W9-BSN-297

# SPACE — FRONTIER OF THE MIND

# Space — Frontier of the Mind
# From Triangle to Tenth Dimension

Ludwig  Auer

National Printers
Ottawa

Copyright © 2003 by Ludwig Auer

All rights reserved

Printed in Canada

First Edition

For information about permission to reproduce
selections from this book write to:

L. Auer

2005–1500 Riverside Drive, Ottawa,

Canada, Ontario, K1G 4J4

The text of this book is composed in Garamond

National Library of Canada Cataloguing-
in-Publication Data

Ludwig Auer, Ph.D.

Space: Frontier of the Mind,

From Triangle to 10th Dimension

Includes bibliographic references and index

**ISBN 0-9731165-0-1**

1. Astronomy – History   2. Astronomy – Mathematics – History

3. Astrophysics – History   I. Title

BD511.A84 2002     520'.9     C2002-902778-0

To my wife D. Ingrid Auer
with  love

## Acknowledgments

The author is indebted to George Abell, Isaac Asimov, John D. Barrow, Peter G. Bergmann, Max Born, Denis Brian, Max Caspar, Bernard I. Cohen, J. L. E. Dreyer, William Dunham, Will Durant, Timothy Ferris, Richard P. Feynman, Albrecht Fölsing, Harald Fritzsch, George Gamow, David L. Goodstein, Judith R. Goodstein, Brian Greene, John Gribbin, Stephen Hawking, Sir Thomas L. Heath, Lancelot Hogben, M. Jammer, Michio Kaku, Morris Kline, Arthur Koestler, Marc L. Kutner, Tullio Levi-Civita, Lloyd Motz, Jefferson HaneWeaver, John North, Anton Pannekoek, Chet Raymo, Jay M. Pasachoff, Sidney Rosen, Bertrand Russell, Raymond Serway, Lee Smolin, Drake Stillman, J. Dirk Struik, Terry Leon, Steven Weinberg, Christopher Walker, Richard West fall, and John Archibald Wheeler. Their publications in astronomy, biography, history, mathematics, and physics, and many others listed under the bibliographic references, provided the background material for this book. Without their work this book could not have been written.

Neil Swan read an earlier manuscript and the final version of this book with great care, especially the mathematics of it, and provided many insightful comments for which I am very grateful. I should like to thank the late Roy Davidson for his comments, in particular for the suggestion to present the mathematical interpretation in diagrams. Rolf Auer and Arnold Ayres read an early manuscript and offered helpful editorial comments and encouragement. Alain LeBel read over the mathematics and made comments. I am happy to acknowledge my excellent editor, Jennifer Latham, who patiently read several versions of the manuscript, gave very detailed and instructive comments, and whose gentle suggestions led to a distinct improvement in the presentation of the ideas in the text—for which I am thankful.

# CONTENTS

# FIGURES

# INTRODUCTION

When in the dark of night the Australian Aborigines look up at the sky they see the Milky Way as wisps of smoke of a camp fire, a fire lit by Nacacork, the creator of the world.[1] When the Tartars of central Asia gaze up they see a great tent with bright lights shining through many tiny holes, the Polar Star holding up the top of the tent. When the Greek philosophers of classical antiquity contemplated the night sky, they sensed beauty and harmony. They observed how the stars and planets moved around the Earth in concentric circles. In their search for a rational explanation, they went beyond mere description and tried to discover what lay hidden behind the appearances. Today, much more is known about "the heavens" but the search for a better understanding of the great unknown continues.

This book is written for laypersons, students at high school or undergraduate university levels, and amateur astronomers who would like to know more about the space we live in. We are all aware, of course, that artificial satellites are orbiting the Earth, that astronauts have landed on the Moon, that a rover explored the surface of Mars, and that spacecraft have gone past the planets Jupiter and Saturn. And we have some idea how it was done. Some of us may have been fascinated when, on television, Captain Picard of *Star Trek, the Next Generation*, ordered the spacecraft Enterprise to shift into warp nine, "To go where no one has gone before." All very well, but we are also told that this is impossible because no material body can travel faster than the speed of light.

1

Today many popular science books are written for the layperson. We have heard of Newton's laws and may have read about the strange paradoxes of Einstein's theory of relativity. Often, such books are easy to read but hard to understand. One reason for this paradox is that authors are reluctant to expose the reader to any mathematics at all. Yet without some mathematics, we can only rely on trust, faith, intuition, or imagination. The Greek philosopher Thales speculated almost three thousand years ago that water was the basic element of all life and that the Earth floated like a cork on an ocean of infinite depth. Convinced that rational thinking could uncover the truth, he opened the doors to scientific research. He was the first to start out from self-evident propositions or basic axioms and arrive at geometric proofs. Others followed. Pythagoras believed that harmony ruled the universe and that it was made by the magic of numbers.

Nearly all the philosophers of antiquity believed that the Earth was at the center of the world, a view held until a few hundred years ago. Then came Copernicus, Kepler, and Galileo, who put the Sun at the center of the solar system and paved the way for Newton. He constructed the ultimate model of the world. Mathematically defined, it functioned like clockwork.

New experimental evidence came along that could not be readily dismissed. Around the turn of the last century Einstein revolutionized physics with his theory of relativity. Not only did he answer some of the puzzling questions of the day, but his work prepared us for a better understanding of nature. He discovered a hidden order, a beautiful but strange order, that no one had ever thought of or seen before.

It is a common belief that Einstein's theory of relativity is very difficult if not impossible to understand. Perhaps there are some good reasons for this belief. One is that certain aspects of the theory *are* very difficult for the average person to understand. Another reason is that many attempts to explain the theory are veiled in cryptic terminology. Even Einstein himself did not find it easy to explain his theory. On one occasion he tried to explain it to Chaim Weizman. Before World War I, Weizman had taught chemistry at England's Manchester University and in later years he became the first president of Israel. In 1921 he happened to cross the

Atlantic with Einstein. When asked about his trip, he responded: "Einstein explained his theory to me every day; by the time we arrived, I was finally convinced that *he* understood it."[2]

Very likely Weizman said it in jest to ward off some of the journalists. Surely, he could have understood if Einstein had used a bit of mathematics. And Einstein probably did. Not all aspects of Einstein's theory require a knowledge of higher mathematics. Consequently, some formulas are included here. Not all of them are immediately linked to astronomy but they can be useful for discussing astronomy later on. Even if mathematics should slow down the reader a bit, ultimately it can make for a better understanding of astronomy.

It is also easier if the scientific developments are traced in chronological order, walking down the path of history. On this path great scientists are encountered who tried to interpret the celestial motion. Starting with the Greek philosophers, their searches are followed, and their lives and times are sketched. Sequentially arranged, focusing on highlights and turning points, some of their fascinating ideas are encountered.

Some mathematics can be used to better understand the underlying logic, the reasoning of the scientists of history. By understanding a few principles of geometry developed at the time of the Greek philosophers Thales and Euclid, it is possible to see how the astronomers of antiquity explored the motions of the planets. Going on from there to Copernicus, Newton, and Einstein we follow the evolution of thought. Although to those who are not mathematicians the approach can be a bit challenging at times, it can also add beauty to the intellectual experience. Readers more interested in the history of astronomy and the fascinating lives of the astronomers can happily read along without having to pause at the math. As well, readers can easily grasp the mathematical concepts sometimes discussed by referring to the user-friendly color diagrams provided, and the glossary of terms given at the back of the book. Each term appearing in the glossary is conveniently marked with a subscript "g" (e.g., apogee$_g$ ).

This book is written for those who are intrigued by the mysteries of outer space. It touches on the philosophy, religion, physics, and mathematics of it. While it is not possible to explore all the nooks and crannies along the way, there is enough material here to make the central ideas at least plausible. If this book should provide a stimulus for some to go beyond what is given here, the aim of the book will be more than fulfilled.

Chapter 1

## THALES OF MILETUS (ca. 624 B.C.–547 B.C.)

*Thales introduced the study of geometry in Greece. He discovered many propositions himself. Thales was also the first Greek Astronomer.*

Sir Thomas L. Heath[1]

In ancient times Ionia$_g$ was a region in Asia Minor, of what is today the southwest corner of Turkey. Situated across from the Greek peninsula, it extended for some 90 miles (145 km) along the Aegean coast. Greeks from Attica first invaded Ionia around 1000 B.C. Their more adventurous culture merged with the old and somewhat decadent Aegean culture$_g$. Handicrafts began to flourish. Textile mills emerged along the meandering rivers. An active commerce developed where the rivers flowed into the sea. Merchants along the coast bought wool, flax, fruit, timber, and metals shipped from inland areas. Ports opened up and trading posts were established. By the sixth century the Ionian merchants had become so rich that they were able to finance new enterprises beyond their borders. In the midst of the region the city of Miletus expanded. Throughout Greece it became known for its wealth and luxury. The Greek historian Herodotus (484–424 B.C.), claimed the city of Miletus was "the most beautiful in the world."[2]

5

In Miletus, a crossroad of east-west merchant trade, new ideas met, material success was pursued, freedom of thought tolerated, and rational thinking appreciated. It was here that the philosopher Thales was born. His father was a wealthy merchant of Phoenician origin who had traveled to distant lands. As his son grew up, he encouraged him to travel. As a young man, Thales came in contact with the belligerent Lydians to the north, the wealthy Babylonians and Phoenicians to the east, and the intellectual elite of Egypt to the south. Through his travels he became acquainted with foreign customs and beliefs, and with new ideas.

Thales of Miletus was the first of the great Ionian philosophers. It is believed he lived from 624 to 547 B.C. and later in history he was considered one of the Seven Wise Men of Greek antiquity.[3] Around 600 B.C. he founded the Milesian School of Philosophy. He also engaged in business, not to accumulate great wealth but only to make a living. His accomplishments in astronomy, mathematics, engineering, business, and statesmanship were legendary.[4]

His place in history is often linked to the solar eclipse of 585 B.C.[5] In that year the Lydians fought under King Alyattes against the neighboring Medes under King Cyaxares.[6] After five years of indecisive battles, their armies fought for the ultimate victory on a field near the Hales River. It was a day of bright sunshine. But in the midst of the raging battle, on the 28th of May of 585 B.C., the light of the mid-day Sun was shrouded by the dark of night. Frightened of the anger of the gods, the opposing armies put down their arms and went home. When the Ionians heard what had happened they breathed a sigh of relief. They could easily have been drawn into the war of their neighbors. What startled some of them even more was that long before the battle Thales had foretold the precise day of the month when the Sun would darken and turn day into night.[7]

**Babylonian Influence**

How did Thales manage to predict the solar eclipse far in advance? It seems that during a lengthy stay in Egypt he had learned of the recurrent cycle of solar eclipses from Egyptian priests. They had borrowed their knowledge of solar and lunar periods from the Babylonians, and they in turn from the Chaldeans.[8] By keeping accurate records Chaldean astronomers had discovered that solar eclipses followed a cyclical pattern, often referred to as the "Saros cycle." Careful tracking had revealed that the Moon eclipsed the Sun every 6585⅓ days (approx. every 18 years).[9] Knowing this, Thales forecasted the day of the eclipse.

For centuries the Babylonian and Chaldean priests had kept records of astronomical events. Unlike the Egyptians and the Greeks, they had developed a sexagesimal system of numbers, similar to our decimal system but based on cuneiform groupings rather than 10 numerals.[10] This number system made it easier to divide numbers by 2, 3, 4, 5, 6, 10, 12, 15, 20, 30. As well, this system lent greater precision to astronomical observations, making it superior to the number systems used by the Egyptians and Greeks.

Archaeologists have gained these insights from the cuneiform writings on Babylonian clay tablets. Unfortunately, most of the tablets were damaged, broken, or illegible. Some of the best preserved tablets have been found in the ruins of one temple in Babylon. They show rows of numbers relating to the outstanding lunar and planetary events of the time. They show, for example, how the Babylonians tracked the movements of the planet Jupiter, listing longitude and zodiacal sign for individual months.[11] By use of purely arithmetical methods, the Babylonians had managed to record the irregularities of the planetary motions during the seasons, years, and decades.

The Babylonian astronomers were priests and not philosophical thinkers. They were concerned with the strict observance of religious rites and were not in search of explanations of the cosmos. From their observatories they interpreted the motions of the planets as the wanderings of luminary deities through the heavens. They kept track of recurrent motions by counting the length of the periods between celestial occurrences. Yet, they did not think to trace the geometric patterns of the stars and planets in a three-dimensional universe.[12]

## Egyptian Influence

The Egyptians, on the other hand, were practical geometers. Under the order of pharaohs and high priests, Egyptian administrators exacted a tithe—an annual part of produce paid as a tax to the pharaoh, the court, and priesthood—from the land-holders. The amount of the tithe was determined in direct proportion to the size of their farms; the larger their holding the greater their tribute. Because the annual spring flooding of the Nile often obliterated the landmarks that distinguished the farmers' fields, borders needed to be re-established every year. Since the fields were irregular in shape, knowledgeable geometers recast borders by method of "triangulation."[13] They measured the land by stretching their ropes into squares, rectangles, and triangles, estimating the size of the farms by adding up the various areas. Experience had taught them how to determine right angles and the sizes of different shapes. They knew, for example, that a triangle with sides measuring 3, 4, and 5 units of length formed a right angle between the two shorter sides. They understood how to find the size of a rectangle by multiplying the lengths of its two sides, or to find the size of a triangle by multiplying one-half of the length of one side with its corresponding height. Being practical men, they knew how to get the job done. For centuries this technique had worked for them. Egyptian geometers measured the size of the fields and did not agonize over the logic behind the method.[14]

## The New Hellenic Philosophy

In Thales' day, the Hellenic$_g$ perception of the world was very different from that of the Egyptians, Babylonians, and other civilizations. Not satisfied with a mere description of the happenings, they searched for the causes behind the events. Thales of Miletus was the first of the Greek philosophers to pursue this vision of exploration. He had gained a great deal of knowledge of applied geometry during his stay in Egypt and while traveling through other countries of the Middle East. History credits Thales as having been the first to go further than the faithful tracking of celestial occurrences or the practical application of simple geometric rules. He brought deductive reasoning to geometry.

### *Deductive Reasoning in Geometry*

In his search for some of the underlying principles of geometry, Thales succeeded in proving, step-by-step, the validity of his geometric propositions. Never before had geometry been thought of, or been taught, in this fashion. His method was unique. Starting from scratch, he invented and defined some of the basic geometric theorems. For example, he has been credited with the discovery that the angles at the base of an isosceles triangle are equal, and that a triangle inscribed in a semicircle is rectangular.

For proof by demonstration he only allowed the use of straight-edge and compass$_g$. He began with a few axiomatic rules that could be taken for granted.[15] Among them, the proposition that if a straight line crosses two parallel lines, the alternate angles at their intersections are equal in size. From this he deduced that the three interior angles of a triangle add up to two right angles (i.e., 180°), irrespective of the triangle's shape (Figure 1.1, Diagrams 1 and 2).

He then defined certain types of triangles as congruent$_g$. To match each other, they had to be equal in any one of three aspects: first, equal in the length of all three sides; second, equal in two sides and the angle between them; and third, equal in one side and its angle at each end (Figure 1.2).[16]

By starting out from these basic axioms Thales demonstrated that the base angles of isosceles triangles—triangles with (at least) two sides of equal length—are of equal size and that any triangle inscribed in a semicircle will have a right angle.

*Isosceles Triangle*

To prove that the base angles of an isosceles triangle are equal in size requires a bit of preparatory work. It illustrates the logic of the method. First ask, how can a straight line connecting two points be cut in half using a compass and a ruler. After constructing several congruent triangles it is evident that the base angles of an isosceles triangle are indeed equal in size (Figure 1.3).[17]

*Right Triangle*

Thales is also credited with the proof that a triangle inscribed in a semi-circle will always be rectangular. For the Egyptian geometers it was essential to have a practical method of staking out and measuring fields of rectangular or triangular shape. For centuries they had known the recipe for doing this by starting out with a right angle. They simply stretched three ropes so that they formed a triangle with sides 3, 4, and 5 units of length. By experience they had learned that the angle between the two shorter ropes always formed a 90° angle.

For Thales, the philosopher, the problem was not one of how to go about forming a right angle, but one of finding a logical method of deduction using only a straightedge and compass, which inevitably yielded a right angle. In his search for solutions he discovered a novel method: a right angle inscribed in a semicircle. Since Thales had already established that the three interior angles of any triangle add up to two right angles or 180°, and that the two base angles of any isosceles triangle are equal to each other, he could demonstrate that a triangle inscribed in a semicircle will always be a rectangular triangle. It was not that it made the work of geometers easier. The merit of his new geometry was that it opened up a road to rational deduction (Figure 1.4).

We are told that upon discovering this theorem Thales was so overjoyed he celebrated the occasion by arranging for a bountiful feast and sacrificing an ox in honor of the gods.[18] If true, it must have been the first of many such worthy occasions.

*Proportionality*

From the priests in Egypt, Thales also learned how to use the "magic shadow stick," an ordinary stick of six-foot length. Its magic was that it made it possible to measure the heights of monuments too tall to reach from level ground. On a sunny day, at a time the vertically held stick cast a six-foot shadow, the shadow matched exactly the length of the stick. If, at this time of day, a monument such as an obelisk cast a shadow of 18 feet, it too had to be 18 feet tall, its shadow matching the monument's height.

The story is told that one day when the Pharaoh came to sacrifice at the tomb of his ancestors, he noticed Thales among a group of selected spectators and inquired about the foreigner.[19] The priests in the Pharaoh's entourage told him about the great knowledge of the young man. The Pharaoh had Thales brought before him. To test his skill he asked him whether he knew of the magic of the shadow stick and if so could he tell him the height of the pyramid. It was a trick question because the vertical stick did not cast a six-foot shadow at that time of the day. The Pharaoh's request raised fear among the priests because no one had ever attempted to measure the height of a structure, let alone a pyramid, at a time of day when the Sun stood low at the horizon. Should the shadow stick fail him, it would clearly be an impious act that could put his own life, as well as theirs, in jeopardy. But Thales—having intuitively grasped the law of proportionality of similar triangles— estimated the height of the pyramid within a few feet. The Pharaoh was impressed and the high priests greatly relieved.[20]

Aside from his ingenious theorems$_g$ of geometry, many other accomplishments have been attributed to him. And even if some of them are legend rather than fact, they symbolize the recognition paid to Thales —he was the first known person in the history of humankind to search for and discover some of the basic principles of geometry, mathematics, and modern science.[21]

## Thales' View of the Universe

While often insisting on rational deductions, on some occasions Thales felt free to speculate. He tried to understand humanity's place in the universe, and the elements and dynamics of the universe's system. To him, water was the key substance of the universe. He saw the germ of all beings, the origin of life, in water. He saw water produce the air and the clouds. Without rain from the clouds, plants did not grow, crops failed, and animals could not forage. Man and beast starved to death. He imagined that the Earth, covered from above by a vault of stars, floated like a cork on waters of infinite depth.

Today, of course, our perception of the universe is very different. We know that the depth of the ocean is finite and that hydrogen and not water is one of the most common elements of the universe. We know that our galaxy alone contains some 100 billion stars and that there are billions of galaxies. And we speculate that the expanse of the universe is infinite.[22]

So, while more than two thousand years ago Thales attributed the existence of the world to water, today it is recognized that hydrogen is a most common element. He appreciated the importance of rational thinking in the study of nature. We still do. He valued the logic of mathematics. So do we. And to him, the world was as fascinating and mysterious as the cosmos appears to us today.

Chapter 2

## PYTHAGORAS (ca.580 B.C.–500 B.C.)

*Pythagoras transformed the study of geometry into a liberal education examining the principles of science from the beginning.*

Proclus[1]

Pythagoras was the son of Mnesarchus, a wealthy Phoenician merchant who lived on Samos, an island off the west coast of what today is Turkey. Through Mnesarchus' business and travels he became acquainted with the customs and cultures of other Mediterranean countries. Legend has it that before one of his trips he asked the Pythian Oracle$_g$ in Delphi, an ancient city in central Greece, whether his next voyage to Syria would be successful. The Oracle replied that it would be very rewarding for him. The Oracle added that his wife would share with him a gift of much greater value, a son surpassing in wisdom all who had lived before.

Their son was born later that year. They named him Pythagoras, after the Pythian Oracle.[2] At the time of his birth, circa 580 B.C.,[3] the people of the island of Samos enjoyed freedom and great luxury, a brief period during which culture and scientific thought flourished before being obliterated by the invasion and tyranny of the Persians.

### Escape From Samos

Having been very successful in his commercial ventures and overjoyed with the progress of his newly-born son, Mnesarchus built a temple and

12

dedicated it to the god Apollo. He had his son educated by the best teachers of the day. While still in his youth, Pythagoras became known for his outstanding knowledge. Threatened under the dictatorship of the Ionian tyrant Polycrates he escaped, when not quite twenty, from the island of Samos in the dark of the night, fleeing to the coastal area of Ionia. In Ionia he came to know Pherekydes and Thales of Miletus, two of the leading philosophers of the time. Pherekydes had the greatest influence on Pythagoras. He taught him a mixture of myth, logic, theology, and philosophy. Pythagoras easily surpassed all other students and Thales greatly admired him. He urged him to sail to Egypt to learn from the priests of Jupiter, where Thales himself had received instruction many years earlier.[4]

## Travels

Not feeling at home in business and commerce, Pythagoras left his homeland to see the world. We are told that he traveled for some thirty years as far west as Gaul (present-day northern Italy), France, and the Netherlands, throughout the Middle East and to Egypt, and as far east as India. Under the guidance of the Egyptian priests, Pythagoras studied geometry and astronomy for more than 20 years. He admired the range and depth of their knowledge and was inspired by their worship of the gods. When the Persians invaded Egypt, Pythagoras was taken prisoner. Escorted to Babylon, a city of wealth and rich culture, he remained there for eight years.

Eventually he returned home to the island of Samos, still ruled by the dictator Polycrates. Revenues from a busy seaport enabled the tyrant to invest in public works. Among other projects, he had a 4500-foot-long water tunnel dug through the island's mountain.[5] The economy boomed but the people felt oppressed. Driven by his desire for freedom and now past the age of 50, Pythagoras left Samos again and immigrated to southern Italy.

## Arrival in Italy

The Greek historian Porphyry gives a vivid description of the arrival of Pythagoras in southern Italy. He reported that when Pythagoras:

> ...disembarked in Italy and reached Croton [he] was a much traveled and exceptional man, endowed by fortune with great natural

gifts. He was tall and of noble aspect, having grace and beauty of voice, of manner, and of every other kind. On his arrival the effect he produced in Croton was immense. With a long eloquent discourse he so moved the magistracy of elders that they bade him pronounce an exhortation suitable to that age to the young men, then to all boys assembled from their schools. Then an assembly of women was arranged for him.

As a result of these meetings his reputation rapidly grew and he gained many disciples in that city, men and women as well—the name of one woman, Theano, has come down to us—and many princes and rulers from the neighboring non-Greek country. There is no account of what he used to say to those frequenting him, for they preserved extraordinary secrecy....He so converted everyone to his way of thinking, ...that he gained two thousand adherents to his discourse. They did not return to their homes, but together with their wives and children, set up a great school [or lecture hall] and created the state of Magna Graecia. They received laws and regulations from him, and respected them as if they were divine covenants.[6]

## The Pythagorean School

His disciples lived within a communal system by a strict set of rules. They were bound by absolute loyalty to their teacher as well as to their fellow students. They dressed simply, lived as vegetarians, were devoted to their studies. They were not allowed to swear, and at the end of each day asked what they had done wrong, what duties they had neglected, and what good they had achieved.[7] Female students received training in philosophy, literature, home economics, and maternal child care. Women trained in the Pythagorean school became role models for others. They were honored by society for their extraordinary qualities.[8]

New students were expected to accept the Pythagorean teachings without question for five years. After this probationary period, they were allowed to study the key subjects under the master himself. The curriculum consisted of five subject areas: geometry, arithmetic, music, astronomy, and harmony. Mathematics was the background to all five, with emphasis on clarity of thought and rigorous deduction of logical proofs.

*Geometry*

The logical study of geometry required the use of a straightedge and compass to construct diagrams based on axioms (statements that can be taken for granted), theorems (statements that must be proven), and proof by demonstration (conclusion reached by previously proven theorems).[9]

*Arithmetic*

This subject was not only a matter of mastering the practical art of reckoning, but also addressed questions of abstract number theory.[10] With respect to numbers$_g$ , Pythagoras divided the "integer$_g$" numbers into "male" (odd) and "female" (even) numbers; distinguished between "prime$_g$" numbers, (e.g., 2, 3, 5, 7, 11) and "composite$_g$"numbers (e.g., 4, 6, 8, 9, 10). He discovered "perfect$_g$" numbers whose factors, when summed, equal that number. For example, the number 6 was the first of the perfect numbers factoring into 1, 2, and 3. Multiplied with each other or added to each other (as in *1x2x3=6* and *1+2+3=6*), yielding the same value, 6. He and his disciples discovered several others. Today 17 such "perfect" numbers are known.

Pythagoras also created sets of "figurate" numbers, which he derived from the expansion of geometric figures. Starting with triangles he enlarged their pattern from 1 unit to 3 units, to 6 units, to 10, and 15 units. He discovered that by adding any two consecutive triangular numbers (1, 3, 6, 10, 15), the sums yielded a series of square numbers. For example, *1+3=4*, *3+6=9, 6+10=16*, and *10+15=25*. Among these sums were the squares of 3, 4, and 5 (Figure 2.1). Knowing that triangles with sides of length 3, 4, and 5 always formed a right angle may have prompted Pythagoras to ponder over the relation between rectangular triangles and squares.

*Music*

It was taught that sounds depended on tension, thickness, and vibration of chords. Pythagoras demonstrated how musical harmony could be determined by proportionate intervals. He discovered that strings drawn to different lengths produced different sounds when plucked, strummed, or hit. Long strings vibrate more slowly, producing sounds of a lower pitch and short strings vibrate faster, producing sounds of a higher pitch.[11]

And he found a harmonic scale, that he created by holding a vibrating chord at the ratios of 2/1 (octave), 3/2 (the fifth) and 4/3 (the fourth). Even though the laws of acoustics were later shown to be more complex, these clearly defined proportions persuaded him that all harmony in nature derived from such numerical relationships.[12] Convinced of the supernatural powers of music, he is said to have played a lyre, a harp-like musical instrument , so that upon waking in the morning and before going to sleep at night his soul could be touched by the divine quality of musical harmony.[13]

*Astronomy*

Pythagoras taught that the universe was a living sphere. He was the first to call the Earth a sphere (from the Greek *sphaira* (σφαῖρα) for globe) and the first to declare that the planets moved independently and, in a sense, opposite to the circular rotation of the stars.[14] He taught that the phases of the Moon depended on which part of the Moon was facing the Sun, and that the lunar eclipses occurred when the Earth was in line with both Moon and Sun so that the shadow of the Earth blotted out the Moon.

He searched for symmetry in the structure of a universe that could be described in numbers. The first to develop the theory of the harmony of spheres, Pythagoras believed that God adorned the world with numbers. He claimed that the first four integer numbers 1, 2, 3, and 4 contained the nature of all things. For example, sets of four were found in spikes of flowers and heads of grain, and nature consisted of four elements said to be water, earth, air, and fire.

*Harmony*

In the belief that the only lasting aspects of nature were numerical, he believed that God's existence is conveyed by numbers and went on to say that "God is number."[15] He enshrined all his cosmic speculations in a bizarre mysticism of numerals. Having discovered that harmonic musical sounds are associated with certain numerical ratios, he postulated that a similar relation existed among the heavenly bodies. He proposed that the planets moved along the heavens in musical harmony, an idea that survived the next 2000 years of western civilization. Throughout antiquity and up to the Renaissance, this was interpreted to mean that harmonic musical sounds were produced as the heavenly bodies moved at different distances and speeds along the firmament. More likely, Pythagoras referred to the perfection of a universe founded on numerical intervals, which he associated with musical harmony.

Pythagoras sought harmony in everyday life. When he first arrived in Croton he found that many of the neighboring cities fought each other, took prisoners, and oppressed each other with slavery. Inspiring the inhabitants with love for liberty and mutual respect, he had them free slaves, restore them to independence, and establish a code of law and order. With a shift from war to peace, the economy of Croton recovered, commerce flourished, and the towns prospered again.[16]

Historians have reported on Pythagoras' many achievements. All of them, however, based their writings on hearsay. To this day we do not know how much is legend and how much is fact.[17] None of Pythagoras' written records have ever been found. We are told that he entrusted his *Commentaries* to his daughter, Damo, and charged her not to release them to anyone. Even though she could have obtained much money for them, she was among his most devoted followers and never let go of his writings.[18] Nevertheless, his teachings of the absolute necessity for clear and rigorous thinking spread far and wide and laid the foundation of scientific thought in western civilization.

### The Great Pythagorean Theorem

It is the geometric construct that brought him immortality. Conceivably, Pythagoras' work on figurate numbers (Figure 2.1), inspired him to search for a link between rectangular triangles and squares. In plain language, the Pythagorean Theorem[19] says that in a right-angled triangle the area formed by the sum of squares on its two shorter sides equals that of the square on its third side.[20] If, for example, the three sides of a right triangle are 3, 4, and 5 units long, the square of the first is 9, that of the second is 16, and their sum, *16+9*, equals the square of the third, at 25 units. It follows that a triangle with sides of lengths 3, 4, and 5 will always form a right angle.

Not surprisingly, the simple combination of 3, 4, and 5 units had been used for centuries by Egyptian and Babylonian builders and craftsmen to construct and verify that the corner angles were "right." They knew *how* to construct a right angle because the recipe had always worked. They had not tried to find out *why* it worked because that did not matter to them.

## The Classical Proof

After Pythagoras' theorem became more widely known, other geometers and mathematicians set about proving its validity. Among the hundreds of proofs that have emerged over the centuries, the Euclidian proof is a classic.[21] It involves the shape and size of several regularly and irregularly shaped triangles. Knowledge of how to determine the size of such triangles was part of the Egyptian geometers' tool box. They knew that the area of any triangle, whatever its shape, is equal to half the size of a rectangle formed by the base and height of the triangle. In Figure 2.2 irregularly shaped triangles are shown to be the sum (or the difference) of two rectangular or right-angled triangles.

Having established this, the classical proof of the Pythagorean Theorem is illustrated in Figure 2.3, Diagrams 2 to 5. This proof of the Pythagorean Theorem is not "squeaky clean." It relies on the fact that if two triangles equal each other in base and height, or if they match each other in the lengths of two sides and the enclosed angle, they will be of equal size. Intuitively, that may be obvious. Euclid, who taught geometry several hundred years after Pythagoras, followed a much more rigorous approach. He introduced his proof only after he had dealt with 46 preliminary propositions, making the proof of the Pythagorean Theorem a fitting climax to the end of his first volume of the *Elements*.[22]

The classical proof of the Pythagorean Theorem reveals the brilliance and elegance of Hellenic logic when applied to an abstract problem of geometry. Pythagoras' great theorem has become an elemental part of many theorems of mathematics and physics. In its most general form, the theorem is the starting point of non-Euclidean geometry and of Einstein's Theory of General Relativity.[23]

## Rational Numbers

Pythagoras was convinced that all the basic elements of nature could be represented by natural and rational numbers (i.e., ratios of natural numbers). It must have come as a horrendous shock to him when the austere logic of his own theorem demolished this belief. Until then he believed that rational numbers spanned the whole domain of numbers. To think of any other kind of numbers must have appeared to him irrational. After all, geometers were able to measure any length in numbers of units and fractions of units.

In his exploration of figurate numbers, Pythagoras discovered that the two square numbers 9 and 16 added up to a third square number 25 (Figure 2.1). When he searched for other triplets, he found that the square numbers $5^2 = 25$ and $12^2 = 144$ added up to $13^2 = 169$. He discovered methods of quickly finding other sets of triplets. The simplest method consisted of multiplying the numbers of one triplet by an integer or a fraction to obtain another triplet. If, for example, we multiply the triplet 3, 4, 5 by 2 to get 6, 8, 10, then $6^2 + 8^2 = 10^2$ or $36 + 64 = 100$. Or, if we multiply it by a fraction, say ½, then $(1.5)^2 + 2^2 = (2.5)^2$ or $2.25 + 4.00 = 6.25$.

While there was an obvious correspondence between the triplets of square numbers such as $3^2$, $4^2$, $5^2$ and the squares of a rectangular triangle with sides of length 3, 4, and 5 units, it was not clear if and how such triplets could be matched with all possible squares of right-angled triangles.

*Irrational Numbers*

The search continued until one day the inevitable happened. Pythagoras, or perhaps one of his students, discovered that the diagonal of a square (i.e., the third side of a right-angled isosceles triangle) could not be any kind of natural number, nor could it be any ratio of two natural numbers. Until then, Pythagoras was convinced that the third side of any rectangular triangle, whatever the length of its two smaller sides, could always be represented by a whole number or fraction of whole numbers.[24] That it could not, was a momentous discovery.

The refutation of it follows the classical mode of assuming the opposite to see if it leads to a contradiction. Formally, the new theorem states that the length of the diagonal of a square is incommensurable with the length of its sides.[25] Simply, this meant that the base of a right-angled isosceles triangle (or the diagonal of any square) cannot be expressed as a multiple or fraction of the length to its two equal sides. To clarify it further, assume the two equal sides of a right-angled isosceles triangle are represented by whole numbers or ratios of whole numbers, not divisible by any integer number greater than 1.[26]

By starting out with the assumption that the base of an isosceles triangle (or the diagonal of a square) is an odd-numbered integer, the immediate contradiction is evident. It is impossible because the two equal sides imply that it must be even-numbered. Evidently, in this case, the squares of the smaller sides of a rectangular triangle, measured in whole numbers, cannot be matched up with another integer number, not divisible by two, on the third side (Figure 2.3, Diagram 6).

This finding must have caused great consternation among the Pythagoreans because their whole theory was built on the belief that God's universe was based on whole numbers. They kept the existence of their newly discovered irrational number$_g$ (i.e., the square root of 2) strictly secret, at least up to the day when a certain Hippasus gave it away. Hippasus is said to have paid for this impious act with his life. Taken out on a boat, he was thrown overboard. As someone put it, the drowning of Hippasus at sea was an early example of "publish *and* perish."[27]

When the murder of Hippasus became known, it enraged the people of Croton. So when Pythagoras and some of his followers were gathered at the house of Milo the people set fire to it. They feared the Pythagoreans might establish a tyranny. Driven out of the building by smoke and fire, Pythagoras escaped and fled to a temple of the Muses in Metapontum where it is said he starved himself to death. All this, if true, because of an "irrational" number?

## Conclusion

In fact, there are many versions of Pythagoras' death.[28] Some are dramatic tales that add to his legendary life and reveal him as a charismatic leader committed to his beliefs and principles to his dying moments.

One version links Pythagoras' demise with a complicated plot of vengeance, battles, and conspiracy that eventually pulls down the Pythagorean sect at Croton. The story goes back several years before Pythagoras' death, to 508 B.C. when Telys of Sybaris, the cruel tyrant of the neighboring state to the north of Croton, overthrew the Sybarite ruling faction. The exiled rulers fled south and asked for asylum in Croton. When a Sybarite envoy demanded their release, Pythagoras intervened on behalf of the exiles because several graduates of his school had been put to death by the followers of Telys. On the advice of Pythagoras, the Crotoniates sent an envoy to Sybaris. The Sybarites massacred the envoy, assembled an army about three times the size of that of Croton's, and marched south.[29]

During the ensuing battle, the Crotoniate flute players threw the invaders' cavalry into disarray. During peacetime the horses of the Sybarite cavalry had been trained to dance to the flute. On hearing the music of the flutes the Sybarite horses began dancing in the midst of the battle. Telys and his army were slaughtered, the city of Sybaris razed to the ground, and the river Krathis diverted to flow over the ruins. Sybaris vanished forever. Milo, the commander of the Crotoniate forces and a famous athlete of Croton, was a loyal follower of Pythagoras. His decisive victory was attributed in large part to the discipline instilled during his training at the Pythagorean school.[30]

Not long after the Crotoniate victory the first signs of a conspiracy against the Pythagoreans rose up. Kylon, a well-known citizen of a leading family of Croton, had been rejected a few years earlier from entering the Pythagorean school because of serious character flaws. He and his friends, all of rich, aristocratic families, vowed to seek revenge. They stirred up and incited a revolt against Pythagoras and his disciples. Jealous of the growing influence the Pythagoreans had on politics and religion, Kylon gave fiery speeches urging the people of Croton not to follow their Pythagorean masters like a herd of sheep. Because of their lofty teachings, the Pythagoreans had become estranged and isolated from the people in town and had lost popular support. When fighting broke out and their buildings were set on fire, the Pythagoreans fled. By now Pythagoras was in his eighties. Students still deeply devoted to him helped him cross a dangerous chasm barring the escape route, by forming a "living bridge" so that he could safely walk to freedom.[31]

Such is the legend of Pythagoras. The fact that his contemporaries preserved and transmitted his teachings to later generations is symbolic of the admiration and authority he commanded. His insistence on searching for the underlying logic of theorems and his belief in expressing the physical structure of nature in numbers revolutionized the thinking of the time. His novel philosophy found many followers and his views prevailed over many centuries. He established not only a new school of thought but also created a spiritual discipline that inspired others to find beauty in nature through search for harmony, order, and numerical relationships.

Chapter 3

# FROM PYTHAGORAS (ca. 580 B.C.–ca. 500 B.C.) TO ARISTOTLE (384 B.C.–322 B.C.).

*All men by nature desire knowledge.*

Aristotle[1]

Much of what is known today of the accomplishments of Pythagoras goes back to Aristotle. In his writings Aristotle did not distinguish between the discoveries of Pythagoras and those of his followers, but simply attributed all to the Pythagoreans.[2] Others have attributed fragments of Pythagorean speculations and findings to individuals. Only those who addressed issues of the cosmos or solved certain mathematical problems that had a bearing on further developments in astronomy are presented here.

## Anaximander (ca. 611 B.C.–546 B.C.): The Infinite Cosmos

Anaximander was a fellow citizen and friend of Thales but with different, somewhat more speculative philosophical views. In true Hellenic fashion his theories were abstract, based on logical reasoning and, as indicated in Chapter 1, independent from those of the Babylonians and the Egyptians. While Thales made water the first principle of the universe, Anaximander believed that it was neither water, nor oil nor air, but some other sort of "infinite substance" from which the Earth and the universe was made.[3]

He also believed that since the young of the human race were vulnerable for too long and required more care and protection than any other species, that mankind must have evolved from earlier forms of life. But Anaximander went beyond this argument and anticipated the modern interpretation. He believed that the evolutionary process dated far back in time and that human beings ultimately evolved from the fish in the sea. He based his belief on fossil finds and concluded that evolution was a continuing process.[4]

In astronomy as well, some of his views were very modern. He took a great step forward when he reasoned that the "Infinite" embraced all the cosmos, that it was ageless, and that generation and destruction of all worlds recurred in cycles. The Infinite was in eternal motion. He speculated that the Earth was surrounded by a vast ring of fire when it came into being, that it was aloft, and not supported by anything. It remained where it was, equidistant from the stars.

He also came up with some ideas that are strange to us today. He described the Earth as cylinder-shaped, being three times wider than it was deep. He thought that the Sun was one big hoop of fire, letting the fire out through a vent and that eclipses of the Sun occurred when the vent was shut. And similarly, he believed that the Moon was a also fiery hoop, with an opening for the light to shine through. Eclipses happened when the opening was blocked. He claimed that the Sun was the same size as the Earth, that the diameter of the Moon's orbit was 19 times the diameter of the Earth and that of the Sun 27 times as large as the diameter of the Earth. He placed the Sun highest, the Moon second, and the planets and stars under both of them. All of Anaximander's beliefs came to us from the writings of others. They did not elaborate on how he arrived at these findings.[5]

Anaximander was admired for his practical talents. He was said to have been the first to draw a map of the inhabited parts of the Earth that went beyond the earlier maps of the Egyptians. He also was said to have set up a sundial in Sparta, on which he marked the times of the day, the seasons, the solstice, and the equinoxes.[6]

## Anaxagoras (ca. 500 B.C.–428 B.C.): Reason Rules the World

Anaxagoras was born in Asia Minor near Smirna, north of Miletus. Although he inherited considerable wealth from his parents, he neglected his possessions to devote himself to science and cosmological questions. Impressed by the orderliness of nature, he believed that "reason rules the world,"[7] and took nature's order as evidence of a regulating force. This was an early attempt of proving the existence of God by the laws of nature.[8]

He recognized the great variety and the enormous number of substances and believed that each was composed of tiny particles which he called "seeds." Merely cutting any substance into ever smaller pieces, he believed, could not yield a different matter. He was convinced that the proportions of different tiny seeds in each substance remained constant. He reasoned that a great variety of such seeds could be combined in many different proportions. With this novel idea he came closer to the modern theory of chemical elements than anyone before him.[9]

For Anaxagoras the ultimate object of life was to investigate the "Sun, Moon and Heaven."[10] Great discoveries attributed to him were that the Moon did not shine by its own fire but was merely reflecting the light from the Sun, that solar eclipses were due to the interposition of the Moon between the Sun and the Earth, and that lunar eclipses were due to the position of the Earth between the Sun and the Moon. He speculated that the world was formed out of a central vortex with a rotary movement that spread out, taking wider and wider circles, tearing out rocks from the Earth and kindling them into stars.[11] He was an early advocate of the biological evolution of humankind and claimed that life existed on other worlds like ours. He also believed in a creative universal mind and a universal consciousness.[12]

His philosophical views were unorthodox for his day. His concept of God was not at all in line with the religion of the state of Athens. After having taught in Athens for 30 years, the state accused him of corrupting the youth and laid a charge of impiety against him. He was found guilty and put in prison. Snatched from there by Pericles, a democratic statesman and commander-in-chief of all forces of Athens, he narrowly escaped from Athens to Lampsacus (in the west of Asia Minor, along the Dardanelles) where he remained in exile and continued to teach in freedom.

### Philolaus (ca. 480 B.C.): The Sun, Hearth of the Universe

Philolaus was one of the leading Pythagoreans who significantly contributed to advancing Pythagorean theories. Philolaus studied the properties of numbers, explored the numerical relationships of harmony in music and related them to the physical universe. In astronomy Philolaus came up with some new and startling ideas. He described the universe as spherical in shape and finite in size, with some changing and unchanging elements. In the history of astronomy, he was the first to abandon the idea that the Earth was the center of the universe; he demoted it to a planet similar to the other five known planets.

He believed that the Earth did not revolve around the Sun but that it circled together with the Sun and the Moon around the glowing fire of the "Hearth of the Universe." At this central fire, invisible from Earth, was the throne from which the god Zeus directed all the movements and activities of the universe. Nearest to the center revolved another planet, a counter-Earth, then the Moon next to the Sun, then the five planets, and outside the planetary orbits was the sphere of fixed stars. The Earth revolved around the central fire, producing day and night. Adding a counter-Earth allowed for lunar and solar eclipses. He asserted that beyond this planetary system and outside the sphere of stars was an infinite void.[13]

## The Sophists: The Practical Art of Persuasion

In 480 B.C., united Greek armies overcame Persian forces on land and in 479 B.C. the Athenians defeated the Persian fleet. For future protection the Athenians organized a league of Greek city states and built up a great naval power. Having successfully repelled the Persian invaders, they lived in peace. It was a critical turning point in their history.[14] Instead of fighting the enemy in navy battles, the Greeks opened up new sea routes causing trade and commerce to flourish. Greece entered a golden age.

Greek migrant teachers traveled from city to city and, for substantial fees, imparted their knowledge to young men of wealthy families.[15] The teachers were Sophists who taught grammar and public speaking and had no use for analyzing the physical nature of things or speculating about the stars in the heavens. They claimed there was no absolute knowledge. Instead, they believed in rhetoric and taught their students how to argue both sides of any case.[16] In a society where commercial success was considered paramount, winning people over became a fundamental virtue. Their ideal was to acquire an all-round virtuosity and skill in the art of persuasion. Opinions were to be tested for their practical use.[17]

The teachings of the Sophists ran counter to what the Greek philosophers of nature, geometry, and the cosmos tried to achieve. Yet, in the art of persuasion a countervailing force existed. When the Sophists were at the height of their power, the Athenian philosopher Socrates (469 B.C.–399 B.C.) made his influence felt. He agreed with the Sophists that a knowledge of physical nature was not nearly as important as the knowledge of human nature. But in contrast to the sophists he believed it was necessary to question and thereby clarify the concepts that lie latent within the human soul.[18]Absolutely straightforward, Socrates invariably said what appeared to him to be right. On trial for corrupting the youth of Athens, he defended himself against charges drummed up by the reigning politicians. They were deeply offended for having been shown their moral and intellectual emptiness. True to his character, Socrates accepted the penalty of death by drinking a cup of hemlock rather than pleading guilty and going into exile.

In his lifetime Socrates had lived from the age of physical and cosmological speculation to the age of humanism.[19] Of course, the periods were not sharply separated but overlapped and, at times, ran parallel to each other. Perhaps because of his search for truth, the interest of the Greek philosophers in the cosmos, nature, and geometry continued for centuries to come.[20]

## Hippocrates (ca. 460 B.C. ):  The Crescent-Shaped Moons

Hippocrates was raised on the island of Chios.[21] This was not  very far from the island of Cos where the better-known Greek Physician, Hippocrates (of the "Hippocratic Oath" fame), was born.

Hippocrates of Chios came from a wealthy family. Having lost a large sum of money in trading operations with some unscrupulous pirates, he tried to recover it. This brought him to Athens where a lawsuit tied him down for many years. Being unsuccessful in his legal and financial pursuits, he joined the philosophers of Athens and supported himself by teaching geometry.[22]

Among the geometers of the day, Hippocrates was best known for having written the *Elements* in which he derived theorems from a few axioms. By doing so he set the stage and provided much material for

Euclid's *Elements*, which would be written about one hundred years later. Unfortunately, no record of Hippocrates' treatise has survived. Among students of geometry he is better known for the "Quadrature of the Lune," the squaring of a moon-shaped figure. He was the first mathematician who successfully demonstrated that a circular geometric figure could be converted into a rectilinear figure of the same size.

For centuries, Egyptian geometers had known how to approximate the area of a circle by multiplying the square of its radius by the ratio 22/7 (the Greeks knew only fractions and not decimals, in decimal notation 22/7 was equivalent to 3.14). Expressed in modern notation it meant that $\pi r^2 \approx (22/7)r^2$. Hippocrates showed that the combined size of four crescent-shaped lunes attached to the sides of a square, equal the size of that square (Figure 3.1, Diagram 1).

Hippocrates knew that the size of a semicircle is proportionate to that of a square. Figure 3.1, Diagrams 1 to 4 show that the triangle ABC covers as much area as the two crescent-shaped lunes (or lunulae) and that the four lunes equal the size of the square.[23]

It was the first time, that anyone had managed to "square" a curvilinear figure, a memorable event in the history of geometry. It inspired his followers to pursue with renewed vigor the search for a geometric method of squaring the circle. Yet, it proved to be a blind alley. Some of their arguments were flawed, and they encountered problems they could not solve.[24] Still, the circle was thought to be an ideal figure and dominated astronomy for more than a thousand years. Eventually, astronomers replaced the circle with an ellipse and in doing so the conversion of a rectangle into a square played a role (see Chapter 7).

Long before Greek geometers succeeded in squaring a circular figure, they had managed to convert a rectangle into a square (Figure 3.2, Diagram 1). The procedure was not as simple as it is today because they adhered to their strict rule of geometry—permitting only the use of compass and straightedge. Years later the great geometer Euclid described the method of this conversion (Proposition 14 in Book II of his *Elements*). A simplified version of his method is illustrated in Diagrams 2 to 4 of Figure 3.2.[25] Somewhat modified, the same idea was later used in connection with the Apollonian geometry of ellipses and, eventually, it reappeared in Newton's analysis of planetary orbits.

**Plato (427 B.C.–347 B.C.): Beauty is Symmetry, Five Platonic Solids**
Plato carried on where Socrates had left off. With the Sophists, Greek philosophers had switched over to a new track, from problems of numbers, nature, and cosmos to those of man, state, and society. Commerce and politics in the state assembly had raised a new set of moral issues: the eternal values of truth, beauty, and goodness.

Plato was the greatest disciple of Socrates. He was not a very systematic philosopher. In his writings he raised challenging questions, searching for Truth and trying to find it through rational thought. His dialogues were written in prose. For the most part they addressed questions of the nature and destiny of the soul after death. He also dealt with the myth of the creation of the universe where the soul of the world was at the center. Often he expressed his thoughts in symbolic narratives and not by logically reasoned arguments.[26]

Plato saw the world as a divine work of art where the Idea ruled supreme. Like the Pythagoreans, he speculated that there was perfect harmony in the heavens. Although Plato did not share the belief of some of the Pythagoreans that the planets produced musical sounds, he *did* believe that the musical scale reflected the harmony of the world. His deductions were abstract. In describing the mechanism of the world, he gave us some details of the planets. He based the distance of the planets from Earth on a mixture of two geometrical progressions, that is, $2^n = 1$, $2, 4, 8, ...,$ and $3^n = 1, 3, 9, 27, ...,$ where n are consecutive numbers, and arrived at the following planetary distances:

| | | |
|---|---|---|
| Moon | = | 1 |
| Sun | = | 2 |
| Venus | = | 3 |
| Mercury | = | 4 |
| Mars | = | 8 |
| Jupiter | = | 9 |
| Saturn | = | 27 |

These relative distances were not based on his observations, but appealed to Plato's appreciation of the abstract.[27] He went further. By inserting other numbers between the two series he formed a musical scale.

Plato claimed that "geometry is knowledge of the eternally existent" and that "geometry existed before Creation." He maintained that it is right to proceed from the second dimension to the third, which brings us to cubes and other three-dimensional figures.[28] Nature, he asserted, adheres to the principle of three-dimensional forms.

The forms, symmetric from all sides, are known to mathematicians as the "Five Platonic Solids." Their sides are made up of congruent triangles, squares, and pentagons. Convinced that geometry ruled nature Plato decided to link the elements of nature with the geometric solids. Following the proposition of the earlier Greek philosopher Empedocles (ca. 430 B.C.), Plato maintained that all of nature is made up of four basic elements: fire, earth, air, and water.[29] He identified these elements with four of the five regular solids: fire with the pyramid-shaped tetrahedron, earth with the cube, air with octahedron, and water with the icosahedron. Since there were five regular solids, however, Plato associated the constellations of heaven with the fifth solid, the dodecahedron (Figure 3.3).[30] In making this choice he said: "The Good, of course, is always beautiful, and the beautiful never lacks proportion."[31] This proposition can be readily accepted. When Plato presents the reader, however, with a pseudo-mathematical statement such as "air is to water as water is to earth" it may be interesting but hardly convincing to mathematicians.

Much of Plato's description of the cosmos dealt with the soul of the world. His ideas were couched in mysticism and difficult to interpret. He made the soul the keystone in the construction of the cosmos and the prime mover of the heavenly spheres. Although not greatly interested in a physical description of the structure of the world, he did formulate one of the most challenging questions to astronomers, then and for centuries to come.

After hearing someone reading from a book of Anaxagoras who asserted that the mind is the cause of all things, Plato wrote:

> I was pleased with this cause, as it seemed to me right in a certain
> way, I was glad to think that I had found a guide of the cause of

existing things. I was prepared to be told in like manner, with regard to the Sun, the Moon, and the other stars, their relative speeds, their turnings-back, and their other conditions, in what way it is best for each of them to be, to act, or to be acted upon so far as they are acted upon. From what a height of hope, then, was I hurled down when I went on with my reading and saw a man that made no use of Mind for ordering things, but assigned, as their cause, airs, aethers, waters, and any number other absurdities.[32]

A rather harsh critique. Plato himself devoted little time to the observation of the heavens and the motions of the planets. Although he found mathematics interesting and considered it an essential part of education, he deemed it inferior to pure philosophy. In all matters, he preferred the theoretical to the practical. In geometry this meant proving or disproving intriguing theorems rather than searching for better ways of measuring land. He frowned upon practical experiments and, if we can believe Plutarch, expressed righteous anger when his students, Eudoxus and Archytas, carried out mechanical experiments.[33]

In the history of astronomy his view of the universe did not play a major role. But since his books were widely read, he helped spread the Pythagorean doctrine.[34] More importantly, he challenged contemporary and future philosophers and astronomers to substantiate their arguments by going beyond the pure description of the world and searching for the underlying causes of change.

## Eudoxus (408 B.C.–355 B.C.): The Universe of 27 Celestial Spheres

Born in Cnidos (an island northwest of Rodhos), Eudoxus set out at the age of 23 to study medicine and geometry. He attended the lectures of Plato. He was poor and unable to afford accommodation in Athens. From his low-cost quarters on the outskirts of the city, at Piraeus, he walked daily to the Academy.

Eudoxus attended Plato's lectures for some months but was not content with the knowledge he could acquire. The insistence on theory without observation frustrated him. He decided to leave Greece. He went to Egypt where he learned of the planetary motions from the priests in Heliopolis. Although the Egyptian priests kept meticulous records of the planetary motions, they had not developed a theory of the universe.[35] After studying in Egypt for nearly two years he moved to Propontine Cyzicus, near the Dardanelles, where he lectured on mathematics for several years.[36]

By the time he was forty, he was back in Athens. He opened a school of science and philosophy that, for a time, rivaled Plato's Academy. Eventually he was called back to Cnidos, his place of birth, to provide the city with a new code of laws. While there, he continued with his studies of mathematics and astronomy and set up an observatory.

In the history of astronomy he is considered to be the founder of a complete theory, based on his own observations, of the spherical motions of the Sun, planets, and stars. His system of the heavens consisted of 27 transparent spheres, 26 of them belonging to the planets and one to the stars.[37] He assigned three spheres to the Sun and Moon each, four to each of the other five (visible) planets, and one to all the remaining stars since he saw them all moving together along the same circular course.

In his model, the Earth was the center of the universe. The Sun, the Moon, and the five planets orbited around it in concentric circles, each within its own set of spheres. The first sphere of each planet revolved in concert with the daily rotation of the fixed stars from east to west. The second sphere was fastened onto the first and revolved counter to it from west to east, for the time required by the planet to traverse the zodiac_g —the twelve constellations the Sun passes through during its annual journey around the celestial sphere.[38] A third sphere was inserted to explain the irregular motions of the planets against the (apparently) uniform background motion of the stars. And finally the fourth sphere, to support the planet itself. By this method, Eudoxus explained all changes in the heavens by circular motion. It was a view of the universe that prevailed, with some modifications, for several centuries.

This, his most famous theory, has been called a "brilliant failure."[39] Nevertheless it was at the time, and still is considered today, an "admirable performance of geometrical sagacity" and "a monument of mathematical ingenuity."[40] It provided a solution to Plato's challenge—making use of the mind for ordering things—by showing how the irregular wanderings of the planets could be explained by perfectly circular motions. And it was based on careful observation and went beyond the mythical beliefs of earlier times.

Later historians of astronomy often brushed aside Eudoxus' theory of the 27 spheres as an absurdity because they did not see that mathematically it was a very elegant solution. This was not recognized until the 1800s when Ideler explained the underlying principles of Eudoxus' 27 spheres in two papers in the *Transactions* to the Berlin Academy in 1828 and 1830. And finally, in 1875, the Italian astronomer Giovanni Virginio Schiaparelli (1835–1910) restored the theory of the Eudoxean spheres and showed how well it could account—qualitatively, not quantitatively—for the motions of the stars and planets as observed with the primitive means available in the days of Greek antiquity.[41]

By careful examination, Schiaparelli demonstrated how close the Eudoxean estimates of the synodic and zodiacal periods came to modern-day estimates. The synodic period$_g$ refers to the time required for a planet to return to the same position relative to the Sun, that is, to the same celestial longitude. Similarly, the zodiacal period refers to the time required for a planet to return to the same constellation of stars. As shown in Table 3.1, with exception of Mars' synodic period the Eudoxean periods came within six percent of today's estimates.

Table 3.1: Comparison of Eudoxean Estimates of Synodic and
        Zodiacal Periods with Modern-Day Estimates

| | Synodic Periods | | Zodiacal Periods | |
|---|---|---|---|---|
| | Eudoxean Estimate in days | Modern-day Estimate in days | Eudoxean Estimate in days | Modern-day Estimate in days |
| Mercury | 116 | 110 | 365 | 365 |
| Venus | 584 | 570 | 365 | 365 |
| Mars | 780 | 260 | 730 | 687 |
| Jupiter | 399 | 390 | 4,334 | 4,383 |
| Saturn | 378 | 390 | 10,758 | 10,958 |

Source: Adapted from Sir Thomas L. Heath, as quoted in W. Durant (1966), p. 502

Schiaperelli found it impossible, however, to reconcile the Eudoxean estimate with modern-day estimates for the planet Mars, no matter how he juggled the inclination of the spheres. The estimation of the Martian orbits had created a problem that had puzzled astronomers for many centuries. It was not to be solved until Tycho de Brahe and Johannes Kepler came along some 2000 years later (Chapter 10). Nevertheless, the Eudoxean model of the planetary system performed amazingly well and we can only admire the imagination and ingenuity of its creator.[42]

In geometry Eudoxus invented the theory of proportions and the "method of exhaustion." Most of the axioms of this theory have been transmitted to us in Book V of Euclid's *Elements*. His "method of exhaustion" was a revolutionary technique and a forerunner of infinitesimal calculus. It made it possible to approximate, to any desired degree of accuracy, the area of a circle, the volume of a cone and a sphere.

Yet, his heart was in astronomy. Astrology and other mysticisms did not appeal to him. He did not want to speculate on things that he could not observe. He was so dedicated to astronomy that he once said "he would gladly be burnt up like Phaeton if at that price he could get to the Sun and ascertain its form, size and nature."[43] His life's work was a brilliant first attempt at a purely mathematical theory of the cosmos, based on actual observations of the heavenly motions.[44]

## Aristotle (384 B.C.–322 B.C.): The Universal Philosopher

Aristotle was Plato's star pupil. Born in the Greek town of Stagira on the Macedonian coast in Thrace, he was the son of Nichomachus, a physician and friend of the Macedonian King Amyntas. Even though Aristotle's parents had passed away when he was young, his father's profession influenced his course of education and the family connection to the Macedonian court prepared the way for Aristotle's employment at the court later in life.

He attended the lectures at Plato's Academy and stayed there, first as a student and later as a member of the Academy, from age 18 to 37.[45] For many years he adhered to Plato's abstract ideas on metaphysics, ethics, aesthetics, politics, and logic. After Plato's death, he left the Academy. He accepted an invitation from Prince Hermias, who at one time had himself attended the Academy. Not long after, Aristotle married the daughter of the Prince. Aristotle was about to settle in Asia Minor when Prince Hermias was assassinated by the Persians because they suspected him of helping King Philip of Macedonia to plan an invasion of Asia. Aristotle fled with his wife Pythias to the Aegean island of Lesbos where she died giving birth to their daughter. Although Aristotle remarried, he never overcame the loss of his first wife and, toward the end of his life, asked that his bones be buried beside hers.[46]

After the death of his first wife Aristotle became tutor to Prince Alexander, the son of King Philip of Macedonia. When Philip conquered Greece in 338 B.C., Aristotle returned to Athens and founded the "Lyceum," an educational institution named after a nearby temple of Apollo, Lykeius. Located in a beautiful section of the city, it was a museum of natural history. In the mornings Aristotle lectured on advanced subjects to regular students and in the afternoons he lectured to a popular audience on rhetoric, ethics, and politics.

Aristotle wrote about all branches of knowledge. He addressed questions of logic, science, metaphysics, esthetics, ethics, and politics. During antiquity his philosophy became known through 27 popular dialogues written for the educated layman. They were lost when the barbarians invaded Rome.

Only his lecture notes remained, covering the last 12 years of his life. In his books on physics he covered motion, space, and time. Instead of addressing the characteristics of nature by observation and experiment, he analyzed the meaning of everyday expressions and words.[47] He wrote eight books on astronomy. The first four dealt with meteorology and the second four with matters of the heavens. Not very interested in empirical verification, he rarely relied on his own astronomical observations, but accepted those of others and freely added commentaries in support of his own ideas. In the treatise *On the Heavens* he argued, for example, that the universe could not be infinite because an infinite universe could not revolve in 24 hours. Since heavenly bodies could not be at an infinite distance, space could not be infinite either.

While Plato had taught that the world had been created to last forever, Aristotle argued that the world had neither a beginning nor an end because one could not occur without the other. He believed that the world was spherical because a sphere was the only body which, during its revolution, continually took up the same space. He was convinced that the outermost sphere was the most perfect because the stars revolved in an unchangeable order. And he believed in a divine cause of motion that extended from the outer sphere to the center and not as Pythagoras had alleged from the center to the outer sphere.[48]

Aristotle felt quite uncomfortable with Eudoxus' mathematical model of 27 spheres. He saw the heavenly spheres as a vast machinery of interacting parts. For him, the problem was how to connect all the spheres, have them revolve around each other and, at the same time, prevent the motion of the outer spheres from being transmitted to the inner ones. To neutralize the interactions between spheres he inserted more of them, reaching a grand total of 55 spheres.[49]

In creating his system he had started with the abstract model of Eudoxus, accepted some modifications that had been introduced later, and superimposed more than 20 additional spheres. He was not very happy with this arrangement because now the number of spheres varied greatly between the Sun, the Moon, the planets, and the stars. Although more complex, his system did not significantly improve on the predictive power of Eudoxus' abstract mathematical model but it was "interactive."[51] He had conceived it as a set of transparent crystalline spheres that were connected to each other. It was the first model of a "world machine" and it was accepted by astronomers for the next five hundred years. By then Ptolemy had developed it further and the two competing models held sway over other models for the next fourteen centuries.[52]

Astronomy was only one of the many subjects that fascinated Aristotle. When Alexander became King of Macedon, he greatly expanded his father's kingdom. Wherever he went with his armies, he had scientists follow to collect animals, plants, and minerals for the Lyceum. Aristotle directed the classification of the materials, taught classes, and wrote extensively on many subjects ranging from zoology, botany, geology, to logic, ethics, politics, and others, including astronomy.[52] His treatises formed an encyclopedia of everything known in his day. It is probably fair to say that nothing rivaled it in scope for the next 2000 years.

Aristotle's conceptual analysis of all things was patterned after a geometric proof, starting with an assumption, followed by a proposition and leading to a logical conclusion. For example, he asserted that heaven is spherical because that shape is most appropriate and because motion "must not change in relation to the Mover. So, from first principles, it must lie either at the center or the circumference. But things nearest the Mover move fastest, and in this case the circumference moves fastest; therefore the Mover is at the circumference."[53] In this case Aristotle started from a plausible but false assumption, mingled it with some logical reasoning, and arrived at the wrong conclusion.

Aristotle maintained that observation yielded only information on the particular and could not yield a knowledge of universal laws of Nature. He stated, for example, that it did not matter how many times a rock was thrown up in the air and its motion observed, it was impossible to conclude from it why the rock fell as it did. This was a monumental error. Perpetuated over the next thousand years, the idea retarded progress in natural science until it was corrected by the observational scientists of the Renaissance.

The death of Aristotle marked the end of the Hellenic (old Greek) era. Alexander the Great had conquered much of what was then the known civilized world. In the midst of plans for reorganizing the government of his vast empire, Alexander suddenly took ill with malaria and, in his thirty-third year, died in Babylon in 323 B.C. As the empire fell apart, the Athenians rose up in revolt against Macedonian rule. They accused Aristotle of being a Macedonian sympathizer and charged him with impiety. Knowing what might await him, he fled and found refuge among the Macedonians in Chalcis. He died shortly after, in 322 B.C.[54]

Chapter 4

## THE ALEXANDRIAN AGE (388 B.C.–190 B.C.)

*When Ptolemy I, ruler of Egypt (323 B.C.–285 B.C.), asked Euclid if there was in geometry any shorter way than that of the* Elements, *Euclid replied that there was no royal road to geometry.*

Sir Thomas L. Heath[1]

Alexander the Great (356 B.C.–323 B.C.), King of Macedonia, was one of the greatest generals in history. His army conquered what was then most of the civilized world. At the same time he brought Greek ideas and the Greek way of doing things to all the countries he subdued.

By today's map, Macedonia ranged from southeastern Yugoslavia, to southwestern Bulgaria and northern Greece. Between 359 and 336 B.C. King Philip II, Alexander's father, expanded his kingdom into central Greece. He organized the Greek cities into a league under his control and began to prepare for war against the Persians. In the midst of this mobilization, however, he was assassinated (336 B.C.).[2]

### Alexander's Conquests

At age 20, Alexander took over his father's kingdom. He also inherited his father's unbridled ambition.[3] Aristotle, his former teacher at the court, had inspired in Alexander an appreciation of Greek literature, a lifelong interest in foreign cultures, and a fascination with natural sciences. But for Alexander, all his learning did not come from books. He met foreign ambassadors and came to know, and often befriended, the sons of rulers of other countries. At the age of 18 he commanded part of the Macedonian cavalry on the battlefield and acted as ambassador to Athens. King Philip was so proud of Alexander's achievements that he said to him: "Oh my son, seek out a kingdom worthy of thyself, for Macedonia is too little for thee."[4]

From early on, Alexander was preoccupied with military warfare and politics. He would have liked to devote more time to study. With a passion for learning and a love for reading, he often enjoyed sitting up half the night conversing with scholars and scientists, even after a day of marching or fighting. He generously supported a great variety of scientific inquiries, set up a commission to explore the sources of the Nile River, and richly endowed institutions of higher learning. He wrote to Aristotle: "I assure you I had rather excel others in the knowledge of what is excellent than in the extent of my power and domain."[5] Yet, it was not to be.

After six years of battle in Afghanistan, Uzbekistan, Kazakhstan, and Pakistan, on the long march back to the Mediterranean, along the Indus Valley, across the desert of southern Persia, he and his army arrived in Babylon. His body was weakened by the elements and heavy drinking and he caught malaria.[6] He died on June 23, 323 B.C. in the palace of Nebuchadnezzar, in his 33rd year.[7]

*Alexander's Legacy*

The Greeks did not view Alexander's death as the end of an era but more as a new beginning. Going back to the eighth century, the Hellenic[g] civilization was marked by an educational system in which the sons of nobility received their education at the court of a prince. The cult of the hero and champion of high performance was promoted. The ideal of a cultivated Greek patriot-warrior emerged.

After Alexander's death the Satraps, Macedonian governors appointed by him, ruled like monarchs. They controlled most of the eastern Mediterranean and the Middle East and provided the framework for the spread of Greek culture. The riches the Persian kings had accumulated in their treasuries were now distributed among the soldiers or spent by the new Satraps on highways, cities, harbours, temples, and statues. The infusion of wealth stimulated the economies.[8]

Greek merchants travelled the trade routes of the near East. They employed a growing proportion of the population and made great fortunes. The spirit of the early Ionian philosophers came into play again. It fused the classical Greek culture with that of the Babylonian and Egyptian civilizations, and this marked the transition from the Hellenic Era to the Hellenistic$_g$ Era of Greece.[9]

At a time when Greek literature and art were already on the decline, Greek science rose up again and reached its zenith during the new age.[10] Had it not been for Alexander's conquests and the merging with other cultures, the unique achievements of the Greek philosophers could well have been lost. Where in astronomy the Greek philosophers had focussed on the abstract, their counterparts in the Middle East and Egypt had kept meticulous records of their astronomical observations, their focus was empirical. Bringing together the two cultures would eventually lead to improvements in astronomy that lasted for more than 1000 years.

*Science*

In particular, the ideas and works of Aristotle were carried into this new age. Aristotle had classified all facts known to him in the form of an encyclopaedia. In it, he distinguished between the forces of heaven and Earth. According to him, objects on Earth followed one set of rules, while those in heaven followed another. Except for temporary disturbances, everything on Earth was at rest, everything in the heavens was in motion. The heavenly bodies followed the law of ideal motion: uniform circular motion. There were some exceptions. While all the stars moved together in perfect unison, the planets did not. Nevertheless, their motion could also be approximated by imposing some form of circular motion. This was accomplished by letting the deviant planets revolve in small circles, called epicycles, on the great circle of uniform motion of the stars.[11]

## Heraclides (388 B.C.–315 B.C.): The Earth Turns on its Axis

Aristotle's view of the universe was not without rival. A contemporary of

Aristotle, Heraclides Ponticus (named after the town Heraclea on the Pontus, at the southern coast of the Black Sea) was famous for his wide-ranging knowledge and his novel ideas of cosmology. However, all of his writings were lost and what is known of his views has been transmitted to us by later authors.

Heraclides was one of the first to believe that the Earth turned on its own axis from west to east; but it is less certain whether he believed the Earth moved in a circular orbit. When Simplicius wrote that Heraclides "thought to save the phenomena" he referred to the conundrum of the wandering planets.[12] Greek astronomers of antiquity had long known that the planets did not always proceed in a forward direction. They believed that for short periods of time, the planets went backward and then resumed their forward course again. Proposing that the Earth revolved around its own axis could not resolve this puzzling phenomenon.

Although it looked like an insoluble problem, Heraclides reportedly came up with a brilliant solution. Having observed that the planets Venus and Mercury were always close to the Sun, he believed them to be satellites of the Sun. Based on that observation he proposed that the planets' orbits around the Sun could be shaped like a corkscrew, with planets tracing out circular motions, at times moving along their orbits backward and away from Earth, and then again forward toward Earth.[13] Whether or not this was what Heraclides did say or meant to say has been questioned, but this is how the great nineteenth century Italian astronomer, Schiaperelli, interpreted Heraclides solution to the wandering planets.[14]

Some of Aristotle's students did not pursue this speculative cosmology, but followed the ideas of earlier mathematicians. They took up where the Pythagoreans had left off and searched for the mathematical laws of the universe. They focussed on the abstract. The greatest names among them were Euclid, Archimedes, and Apollonius.

## Euclid (ca. 300 B.C.): The Laws of Geometry

Very little is known about the life of Euclid. It is likely that he received his education at Plato's Academy in Athens. It is also fairly certain that he opened a school in Alexandria where graduates of his school excelled over those of other schools. Historians tell us that he was a very modest and kind man, and that he cared very little for money.

In the 13 volumes of his work, the *Elements*, he gave a vast systematic account of the laws of geometry and numerical analysis that had been discovered during the earlier Hellenic era.[15] Like his great predecessors, he confined himself to demonstrations and proofs that required no instruments other than straightedge and compass, proceeding from proposition and diagrammatic illustration to proof and conclusion. He began his exposition with 23 definitions, five postulates, and five axioms.[16] Omitting all he considered superfluous, he proceeded to select and arrange in due order the key elements and proofs from which all the rest follows.[17]

Euclid's theory of proportions and most of the propositions of Books V and VI originated with Eudoxus (see Chapter 3).[18] Using only a straightedge, it had always been possible to represent addition and subtraction by simply lengthening and shortening straight lines. The new theory of proportions made it possible to geometrically represent multiplication and division. By combining parallels with triangles, straight lines could be multiplied, divided, and ratios transferred from one line to another (Figure 4.1).[19] Eventually, the estimation by trigonometric ratios evolved from this method.

Euclid's writings were based on the discoveries of earlier mathematicians, going as far back as Thales and Pythagoras. Euclid did not explicitly acknowledge their contributions, most likely because he thought of his own contribution as merely a summary of what was known in geometry at the time. Yet, his method of logically progressive exposition was so successful that "Euclidean Geometry" was taught from the *Elements* for the next 2000 years. An incomparable record in the history of science, no other textbook even came close to it until modern times.[20]

## Archimedes (287 B.C.–215 B.C.): The Greatest Mathematician of Antiquity

Archimedes was the best-known mathematician and scientist of antiquity. The quality and scope of his work were not matched until Isaac Newton's in the seventeenth century. Born at Syracuse, on the island of Sicily, his father was the astronomer Pheidias. Astronomers were highly respected and well paid. His father was wealthy enough to send Archimedes to Alexandria to study at the same institution where Euclid once taught. The lectures so inspired Archimedes that he decided to pursue the study of mathematics and science for the rest of his life.[21]

After completing his studies in Alexandria he returned to Sicily where he lived and worked in a secluded, austere manner. When on the trail of a new theorem he often neglected food and drink while drawing geometric figures on the floor strewn with sand. His writings were not directed at students but were addressed, in the form of monographs, to other scholars who shared his interests.

His curiosity and inventiveness went far beyond the purely theoretical aspects of mathematics, science, and astronomy. While a student in Alexandria he invented a mechanism, the Archimedean screw, that was still used in the 20th century to raise the waters of the Nile for irrigation purposes. He is also known to us for his discovery of a basic law of hydrostatics, sometimes referred to as "the Principle of Archimedes."

The story of how he discovered this principle involves King Hieron of Syracuse, who had commissioned a goldsmith to make a crown for him out of pure gold. But when he received it, the King doubted that it was really made of pure gold. He asked Archimedes to find out, without damaging the crown, if the goldsmith had cheated him by adding silver to it. Archimedes had worked out the mathematical formulas for determining the volumes of spheres, cylinders and other geometric figures, but not for such an irregularly shaped form.

One day, when he stepped into a tub of water at the public bath, and the water ran over the rim, it suddenly struck him how to measure the volume and how to determine the specific gravity of the crown. He was so excited that he ran naked from the public bath and through the streets of Syracuse shouting "*Eureka, Eureka* (εὔρηκα, εὔρηκα) , I have found it, I have found it!" Bursting into his home, he weighed a lump of pure gold, then placed it in a container filled to the brim with water. He then measured the amount of water it displaced by the overflow. Next, he weighed the King's crown, immersed it in a container filled with water, and measured its displacement by the overflow. Since the overflow of water was a measure of the metal's volume, Archimedes found that the King's Crown displaced more water than it would have if it had been pure gold. So, it came out that the goldsmith had replaced some of the gold with a lighter metal. This was the serendipitous discovery of the Archimedean Principle, one that may have cost the goldsmith more dearly than the gold he had stashed away.[22]

Only ten of Archimedes' written works have survived to this day. In *The Method*, he explained to his friend Eratosthenes how mechanical experiments could help extend knowledge in geometry. He tells how he discovered certain theorems of geometric areas and volumes by first physically weighing the elements of one figure and comparing them to another simpler figure, and then furnishing the scientific proof by rigorous demonstration using orthodox geometric methods. In the *Collection of Lemmas* he deals with various hypotheses in geometry. In the *Measurement of a Circle* he estimates a value for $\pi$. In other treatises he provides proofs of theorems on the sphere and the cylinder, the quadrature of the parabola, theorems on spirals, on floating bodies, and on conoids and spheroids. In *The Sand-Reckoner* he switched from geometry to arithmetic, introducing the equivalent of exponential powers.[23]

His treatise, *Measurement of a Circle* consisted of only a few pages, yet it had an enormous impact. In it Archimedes provided not only a very accurate estimate of $\pi$ (the Greek letter *pi* for the factor that, multiplied by the diameter of a circle, yields the circumference), but applied the method of exhaustion. This technique could be taken as a forerunner to integral calculus, a method not discovered until many centuries later by Newton and Leibniz (see Chapter 12). Some essential elements of the method were missing, however, which left a gap that even Archimedes could not bridge. Nonetheless, it was the quality and precision of the work that made his treatise a classic.[24]

Long before Archimedes, people knew how to calculate the area of a triangle, rectangle, or square. They also knew how to approximate the area of a circle. According to the Rhind Papyrus—an Egyptian text dating back to 1650 B.C. and named after the Scottish Egyptologist A. Henry Rhind who bought the papyrus in 1858—the area of a circle was of the same size as that of a square with sides 8/9 times[25] the length of the diameter. If, for example, the diameter was 2, the ancient Egyptians estimated the area of the circle at *(2 ×{8/9})² = 3.16* . This ancient estimate came close to 0.6 % percent of today's value *(i.e., 3.16/3.14 = 1.006)*. Considering that it was arrived at by empirical approximation more than 3500 years ago, it was an excellent estimate.[26]

Archimedes was the first to devise a mathematical procedure for estimating the value of π. His idea was to approximate the circumference of the circle by calculating the perimeters of a many-sided polygon. It was done by calculating the polygon's perimeter once circumscribing the circle from the outside and once inscribing it from the inside. For a given number of the polygon's sides the perimeter circumscribing it exceeded the circumference of the circle, while that of the inscribed polygon fell short of it. This technique enabled him to approximate the area of the circle between an upper and a lower bound (see Figure 4.2). By increasing the number of sides, he could bring the two bounds closer together and thereby improve on the estimate of π.[27]

In dealing with the estimation of curvilinear areas and volumes of geometric figures, Archimedes applied this method of exhaustion that minimized, to any desired degree, the deviation from the true values.[28] The underlying proposition was given in Euclid:

> If from any magnitude there be subtracted a part, not less than its half, and if from the remainder one again subtracts not less than its half, and if the process of subtraction is continued, ultimately there will remain a magnitude less than any preassigned magnitude of the same kind.[29]

Although Eudoxus is credited with originating the concept, Archimedes was the first to describe it formally and to apply it to specific problems. Figure 4.2 illustrates his approach. By repeating this process he could obtain perimeters of polygons of 12, 24, 48, and 96 sides, with each yielding a better approximation.

To calculate the circumference of successive polygons Archimedes applied an ingenious algorithm.[30] The underlying concept was to estimate at what rate the lengths of the polygon's sides diminish relative to its radius as the number of sides are doubled. Although it is likely that Archimedes was aware of trigonometric ratios, he chose to abide by the Euclidean geometry of straightedge and compass. Instead of following his very ingenious but rather difficult geometric approach, a simplified trigono-metrical shortcut to calculating the circumference of successive polygons is shown in Chapter 6.

As a close advisor to King Hieron, the mathematical services of Archimedes came to be appreciated in more practical matters. When the king heard of the physical power Archimedes could apply by use of lever and pulley, he asked for a demonstration. Archimedes arranged a series of cogs and pulleys in such a way that he, all by himself and without much exertion, pulled a fully loaded vessel out of the water onto land. Deeply impressed, the king asked Archimedes to apply his knowledge to the design of machinery of war. Archimedes did and Hieron was delighted. Yet, as a peace-loving monarch he never made use of them.[31]

After Hieron's death, Syracuse was drawn into conflict with Rome. The Roman Commander Marcellus attacked by land and sea. Even though Archimedes was in his mid-seventies, he oversaw the deployment of the defences. Behind the fortified walls that protected the city, catapults were installed that hurled rocks at the enemy on land. Cranes dropped monstrous rocks on the Roman ships when they came close to the harbour's walls. Others lifted the ships with massive hooks right out of the water and smashed them against the rocks at the base of the walls. Mirrors were used to set the ships on fire. In the end the Roman soldiers dared not come close to the walls and retreated if as much as a rope showed above them.

When his soldiers refused to prepare for another attack, Marcellus withdrew and decided to conquer Syracuse by siege. After seven months, the starved-out city surrendered. The Roman conquerors plundered the city. Marcellus had its works of art and many statues removed to Rome. By 210 B.C. the whole island of Sicily had fallen into Roman hands and had been reduced to a granary. The once great city of Syracuse withered away. It was not to recover for a thousand years.[32]

As the story goes, during the pillage of Syracuse, Marcellus gave the order to bring Archimedes to him. A Roman soldier found him in his garden, drawing figures in the sand. When he saw the shadow of the soldier obscure his drawings, Archimedes exclaimed: "Don't disturb my circles!" Intensely occupied with the proof of a theorem, he asked the Roman soldier to wait until he had worked out his mathematical problem. The soldier drew his sword and killed him on the spot.

When Marcellus found out what had happened, he was shocked and grieved. He did everything he could for the scientist's family. He had an imposing tomb erected. As Archimedes had wished, engraved on it was a sphere within a cylinder.[33] A century later when Cicero, a distinguished Roman orator and statesman, became the treasurer of Sicily, he could not find anyone who had ever heard of Archimedes, let alone knew of his grave. After a long search he found the marble tomb among thorny bushes, totally covered in weeds. He had the burial plot cleared and the inscriptions refurbished.[34] Today, more than 2000 years later, nearly every high school graduate has heard of Archimedes.

## Apollonius (262B.C.–190B.C.): Master of Conic Sections

The next great mathematician after Euclid and Archimedes was Apollonius of Perga.[35] He revived some of the lost writings of Euclid by making Euclid's *Conics* the starting point of his own treatise. He, too, had studied and taught in Alexandria until he moved to Pergamon, an important center of scientific studies on the coast of Asia Minor.

Apollonius was famous among astronomers. They referred to him as the "Great Geometer" and nicknamed him $\epsilon$ (epsilon) because much of his outstanding work was on the motion of the Moon and $\epsilon$ (epsilon) was the traditional Greek symbol for the Moon. No written record exists of his work on astronomy.[36] Nevertheless, he had a decisive impact on the evolution of astronomy ( Chapter 7).

He rivalled Archimedes as a geometer. It is said that his writings were laborious and verbose, but as definitive as the work of Euclid. He expanded on Euclid's work and comprehensively described his discoveries in eight books. His writings, with nearly 400 propositions on conic sections, are considered a classic on the subject. Apollonius was the first to discover that the parabola, the ellipse, and hyperbola could all be generated as sections by varying the angle of the cutting plane of a circular single cone or a circular double cone (Figure 4.3).[37] This discovery led to an elegant unification of proofs of his propositions.

In his books, Apollonius proved that the midpoints of chords stretched parallel to the major axis of an ellipse fall on the minor axis of it. He explored how to draw tangents to conic sections, examined a variety of ways in which conic sections can meet each other, described how lines of minimum and maximum length can be drawn to a conic from various points, treated congruent and similar conics, and discussed diameter issues.[38]

In the present context only a few properties of the ellipse will be introduced. More properties will be explained in Chapter 7. An ellipse can be thought of as a stretched circle. A circle can be traced out with a string attached around its one center point. An ellipse can be described with a string wrapped around two central points. The two points are usually called "foci." The longer the string, the greater the ellipse. If the foci are fixed, a string of given length will determine the shape and size of the ellipse.

A tangent line that touches the circumference of an ellipse forms two angles of equal size with the rays connecting the tangent point with the two focus points. A ray coming from one focus point is deflected just like a mirror would deflect a beam of light. The ray is deflected by the tangent at the precise angle required to meet with the second focal point. This phenomenon is referred to as the "optical property" of the ellipse. Some 1800 years later it played a key role in Kepler's discovery that the planetary orbits are elliptical. Figure 4.4, Diagrams 1 to 6, illustrate the kind of geometric proof (simplified and abbreviated) Apollonius provided. It describes an obscure theorem that Newton made use of when he analysed the impact gravity has on the shape of the planetary orbits.

Aside from his theoretical work on conics, Apollonius is said to have derived an empirical estimate of the value of π (pi, the ratio of a circle's circumference to its diameter) that was even more accurate than Archimedes' estimate.[39] Applying the Eudoxean method of exhaustion, Archimedes had derived estimation procedures for the areas of the circle and segments of the parabola but not for the ellipse and segments of the hyperbola. In that respect, Apollonius did not go beyond Archimedes even though Archimedes had correctly guessed that the entire area of an ellipse equaled the product of π and its minor and major axes. Neither Archimedes nor Apollonius supplied a proof of this proposition.

When questioned about the value of his results, Apollonius is said to have replied: "They are worthy of the acceptance for the sake of the demonstrations themselves, in the same way as we accept many other things in mathematics for this and no other reason."[40] Yet, many centuries later his work on the circle, the parabola, the ellipse, and the hyperbola formed the basis for studying theoretical aspects of projectiles, navigation, and astronomy.[41]

Chapter 5

## ARISTARCHUS (310 B.C.–230 B.C.) AND ERATOSTHENES (273 B.C.–192 B.C.)

*The center of scientific research shifted from Athens to Alexandria, the most successful of Alexander's new cities, the meeting place of scholars from all over the world.*

Bertrand Russell[1]

About 300 B.C. Athens had passed its zenith and was on the decline. Alexandria was taking its place as the center of Hellenistic culture. The new city had been founded by Alexander the Great in 332 B.C. after the start of his Persian campaign. He named the city after himself. It was to be the capital of his great Egyptian dominion. Alexander had chosen its location because it was an ideal site for a naval base that could control the Mediterranean.

Not long after Alexander's early death, Ptolemy, one of his generals, started building the new city. Like Alexander, Ptolemy was a student of Aristotle. He founded the great Egyptian dynasty of the Ptolemies. Ptolemy was keenly interested in education and the promotion of knowledge and information. He built the great library of Alexandria and let it be known that scholars were welcome.

Liberated from the oppressive force of Phoenician power, Alexandria profited from the growing trade with the Mediterranean countries. Shipping from the East passed through a canal connecting the Nile River with the Mediterranean and the Red Sea. Within a century of its founding Alexandria became the greatest city in the world, a center of Greek scholarship and new science. Many great scholars studied and taught at Alexandria. The mathematicians Euclid and Archimedes, the geographer Eratosthenes, and the astronomer Ptolemy all attended the Museion, the unique Research Institute of Alexandria.[2]

## Aristarchus (ca. 310 B.C.–230 B.C.)

Aristarchus was a contemporary of Archimedes. He came from Samos, the same island Pythagoras had escaped from three centuries earlier. He was a student of Strato of Lampsacus, the head of the peripatetic$_g$ school, so later named after its founder, Aristotle.[3] Aristarchus was a skilled geometer and astronomer. Of his writings only the treatise *"On the Sizes and Distances of the Sun and the Moon"* survived. He is also credited with a more precise value for the length of the solar year. Today a lunar crater, in the center of the brightest formation on the Moon, is named after him.[4]

Aristarchus was one of the scientists who found a home in Alexandria. Today he is best known as the first astronomer who conceived of a heliocentric (Sun-centered) planetary system. He stated that the Earth revolved on its axis while circling the Sun, which he asserted was at the center of the solar system. Even for the speculative philosophers of Greece his heliocentric concept was too much. It was too radical a break from the traditional geocentric (Earth-centered) concept of an Earth, stationary at the center of the universe. It meant the stars did not revolve around the Earth and sunrise and sunset were not for real because the Sun did not rise and set. Although controversial in his views, Aristarchus was a great mathematician and astronomer, one of only a few philosophers of his time who possessed a deep knowledge of all branches of science.[5]

Unfortunately, none of his writings on the formulation and reasoning behind his heliocentric model have survived. We only know of it because Archimedes' treatise, *Sand-Reckoner*, referred to Aristarchus' heliocentric model:

> You [King Gelon] are aware that "universe" is the name given by
> most astronomers to the sphere at the center of which is the center

of the Earth, while its radius is equal to the straight line between the center of the Sun and the center of the Earth. This is the common account, as you have heard from astronomers.

Aristarchus' hypotheses are that the fixed stars and the Sun remain unmoved, that the Earth revolves about the Sun in the circumference of a circle, the Sun lying in the middle of the orbit, and that the sphere of the fixed stars, situated about the same center as the Sun, is so great that the circle in which he supposes the Earth to revolve bears such a proportion to the distance of the fixed stars as the center of the sphere bears to its surface.[6]

See Figure 5.1 for illustrations of the geocentric and heliocentric universes.

## The Assumptions

Archimedes did not elaborate on the assumptions Aristarchus enlisted in support of his heliocentric system. Aristarchus' treatise, *On the Sizes and Distances of the Sun and the Moon,* gives us a hint why he opted in favor of the heliocentric model. In introducing his work on astronomic distances he followed the classical tradition of setting out his assumptions first. They were:

- the universe is infinitely great not only in relation to the Sun but relative to the orbit of the Earth as well;

- the apparent angular diameter of the Sun is $2°$ (2 degrees$_g$ or 1/180th part of the Zodiac$_g$ Circle, the band of constellations through which the Sun moves during the course of a year (Diagrams 1–4 of Figure 5.2);

- the angular diameters of the Sun and Moon are equal at the center of the Earth;

- the great circle which divides the bright and the dark portions of the Moon, when the Moon appears to us exactly halved, is in line with our eyesight;

- at the time of half-Moon the centers of the Sun, Moon and Earth form a right-angled triangle at the center of the Moon;

- the corresponding angle of this right triangle at the center of the

51

Earth is 87°; and

- the shadow of the Earth is twice the width of the Moon when it traverses it.[7]

Although the term Zodiac Circle is derived from the Greek words animal sign, *zodion* (ζῴδιον), and circle, *kyklos* (κὐκλος), the expression was coined by Sumerian astrologers hundreds of years earlier (Figure 5.2). Like other Greek astronomers Aristarchus was not interested in the pseudoscience of astrology but fascinated by the mathematical structure of the cosmos.

From these assumptions and a set of geometric constructs, Aristarchus estimated the size and the distance of the Moon and the Sun. He was hampered, of course, by a lack of instruments. The underlying astronomic measurements were the best available in his day, but by today's standards they were very inaccurate.

**Astronomical Distances**

Aristarchus was the first astronomer to compute astronomical distances. In estimating how far it was to the Moon, he started with the fact perhaps commonly accepted among astronomers of his day that the diameter of the Moon measured 180th of the Zodiac Circle, the great band of star constellations encircling the Earth at night (Figure 5.2). This made the width of the Moon $360°/180 = 2°$.[8]

*Distance to the Moon*

He geometrically illustrated his estimation procedure by drawing two lines from the center of the Earth tangential to the circle representing the lunar sphere. By connecting the tangents' points to the center of the Moon, he constructed two rectangular triangles. From the ratios of two of their sides he estimated the distance to the Moon. It is not known how he arrived at these ratios. Perhaps they were already known among mathematicians of his day and he simply included them in his assumptions. From these ratios Aristarchus estimated how many lunar spheres it would take to fill the distance from the Earth to the Moon. He concluded that the Moon-Earth distance ranged from 22.5 to 30 diameters of the Moon (Figure 5.3[9]).

His estimates were far off the mark. By today's measure the diameter of the Moon is 2160 miles (3476 kilometers) and its mean distance from Earth 238,863 miles (384,403 kilometers). Aristarchus' estimate put the Moon's distance from the Earth at 46,468 to 64,624 miles (78,000–104,000 kilometers). His estimates fell short, not because of an error in logic but because of a faulty assumption. The angle of the Moon's width is not 2° but close to ½°. Had Aristarchus based his calculation on ½°, he would have arrived at an estimate of some 248,555 miles (400,000 kilometers). That would have been within less than five percent of the correct distance.[10] His erroneous estimate could have been due to the lack of astronomical equipment, but it could also have come from his overriding interest in theory and his lack of concern for accurate empirical verification.

*Distance to the Sun*

Using the Moon-Earth distance as a base, Aristarchus went on to estimate the distance of the Sun from the Earth. About three centuries earlier Anaximander (ca. 611–545 B.C.) had speculated that the Sun was one and a half times farther away from the Earth than the Moon; Eudoxus (408–355 B.C.) believed it was 9 times farther away and Phidias, the father of Archimedes, claimed it to be 12 times farther away. Aristarchus estimated that the Sun was 18 to 20 times farther away from the Earth than the Moon, again an improvement over earlier estimates.

We do not know how the earlier astronomers arrived at their conclusions. They left no written record of it. Aristarchus did. He described his method in the treatise *On the Sizes and Distances of the Sun and the Moon*. His method was similar to the earlier one of finding the Moon-to-Earth distance.[11]

Aristarchus based his estimate on the triangulation of Sun, Moon, and Earth. During the first quarter of the lunar month the Moon waned from full Moon to half-Moon. After that it waxed to full Moon, then waned and reached half-Moon again in the last quarter. Some time during the period of half-Moon, the line between the light half and the dark half cut the lunar sphere exactly into two halves. From this Aristarchus deduced that when the Moon appeared precisely halved, the centers of the Sun, Moon, and

Earth formed a triangle with a right angle at the Moon.[12] He added to this the assumption that the imaginary lines connecting the Earth to the Moon and the Earth to the Sun formed an angle of 1/30 less than a right angle (i.e., 90°-3° or 87° ). The remaining third angle formed by the lines connecting the Sun to the Moon and the Sun to the Earth, therefore, amounted to 180°-90°-87° = 3° (Figure 5.3).

With this information on hand, Aristarchus set out to prove that the distance of the Sun from the Earth was 18 to 20 times farther away from the Earth than the Moon. The actual Sun-Earth distance is 389 times the Moon-Earth distance, or about 20 times greater than the distance Aristarchus estimated.[13] This disparity is much greater than the earlier discrepancy of his estimate of the Moon-Earth distance, partly because it was based on inaccurate observations, and partly because reliance on the earlier estimates of the lunar distance compounded the error.

*Sizes of the Moon and Sun*

Having deduced how far the Sun was from the Earth, Aristarchus tried to find out how big the Sun was. He based his estimation on two assumptions:

1.   The apparent angular diameter of both the Sun and the Moon is 2° as seen from the Earth, and

2.   The diameter of the Moon is half as wide as that of Earth.

The first assumption may reflect a common misconception among astronomers of his day. The second assumption was probably based on a lunar eclipse (when the shadow of the Earth passed across the Moon). The curvature of the shadow's edge may have suggested to him that the cross section of the Earth was twice as large as that of the Moon.

Aristarchus incorporated the two observations in a diagram showing the line-up of the Sun, the Earth, and the Moon as they appeared to him during a lunar eclipse. Since he assumed the visual angles of the Sun and Moon to be of equal size, the Sun was 19 times farther than the Moon-to-Earth distance. It followed from the similarity of the visual angles and the geometry of proportions, that the Sun's diameter was also 19 times that of the Moon. Since Aristarchus reckoned that the width of the Moon was only half that of the Earth, he concluded that the Sun's diameter was nearly 10 times that of the Earth (Figure 5.4).[14]

Modern-day estimates put the Sun's diameter at 109 times greater than the Earth.[15] This is more than 10 times larger than Aristarchus had estimated. His error was to inaccurately measure the angles of the triangle formed by the imaginary lines connecting Earth, Moon, and Sun. Using the naked eye to estimate the visual angle of the Sun was imprecise. As well, he had underestimated the Moon-Earth distance by a substantial margin and that accentuated the error.[16]

Nevertheless, it was an extraordinary achievement. His geometric analysis had clearly convinced him that the Sun was much larger than the Earth, nearly 10 times as large. This, of course, raised the next question of why this huge Sun should revolve around the much smaller Earth. Why should the tail wag the dog? To answer this question Aristarchus stated that the Earth was not the center of the universe and that the Earth and the planets all orbited around the Sun.

## Why did Aristarchus' Heliocentric Model Not Prevail?

No written record of Aristarchus' heliocentric view has ever been found. It is only known because Archimedes mentioned it in his book, *Sand-Reckoner*. Archimedes did not leave the impression that he found Aristarchus' proposition very convincing.

There were several reasons why Aristarchus' heliocentric arguments did not prevail. Many years earlier Aristotle had pointed out that if it were true that the Earth revolved about the Sun, then the stars would not stand still but ought to move the other way. Yet, they did not. And if the universe were to be of infinite size, as Aristarchus suggested, the stars would have to move faster according to how far away from Earth they are. At an infinite distance the stars would have to move at infinite speed. As anyone could plainly see, the stars stood still. It is not known if astronomers questioned the accuracy of the astronomical estimates Aristarchus had used. While the precision of his observations was unsatisfactory, his geometric reasoning was based on impeccable logic.

Moreover, a heliocentric world was not a welcome concept. Two centuries earlier the Greek philosopher Anaxagoras (500 B.C.–428 B.C.) had asserted that the Sun was a huge flaming rock and for this he was tried for blasphemy, impiety, and atheism in the court of Athens. In his great wisdom he fled from Athens. Aristarchus had gone much further. He had proved mathematically that the Sun was not only greater than the Earth, but he had displaced the Earth from the center of the universe. Cleanthes, a stoic philosopher who lived at the time of Aristarchus, was strongly opposed to this radical view. He considered it a blasphemy of the gods and publicly advocated Aristarchus be tried in court. Yet, it did not come to that.[17]

Aristarchus' very novel idea left no great impression on his contemporaries. Even Archimedes treated it as no more than an oddity and so, for nearly 2000 years the heliocentric theory did not surface again. It may seem strange that the speculative philosophers of Hellenistic times did not embrace the heliocentric view. Perhaps they did not because something else was in the making. Rather than dramatic developments in abstract geometry, there was a drastic change toward greater precision in observation and empirical measurement of the celestial motions.

## Eratosthenes  (273 B.C.–192 B.C.)

In his day, Eratosthenes was best known as a mathematician. Archimedes knew him as a colleague and friend and frequently communicated with him. Today we know of him as the first mathematical geographer, the first to estimate the circumference of the Earth by a correct geometric procedure.

He was born in Cyrene, the capital city of Cyrenaica, of what is now eastern Libya. The first Greeks had landed there around 700 B.C. and colonized the region. It did not take the Cyrenaican aristocracy very long to adopt the Greek language and culture. After Alexander's death, his general Ptolemy devoted himself to consolidating his position in Egypt by promoting agriculture, industry, and commerce. He built a strong fleet to secure Egypt against attack. In time, he established Greek-Egyptian rule over Phoenicia, Syria, Palestine, and some of the major islands of Mediterranean Sea. During his reign Cyrenaica became an Egyptian province.[18]

While still in his teens, Eratosthenes left home for Athens to study at the Academy and the Lyceum. By age 30 he had completed his studies. A man of many talents, he wrote poetry, produced a history of comedy, assembled a time table of the major historical events around the Mediterranean, edited a *Geographica* in which he summarized the reports of Alexander's surveyors, wrote mathematical monographs, and described his astronomical observations.[19] In mathematics he invented, for example, a simple method of picking prime numbers (*Sieve of Eratosthenes*), and a mechanical method of doubling the volume of a cube. And in astronomy he maintained the geocentric view, and put the Sun next to the Moon. Other mathematicians, who agreed with him on this, differed from him only in the order of the planetary distances from the Earth, some putting Venus and others Mercury next to Earth.[20] Unfortunately, only some fragments of his writings survived.

His works attracted so much attention that Ptolemy III of Egypt invited him to become his son's tutor. He also served as a librarian at the library of Alexandria. Within a short time he was promoted to senior fellow and then chief of the library.[21] Under his administration the library of Alexandria expanded in size. With a collection of some 600,000 manuscripts, it became the greatest library in the world. For nearly 50 years Eratosthenes guided its development along scientific lines rather than literary arts. With his successors following his lead, Alexandria became the center of science for the next 500 years.[22]

**First Measure of the Size of the Earth**

Eratosthenes is best known as the first to have arrived at an accurate measure of the size of the Eartha most remarkable achievement. He estimated the circumference of the Earth long before anyone had ever traveled around the globe.

In his book, *On the Measurement of the Earth*, he described his estimation procedure. Following the classical pattern of deductive reasoning in plane geometry he first stated his assumptions:

1. The Earth is a perfectly shaped sphere;

2. Sunbeams, originating at a great distance, are parallel; and

3.  An imaginary straight line passing from the Sun when it is directly overhead extends straight to the center of the Earth.

He knew that in midsummer the noonday Sun was reflected in the water of a very deep well on Elephantine Island, a small island situated in the Nile River near Syene (the modern-day Aswan). Once a year, at the time of the summer equinox on June 21, the Sun's reflection was so intense that it lit up the well to its full depth.[23] This meant that precisely on this day the Sun stood straight overhead at noon. Not so, however, in Alexandria. The city was nearly 500 miles due north of Syene. There, Eratosthenes observed that the Sun shining on a pillar-like obelisk at noon of the same day at the time of the summer solstice when the Sun stood highest above the horizon threw a distinct shadow. The shadow's angle measured 1/48 of a 360-degree circle, an angle of *360/48 = 7.5°*. Knowing from plane geometry that if lines are parallel, their alternate interior angles are equal, then the imaginary angle at the center of the Earth had to be a 7.5° angle (Figure 5.5).[24]

The distance between Syene and Alexandria was approximately 5000 stadia$_g$. Therefore, a straight line drawn through the two cities and extended around the globe was *50 x 5000 = 250,000* stadia. After some additional readings and corrections for errors he obtained a final estimate of 252,000 stadia. Converted to miles (at 10.218 stadia per mile) this amounted to 24,662 miles (39,689 km) for the circumference or roughly 7850 miles (12,633 km) for Earth's diameter from pole to pole.[25] His calculations were very accurate estimates that came within one percent of the true values, the result of a combination of elegant geometry and empirical knowledge—truly a great achievement.[26]

Chapter 6

# THE LAST OF THE GREEK ASTRONOMERS
## ( 180 B.C.–180 A.D. )

*The* Almagest, *the astronomical and mathematical encyclopaedia compiled about 140 A.D. by Claudius Ptolemy, served as the basic guide for Arab and European astronomers until about the beginning of the 17th century. It was first translated from Greek into Arabic in 827 A.D. and then re-translated from Arabic to Latin in the last half of the 12th century.*

*Encyclopaedia Britannica*[1]

Hipparchus and Ptolemy were the greatest astronomers of the Hellenistic era. Their outstanding achievements in astronomy were perhaps the most important result of the Greek-Oriental contact. The cultural exchange brought together the abstract theoretical thinking of the Greek astronomers with the observational perspectives of the Oriental astrologers. The result of this confluence of thinking would last for the next thousand years.[2]

## Hipparchus (ca.180–100 B.C.)
Hipparchus was the greatest astronomer of Hellenistic times. His outstanding achievements were perhaps the most important result of the

Greek-Oriental contact. They were linked to the Babylonian observational astronomy that was in full bloom in his day.

He was born around 180 B.C. near the city of Byzantium, today called Istanbul (Turkey). It is known that he spent three decades (160 B.C.–129 B.C.) recording and analysing astronomical observations in Alexandria.[3] He then moved on to the island of Rhodes, a rich commercial center and intense rival to Alexandria in all matters of arts and science. He was invited there to set up an astronomical observatory, a position which allowed him to work on his observations for a number of years. Unfortunately, nearly all his written treatises have been lost.[4] Nevertheless, most of his astronomical findings were transmitted to us by Claudius Ptolemy, the last of the Greek astronomers, who is featured later in this chapter.

Historians have been able to credit Hipparchus as a very accurate and patient researcher, a careful collector of astronomical data, a very gifted man with a great curiosity, a brilliant theoretician, and a great scientist forever in search of truth. Many achievements have been ascribed to him, among them:

- the translation of the Babylonian records for determining the solar, lunar, and sidereal$_g$ lengths of years;

- improvements to Babylonian astronomical instruments;

- the invention of longitudes and latitudes;

- the first western discovery of a supernova and the creation of a star catalogue;

- assembling the first trigonometric tables of sines$_g$; and

- estimating the distance to the Moon with greater accuracy.[5]

*Translation of the Babylonian Records*

Hipparchus was in full possession of all the observations the Babylonian astronomers had recorded.[6] Other Greeks before him, like Thales, had obtained information on certain aspects of Mesopotamian astronomy. But Hipparchus was the first to have access to all the Babylonian records dating as far back as the eighth century B.C. After Alexander the Great's conquest of Babylonia the exchange of such information became possible. It is plausible that one of the astronomer scribes of Babylonia personally instructed Hipparchus and supplied him with the material. As well, he knew their techniques for predicting lunar and planetary phenomena. It was an enormous amount of information.[7]

Even after the Babylonian records were translated into Greek, it must have been a huge task for Hipparchus to convert all the lunar data (the dates of the waxing and waning of the moon) of the Babylonian kingdoms into the Greek calender. He also had to convert all numerical data from the Babylonian sexagesimal system into the Greek number system. The Babylonians used cuneiform inscriptions with wedge-shaped characters, for writing. To write numbers they arranged characters in groups of wedge-shaped symbols, each group denoting the next higher level in the sexagesimal system. Whereas the Greeks used letters (analogous to the Roman numbers) and fractions of integers in their numerical notation.

With their focus on astrology, Babylonian astrologers predicted future events from recurring celestial phenomena. Around 500 B.C. they started using linear zig-zag functions. For example, they recorded the luminosity of the Moon over periods of 30 days, the lunar month. At the beginning of the month the Moon was hardly visible, it reached a full Moon in the middle of the month, and diminished to zero at the end of the month (Figure 6.1, Diagram 1).

They also kept detailed records of periodic changes in the positions of the planets Mars, Jupiter, and Saturn, as well as the times of lunar and solar eclipses.[8] To record the occurrence of celestial events and changes in the planets' positions the Babylonians used mechanical instruments that functioned like an astrolabe (Figure 6.1, Diagram 2). The term astrolabe comes from the Greek expression *astrolabon organon* (ἀστρολάβον ὄργανον) or "astronomic instrument," a term that is not nearly as specific as the English word "astrolabe." After recording the periodicities$_g$ they used them for their astrological forecasts and for adjusting their annual calendar when necessary. Notably, the Babylonians considered the astrological forecasts as more important than tracking their calendar.

61

*The Invention of Longitude and Latitude*

Greek philosophers had no interest in astrology. They were not interested in observing and continuous recording of motions of the Moon, the planets, or in keeping records of celestial events such as eclipses of the Sun and the Moon. In keeping with the Hellenic philosophy of abstract generalizations, they followed in the footsteps of Pythagoras and Aristotle.

Greek philosophers knew that the North Star, Polaris, was the closest marker to the celestial pole$_g$. Polaris was so close to the pole that it did not move like the other stars.[9] Not a very bright star, it could be found with the aid of the two most familiar constellations, the Big Dipper and the Little Dipper. In Greek culture, as in many other cultures, these two constellations were associated with the image of bears even though they hardly resembled them. It has been suggested that the configurations of the two constellations slowly changed and that some 250,000 years ago they may have looked more like the outline of a bear.[10] In the same neighborhood is a bright star which the Greeks named Arcturus from the Greek for bear keeper (αρκτοῦρος ). The Greek philosophers also knew that the five planets circled the Earth in a somewhat erratic pattern and they called them *planetes* (πλᾰνῆτης), Greek for wanderers or hobos.

Hipparchus set a new course in astronomy. He could not believe that confusion ruled the heavens. To get at the underlying design he wanted to accurately position the celestial events and planetary motion in three-dimensional space, over a period of months and years. Obviously, there was some order in the skies. On evenings he could observe the stars rise in the east, saw them revolve during the night in a great circle around the North Star, and then toward morning he saw them disappear in the west. Around the Mediterranean only the constellations near the celestial pole, such as the Great Bear (or Big Dipper), the Little Bear (or Little Dipper) and some others, never vanished below the horizon. And there were the five wandering planets.

The pictorial impressions of the constellations were inadequate for accurately predicting the motions of celestial objects. To attain the needed precision he invented a coordinate system that conceptually corresponds to today's longitudes and latitudes of geographic locations. Drawn on the sphere of a globe the longitudinal lines run 63 from north 63to south, each representing half a circle from North Pole to South Pole (like the seams separating the sections of an orange). Any location on the line connecting north to south, when the Sun is exactly overhead at noon, is the meridian (from the Latin *meridies* for mid-day or south), that is, the longitude of that specific location. By contrast, the lines of latitude run parallel to the equator. The equator forms the great circle. The latitudes above and below the equator make smaller circles just like the slices of an orange get smaller when cut from middle to outer end (Figure 6.2, Diagram 1 and 2).

No coordinate system of the Earth had ever been designed before. Hipparchus started from scratch. Following earlier philosophers he believed that the Earth's globe extended to the sphere of the universe. He let the Earth's axis be aligned with the North Star, Polaris. He marked the meridian of his locale on the base of his new astrolabe when the Sun stood highest and his scope pointed straight south. The complete circle of the base was 360°. When observing the stars at night he could line up the scope of his astrolabe with a star. While tracking it along the ecliptic$_g$, he found that pointer at the base advanced every hour by 15° as the stars appeared to moved from east to west (i.e., one 24th of 360° with the Earth's revolution). It was possible, therefore, for him to measure the hourly motion of planets by longitudinal degrees (Figure 6.3, Diagram 1 and 2).

To pinpoint the position of a celestial object he needed, in addition to longitude, to find its precise latitude. Having divided the circumference of the globe into 360°, Hipparchus set the range in latitude at one quarter of the globe from 0° to 90°, spanning the distance from the celestial equator (at 0°) to the North Pole (at 90°). To find the latitude at any location, he redesigned the Babylonian astrolabe so that changes in the scope's line of sight allowed him to read the latitude directly from a scale on his astrolabe.

Hipparchus began with a conceptual model (Figure 6.3, Diagram 3). Since the light from the star Polaris appeared straight north irrespective of the observer's place, he correctly assumed that the light rays from the stars reached the Earth in parallel. To estimate the latitude at his location he only needed to determine the angle formed between the North Star and the line extending to the horizon. This immediately gave him the angular distance between the equator and his locale. To determine the altitude of a celestial object in the sky he chose its angular distance from the North Star. For example, assume the angle of latitude was 40° and the angular distance of the celestial object as measured from the North Star was 16°. The latitude of the observed star or planet was then estimated at 74°. Although at another location the geographic latitude differed, the altitude of the celestial object measured by the angular distance from the line of sight of the North Star, remained the same (Figure 6.3, Diagrams 4 and 5).

Since the geographic longitudes and latitudes differed among locations, Hipparchus searched for methods yielding universally acceptable coordinates. His method of estimating latitudes would have yielded the same results irrespective of geographic location. The determination of longitudes, however, hinged on east-west comparisons of time and distance. This would have required the cooperation of astronomers and geographers around the Mediterranean. Hipparchus attempted to have astronomers of the Mediterranean make observations to identify the exact location of their cities.[11] He did not succeed in this venture, however, because in his day the few astronomers were scattered far and wide, in location and time. Also, he suggested that the geographic longitudes could be determined by observing the duration of solar eclipses, an acceptable method in theory but not a practical one in his day.[12]

Nevertheless, with his new coordinate system he could translate the Babylonian files into systematic astronomical records allowing him to trace the motions of celestial objects over long periods of time, in some cases going back through centuries. In measuring changes in the positions of celestial objects he did not need to rely on images of star constellations$_g$, but could pinpoint their latitude in relation to the equator and their longitude by the angular distance from the North Star. By this novel technique astronomical observations could be made comparable among different geographic locations and, of course, Hipparchus could augment the Babylonian records with his own observations of several decades.

*Celestial Survey*

Hipparchus assembled the first accurate star catalogue. Reportedly, this came about when he discovered an unusually bright star in an area of the sky where he had never seen a star before.[13] It was a new star, possibly a nova or supernova appearing in the year 134 B.C.[14] Until then, astronomers had believed that the stars were firmly attached to the heavenly sphere. It is doubtful that Hipparchus would have believed otherwise, had he not seen the birth of this new star with his own eyes. The closer contact with the Babylonian culture and the overriding interest of their intellectual elite in astrology, gave a new economic incentive to astronomy in the Hellenistic world. It, too, may have encouraged Hipparchus to produce the star catalogue.[15]

By then he had modeled the universe in his systematic frame work of coordinates. He had longitudinally divided the sphere of the stars into 360 equal parts, then each part into 60 more, and each of these into 60 parts again.[16] And he had latitudinally split the diameter of this imaginary sphere into equal parts, and any fractions of it into the equal (sexagesimal) parts again. Based on this framework he mapped the stars.

He started with the twelve Zodiac constellations,[17] listed the groups of stars in each segment, and rated each star according to brightness. Designating for each star the celestial coordinates by longitude and by its angle from the North Star, he fixed their relative positions.[18] He compiled a catalogue of 850 stars. Each star he classified into one of six categories of brightness or magnitude.[19]

During the assembly of the star catalogue Hipparchus discovered that the nodes of ascension of the stars (when they appeared to cross the celestial equator from south to north) had changed by roughly 5° since the time Babylonian astronomers had kept track of them some 350 years earlier. This change worked out to an approximate decrease of 1.4° per century. Although not known in Hipparchus' time, this was the result of recession, a very slow wobble of the Earth's axis somewhat like the wobble of a spinning top. It is caused by the gravitational influence of the Moon and the Sun acting on the Earth.[20] And just as it takes many revolutions before the axis of a spinning top completes one circle, it takes the Earth's axis about 25,800 years to complete a full circle.[21]

*Trigonometry*

As discussed in Chapter 1, the geometers of ancient Egypt had adopted certain rules essential to their craft. Experience had taught them that any area with straight borders could be divided into triangles and that irregularly shaped triangles could be further broken down into smaller, rectangular triangles. Once they had staked out and measured areas in this fashion, they added them and arrived at the size of the larger land area. Although time consuming, the method worked and formed the starting point for Hellenic geometry.

Trigonometry was a decisive break away from the strict rules of classic Hellenic geometry. The Greeks coined the word for "trigonometry" for the new method of geometric measuring. The first part "trigono-" comes from the Greek word *trigonon* (τρίγονον) meaning triangle and the second part "-metry" stems from *metrein* (μετρεῖν), meaning to measure. Trigonometry deals with the numerical relationships among the sides and angles of a triangle. The new rules of trigonometry made it possible to quickly find solutions for any shape of triangle if only three particular elements were known: the measured length of the three sides, the two sides and the enclosed angle, or one side and the degrees of the two adjacent angles. This new method could be applied by astronomers, navigators, geometers, and surveyors. It yielded more accurate results, in shorter time than could be achieved by plane geometry.

In Hipparchus' time systematic and comprehensive tables of trigonometric ratios did not exist. In his zeal to observe and accurately record astronomical observations he was the first to construct and use trigonometric tables. Reportedly, he summarized the numerical ratios in 12 books. It took him that many books to describe his method for derivation of trigonometric ratios and to assemble the trigonometric ratios for angles of all sizes.

Where Euclid stressed the similarities and congruence of triangles, Hipparchus probed into their numerical relations. Although trigonometry deals with any type of triangle, it is convenient to approach it through rectangular (right) triangles. For any angle $\alpha$ there are six trigonometric ratios$_g$. To simplify, we look at only the first two of them for a specific angle $\alpha$ (alpha) of a triangle inscribed in a semicircle. The angle $\alpha$ is located at the central vertex of the triangle. Letting the radius $r = 1$, the sine ratio is defined by $a/r$ and the cosine ratio by $b/r$ as in Diagram 1 of Figure 6.4.

A regular hexagon can be used to illustrate how the size of its perimeter can be derived by trigonometry (for a description of Archimedes' method see Figure 4.2 of Chapter 4). The hexagon can be thought of as being composed of six congruent triangles, each having three sides of equal length and three angles of 60° each. Inscribed in a circle, six of these triangles fill the 360° circle. If each triangle is split in half, twelve congruent triangles emerge. To illustrate the method it is shown how the perimeter of the hexagon can be computed trigonometrically (Figure 6.4, Diagram 2). In this case the answer is obvious. But if the method is to be used for estimating the circumference of a circle, it is necessary to add many more sides to the polygon. To do so Hipparchus computed the trigonometric ratios of smaller angles, also essential for his astronomical estimates (shown in Table 6.1 below).

*The Half-Angle Theorem*

For the derivation of more refined trigonometric ratios, Hipparchus applied a geometric approach.[22] He started out with the half-angle theorem. Again a triangle is inscribed in a circle with two of its sides made up of the radius and the third connecting the endpoints of the two, thereby forming two interior angles that are half the size of its exterior angle. From any angle of given size, Hipparchus could derive another angle half its size (Figure 6.4, Diagram 3).

Hipparchus used this theorem to compute his trigonometric tables. Once he had calculated the trigonometric value for an angle of size $\alpha$, he computed the value for $\alpha/2$. To do this he derived special trigonometric formulas based on sine and cosine values. If knew the sine and cosine values of an angle $\alpha$, he could compute sine ratios of angle $\alpha/2$. The method is briefly described in Figure 6.4A, Diagrams 1 to 4, and in Appendix A of this Chapter. Further explanations and a practical application to the Earth-to-Moon distance are given in Appendixes A and B of this Chapter. Instead of going here into the derivation of more complex trigonometric formulas,[23] an example may illustrate the new technique.

## *On Measuring the Circle*

The great philosophers of Greek antiquity, from Pythagoras to Aristotle and from Archimedes to Aristarchus, were fascinated with the characteristics of the circle. They sensed beauty and harmony in the circular motion of celestial bodies and were intrigued by the circle's elusive properties of geometry and measurement. They searched for the numerical value of π (the Greek letter pi), the mysterious number that defines the relation between the circle's diameter, its circumference, and its area.

Archimedes had estimated both values, a circle's diameter and area, by applying a rather complex geometric technique. Following Hipparchus' new trigonometric approach, it became much easier to tackle the problems that had challenged mathematicians for so long. Archimedes and Hipparchus had succeeded by computing two sets of estimates, one based on polygons inscribed in the circle and the other based on polygons circumscribing the circle. The principle of trigonometric estimation can simply be illustrated by looking at only one set of estimates.[24]

Setting the radius of the circle equal to 1.0, the size of the circle's circumference can be estimated by inscribing a polygon in the circle. By inserting regular-sided polygons (of 6, 12, 24, 48, 96, etc., sides) in the circle, its circumference can be ever more closely approximated. Starting with a hexagon, divide it into six isosceles triangles and then split it further into rectangular triangles (as was done earlier in Figure 6.4, Diagram 2). By adding more sides to the polygon ($2n = 12, 24, 48, 96$, *etc.*), the sine ratios gradually converge toward a more accurate value of the circle's perimeter. The closest estimate of the circle's circumference came from a polygon of 96 sides yielding a fairly good estimate of the circle's circumference (Table 6.1).[25]

This example illustrates how Hipparchus could simplify an otherwise very complex and more difficult estimation procedure. Similarly, his comprehensive tables of trigonometric values could be effectively used for astronomical estimates.

*The Distance to the Moon*

Some hundred years earlier Aristarchus had tried to estimate the Moon-to-Earth distance by direct observation and triangulation. Hipparchus came up with two new ideas. Instead of measuring the left-to-right angle of the Moon's diameter by direct observation as Aristarchus had done, he measured the difference in the Moon's angle when viewed from two locations

Table 6.1:  Trigonometric Approximation of $\pi$ Based on Polygons
Inscribed in a Circle of Radius $r = 1$

| No. of sides | No. of triangles 2n | Angle $\alpha$ at center $360°/2n$ | $\sin \alpha$ | Polygon's Perimeter $2n(\sin \alpha)$ | Approx. value of $\pi$ |
|---|---|---|---|---|---|
| 6 | 12 | 30° | 0.5 | 6.0 | 3.0 |
| 12 | 24 | 15° | 0.2588 | 6.2117 | 3.1058 |
| 24 | 48 | 7.5° | 0.1305 | 6.2654 | 3.1327 |
| 48 | 96 | 3.75° | 0.0654 | 6.2784 | 3.1392 |
| 96 | 192 | 1.875° | 0.0327 | 6.2822 | 3.1411 |

on Earth, separated by a known distance. Instead of measuring the distance in terms of diameters of the Moon, he estimated it in terms of the diameter of the Earth. Eratosthenes (see Chapter 5) had estimated the circumference of the Earth and, based on this estimate, the diameter of the Earth came to 7850 miles (12,633 km).

Capitalizing on his knowledge of trigonometric ratios, Hipparchus derived the Moon-Earth distance from the angles of the lines of sight, as illustrated in Figure 6.5.[26] More detail on the method of estimation is given in Appendix B to this chapter. Hipparchus estimated the Moon-to-Earth distance at 30 times the diameter of the Earth, roughly 235,000 miles (378,186 km). His estimate falls within the range of the shortest and greatest Moon-to-Earth distance, which is between 221,462 miles (356,399 km) and 252,718 miles (406,699 km) (the Moon follows an elliptical oval-shaped orbit around the Earth). His estimate was about four times that of Aristarchus and it came within less than 2% of today's estimate of the average Moon-to-Earth distance of 238,863 miles (384,402 km).[27]

Aristarchus had attempted to measure the distance of the Moon from the Earth by a geometric method. His geometry was flawless, but his observations were not. Hipparchus came much closer. He had also developed an ingenious method of determining geographic latitudes. This, combined with his new method of trigonometry, allowed him to estimate not only the distance of the Moon from Earth but to compute the apparent motions of the Sun, planets, and stars with much greater accuracy.

Hipparchus saw the Sun move during the course of a year at varying angular speeds. If the Sun orbited the Earth in a 360° circle in the year, it should have swept out an angle of 90° quarterly. But the time interval per quarter varied from 88.125 days (between the autumnal equinox and the winter solstice) to 94.5 days (between the vernal equinox and the summer solstice). If the Sun circled the Earth at a steady speed, and perfection in celestial motion demanded it, a change in design was needed to keep up the appearance of the Aristotelian circular motion. Hipparchus decided in favor of an eccentric model of solar motion. This model allowed for a circular orbit of the Sun, traversing the course at a steady speed, and it accommodated the variations in quarterly orbital time periods. He calculated the eccentricity[28] of the solar orbit at 1/24 of the solar orbital diameter (Figure 6.6).

Modeling the lunar orbit was more difficult. Hipparchus was interested in the precise timing of the periodic eclipses of the Sun and the Moon. Able to compare his own data with Babylonian records, he devised an epicyclic model[29] of the Moon's orbit so that the model's predictions were accurate enough to fit the observations. Hipparchus made the Moon move along the circumference of a small circle, the epicycle$_g$, and the center of this epicycle revolve around the Earth on a larger circle, the deferent$_g$. With this design he could reproduce the observed lunar orbital positions without abandoning the Greek dogma that only allowed circular motions in the heavens (Figure 6.7).

Most of what we know about Hipparchus' accomplishments in astronomy was transmitted to us by Ptolemy, a great astronomer who lived nearly 300 years later. Hipparchus' achievements were revolutionary in the history of astronomy. He had invented a new mathematical technique that moved mathematics forward from ingenious and elegant geometric concepts to a method of estimation that was to become an essential feature of astronomy, a basic tool for nautical and aeronautical navigation, geographical surveys, and many other fields of engineering.[30] The discovery of a new branch of mathematics was a first in the history of astronomy.

His contribution in the field of mathematics was only surpassed by the precision of his astronomical observations. It is known, for example, that:

- he determined with impressive accuracy the synodic$_g$ periods of the planets, the obliquity$_g$ of the ellliptic$_g$, the Moon's orbit, the apogee$_g$ the Sun, and the parallax$_g$ of the Moon;

- he estimated the solar year at 365¼ days minus 4 minutes and 48 seconds, only 6 minutes off current calculations; the lunar month at 29 days, 12 hours, 44 minutes and 2½ seconds, less than a second off today's figure;[31] and that

- he discovered the precession$_g$ of the stars, the extremely slow eastward shift of the fixed stars by about 1° degree in 75 years, very close to the modern-day estimate of 50.26".

## Ptolemy, the "Euclid of Astronomy" (ca.100 A.D. – ca.170 A.D.)

Although Hipparchus was the greatest of the Hellenistic astronomers, very few of his writings survived. No doubt, all of his important findings would have been lost had Claudius Ptolemy not written the *Almagest*. Little is known of Ptolemy's personal life. It is known that he lived in Egypt, was granted Roman citizenship and was given the Latin name Claudius Ptolemaeus.[32]

*Author of the Almagest*

Ptolemy gathered his astronomical observations at Alexandria and described his astronomical theories and findings in a 13-volume treatise which came to be called the *Great Collection*. Later, the Arabs shortened the title to *The Greatest* or the *Almagest*.[33] Although Ptolemy was an excellent mathematician, he is best remembered for his treatise in astronomy, most of which was based on the work of Hipparchus and that of other Greek astronomers.

*His Great Cosmological Model*

Perhaps the greatest contribution of Ptolemy—it has also been called an "immense monument of wrongheadedness"[34]—was his geocentric model of the heavens. Hipparchus had already discovered that the earlier theories of revolving spheres by Eudoxus, Aristotle, and others did not fit very well with the actual planetary motions, and had collected data on the planetary motions for his successors to use. Ptolemy collected more data and eventually used a model that was to prevail for more than a thousand years. Ptolemy's *Almagest* became the European astronomer's text book. Thus, Ptolemy became to astronomy what Euclid was to geometry.

Ptolemy, like Hipparchus, Aristotle, and others before him (except Aristarchus who had designed a heliocentric model), thought the Earth to be at the center of the universe with all the heavenly bodies revolving in circles around it. Careful observations by Hipparchus and Ptolemy himself revealed that the planets did not move unerringly in perfect circles. At times they saw them wander backwards only to turn around again to pursue their earlier course.

The challenge was to integrate these motions into an Earth-centered (geocentric) system of circular motion. Ptolemy solved the problem by having the planets revolve—while traveling in their grand orbit, the deferent$_g$—counter-cyclically on an epicycle, a smaller circular orbit on top of the grand circle. Hipparchus had incorporated in his lunar model an epicycle on which the Moon orbited the epicycle's center clockwise, moving in the opposite direction as the deferent circled the Earth. Ptolemy had the planets move on epicycles counter-clockwise in the same direction as the deferent circle orbited the Earth. Although it was an ingenious piece of geometry, it still did not fully explain the observed angular motion of the planets. To adjust it further, Ptolemy had the epicycles revolve around an equant$_g$, slightly off-center of the deferent orbit on the opposite side of the center of the Earth so that the epicycle moved at more uniform speed (Figure 6.8, Diagram 1).[35]

As the center of the epicycle continued to move along the perimeter of the planetary orbit, the retrograde motion occurred after the planet wandered off its regular orbit. It appeared as if a planet had to slow down, go backward, and then return to its deferent orbit.[36] A plotting of their motions against the background of the constellations of stars could easily give the appearance of a backward loop with retrograde motion (Figure 6.8, Diagrams 2 and 3). In reality the strange behavior of the planets was due to the earth-centered geocentric theory of celestial motions. Eventually, the puzzle of the mysterious wanderings of the planets would be solved. But the mystery persisted until Copernicus came along some 1500 years later. (His theory will be discussed in Chapter 8.)

Ptolemy never claimed that his geocentric system represented reality. His intricate model matched empirical observations. And it was all done by circles. It performed so well that astronomers used it to predict the motions of the planets. It was a marvelous edifice of intricate mathematical modeling that was to stand the test of time for more than a thousand years.

## Appendix A: Computing Trigonometric Sine Ratios[37]
Figure 6.4, Diagram 3, showed the half-angle theorem. It illustrates how an isosceles triangle can be used to geometrically divide an angle in half.

Hipparchus used this theorem for the construction of his trigonometric sine tables. Once he had calculated the trigonometric value for an angle of size $\alpha$, he could compute the values for $\frac{1}{2}\alpha$. This could not be done by just dividing the sine values in half, the derivation of it was somewhat more complicated. As shown in Figure 6.4, Hipparchus could compute $sin^2 \frac{1}{2}\alpha = \frac{1}{2}(1 - cos\,\alpha)$ and, after taking the square root, obtain the value for $sin\,\frac{1}{2}\alpha$. Using the half-angle formulas, Hipparchus was able to compute the sine and cosine values for smaller and smaller angles. It may appear strange that the angles are expressed in fractions rather than decimal notation but numerical fractions came naturally to the Greek mathematicians because they had never developed a decimal system.

## Appendix B: Trigonometric Estimate of the Moon-to-Earth Distance[38]

In approaching this problem, Hipparchus came up with a novel idea. He measured the difference in the Moon's angle when viewed from two locations. From the different angles and knowledge of the Earth's diameter he deduced trigonometrically the Moon-to-Earth distance.

As suggested by Lancelot Hogben, to arrive at this distance Hipparchus may have applied the sine rule and the cosine rule. Both will be described in greater detail later (Chapter 10 on Kepler). The example below is simplified; it only uses the sine rule.

Given any triangle *ABC* with sides *a, b, c*, and the corresponding angles at the corners *A, B,* and *C* (opposite the sides *a,b,c*), the sine rule states that:

$$a \div sin \triangle A = b \div sin \triangle B = c \div sin \triangle C.$$

Denoting the distance *MC* (Figure 6.4) from the center of the Moon to the center of the Earth by *d*; the radius of the Earth by *r*; the distance from the observer's station *O* on Earth to the center of the Moon *M* by *m*; Hipparchus needed to determine the size of the angles $\triangle 1, \triangle 2, \triangle 3$, and $\triangle 4$. His estimate of the latitude of the observatory at location *O* matched angle $\triangle 1$ at the center of the Earth, angle $\triangle 4$ was formed between the line of sight of the Moon OM and the plumbline *OE*. By subtracting $\triangle 4$ from 180°, he obtained $\triangle 2$. He then found $\triangle 3$ by subtracting angles $\triangle 1$ and $\triangle 2$ from 180°. In addition he knew Eratosthenes' estimate of the Earth's diameter.

At Alexandria the angle of latitude is $\triangle 1 = 31.1°$. If Hipparchus found the difference between $\triangle 4$ and $\triangle 1$ to be ½° , he could find angle $\triangle 2$ as $180°-(\triangle 4-\triangle 1)= 179 ½°$ and the remaining angle as $\triangle 3 = 180°-179 ½° = ½°$. He also knew of Eratosthenes' estimate of the Earth diameter of 7850 miles (12,633 km) or radius of 3925 miles (6316 km).

With this information at hand, Hipparchus capitalized on his knowledge of trigonometric relations. To compute the Moon-to-Earth distance he applied the sine rule. Related to Figure 6.5 in the text, that rule implies:

$$m \; / \; \sin \angle 1 = r \; / \; \sin \angle 3$$
$$m \; = \; (r \sin \angle 1) \; / \; \sin \angle 3)$$

Inserting the values for $r$, $\sin \angle 1$ and $\sin \angle 3$, yields:

$$m \; = \; (3\,925 \sin 31.1°) \; / \; \sin 0.5°$$
$$= \; (3\,925 \times 0.5265) \; / \; 0.0087$$
$$= \; 2066 \; / \; 0.0087 = 237\,471 \; mi \; (382\,091 \; km)$$

This is the estimate of $m$, the distance from the center of the Moon $M$ to the observer stationed at $O$. It is somewhat less than the distance d to the center of the Earth. This distance will be no greater than $m + r = 237,471$ $mi + 3925 \; mi = 241,396 \; mi$. It follows that the estimate falls between 237,471 miles (382,162 km) and 241,397 miles (388,480 km) a Moon-to-Earth distance that comes very close to today's (mean) value of 238,857 miles (384,392) km or the better known space-age figure of 240,000 miles (386,232 km).

Chapter 7

# THE LOST MILLENNIUM (ca. 500 A.D.–1500 A.D.)

*The Arabs controlled the Mediterranean; they sacked the city of Rome in 846 A.D. From the north the Vikings came looting and conquering, from the east the Magyars invaded and devastated Western Europe. Economic life had dwindled to a miserable agricultural activity carried on by ignorant serfs who were ruled by lords and priests hardly less ignorant than themselves.*

Anton Pannekoek[1]

With Hipparchus and Ptolemy, Greek astronomy had reached its zenith. Greek astronomy and science were on the decline. The change mirrored the gloomy trend of futility initiated by Greek philosophers several hundred years earlier. The adherents of passionless philosophies anticipated the change.

This chapter gives a brief historical overview focusing only on influential movements and a few advances in the study of mathematics and astronomy. Although the decline of Greek science began earlier, the final destruction of the Alexandrian library around 389 A.D. and the closing of the Schools of Athens in 529 A.D. marked the end of Greek science. The next innovative astronomer would not appear until a millennium later, when Copernicus published his Sun-centered (heliocentric) system of celestial motion in 1543 A.D.

## Shift of Focus in Philosophy

Preaching an ascetic doctrine of simplicity and faith in God, the stoics planted the seeds for the new trend. It is as if they anticipated the economic decline and prepared for the hardships that were to follow.

### Pyrrho (365 B.C.–275 B.C.)

He lived  serenely in poverty, taught philosophy, and promoted the idea that certainty was not attainable and that all theories were likely to be false. To him life was not necessarily rewarding, death not necessarily evil, desire an illusion, and dispute irrelevant. Advocating that wise people should seek tranquillity rather than search for truth, he considered  it  best  to accept the myths and conventions of the day. One should not take sides but calmly accept it all. He made no effort to prolong his life but lived to the age of 90.[2]

### Epicurus (341 B.C.–270 B.C.)

He was one of the Greek philosophers who followed Alexander's army to India. From Pyrrho he adopted the doctrine of tranquillity, from other philosophers the wisdom of pleasure and atheism. Living in stoic simplicity, he was content with water, bread, a little wine and cheese. While protecting his privacy, he wrote some 300 books between his lessons and loves.

He disliked religion because it built barriers against knowledge, and darkened life with the threat of God's eternal punishment. According to him the real function of philosophy was not to explain the world but to guide humanity in the search for happiness.

### Zeno (ca. 340 B.C.–265 B.C.)

He, too, followed the stern simplicity of a simple life. Lecturing his students from the colonnade,[3] he espoused an "anarchist communism." He and his followers recognized religion as a basis of morality. They made an honest attempt to bridge the gap between religion and philosophy.[4]

Philosophers had grown wary of the search for the ultimate truth.[5] Their state of mind was not simply the outcome of a philosophical trend but the result of pervasive changes in the economic and social environment. The vast expansion of the Alexandrian Empire and the subsequent breakup, had initiated economic down-drift that put philosophy on a different course.

## Shift in Economic Powers

Alexander's death brought his generals to power. Eventually, after the wars of succession had ended (ca. 275 B.C.), they split the Alexandrian empire into three kingdoms ruled by the Antigonids from Macedonia, the Ptolemies from Egypt, and the Seleucids from Asia.

Rome was on the way to becoming the fourth great power. Rome's army did not conquer Greece by battle but took advantage of the disintegration of Greek civilization. Will Durant thought of this as a natural course of evolution. He wrote:

> No great nation is ever conquered until it has destroyed itself from within.... the migration of trade routes, the disturbance of economic life by political disorder, the corruption of democracy...the decay of morals and patriotism...revolutions and counterrevolutions—all these had exhausted the resources of Hellas [Greece].[6]

Antigones, ruler of Macedon, and his successors fought the Romans until, eventually in 168 B.C., Rome annihilated the army of Macedon, destroyed 70 cities, banished the upper classes to Italy, sold 100,000 into slavery, and divided up the kingdom. Shortly after, Greece surrendered its freedom to Rome.[7]

During the first century B.C. Julius Caesar added Asia Minor, Syria, Egypt, and Gaul to the Roman empire. A series of civil wars among his successors led to the establishment of Imperial rule. Octavian, the adopted son of Caesar, re-established order. For the next 200 years the Roman empire enjoyed stability and peace. Under the emperors Hadrian and Antoine prosperity reigned but, in the end, all this changed.[8]

## Diophantus (ca. 200 A.D.)

In this time of economic change, Diophantus made a significant contribution to mathematics. His fame rests on the great treatise *Arithmetica*, a brilliant work that stands on its own outside of the mainstream of Greek mathematics. Before his time, questions relating to unknowns and equations were described in words. Diophantus was the first to set them out in symbolic form. He introduced symbols for subtraction, for exponents of higher orders, and for the known and unknown variables of equations.[9]

In his treatise Diophantus describes the solutions to some 150 problems. They make up a fascinating collection of determinate (e.g., $25 x^2 = 9$ so that $x = 3/5$) and indeterminate equations (e.g., $xy = 24$). For example, in order to find two numbers whose sum equals 10 and whose some of cubes equal 370, he designated the two numbers not as $x$ and $y$ but as $(5 + x)$ and $(5 - x)$. Then he added the second condition as $(5 + x)^3 + (5 - x)^3$ giving $x = 2$ as the answer. So that $(5 + x) = 7$ and $(5 - x) = 3$ and $7^3 + 3^3 = 343 + 27 = 370$. Although most of his equations are indeterminate because they often contain two or more unknown variables and have a great many solutions, he only allowed for solutions in rational numbers and usually gave only one solution.[10]

## The End of Alexandria's Era (ca. 400 A.D.)

When the wars of Rome's victorious expansion ended, the supply of cheap labor dried up. Having exploited the silver and gold mines of Spain, Rome's imports diminished because of lack of finances and commerce entered a state of paralysis. Its military might faded away. Rome fell to the invasion of the Goths. The Roman Emperor Constantine turned to Christianity.[11]

Rome had excelled in large scale government administration where the city states of Greece had failed. Although much of Rome's culture had been derived from Greece, the Romans had made no attempt to preserve the literature of the Greeks. Part of the great Alexandrian library was burnt down when Caesar landed with his fleet in Alexandria. Some of the works of Alexandrian scholars were reassembled later. But in 389 A.D. Christian monks destroyed most of what was left. After a few years all that remained were the burned-out ashes. With the decline of Greek society and Rome's lack of interest in science, the Alexandrian school died.

It was a slow death. Some of the remaining staff tried to save whatever they could. In the closing phase of Greek mathematics and astronomy three names were notable: Pappus, Theon, and Theon's daughter, Hypatia. They produced extensive summaries and commentaries on the works of their great predecessors—Pappus and Theon on Ptolemy, Hypatia on Diophantus and Apollonius.

Their commentaries preserved the key elements of Greek science. Had it not been for the work of these philosophers, and others who treasured and saved what they found, the great legacy of the Greek philosophers might have vanished forever. Translated into Arabic, their works became known to philosophers of the Near and Far East. Eventually they made their way back to Europe, but not until a millennium later.

### Pappus (ca. 320 A.D.)

In his book *Synagoge* (from the Greek word *synagogois* (συνᾶγωγεύς) meaning gathering, collection) Pappus, a late Greek geometer of Alexandria, gave a systematic account of Greek mathematics, with historical annotations, some alterations, and original material.[12] It consisted of eight books covering arithmetic and problems of plane and solid geometry. Pappus described how the five Platonic solids (Chapter 3, Figure 3.3) could be inscribed in a sphere (used later by Kepler, see Chapter 10). He considered properties of various curves, enumerated the works of Euclid, Apollonius of Perga, and Eratosthenes; and commented on Euclid's theory of irrational numbers. Some of Pappus' works survived only in Arabic translations.

### Theon (ca. 380 A.D.)

Like Pappus Theon was also a professor of mathematics and astronomy at Alexandria's *museion*. He proved himself competent in technical matters. He worked out a practical method of finding square roots needed in astronomy for determining the values of trigonometric ratios (Chapter 6, Figure A6.1). To derive the numerical value of a square root he started by first taking a guess at its value.[13]

If, for instance, he wanted to find the square root of 2.00 he tried initially *(1.4)(1.4) = 1.96* and *(1.5)(1.5) = 2.25*. Evidently *1.4* was a bit too small and *1.5* a bit too large. Choosing the smaller value of the two, he would set up an equation. In Equation 7.1 the symbol $\Delta x$ refers to the unknown difference between the initial estimate and the actual value. Compared with the value of *(1.4)$\Delta x$*, $(\Delta x)^2$ is of a second order of magnitude and can be ignored. By solving for $\Delta x$, Theon arrived at a revised value of *1.414* for $\sqrt{2}$. If Theon wanted to obtain an even better estimate for the square root, he simply substituted *1.414* for the initial value of *1.4* in Equation 7.1 and repeated the estimating procedure.[14]

Equation 7.1: Theon's Method of Estimating a Square Root

$$(1.4 + \Delta x)^2 = 2$$

$$1.4^2 + 2\,(1.4)\,\Delta x + (\Delta x)^2 = 2$$

$$1.4^2 + 2\,(1.4)\,\Delta x = 2$$

$$\Delta x = \frac{2 - 1.4^2}{2\,(1.4)} = \frac{2.0 - 1.96}{2.8} = 0.014$$

$$(1.4 + 0.014)^2 = 1.9994 \approx 2, \quad and$$

*therefore:* $\qquad 1.414 = \sqrt{2}$

---

*Hypatia of Alexandria (ca. 370 A.D.–415 A.D.)*

Theon also wrote a commentary on Ptolemy's *Syntaxis* (from the Greek σύνταξις for order or survey). In it he acknowledged the help of his daughter Hypatia, a very gifted mathematician and philosopher.[15] She became the recognized head of the Neoplatonic school of Alexandria. Because of her eloquence, modesty, beauty and intellect, she attracted a large number of students. She wrote commentaries on the classical works of the great mathematicians, on Ptolemy, on the equations of Diophantus, and on the conic sections of Apollonius of Perga.

*Commentaries on Apollonian Conics*

A sample of Apollonius' work was given earlier in Figures 4.3 and 4.4 of Chapter 4. Others are shown here in Figures 7.1 and 7.2 because they too will reappear in Isaac Newton's analysis some thousand years later. Newton simply refers to Apollonian theorems as selected properties of conic sections, proven by writers on conic sections.[16] It would be difficult to follow Newton's analysis without knowing anything about conics. Yet, a rigorous proof is lengthy, complicated and not given here.[17] It is simplified by relying more heavily on intuition than rigor. In this form it can still serve as useful background for later analysis (see Chapter 12).

In Chapter 3 it was shown how a rectangle can be converted into a square by integrating both in a circle (Chapter 3, Figure 3.2). At first glance the theorem of Apollonius has little to do with this conversion (Figure 7.1, Diagram 1). Yet, it does. Interpreted as the ratio of a rectangle over a square, the two figures can be integrated in an ellipse. It is as if only the perspective had changed, going from an overhead view to an angular view. As a result the circle is converted into an ellipse and the rectangle and square into two parallelograms. After the conversion, the two rectangles remain equal in size.[18] Converted back into a rectangle and square, the equality is maintained. To this are added the conjugate diameters[19] of the ellipse which are of equal length. Combining the two characteristic properties of the ellipse, it is concluded that $(Gv)(Pv)/(Qv)^2 = (PC)^2/(CD)^2$ as in Figure 7.1, Diagram 6. While this method lacks the precision of the classical proof, it has sufficient intuitive appeal to make the theorem plausible.

Following the same intuitive approach, another characteristic of conic sections is added. The quadrant of a circle will keep its size when turned around its center in the same plane (Figure 7.2, Diagrams 1 and 2). Although not obvious, the same idea applies to ellipses. The quadrant of an ellipse keeps its size as the frame is changed, tangential to the ellipse, from a rectangle to that of a parallelogram (Diagrams 3 and 4). It also keeps its size when the shape of the quadrant is changed back to a rectangle as in Diagram 5. From these transformations, certain equalities are derived that will reappear later in Newton's analysis (see Chapter 12).

Now back again to Hypatia. Greatly respected and admired for her knowledge, she often appeared before the city magistrates as an advisor. At a time of political stress this connection became the focal point between Christians and non-Christians.

Hypatia represented science. At the time such knowledge was largely identified by the early Christians with paganism. Anybody who was not a Christian was marked a pagan and perverted religious zealots took the opportunity to murder her, one of the few women of outstanding achievement in the field of mathematics. The sadistic murder of Hypatia symbolized the end of Alexandria as the greatest center of learning of the Western World. Some of the pagan professors escaped to Athens where non-Christian teachings were still allowed. Yet the schools of Athens were on the decline too.[20]

*Proclus Diadochus (ca. 410 A.D.–485 A.D.)*

Among the last to teach in Athens, Proclus Diadochus lectured at the Neoplatonic Academy Plato had founded in Athens nearly a thousand years earlier. In his writings he annotated the works of the classical philosophers. For instance, in the introduction to his *Commentary on the First Book of Euclid's Elements*, he elaborated on Euclid's intentions. He distinguished between Euclid's aim to inform the student of geometry and Euclid's grand plan of providing a better understanding of the universe. According to him Euclid tried to explain not only the elements of geometry but as well the structure of the universe. By interpreting Euclid's *Elements* in this fashion he expressed an opinion that prevailed at the time, though Euclid had never mentioned any such link.[21]

Proclus was aware that neither Plato nor Aristotle ever wrote about epicycles, eccentrics, or equants$_g$ of planetary motion. He also knew that Ptolemy's eccentric-epicyclic theory fitted the observations of the planetary motions better than Aristotle's system of concentric spheres. It was a dilemma for him. He questioned how the stars could revolve in concentric circles around the Earth when the planets revolved in eccentric circles and in epicycles around some other centers. He expressly appreciated the beauty and precision of Ptolemy's abstract model. It appealed to his logical mind. Yet he found its structure to be incompatible with the divine nature of the universe as conceived by Plato.[22]

Once the Christians entered the leading circles of Athens, they made it difficult for philosophers and students of the Academy who still believed in the gods of ancient Greece. Proclus had to flee. He managed to escape to Asia Minor where he found shelter at a friend's home. His friend was eager to learn what the Greek philosophers of classic times had taught in astronomy. Having promised to teach him on his return to Athens, Proclus wrote an *Outline of the Astronomical Hypotheses*. Proclus ended his book by stating that the Ptolemaic system was designed to arrive at more precise measures of the planetary motion. He considered it a serviceable mathematical construct, but had his doubts that it represented physical reality.[23]

### Boethius (ca. 480A.D.–ca. 524 A.D.)

Born during the lifetime of Proclus, he was a scholar and statesman who made the mistake of alienating the Roman Emperor Theodoric. He spent the last years of his life in prison. While in prison he wrote manuals for the liberal arts, a volume on ethics, a book on arithmetic, and another called the *Consolation of Philosophy*. The *Consolation* became perhaps the most widely read book during the Middle Ages. He intended to translate the works of Plato and Aristotle but he only managed to finish Aristotle's book on logic when the executioner came for him. During the next centuries his translation of Aristotle's treatise became the basic text for students of logic.[24]

Beginning with the reign of the Emperor Justinian (483A.D.–565 A.D.) and his conquest of the north African coast, the southern coast of Spain, and the western Mediterranean islands in the early sixth century, the ecclesiastical power of Rome was strengthened. Rome imposed Latin as the language of communication. Since Greek was considered the language of pagans, no attempt was made to translate scientific works into Latin. Knowledge of Greek literature faded away in the West. Copies of the original writings of Plato, Aristotle, and of the works of the Greek mathematicians and astronomers were lost.

### The Near East

Under the Roman Emperor Justinian (483 A.D.–565 A.D.) the "pagan" Academy of Athens closed its doors in 529 A.D. Meanwhile, however, new centers of learning had opened in Constantinople and in other cities of the Near East$_g$. There, commentators perpetuated the memory of the classical works of Greek science and philosophy.[25]

Theodosius I founded the Byzantine Empire in 394 AD. He had made Constantinople its capital. It became the administrative center of the empire. While holding off the forces from the east, north, and west, it became a bridge between the West and the East.[26]

With the decline of mathematics in the Greek and Roman empires the center of science shifted to Mesopotamia. Arabic treatises dealing mainly with astronomy clearly showed the enormous impact of Ptolemy's work. In the field of mathematics they improved on the more conventional trigonometry. Some of their work showed considerable ingenuity.

## The Far East[27]

China's astronomical records go further back than anywhere else in the world. The length of power of a dynasty formed the basis of their calenders; each new dynasty ushered in a new calendar. For example, since the advent of the Ming dynasty in 1368 A.D. some forty new calendars have been introduced. Over the centuries Chinese astronomers improved on the accuracy of their calendars. During the Tang dynasty (618 A.D.– 906 A.D.) their estimates of the lunar month came close to modern-day estimates. Chinese records of celestial observations were remarkably detailed. Their earliest star charts go back to at least 2000 B.C. Two centuries before Hipparchus, their astronomers had identified 1464 stars and grouped them into 284 constellations. Yet, as late as 500 A.D., during the Tang dynasty, their star charts had no coordinate system and, therefore, were quite imprecise.

Since ancient times Chinese astronomical records were guarded as secrets. Unusual celestial events were taken as pointers of serious faults in government administration that were usually followed by disasters. Rulers did not want their people to know of such divine censures. Astronomy became an integral part of administration. It was part of a most elaborate bureaucracy that actively discouraged the study of astronomy outside of government confines.

As a result of this kind of thinking, their theories were vague enough so as not to offend the Chinese Emperor. The earliest theory described the sky as a vault above a gently curved Earth. The vault of the heavens rotated daily at a great distance around its axis through the center. The second theory, put forth between 140 B.C.–104 B.C., described the heavens to be like a hen's egg with the Earth like a yolk at the center, the heavens being large and the Earth small. The third theory, proposed during the Han dynasty (25 A.D.–225 A.D.), implied that the Sun, Moon, planets, and stars floated in empty space carried along by a "hard wind." Whenever the wind shifted, the planets reversed their course of direction. Speculation of this kind continued into the third and fourth centuries.

By 500 A.D. the astronomers of the West had became thoroughly acquainted with the Babylonian observations. Hellenistic astronomers had designed an intricate mathematical theory of the Heavens to which Chinese astronomers could not add anything significant.

The Chinese idea of divinely inspired rulers carried over into Korea. Japan's astronomy did not become a science until long after the contact with the cultures of Korea and China.

*India*

India's astronomers were aware of certain regularities in the motions of celestial bodies between 1000 B.C. and 500 B.C. Passages in texts gave instructions for the practice of important rituals that were to be performed at certain times of the year. Since the twelve lunar months did not quite make up a full year, some extra days were inserted. Indian astronomers introduced them during the sixth and fifth century B.C. This was not, however, until after they became acquainted with the Babylonian astronomy.[28]

During the fifth century B.C. the Persian Empire reached its greatest expanse, from Greece, Lybia, and Egypt to the Indus river of India. With permanent troops stationed at strategic locations, the civilian and military administration was facilitated by an enormous royal road system. Best known among them was the imperial all-weather road that reached from Sardis in the western part of what is today Turkey to Susa in the southern part of what is today Iran.[29] Toward the end of the Persian reign, around 400 B.C., a text on numerical theories of astronomy, based on linear zigzag functions, came to India from Iran. Indian astronomers then used the Iranian method for predictions of recurrent planetary phenomena.

Around 300 B.C. the Babylonian planetary theory was fully developed. It was passed on through Greek intermediaries and appeared in Sanskrit translations of Greek astronomical treatises between 300 and 200 B.C. Other Sanskrit translations included elements of Hellenistic astronomy, especially those of Hipparchus.

In later years Indian mathematicians and astronomers made significant contributions to trigonometry and to the epicycle theory of Ptolemy, but they added very little to the earlier empirical observations. Yet one of their mathematical inventions, the decimal system, was of great significance and had a far reaching impact. Its use first showed up on an Indian plaque of the year 595 A.D. Long before this inscriptive record, however, the Indians had expressed large numbers in words arranged by positional values. As well they had invented the zero. The decimal system slowly made its way along the caravan routes into Persia and Egypt. It may have already existed earlier, side by side with other number systems, at a time when the zero came into use in Babylonia. Some believe that place-value numerals reached the West through Alexandria as early as 450 A.D.[30] The Arabs adopted the decimal system from India over the next 300 years. It was to take another 500 years before it began to spread through Europe, around 1200 A.D.

## Muslims on the Move

Beginning around 620 A.D., Muslims conquered large sections of western Asia. They first expanded their empire to the south and took Alexandria in 630 A.D. As they took over the administration of government, they replaced the upper layer of society. They did not destroy the great library of Alexandria since little if anything was left after the rampages of previous centuries. Their invasion may have had some adverse effects on scientific work, but their study of mathematics followed in the footsteps of earlier tradition.[31]

Impelled by the preaching of their prophet Mohammed (570 A.D. –632 A.D.), they converted the conquered peoples to the religion of Islam, by force or persuasion. After solidifying their hold on the Arab countries they conquered the eastern provinces of the Roman Empire. From Egypt they pushed westward along the southern shores of the Mediterranean Sea. Early in the eighth century they crossed over from Morocco into Spain.[32]

In less than a century they had conquered much of the Roman Empire and occupied Sicily, North Africa, and Spain. Wherever they went, they made Arabic the official language, replacing the Greco-Roman language with that of Islam. Although Arabic was now used for scientific documents, much of the traditional culture of the land remained intact.[33]

### *Al-Khwarizmi (ca.820 A.D.)*

During the Islamic period the mathematics of the various cultures came together. In Bagdad the Islamic caliph Al-Ma'mun (813A.D.–833 A.D.) built a "House of Wisdom" with an extensive library and an astronomical observatory. The most influential scholar of this period was Al-Khwarizmi. He wrote books on mathematics and astronomy in which he addressed, among other topics, questions of the Hindu system of decimal numeration and of algebra. Although his books were lost, western scholars became aware of them through a Latin translation of the twelfth century. It acquainted them with the decimal notation. It also familiarized them with algebra: linear and quadratic equations. In fact the word *"algebra"* stems from the original Arabic title of his treatise that referred to the reduction of unknowns and solutions of equations. His astronomical and trigono-metric tables of sines and tangents were also translated into Latin and thus reached the West.[34]

### *Arzachel (1029 A.D.–1087 A.D.)*

Arzachel was an important astronomer, known for the precision of his astronomical observations. He worked at Cordoba in Spain, another center of learning established under Islamic rule. He was the editor of the *Toledan Planetary Tables*. They were translated into Latin and became the authoritative source for several centuries.[35]

### *Omar Khayyám (ca. 1050 A. D.–1123 A.D.)*

Perhaps best known for his poetry (*The Rubáiyát*), he was also interested in mathematics and astronomy. He wrote a book on algebra and reformed the old Persian calender, surpassing the Gregorian calender in accuracy. Other mathematicians of Persia followed the directions taken by their predecessors and enriched the knowledge of algebra by their contributions.[36]

*Ibn Tufayl (ca.1110 A.D.–1185 A.D.)*

He served as a physician to the court of the Sultan of Morocco. Astronomy inspired him. His conceptual model of the universe differed from Ptolemy's. It did not rely on eccentrics or epicycles. If he ever did record his thoughts, nothing has come down to us. But Al-Bitruji, one of Tufayl's students, did write a book that was later translated into Latin (by Michael Scot in 1217). In it Al-Bitruji rejected the ideas of eccentrics and epicycles and followed the Aristotelian principle asserting that the motions of all heavenly bodies were concentric to Earth, which was believed to be the center of the universe.[37]

*Ibn Rushd (1126 A.D.–1198 A.D.)*

Introduced to the Sultan of Morocco by Ibn Tufayl, he became the Sultan's court physician in 1184.[38] Keenly interested in the writings of the classical Greek philosophers, he was convinced that Aristotle had grasped all the truth that human nature could comprehend. Astronomy fascinated him. Yet, the Christian theologians rejected his philosophical views.

This rejection was part of the Catholic counter-offensive. At the time Spanish society was divided. Ruled by Muslims, many Spaniards had become converts to Islam. The Jews had joined them because they found the Muslims more tolerant than the Christians. A large majority of Spaniards, however, had kept their Christian faith even though they had adopted Islam's manners and mores. Underneath this fragmented society the Catholic Church was still alive. Looking at any compromise with the Muslims as a victory of Anti-Christ, the representatives of the Catholic Church fanned the flames of vengeance. After the eleventh century, Spain's Christian princes started to reclaim their lost lands. Christians turned on Muslims. They forced them to deny their faith, drove them out of the country, and uprooted the Spanish-Muslim culture.[39] Forced to flee, Ibn Rushd found exile in Morocco.[40]

In his younger years he had vigorously criticized the Ptolemaic ideas of eccentrics and epicycles. He asserted that an eccentric could not exist because revolving around a center that did not exist was impossible for a heavenly body. Similarly, he argued that epicycles would require the existence of additional bodies in outer space that would imply that the Earth was not unique and that other bodies existed for the sole purpose of filling empty space.[41]

Of all the Islamic commentators on Aristotle's works, Ibn Rushd was the most celebrated. His writings were translated into Latin. Early in his career he had hoped to complete his researches in astronomy and come up with a superior alternative to eccentrics and epicycles, but in old age he admitted that he had to abandon his dream. For him, the astronomy of his day did not exist in reality. He challenged others to search actively for a better explanation because, if not, it could leave the wrong impression that eccentrics and epicycles must simply exist for a lack of a better explanation.

Ibn Rushd's eloquent commentaries spread far and wide under his Latinized name, Alvarez. Through these commentaries Aristotle became known as "The Philosopher" and Ibn Rushd as "The Commentator." The issues Ibn Rushd raised not only challenged astronomers of his day, but the revival of Hellenistic paganism haunted Christian theologians for centuries to come.[42]

*Symmetry*

A curious by-product of the advance of Islamic culture was the adherence of symmetric patterns in Islamic art. The architecture of Mosques is an expression of this art. The vast expanse of buildings and intricate, ornate decor spiritually represents the infinity of God. The mosque's essential structure is similar throughout the Muslim world. Examples of this architecture are the great mosques of Damascus and Jerusalem. Although the buildings were monumental, Muslim architects emphasized surface decor.

The most striking feature of this Islamic decor was that the design was not figural but abstract. The prohibition against figural representation is not part of the Koran but goes back to the Prophet Mohammed himself.

He is said to have found his young wife making a pillow with a picture on it and warned her: "Don't you know that angels refuse to enter a house in which there is a picture? On the Last Day makers of pictures will be punished for God will say to them: 'Give life to that which you have created'."[43]

In the eighth century, about 200 years after Mohammad lived, all human and animal figures were banned from religious art. With that restriction, presumably to prevent idolatry, Arab architects and artisans turned to abstract design. They developed intricate geometric patters, covered ceilings and walls with plaster and stucco, and floors with decorative tiles. Symmetric in design, intermingled with beautifully written words in praise of God, no area of the mosque was left unembellished, accentuating the arabesque design of God's infinity.

Examples of such architecture are found as far west in Europe as the famous Mosque of Cordoba and the Alhambra Palace of Grenada. Adherence to strict geometric designs of tiles are still commonplace in Spain today (Figure 7.3). This symmetric ornamentation did not come from Greece, but is a distinct contribution of the Middle East. Inadvertently, it found its way into physics and astronomy many centuries later.

## Thomas of Aquinas (1225A.D.–1298 A.D.)

Eventually, a new Christian-Catholic philosophy emerged. Founded on Aristotelian thought and Christian faith, it was very much influenced by the writings of St.Thomas Aquinas.[44]

Born into the family of the Counts of Aquino he attended the University of Naples for six years and after graduation decided to join the Dominican order. His family was so opposed to the idea that his brothers seized him on his way to France and put him under house arrest. Released a year later, he acquired knowledge under Albertus Magnus (ca.1206 A.D.–1280 A.D.), a renowned German theologian, philosopher and scientist. He first studied under him in Paris, and later, in Cologne.[45]

Aristotle's doctrines on the nature of the universe led people to doubt the Christian doctrine of revelation. The Church could no longer turn a deaf ear to the rising agitation and sent Aquinas to Paris to calm down the restless din. Rather than denounce the Aristotelian tenets, he examined them point by point—in a 21-volume treatise written during a ten-year period from 1259 to 1269—accepting some and refuting others.

In his *Summary of Theology* he touched on the issue of eccentric and epicyclical motions of the planets. He agreed that these hypotheses could be useful in showing how celestial movements appear to the astronomers. Yet, he did not consider the underlying arguments as entirely conclusive. He surmised that the heavenly phenomena could be explained in some other way, not yet understood by humans. Thus, he accepted eccentrics and epicycles as accurate perceptions of planetary appearances but did not regard them as the ultimate truth.[46]

Aquinas agreed with Aristotle that the goal of life is to search for truth. In elaborating on this point he asserted that truth did not solely come by divine revelation but by a deliberate application of the God-given human mind. He agreed with Aristotle that every effect has a cause and that ultimately every cause could be traced back to a first cause. Tracing all creation back to a divine first cause, he declared, proved the existence of God.[47] And since God was the ultimate authority, any differences between Christian and Aristotelian philosophy could only be attributed to faulty reasoning. Thus, Aquinas became the trusted teacher and the icon of information to the Church of Rome.[48] Rome had lost its political power but the Church of Rome managed to retain its spiritual power over the soul, at least for the time being.

## Summary

The legacy of Greek astronomy and mathematics was enormous. With Hipparchus and Ptolemy Greek astronomy and mathematics had reached its peaks around 200 B.C and 200 A.D. Later philosophers searched for peace and tranquillity. They had grown wary of the search for truth and did not believe in Science. Yet, a few persisted. Diophantus initiated algebra. Others tried to salvage what was left. They cherished the rigor of general propositions, logical deductions and formal demonstrations, and they prepared summaries of Aristotle's philosophy, Euclid's geometry, Ptolemy's astronomy, and Apollonius' conics. Their work helped to pass the legacy on to others.

After the great library of Alexandria was destroyed, and the Church of Rome closed the doors of the pagan School of Athens (ca. 500 A.D.), the torch of knowledge was passed on to the Middle East and carried beyond. On the way little was added to astronomy but the invention of the decimal system eased the burden of computations. With the Muslim invasion, astronomy and mathematics were swept back to the West. Ptolemy's Earth-centered (geocentric) system initiated a vigorous debate among the elite. It raised technical questions about the reality of deferents, epicycles, and equants. Thomas of Aquinas reconciled Aristotle's logic with the doctrine of the Church. He let in the light by opening the door to further search.

Chapter 8

## COPERNICUS (1473–1543),
## A THEORY NOT PLEASING TO ALL

*In 1543, as he lay on his deathbed, Copernicus finished reading the proofs of his great work; he died just as it was published. His* De Revolutionibus Orbium *was the opening shot in a revolution whose consequences were greater than those of any other intellectual event in the history of mankind.*

*Encyclopaedia Britannica*[1]

After a millenium during which free western science was suppressed, a time when scientific thought was considered to come exclusively under the domain of the Church, Europe was poised at the edge of a new science at the opening of the sixteenth century. In particular, the study of astronomy was reawakened with a fervor.

The scientific revolution of Europe did not come about overnight. Some vestiges of ancient astronomy had remained. Dates of important holy days of western Christian religion needed to be set. For example, the first Nicene Council—held in Nicaea in 325 A.D., in todays town of Iznik in northwest Turkey— decided on a method for determining the date for Easter. It falls on the first Sunday, after the first full Moon, on or after March 21. It cannot come before March 22 or after April 25. Thus for

94

Easter, as well as other holy days, some ecclesiastics were needed with a knowledge of the Moon cycle and the apparent movement of the stars, to derive the accurate calender dates from these motions. The English monk Bede Venerablis (ca.700 A.D.), for example, computed lists of Easter dates. The variations of Easter dates were recognized by a monk Notker of the Gall monastery, a renowned center of studies. Pope Sylvester wrote a book on the astrolabe (ca. 1000 A.D.). In this fashion some interest in astronomy survived, albeit only for the purpose of setting the dates of religious holidays.[2]

The Renaissance (from the Latin *renascere*, i.e., to be born again) began with the rise of the House of Medici in Florentine, Italy. International merchant trade and banking brought economic wealth and liberated the senses. Money brought forth delight in the arts. Taking human nature as its subject, the new spirit of the age found expression in beauty, it discovered truth in all philosophical schools, and it stressed the dignity of the individual. During the next two centuries the Renaissance spread throughout Europe. Adventure and curiosity swept away the rigid customs and institutions that had stifled progress for so long.

After the fall of Constantinople to the Turks (in 1453) many scholars fled from the East to the West. Steeped in the tradition of classical Greek scholarship, they brought with them important books and manuscripts. While the arts flourished in Italy, scholarship spread in Europe. Gutenberg's new printing press with movable type (ca.1440) made knowledge accessible through the quick production and reproduction of manuscripts. Education, communicaton, and scholarship became widespread.

A true Renaissance man was a person of broad intellectual and cultural interests, possessing universal knowledge.[3] There were many outstanding representatives of this ideal. Erasmus of the Netherlands (ca.1450) brought Christian thought into harmony with Greek philosophy. Shakespeare of England expressed the spirit of the Renaissance in his plays. Christopher Columbus, the Spanish-Italian navigator, represented the spirit of exploration in his discovery of America (1492), Michelangelo of Italy painted the frescos of the Sistine Chapel for the Vatican (ca.1510) and later designed the dome for St. Peter's Church (1550) in Rome. In

Germany it was Martin Luther who began the Protestant Reformation (1517). And in the field of astronomy, it was Nicolaus Copernicus of Poland who demonstrated that the Earth and the planets revolved around the Sun (1543). Galileo Galilei of Italy founded modern experimental science and contributed to astronomy (ca. 1600) and Tycho de Brahe of Denmark brought new observational precision to astronomy.

In this chapter the focus will be on Nicolaus Copernicus.

## Nicholaus Copernicus (1473–1543)

Named after his father Nicklas Koppernigk, Nicolaus was born into a well-to-do family. Later in life he adopted the Latinized name Copernicus but continued to sign official documents with "Coppernic."[4]

The Koppernigks were of German origin. They had migrated from Silesia to Poland early in the fifteenth century, not unusual for the time. In the records of the city of Kraków one Johann Koppernigk , was listed as a merchant and banker. He was the father of a Nicklas Koppernigk who was also a merchant and banker. Nicklas moved from Kraków to Torun where he married the daughter of a local aristocratic family. A son was born to them in midwinter, on February 19 of 1473.

### Early Years

Nicolaus was only ten years old when his father died. So it came about that his uncle Lukas Watzenrode (his mother's brother ) adopted Nicolaus and also his three other siblings. A few years later (in 1489) Watzenrode, a prosperous clergyman, was appointed Bishop of Ermland.[5] For Nicolaus, this family connection opened the door to a career in the clergy in later years. As a member of the clergy, he would be assured of an income from the diocese for the rest of his life. To reach this goal, however, he was expected to graduate with an advanced degree from a recognized institution of higher learning.[6]

As a youngster Nicolaus went to church schools, first in Toruń and later in Włocławek. In Włocławek he was taught by Mr. Vodka who, for good reasons, had Latinised his name to the more temperate Abstemius. Mr. Vodka was very enthusiastic about astronomy and, with the assistance of his student Copernicus, he constructed and mounted a sundial on the wall of the town's cathedral.[7]

## University

At age 18, following the advice of his uncle, Copernicus enrolled at the University of Kraków. Not only did it happen to be his uncle's alma mater but Copernicus' sister was also in Kraków, having married a local merchant.[8]

The University of Kraków was widely known for the strength of its faculty of mathematics. It attracted many foreign students, among them Copernicus whose mother tongue was German. As at other European universities of the day, Latin was the language of instruction. It is not known where or when Copernicus mastered Latin, but he received his excellent training in the fundamentals of astronomy at the University of Kraków.[9] Adalbert Brudzewski, his professor of astronomy, was acquainted with the *Epitome in Ptolemaei Almagestum* and may have introduced Copernicus to the Ptolemaic universe.[10] Later, in a more advanced course, Peurbach's (1423–1461) *New Theory* was taught. It attributed the variations in the brightness of the planets to their eccentric orbits. He may also have learned of Peurbach's eclipse calculation and have heard of Wellingford's critique of the Ptolemaic system.[11]

Richard of Wellingford, an outstanding and most original mathematical astronomer of England, questioned the physical realism of the Ptolemaic hypothesis:

> In the heavens there are no such eccentrics or epicycles as devised by the astronomical imagination for its own use. No educated person could regard them as probable. Without such imaginative astronomical constructions, however, no systematic science of the motion of the stars can be established which would pinpoint their positions at any moment as to be in accord with what we see.[12]

At about the same time, the University of Kraków received a gift of some up-to-date astronomical instruments and Copernicus helped to set them up. These instruments enabled him to make first-hand astronomical observations.

A few years later (in 1496), again at the advice of his uncle, Copernicus left Kraków and enrolled at the University of Bologna in Italy. With his brother Andreas, he crossed the Alps by foot. At Bologna he studied astronomy under Professor Dominico Maria de Novara (1454–1504), not so much as a student but as his assistant. Copernicus expanded on his earlier astronomical observations. In 1503, after more studies, a lectureship in mathematics in Rome and doctoral studies in canon law at the University of Ferrara,[13] Copernicus returned home to Poland, to the diocese of Ermland, for good. His mother had been ailing and by then she was nearing the end of her life.[14]

*Canon at Frauenburg*

Coprnicus' uncle succeeded, on second try, in having him appointed a canon of the cathedral of Frauenburg, a chapter of the district of Ermland. Soon after, he also managed to have Copernicus' younger brother Andreas appointed. Unfortunately Andreas died very young and did not profit nearly as much as Nicolaus from the financial security that came with the canonry.

For Copernicus the student days were over. Now 30 years old, he had studied mathematics, astronomy, medicine, canon law, and picked up a working knowledge of several languages, including Greek. Having gained a thorough grounding in many areas of knowledge, he was on his way to becoming a true Renaissance man.

On his return to Poland his uncle appointed Copernicus as his secretary, and made him his legal advisor and personal physician as well. A hothead in political negotiations and not a man of good health, his uncle relied heavily on him. He had Copernicus actively participate in politically sensitive negotiations, had him write innumerable memoranda and reports, called on him when tempers flared, and had him take care of his fragile health. All this kept Copernicus very busy and left him almost no time for his passion—astronomy.[15]

After his uncle's death in 1512, the workload eased. He took up the canonry at Frauenburg (Frombork), a small obscure Baltic town.[16] It was a position of lower rank. Quite possibly Copernicus had little choice in the matter. Perhaps some elderly officials did not appreciate it that the bishop had promoted his nephew over their heads.[17] Nevertheless, a few years later, when the Teutonic Knights attacked Poland to secure complete independence for East Prussia (1519), he was recalled as secretary and chancellor of the diocese of Ermland.

In this position he served the King of Poland. He prepared a memorandum on the state of the economy and provided documentation used as a basis for peace negotiations. He also wrote a treatise on currency reform *(Monetae Cudendae Ratio)*. In it he advocated that the minting of coins in Poland and East Prussia not be controlled locally, but within the broader context of national currencies. He also recommended that price inflation be curbed by regulating the money supply. Interestingly, both of these ideas are relevant to issues of modern-day monetary policy.[18]

Having become an important personage as the chancellor of the diocese of Ermland, the enticing prospect of promotion to high office seemed likely. Yet at this point, in 1523, Copernicus withdrew and returned to the little town of Frauenburg. As a canon of this tiny diocese he had ample spare time for astronomy. It is quite possible that he had already formulated a heliocentric hypothesis during his student days and started working on it seriously during his earlier stay in Frauenburg (1513–1516). Although Copernicus had also become a physician of some renown, he was ready to focus his energies on verifying his theory.[19] He met the quantitative challenge of the Ptolemaic theory head-on.

The geocentric (Earth-centred) theory of Ptolemy had stood the test of time because it predicted the planetary motions and other celestial events with impressive accuracy. Astronomical observations confirmed the theory. Long before Ptolemy, the Greek astronomer and mathematician Aristarchus had elaborated on a heliocentric (Sun-centred) theory. His revolutionary idea had caused hardly a stir because he did not verify it by astronomical observations. Hipparchus' excellent astronomical records did not become available until much later. The quantitative challenge of the Ptolemaic system, therefore, was to demonstrate, by use of empirical observations, an alternative model that could explain the celestial motions better than the geocentric system.

## The Copernican Theory of the Solar System

Copernicus' early summary of the design of his new model of the solar system was called *Commentariolus*. It is possible that Copernicus responded to a request from Johann Widmannstadt, then Secretary to Pope Clement VII, to release the *Commentariolus*.[20] Widmannstadt had presented a copy of it to the Pope in 1533. Three years later, after extensive discussions within the Church, Cardinal Schönberg wrote a letter urging Copernicus to provide a fully detailed account of his theory. And there were others who encouraged Copernicus to publish. Eventually Copernicus presented his theory in great detail in a book under the title *On the Revolutions of the Celestial Spheres (De revolutionibus orbium Coelestium)*.[21]

In dedicating his work to Pope Paul III, Copernicus wrote in the Introduction:

> I can reckon easily enough, Most Holy Father, that as soon as certain people learn that in these books of mine which I have written about the revolutions of the spheres of the world I attribute certain motions to the terrestrial globe, they will immediately shout to have me and my opinion hooted off the stage. Therefore, when I weighed these things in my mind, the scorn which I had to fear on account of the newness and absurdity of my opinion almost drove me to abandon a work already undertaken.
>
> But my friends made me change my course in spite of my long continued hesitation and even resistance. First among them was Nicholas Schönberg, Cardinal of Capua, a man distinguished in all branches of learning; next to him was my devoted friend Tiedeman Giese, Bishop of Culm, a man filled with the greatest zeal for the divine and liberal arts: for he in particular urged me frequently and even spurred me on by added reproaches into publishing this book and letting come to light a work that I had kept hidden among my things for not merely nine years, but for almost four times nine years. Not a few other learned and distinguished men demanded the same thing of me, urging me to refuse no longer—on account of the fear I felt—to contribute my work to the common utility of those who are really interested in mathematics: they said the absurder my teaching about the movement of the Earth now seems to very many persons, the more

the wonder and thanksgiving will it be the object of, when after the publication of my commentaries those same persons see the fog of absurdity dissipated by my luminous demonstrations. Accordingly I was led by such persuasion and by that hope finally to permit my friends to undertake the publication of a work which they had long sought from me.[22]

In the Introduction Copernicus also drew attention to the fact that the Lateran Council[23] under Pope Leo X could not reform the ecclesiastical calender. The length of the year and months had not been determined with sufficient accuracy. Astronomers had been uncertain about the precise movements of the Sun, the Moon, and the other five planets. When in 1475 Pope Sixtus IV asked Johann Müller of Vienna (also known as Regiomontanus) to correct the disparities of the calender, he failed to do so because he lacked the necessary data.[24] Those who believed in the geocentric spheres had been unable to precisely match them to the apparent motions of the planets. Others had postulated the planets traced out eccentric circles and epicycles. They had either omitted something necessary or added something foreign to the system and in so doing contradicted the first principle of regular motions.[25]

The first principle of regular motions was a principle Hipparchus and Ptolemy set forth when they observed variations in the speed of lunar and planetary motions. They had resolved the problem by allowing for off-center equants and by adding smaller epicycles moving on larger circular deferents.

In his arguments for a heliocentric system Copernicus relied heavily on the recorded astronomical observations of antiquity. He even followed Ptolemy's Euclidean order of axiom first, new theorem second, and logical proof third. His description was very complex and elaborate. Only a few snippets of the vast amount of material Copernicus assembled are presented here. First, a few of his axioms are shown, followed by his central theorem, and then illustrated by some of his geometric proofs.

*The Axioms*

For the most part, the axioms listed by Copernicus would be accepted today without hesitation. His supporting arguments may not be as easily embraced. Some of them recall Aristotle's reasoning. Copernicus wrote, for example, that "the Earth is globe-shaped" not flat, and elaborated that mountains and valleys modify it to a small extent.[26] People traveling toward the north saw stars that never set and did not see stars they may have seen rise further south. The star Canopus, for example, could not be seen in Italy but was visible from Egypt. Yet the last star of Fluvius could be seen in Italy but was not visible in the North.

Voyagers traveling on water could not see the land ahead when it could be clearly seen from the top of the ship's mast. The land rose above the ocean because water did not climb the shore any further than the convexity of the earth allowed. And Copernicus added that America had been discovered in his day, and that it should not come as a surprise if, for reason of symmetry, America was situated on the globe opposite to India.

"The world is spherical," read another heading in his book. Again Copernicus listed some reasons for it. It was a spherical globe because this figure is perfect, it needs no joints, it is a figure that has the greatest volume and is best suited to conserve all things.[27]

Under the heading "The Movement of the Celestial Bodies is Regular, Circular, and Everlasting—or Else Compounded of Circular Movements," Copernicus asserted that spheres turn in circles and that the planets move in many circles. They move differently, at times more slowly and at times more quickly. Sometimes they retrograded, straying toward the south and then north again. Sometimes they were nearer to the Earth and then again farther away from it. But their movements followed a constant law, with fixed periodic returns. In Aristotelean fashion he claimed that their orbits, therefore, must be circular.[28] He was adamant on this point. After giving more details on planetary motions, Copernicus asserts:

> We must confess that these movements are circular or are composed of many circular movements, in that they maintain these irregularities in accordance with a constant law and with fixed periodic returns: and that could not take place, if they were not circular. For it is only the circle which can bring back what is past and over with. [29]

He continued with the idea that the orbits of the planets followed a definite order because nobody was doubting that the fixed stars were "highest up" (most distant from Earth) in the heavens. Euclid had already proved that the more distant planets move more slowly than the nearest planet, the Moon. Saturn completes the longest circuit in the longest period, and therefore was farthest away, Jupiter's orbit was closer, and that of Mars closer yet.[30]

*Some Problematic Issues*

After listing these axioms as obvious truths, Copernicus discussed some problematic issues. In doing so he came to the central theme of his treatise, the theorem that the Earth is a planet orbiting the Sun just as the other five planets do.

It was not an entirely new idea. Long before Copernicus the Greek astronomer Aristarchus had suggested that the Sun was stationary, and that the Earth revolved around the Sun while rotating around its own axis.[31] Aristarchus, however, didn't attempt to prove his hypothesis by linking it to astronomical observation of the heavens. Copernicus did.[32] Before delving into the empirical evidence, he offered some additional background information. First, he asked: "Does the Earth have a circular movement?"[33] Copernicus referred the reader to the many authorities who claimed that the Earth rested at the center of the universe and that anything to the contrary was ridiculous. For him, that question was far from decided.

Copernicus recalled that the ancient Pythagoreans believed the Earth revolved at the center of the universe. If that were so, it was not clear whether the planets were sometimes nearer and sometimes farther away because the Earth came nearer to them and then drew away, or whether the planets came closer to the Earth and then moved farther away from it again. Therefore, it was not surprising that a Pythagorean, Philolaus, is supposed to have held that the Earth was one of the planets, moving in a circle and also following some other movements.[34]

The widely held contrasting view was that the Earth was at the center of the universe, that it was immovable, and that the celestial bodies closest to it moved slowest. The traditional view concurred with Ptolemy

and other philosophers of antiquity who believed that the Earth was at
rest at the center of the universe. The Earth being the heaviest element,
all things of any weight would be attracted and fall upon the Earth. If,
however, the Earth were to revolve around its axis and whirl along its
own orbit at unsurpassable velocity, Ptolemy feared it would have been
scattered beyond the heavens long ago. At such orbital speeds a rock
thrown high up in the air could never land near the same spot and all the
clouds would be seen to swoosh by in the sky from east to west.[35]

To this Copernicus countered that if Ptolemy was so concerned that
the orbital velocity would tear the Earth apart, why did he not fear
that the whole universe would fly apart? He wrote: "We should be even
more surprised if such a vast world should wheel completely during the
space of twenty-four hours rather than its least part, the Earth."[36] And
he continues this line of reasoning by asking:

> Would the stars of the heavens not have to be carried around at an
> incredibly high speed since the circumference of the heavens is far
> greater than that of the Earth? Would that not make the universe
> disperse outward at even greater speed? Yet, they say that beyond
> the heavens is nothing, not even space, and therefore the heavens
> cannot move outward. How is it possible that something as big as
> the universe can be held together by nothing at all? [37]

Copernicus responded to these questions by pointing out that it has long
been known that the planets tracing out a smaller circle revolve more
quickly than those describing larger circles. The Moon—without doubt
the planet closest to Earth—revolved around the Earth once every month
while Saturn, the highest (most distant from Earth) of the wandering
planets took 30 years to go around once.[38]

### The Copernican Empirical Analysis
Having outlined some problematic issues of the Ptolemaic system,
Copernicus elaborated on the heliocentric system. He turned to the fundamental question of whether or not all the apparent motions of the
heavens can be attributed to the orbital motion of the Earth. He believed
that the wanderings of the planets, their retrogressions, and progressions
were not of their own making but were due to the motion of the Earth.

The planets did not revolve around the Earth, but like the Earth, they orbited the Sun at the center of the system.[39]

In his reasoning, some of the ancient laws still held. For example, the sphere of the stars still made up the first and highest (most distant) of all celestial spheres, and it still encompassed everything. Saturn, the highest (most distant) of the planets followed next, completed its orbit in 30 years. Then came Jupiter, moving around in 12 years. In third place was Mars, completing a revolution every 2 years. But then, instead of the Sun, came the Earth with a one-year revolution, orbited by the Moon in a 30-day revolution. In sixth place was Venus completing its revolution in 7.5 months, in seventh place was Mercury with an orbital period of 88 days. Finally, in the center of it all, rested the Sun (Figure 8.1, Diagrams 1 and 2).[40]

In examining the revolutions and wanderings of the planets, Copernicus differentiated between the motions of the Earth and those of the other heavenly bodies. He allowed for a threefold movement of the Earth: first, the daily west-to-east revolution of the Earth on its axis; second, the annual west-to-east orbit around the Sun; and third, the annual variation in the inclination (a term to be explained shortly). He then correlated all the orbital movements of the planets with the revolutions and orbital motion of the Earth.[41]

In Euclidean fashion, Copernicus started with a variety of theorems of plane and spherical geometry that he used later in his proofs. He provided some definitions of astronomy relevant for an understanding of the text. He described his astrolabe, referred to the inclination of the Earth's axis, and catalogued the longitudes, latitudes, and magnitudes of many stars. Only a few selected items are presented here.

*The Inclination of the Earth's Axis*

The Earth travels around the Sun once a year in roughly 365 days.[42] During this trip the night sky slowly changes as the visible stars vary with the time of the season. The star combinations or constellations that can be seen in the spring and summer cannot be seen in the fall or winter as they gradually disappear from the night sky.

From season to season the Sun appears to change its position in the sky. The daylight hours change during the year in all parts of the world because the Earth tips first one pole toward the Sun and then the other. In regions closer to the poles the seasonal changes in daylight are more pronounced than near the equator where the seasons are barely noticeable. Come spring the days lengthen. At the time of the summer solstice, on June 21, the Sun reaches its highest point above the horizon. After that, the hours of daylight gradually diminish. The Sun reaches its lowest point at the time of the winter solstice, on December 22. (Figure 8.2).

Copernicus realized that the seasonal changes in outdoor temperatures could not be attributed to changes in the Sun's apparent elevation in the sky, but were caused by the inclination of the Earth's axis. During the winter months the northern half of the Earth tilts away from the Sun and during the summer months it tilts toward the Sun. For the southern half of the Earth the seasons are reversed, so that it is summer there when it is winter in the north, and vice versa. During the winter the daily temperatures are lower than during the summer because the Sun's rays are spread out over a larger area. During the summer months, when the Sun stands highest, the daily temperatures are higher because the Sun's rays cover a smaller area so that the sunshine is more intense. (Figure 8.3, Diagram 1).

Copernicus was also aware that the length and angle of the Sun's shadows varied with the seasons. In midsummer, at the time of the summer solstice, the Sun threw the shortest shadow. In midwinter, at the time of the winter solstice the Sun threw the longest shadow. From this difference in angle, Copernicus wanted to derive the angle of inclination or tilt of the Earth's axis relative to the orbital plane (Figure 8.3, Diagram 2).

*Astrolabe*

To derive the inclination of the Earth axis, Copernicus used his astrolabe. Ancient astronomers had explored the stars of the celestial sphere with such an instrument. Essentially, it consisted of a metal disk with a sight (a protractor), a plumb line that remained vertical, and graduations for measuring the angle of stars and planets against the horizon (schematically illustrated in Chapter 6, Figure 6.3). Ptolemy had added some further improvements to Hipparchus' astrolabe and had estimated the angle of the apparent annual path of the Sun, the ecliptic$_g$, at $23°51' 20"$.

Copernicus used a more complex astrolabe that described this angle (between ecliptic and equator) in some detail, since he had decided to base the analysis of his heliocentric system on the same data of the geocentric universe. Copernicus' astrolabe consisted of six circular metal frames that could be turned about each other. It had a meridian circle, a northern pole pointing to the Polar Star, one outer circle, and two inner circles. He could adjust the circles to model variations in the latitudes and longitudes of the planetary orbits (Figure 8.4, Diagrams 1 and 2).

With this astrolabe Copernicus could also exactly measure the seasonal changes in the angle and lengths of the Sun's shadows. His objective was to measure the inclination of the Earth's axis against the imaginary plane of the Earth's orbit around the Sun. To accomplish this he measured the angular deviation of the Earth's equator from the plane.[43] At the time of the summer solstice the shadow thrown by the Sun at midday forms the narrow angle. At winter solstice it forms the larger angle. The average of the difference between the two angles yielded the Earth's angle of inclination (Figure 8.5, Diagrams 1 to 5).[44]

Copernicus estimated, at winter solstice, the angle of the Sun's shadow at close to $50°$. At summer solstice, he measured it at close to $3°$. The difference between the two was $47°$. Following the arguments given in Diagram 5 of Figure 8.5, dividing it in half yielded $23.5°$ for the inclination. Actually, Copernicus estimated it at $23°29'$.[45] The modern-day estimate is between $23°26'$ and $23°27'$.[46] Considering that Copernicus worked with less sophisticated tools than are available today, the accuracy of his estimate is impressive.

According to Copernicus, Ptolemy took note of the positions of the stars in relation to the spring equinox. The spring equinox was the time of the year (on or about March 21) when day and night were of equal length. Referring to it, Copernicus wrote:

> For example, in the 2nd year of the Emperor Antonius Pius, on the
> 9th day of Pharmuti, the 8th month by the Egyptian calender,
> Ptolemy, who was then at Alexandria and wished to observe at the

time of sunset the position of the star which is in the breast of the Basiliscus or Regulus, adjusted his astrolabe to the setting Sun at 5 equatorial hours after midday. At this time the Sun was at 3 1/24° of Pisces.[47]

Although Copernicus used Ptolemy's observational data, he decided against using the spring equinox as the starting point for counting the degrees of celestial longitude.[48]

In Book IV of *On the Revolutions of the Celestial Spheres* Copernicus gave a detailed analysis of the precession of the solstices and equinoxes, summarizing his findings of the anomalies, and providing tables for the adjustments necessary to correct for the motion of the equinoxes. He concluded that the precession of the equinoxes and solstices is linked to the very slight changes in the inclination of the Earth's axis and attributable to the very small but detectable variations of the tilt of the poles.[49]

Copernicus did not rely on the positions of the stars as determined by the date of the equinoxes, but related them to the fixed positions of other stars. He decided to begin his analysis of planetary motion with a fixed star from an unchanging starting point, that is:

> With the Ram [i.e., the Zodiac sign] as being the first sign, and with its first star, which is in its head—so that in this way a configuration which is absolute and always the same will be possessed by those stars which shine together as if fixed and clinging perpetually and at the same time to the throne which they have seized.[50]

He was aware that the position of the equinoxes changed slowly (against the background of the stars) over the centuries and was determined to go beyond vaguely associating the coordinates of individual stars with the twelve constellations of the Zodiac. By assigning degrees of longitude and latitude, he fastened each of 1024 stars to a permanent position in the celestial sphere.[51]

Modern-day astronomers know, of course, that the exact coordinates of a star at the time of the equinox are not fixed permanently but inch along the ecliptic, against the constellations in the background. The repositioning of the equinox is attributable to a 26,000-year, very finely tuned wobble of the Earth's axis. Today's coordinates of the spring equinox are still in the constellation of Pisces. After the middle of the next millennium (between 2500 A.D. and 2700 A.D.), they will cross over into the adjacent constellation of Aquarius and slowly continue from there.[52]

### The Apparent Retrograde Motion of the Planets

After a detailed discussion of the revolutions of the Earth around the Sun and of the Moon around the Earth, Copernicus turned to the motion of the planets. Like the astronomers of ancient times, he relied on observations with the naked eye and could only observe the motions of five planets. He distinguished movements clearly:

> One of them is on account of the movement of the Earth, we said; and the other is proper to each planet. We may rightly call the first the movement of parallax, since it is the one which makes the planets appear to have stoppings, progressions, and retrogradations$_g$ —not that the planet which always progresses by its own movement, is pulled in different directions, but that it appears to do so by reason of the parallax caused by the movement of the Earth, taken in relation to the differing magnitudes of their orbital circles.[53]

Some fifteen hundred years earlier, Ptolemy and Hipparchus had explained the irregular motions of the five planets by adding epicycles to their orbits. Copernicus attributed them to the "parallax$_g$" (from the Greek word *parallax* (παραλλάξ), which translates into "not aligned with each other").[54] As seen from Earth he attributed the apparent meanderings of the planets, and especially their retrograde motion, to the variations in the alignment of their orbital positions.

For example, Copernicus observed that the alignment of the planet Mars varied from month to month. Although most of the time Mars, as seen from the Earth, travels from east to west, at times it appears to move in a "retrograde" motion from west to east, only to turn around after a while and resume its course west again (Figure 8.6).

Astronomers of antiquity had observed the apparent reversals in direction of all five planets. These retrograde motions were more pronounced for Mars than for the more distant planets Jupiter and Saturn. To explain this strange behavior of the planets, Ptolemy followed that

Aristotelian doctrine that all celestial motions must be circular and superimposed circular epicycles on the planetary orbits of his geocentric (Earth-centered) model (Figure 8.6). In doing so Ptolemy let the planets move along the circumference of epicycles. He let the center of each epicycle travel on a larger deferent$_g$ orbit.[55] The deferent orbit was circular as well, but slightly off center, so that it approximated the actual shape of the planet's orbit (this theory was illustrated in greater detail in Chapter 6, Figure 6.8). By combining epicycle and deferent, Ptolemy stuck to and preserved the time-honored Aristotelian ideal of circular motion of heavenly bodies. Astronomers used his model of planetary motion for their predictions over the next thousand years.

Copernicus' new geometric model terminated the 1000-year reign of the strange epicycles. Copernicus eliminated most of the epicycles from the deferent by switching over from Ptolemy's geocentric to his heliocentric system. As illustrated in Figure 8.6, the apparent positions of Mars, when observed at regular intervals, could be attributed to the combined effects of the orbital motion of both Mars and Earth. Mars takes nearly twice as long as Earth for one orbital revolution around the Sun—689 days compared to 365 days. As a result, the parallactic alignment between the two changes continually and this leads to the apparent retrograde motion of Mars. The parallactic alignment corrects for the retrograde motions of the other planets, although the time intervals vary with their distances and orbital speeds relative to that of Earth.[56]

Thus with a single stroke—by abandoning the age-old idea of a stationary Earth at the center of the universe—the Copernican heliocentric model accounted for most of the irregular planetary motions. As well, he accounted for the periodic variations in the brightness of the planets caused by the changes in the distance between the planet and Earth, especially noticeable in the case of Mars. He did so by inventing new techniques for estimating the planetary distances. Before pursuing these techniques, this Chapter looks at how Copernicus considered the time it takes planets to complete their orbits.

*The Planetary Periods*
Copernicus made it clear that the planets can rarely be observed from

Earth at their true orbital positions. That was only possible at the precise point in time when the Sun and Earth were perfectly aligned with a given planet. At that time, a planet seen from the Earth is in the exact opposite direction to the Sun. Copernicus described it as follows:

> It is clear that the true position of Saturn, Jupiter, and Mars become visible to us only at the time when they are in opposition to the Sun; and that occurs approximately in the middle of their retrogradations$_g$. For at that time they fall on a straight line with the mean position of the Sun, and lay aside their parallax."[57]

In Figure 8.6, for example, Mars is at the point of opposition when it arrives at position four.

Copernicus then turned to some orbital characteristics of the five major planets. Referring to the observations of Ptolemy and Hipparchus, he wrote:

> Ptolemy surveyed the circuits through a number of years, according as he acknowledged, he got them from Hipparchus. Now he means solar years to be understood as the years measured from equinox or solstice. But it has already been made clear that such years are not equal; on that account we shall use years measured from the fixed stars, and by means of them the movements of these five planets have been reconstituted more correctly by us.[58]

In doing so Copernicus distinguished between synodic years on one hand and sidereal years on the other. The term synodic stems from the Greek word *synodos* (σύνοδος) meaning "reunion." In astronomy the "synodic period$_g$ " refers to the average time it takes a planet to "reunite with" the same orbital position with respect to the Sun as seen from Earth.[59] The term "sidereal" comes from the Latin noun *sidus* for constellation and its adjective *siderus* for pertaining to the stars. The "sidereal year$_g$" refers to the time it takes a planet to complete one orbit around the Sun with respect to the same stars of a particular constellation. This customary period of a year is nowadays timed at 365.25636 days.[60]

Copernicus had sufficient data to describe both periods with precision. Relying on ancient records kept by Hipparchus and Ptolemy and on his own observations, Copernicus computed the duration of the synodic years. For example, in referring to the planets Jupiter and Venus he listed the synodic years at 398 days and 583 days, respectively. In describing the sidereal periods he wrote: "Jupiter is outrun by the Earth 65 times in 71 solar years minus 5 days 45 minutes 27 seconds: during this time the planet by its own movement completed 6 revolutions minus $5°41'2\frac{1}{2}''$."[61] Roughly—ignoring days, minutes, and seconds of solar years as well as fractions of degrees—that translates into 71 solar years and 6 revolutions, or $71/6 = 11.83$ years per sidereal period. Copernicus estimated the sidereal year of Jupiter more accurately, not ignoring days and fractional hours, at 11.86 years. Analogously, he deduced the sidereal periods for the other planets (Table 8.1).

**Table 8.1: Copernican and Modern-Day Estimates of Planetary Periods and Distances**

| Planets | Estimates by Copernicus | | | Modern-day Estimates | | |
|---|---|---|---|---|---|---|
| | Synodic Period (days) | Siderial Period (years) | Average Distance (A.U.*) | Synodic Period (days) | Siderial Period (years) | Average Distance (A.U. *) |
| Mercury | 115.1 | 0.241 | 0.387 | 115.9 | 0.241 | 0.387 |
| Venus | 583.1 | 0.615 | 0.719 | 583.9 | 0.619 | 0.724 |
| Earth | - | 1 | 1 | - | 1 | 1 |
| Mars | 779.2 | 1.881 | 1.52 | 779.9 | 1.891 | 1.523 |
| Jupiter | 398.2 | 11.86 | 5.219 | 398.9 | 11.86 | 5.202 |
| Saturn | 378 | 29.50 | 9.174 | 378.1 | 29.46 | 9.529 |

* Distance is given in astronomical units$_g$, that is Sun–Earth distances.
Sources: Copernicus, Nicolaus (1994 [1939]), *On the Revolutions of Heavenly Spheres*, p. 231, and Mitton, Simon ed. (1977), *The Cambridge Encyclopaedia of Astronomy*, Table 9.1, p. 161.

These estimates, and those of the other three planets, came very close to our modern-day values, differing by less than 1%. His estimates were less accurate for the synodic than the siderial periods because of annual variations tn the periods from equinox to equinox. Except for Saturn, his estimates of the siderial periods and average distances were comparable to our modern-day estimates—an extraordinary achievement considering that Copernicus based them on the records of astronomers of antiquity and some of his own observations, all obtained without the aid of modern telescopes or accurate clocks.

## The Distances of the Planets

Before estimating the solar distances Copernicus reviewed Ptolemy's findings. He considered the periods of the planetary oppositions, the apparent movements and angles between successive positions, the positions on the epicycles as they move along their orbits, and their degrees of eccentricity; he found them to be in good agreement with his own observations. Where he noticed differences, he elaborated and improved on the precision of findings.

### *The Exterior or Outer Planets*

The outer planets are those that are farther away from the Sun than is the Earth. In Copernicus' time the known outer planets were Mars, Jupiter, and Saturn. [62] They are in perfect alignment with the Earth and Sun when they reach the point of "opposition$_g$" on their orbits around the Sun. At that point in time an outer planet, seen from Earth, lies on a perfectly straight line connecting outer planet and Sun (Figure 8.7, Diagram 1).

While both the outer planet and the Earth continue their orbital course, the Earth approaches and passes the planet since it is orbiting the Sun faster. Viewed from the Earth this creates an angle between the Sun and the planet. As the Earth pulls farther ahead of the planet, the angle gradually narrows. When the Earth has moved far enough ahead, the planet can be observed at the point of "quadrature$_g$." It is at this point that the imaginary lines connecting Sun, Earth, and planet, form an angle of precisely 90° (Figure 8.7, Diagram 2).

From the sidereal motions (against the background of the stars) of the planets and the Earth, Copernicus estimated the angular sweep, that is, the change in angle formed by the two (imaginary) lines connecting the Earth to the Sun and the Earth to each planet. To find the size of the angle

Copernicus began at the point of quadrature when the angle between those two lines measured 90°. Applying trigonometry, he then estimated the planet's distance from the Sun. By this method Copernicus estimated Jupiter's distance from the Sun as shown in Figure 8.7, Diagram 2.

Actually, he computed it more accurately than shown in Figure 8.7, Diagram 2, at 5.219 times the Sun-Earth distance.[63] His estimate was well within 1% of the modern-day value. Except for the distant planet Saturn, his estimates for the other outer planets were just as close (Table 8.1).

*The Interior or Inner Planets*

Venus and Mercury, the inner planets, are closer to the Sun than the Earth. To arrive at their solar distances Copernicus took an approach that differed somewhat from his method of determining the distances of the outer planets. Here he applied the concept of "the greatest angular elongation."[64] Again, it involved a comparison of the planet's orbital position with its line-up of the Sun and the Earth. All three were lined up precisely at the point of "inferior conjunction" (Figure 8.8, Diagram 1).

As the planet moves counterclockwise along its orbit, it forms an angle with the line of inferior conjunction. This angle reaches its maximum when the imaginary line between the Earth and planet just touches or is tangential to the planet's orbit.[65] As seen from Earth these are the points of greatest angular distance or "maximum elongation" (Figure 8.8, Diagram 2).

Referring to the observational records of Ptolemy, Copernicus wrote that in the year 119 A.D., in the morning of the fourth day before the Ides [15th day] of October, Theon of Alexandria observed the planet Venus at the greatest angular distance of 47½° from the mean position of the Sun. In the year 132 A.D., on the evening of the eighth day before the Ides of March, Theon observed Venus at 47¼° from the mean position of the Sun. And in 142 A.D., Ptolemy observed the maximum elongation on the morning of the third day before the calends (first day) of August and found that the angular separation was again 47¼°.[66]

Copernicus added these observations to his own. For the angular distance of Venus from the Sun at the points of maximum elongation, he allowed a range of 44.8° to 47.3°. From these angular estimates he deduced the solar distance of Venus by trigonometry (Figure 8.8, Diagram 2).

In the final chapter of *On the Revolutions of the Celestial Spheres*, Copernicus discussed the orbital inclinations of the planets. As he did throughout his book, Copernicus used the observations recorded by Ptolemy. He called Ptolemy the "most outstanding of mathematicians" and followed him, as Copernicus put it, with the exception of a few cases.[67] The most important exception among the few was, of course, the change-over from Ptolemy's geocentric to his heliocentric system (Figures 8.1 and 8.6). It was a masterpiece of intricate geometric reasoning that has been greatly simplified here.

Unlike Aristarchus of antiquity, Copernicus not only put the Sun at the center of the universe, but supported his heliocentric model by an enormous amount of empirical information. He reconciled the recorded astronomical observations of the Hellenistic astronomers with his own heliocentric model. Most importantly he arranged, for the first time in history, the orbits of the Earth and the major planets in the correct order at their proper distances.

By use of this model Copernicus managed to eliminate most of the retrogressions of the planets—the most glaring irregularities of the planetary motions. Even so, some inaccuracies remained. He corrected for them by retaining some of the epicycles and eccentricities first introduced by the astronomers of antiquity.

## The Copernican System, Not Pleasing to All

Copernicus was well aware that he had only initiated the reform, yet he was confident that his "solar system" would stand the test of time. He had put the heliocentric theory on solid foundations. He had based it on extensive and complex arguments of plane and spherical geometry. Of these, only a few have been provided here.

To his future critics Copernicus had this to say: Those "idle talkers who take it upon themselves to pronounce judgment, although wholly ignorant of mathematics, and if by shamelessly distorting the sense of some pass age in Holy Writ to suit their purpose, they dare to attack my work; they worry me so little that I shall scorn their judgments as foolhardy." [68]

*On the Revolutions of the Celestial Spheres* was published in 1543. A few years earlier Jan Flachsbinder, the new Prince-Bishop of Ermland (Warmia) had been elected. Copernicus had opposed him in favor of another candidate. Plagued by years of political harassment on petty issues, Copernicus' health had deteriorated. A stroke and other ailments that came with his advancing age added to wear and tear. Nevertheless, he had managed to complete his manuscript and entrusted it to his friends for publication in Nürnberg, Germany. The first printed version of his book appeared in March of 1543. A copy of it reached him in May 1543, just a few hours before he died at age 70.[69]

Copernicus had delayed the publication of his book because he was concerned about criticism. He was more apprehensive about ridicule from intellectual circles than the adverse reaction of the Catholic Church. In fact, the Church did not react immediately, perhaps because the book had been dedicated to The Most Holy Father, Pope Paul III. Also, the author believed in the doctrine of the Church—established some 300 years earlier by Thomas of Aquinas—that faith and reason need not be in conflict. The introduction to his book reminded the reader that "the conceptions of a philosopher are placed beyond the judgments of the crowd because it is his loving duty to seek the truth in all things, in so far as God has granted that to human reason."[70] No objections were raised in other Roman Catholic countries of Europe. The English even welcomed the Copernican theory.

## Reactions to Copernican Theory

The Copernican theory ushered in a new era in astronomy. Long before Copernicus, even several hundred years before Ptolemy, the Greek philosopher and mathematician Aristarchus had proposed that planets revolve around the Sun and not around the Earth. But it was pure speculation. Copernicus used astronomical records to prove that his heliocentric theory was more powerful than Ptolemy's geocentric theory. He showed that the planetary loops were not real but largely the result of the Earth's motion. According to Copernicus the other planets did not stop and reverse direction but merely appeared to do so because of the Earth's changes in orbital position. True, the theory was in need of refinement but the stage was set.

The Copernican theory was based on mathematics, and it promoted an idea that contradicted the Bible. The early theological confrontation did not come from the Catholic pulpit but from the Protestant altars. Also, the opposition was associated with the heresy of Neoplatonism.

*Neoplatonism*

The Copernican theory was detached from visual impressions. It was a theory of abstract ideas and, so it seemed, not of the real world. It could be interpreted as an offspring of Neoplatonism. Central to Neoplatonism was the theory of Trinity: One, Nous, and Soul. In order of importance, "One" was considered the highest form beyond being, it was everywhere and nowhere. "Nous" was the spirit of self-awareness. The "Soul" was the inner aspect directed toward Nous. This Neoplatonic idea of trinity was in conflict with the Christian orthodox theory of trinity: God, God's Son, and the Holy Gost. At the time of Copernicus the Neoplatonic concept of Trinity was heresy.[71]

During his studies in Italy Copernicus had come under the influence of the Neoplatonism of his teacher Domenico Maria de Novara. Neoplatonists attributed some mystical value to mathematics which, they believed, emanated from the harmony of the Soul. They also believed that the good of God was revealed by the light of the Sun.

Copernicus was the nephew of a Bishop, and while a canon of the Catholic Church he himself never became a priest but, in later life, enjoyed the ecclesiastical privilege of a leisured occupation. Free from daily duties, he could pursue the study of astronomy in seclusion. Perhaps he did have some Neoplatonic leanings. Certainly, a quote from Copernicus hints toward the Neoplatonic direction. He wrote:

> In the middle of all sits the Sun enthroned. In this most beautiful temple could we place this luminary in any better position from which we can illuminate the whole at once? He is rightly called the Lamp, the Mind, the Ruler of the Universe; Hermes Trismegistus names him the visible God, Sophocles calls him the All-seeing. So

the Sun sits as upon a royal throne ruling his children the planets which circle around him.[72]

Neoplatonism also implied a turning away from the "real world," from the politics and arts, and even from practical mathematics. It encouraged secrecy and occult. It may have played a role in some of Copernicus' decisions, made when he abandoned his diplomatic career of earlier years and, again, in later years when he delayed publication of his book.

A widespread antipathy towards Neoplatonism may explain why the Copernican theory was nearly universally rejected. An immediate reaction came from Martin Luther. Being a staunch believer in the Bible, his response was hostile. He said:

> That is how things go nowadays. Anyone who wants to be clever must not let himself like what others do. He must produce his own product as this man does, who wishes to turn the whole of astronomy upside down. But I believe in the Holy Scripture, since Joshua ordered the Sun, not the Earth, to stand still.[73]

Other critics followed. The astronomer Tycho de Brahe wrote:

> What need is there without any justification to imagine the Earth, a dark, dense and inert mass, to be a heavenly body undergoing even more numerous revolutions than the others, that is to say, subject to a triple motion, in negation not only of all physical truth, but also of the authority of the Holy Scripture which ought to be paramount.[74]

But there were also some positive reactions. In Germany Erasmus Reinhold (1511–1553), a Professor in Wittenberg, hailed the forthcoming text as the opening of a new era and approved of it enthusiastically. In England Robert Recorde, a mathematician, was in favor of the Copernican system of the universe and approved of it publicly, although in a guarded manner. Thomas Digges, a English mathematician who published a book in 1576, thought that Ptolemy's system was too awkward to believe and considered the Copernican system to be a perfect model of the world. In Italy Giovanni Battista Benedetti (1530–1597) preferred the "theory of Aristarchus, explained in a divine manner by Copernicus, against which the arguments of Aristotle are of no value."[75] Yet those who agreed with the Copernican theory were far outnumbered by others who objected to it.

Lutherans, Catholics, and Calvinists alike dismissed the Copernican view as an absurdity because it contradicted the Bible. Astronomers did not endorse it and members of other faculties considered it to be implausible. Public opinion was against it. Only members of the Pythagorean-Hermetic fringe of the established educational and religious institutions shared the Copernican view. They were in favor of it because it was one of their axioms that the Sun held a central place in the universe.

Although under pressure because of their unpopular beliefs, the Neoplatonic view survived. Several Italians were associated with the movement. Among them was Francesco Patrizzi (1529–1597), who published a volume on hermitic writings which he dedicated to Pope Gregor XIV. His book was to encourage the teachings of Plato, of the early church fathers, and their followers.

*Hermetism*

Best known among the members of the Neoplatonic fringe is Giordano Bruno (1548–1600), the Hermetist. Born near Naples, Italy, he became a Dominican in 1563 and a wandering scholar. He taught the hermetic tradition with enthusiasm—sometimes ascribed to the Egyptian god Thoth and identified with various mystical, religious, philosophical, and astrological ideas as promoted by an Egyptian priest in ancient times—he saw the Sun at the center of a magical universe, and believed that the universe was pervaded by invisible forces. It so happened that the Copernican system fit his hermetic preconceptions. Bruno regretted that Copernicus was more of a mathematician than a student of nature and could not let his mind freely soar. And so Bruno did it for him by transforming Copernicus' mathematical analysis into a religious doctrine to his own liking.[76]

It was the calm before the storm. By the turn of the century the first lightning struck. Bruno wanted to see the Church return to early principles. Yet, he went much further and advocated that the Church should be drastically reformed by incorporating the ancient Egyptian outlook. His "hermetism" was a strange mixture of magic and metaphor, mysticism and meditation, Pythagorean numerology and Neoplatonism. During his stay in England he lectured on the hermetic writings and intertwined them loosely with the Copernican theory.

The University of Oxford did not take kindly to all this. He fled to France and Germany. Invited to Italy, he was imprisoned. The charges against him were his denial of the divinity of Christ and his polemical promotion of religious magic and mysticism. Caught in the claws of the Inquisition, he was burned at the stake in 1600.[77] Although he was never charged for advocacy of the Copernican system, unfortunately, by then the Copernican theory was linked to Bruno's condemnation. It took many years before the link was broken.

Chapter 9

# TYCHO (1546–1601),
# THE OBSERVATIONAL ASTRONOMER

*Tycho de Brahe was the first to break through the accuracy barrier in the measurement of angles. With his instruments and with his skill, he was able to record co-ordinates to an accuracy of better than one second of arc. This surpassed the measurements made by the best Asian astronomers.*

N. M. Swerdlow[1]

Tycho de Brahe was a man of many talents, a Renaissance man. Wealthy by his uncle's good fortune, he surrounded himself with beautiful things. A craftsman at heart he established a printing shop to produce and bind his own books. He brought craftsmen in from southern Germany to construct the finest astronomical instruments money could buy. He enticed Italian and Dutch architects to design and decorate his astronomical observatory. A castle-like structure, he called it Uraniborg, after Urania, the Muse of astronomy. It housed his instruments and his many assistants. With their help he collected an enormous amount of astronomical data. His observations were so accurate that they allowed him to substantially correct every previously known astronomical record. Learned men from all over Europe visited him and he liked their company.

## Tycho de Brahe (1546–1601)

Tygge de Brahe was a great astronomer. In literature he is often called Tycho, the Latinized version of Tygge. He was born in 1546 in the then Danish province of Skanic of what is now the southernmost region of

Sweden. Descended from a long line of feudal lords, his father was the governor of Helsingborg Castle and a member of the Danish Council of State. His mother was mistress of the Queen's Robes.[2] His uncle, Joergen de Brahe, was known as an irascible vice-admiral of the Danish navy. Although in later life Tycho entertained kings, he was bored with the nobleman's life style of luxury, leisure, horses and dogs.

*Early Years*

By a bit of pirate-like kidnapping and a subsequent brotherly agreement, his Uncle Joergen (Jørgen) "adopted" and raised Tycho. He saw to it that Tycho received the best education.[3] At age seven Tycho had been taught to converse fluently in Latin, to compose music, and to write poetry. In discussing problems of logic, he soon outdid his uncle. At age 13, in family tradition, his uncle sent him to the University of Copenhagen to study rhetoric and philosophy to prepare for a career as a diplomat or statesman.

While at Copenhagen, he heard a professor describe a forthcoming solar eclipse. It impressed Tycho deeply that astronomers could predict the precise time of the event. To him, the ability to foresee and accurately forecast this celestial phenomenon was something so "divine" that he at once decided to study astronomy.[4] He started buying books on astronomy, among them the classic treatise of Ptolemy. He intensely studied Ptolemy's famous treatise, the *Almagest*, (see Chapter 6), and was convinced by Ptolemy's arguments that the Earth was at the center of the universe. From then on, Tycho never abandoned the geocentric view of classical antiquity.[5]

*University Years*

At age 16 his uncle, the vice-admiral, sent Tycho to the University of Leipzig in Germany. Studying law by day and observing the planets and stars at night, his uncle was worried that Tycho might suffer a physical and nervous breakdown.[6] As a precautionary measure his uncle sent along a tutor, Anders Sorensen Vedel, who was instructed to cure Tycho of his fascination with astronomy.

His tutor failed. Tycho bought himself a globe to learn the names of the celestial constellations, and hid it under the blanket of his bed. Later he acquired and hid a cross-staff, a portable instrument commonly used by navigators for finding the latitude at sea. Based on the same principle as the astrolabe (described in Chapter 6, Figure 6.3) the cross-staff could also be used for measuring the angular distance between two celestial objects (Figure 9.1).[7] Tycho used the equipment at night while his tutor was asleep. After a year of close supervision, his tutor gave up. He finally realized that Tycho was star struck beyond redemption and let him pursue his passion for astronomy.[8]

Some 35 years later Tycho would bitterly recall that his tutor had refused to give him the money to buy proper equipment. It had left Tycho little choice but to make his astronomical observations with improvised instruments. Nevertheless, while at the University of Leipzig, Tycho managed to carefully observe the conjunction of Jupiter and Saturn. The two planets came so close together that he could hardly distinguish between the two. They looked like one. He searched in the Alphonsine planetary tables—based on Ptolemaic observations and assembled by Arab and Jewish astronomers at the request of King Alphonso X of Spain nearly 300 hundred years earlier—for Jupiter's and Saturn's predicted positions and discovered that the table values were in error by a whole month.[9] Even the more recent Copernican tables were off by several days.[10] When Tycho first observed the partial eclipse of the Sun, he was awed by the accuracy of astronomical predictions. Now, he was shocked by the "astronomical" size of the error. When he detected that even the observations of the "incomparable Copernicus" did not agree with his own, he became convinced that greater accuracy was needed.[11] Was it any wonder that his family had such a low opinion of astronomy? He decided right then and there to change that. The errors of observation needed to be corrected. Tycho would show his family and the astronomers of the world how it ought to be done.[12]

About this time, the state of Tycho's family fortune changed. After a victorious naval battle against the Swedes the vice-admiral was ac-companying King Frederick II on his way home to Denmark.[13] The king was known to like his spirits and after winning a hard-fought battle was indulging in a drink or two, when he fell overboard. The vice-admiral jumped in after him and saved his life. Upon their return home King Frederick rewarded him generously. Unfortunately, the vice-admiral did not live long enough to enjoy his newly gained wealth. In saving the king from the ice-cold waves of the Baltic Sea, he had caught pneumonia and promptly died. He left all of his great fortune to young Tycho, his adopted son.[14]

Tycho settled the affairs of the estate and hurried back to Germany, this time to the University of Wittenberg where he delved into more astronomy and mathematics. The year was 1565 and Tycho was now 19 years old. When the plague unexpectedly struck Wittenberg, he moved on to Rostock.[15] Although he escaped the plague, it was a move that cost him dearly.

Tycho was as eccentric and irascible as the vice-admiral had been. While at Rostock, he fought a duel with another Danish nobleman on the university campus. Contesting who was the better mathematician, the other duellist sliced off a good part of Tycho's nose. For the rest of his life Tycho wore a shiny replacement made of a precious gold, silver, and copper alloy. To ensure that it stayed in place, he always carried a snuff-box containing a glutinous ointment, which he frequently applied.[16]

After Rostock, Tycho continued his astronomical observations and studies at the University of Augsburg in southern Germany and at the University of Basle in Switzerland. While in Augsburg he met town councillors, Paul and Johann Hainzel. They devoted much of their spare time to astronomy. Seeing how seriously they took their hobby, Tycho designed for them a wooden quadrant with a 19-foot radius. Suspended from the ceiling by its centre, the angles of observation could be read off with an unheard of accuracy of 10 seconds from the vertical plumbline.[17] An accuracy of ten seconds is equivalent to dividing one degree into 360 equal parts. This degree of accuracy was achieved by enlarging the quadrant of an astrolabe to a radius of 19 feet and by precision workmanship (Figure 9.2).

For use on his travels Tycho had designed a smaller and much lighter sextant-like instrument. By looking through two sights, one fixed and the other movable, Tycho could read the degrees of the angle of observation. By adding an inner and outer circle he attained a further ten-point subdivision. In principle this subdivision was comparable to that of a micrometer, a device for measuring minute distances. It improved the precision of observation so much that Tycho applied it later to all of his astronomical measuring instruments.[18]

Tycho completed his university education at age 26 and returned home to Denmark. For the next few years he lived with his uncle, Bill Steen. Steen had founded the first paper mill and glassworks in Denmark. He was the only one of Tycho's family who approved of his stargazing. In his spare time Steen dabbled in alchemy and Tycho sometimes helped him in the laboratory.

*Tycho the Astrologer*

Tycho also dabbled in astrology and cast some horoscopes. Although he did not think highly of astrologers, he did believe that the stars influenced a person's character and destiny.[19] Judging by some of his better horoscopes, it appears that Tycho's predictions were on the cautious side. As was customary in his day, wealthy people had horoscopes cast soon after the arrival of a newborn. King Charles IX of Sweden asked Tycho to prepare a horoscope for his newly born son, Gustav Adolf, Tycho predicted the boy would become King of Sweden, and eventually he did. After Suleiman the Magnificent, the 10th ruler of the Ottoman empire, threatened to conquer Europe, Tycho cast a horoscope confidently predicting that Europe would be saved by Suleiman's premature death. Ironically, after casting the horoscope, it was discovered that Suleiman had already died.

Tycho did not cast a horoscope before his own marriage. He was already convinced that the best match for a busy astronomer was a simple housewife; he shocked the Danish aristocracy by marrying a peasant girl.[20]

**Tycho, the Best-Known Astronomer**

On the evening of November 11, 1572, coming back from his uncle's laboratory, Tycho discovered a new star, brighter even than the planet Venus at its brightest. He could not believe his eyes. It appeared just northwest of the constellation Cassiopeia, at a point where he had never before seen a star. How could it be that a new star appeared suddenly from nowhere? Had Aristotle not said that the heavens were perfect and forever unchangeable?[21] Were comets, meteorites, and other imperfections not confined to the regions closest to Earth? (Figure 9.3)[22]

*Supernova of 1572*

Baffled by the sudden appearance of the new star, Tycho asked several peasants he met on the way to tell him if they could confirm what he saw. They did. Not only was the new star clearly visible at night, but people with good eyesight could make it out in broad daylight. It was a mysterious and wonderful phenomenon. A friend of Calvin, a leader in the Protestant Reformation, thought it was the second star of Bethlehem announcing the return of Christ. Others predicted dire calamities. Had Aristotle not taught that the world of stars was unchangeable and eternal? Was it perhaps a comet condensed from a fiery vapour of gas? It stirred the imagination of all, common people and scholars alike.[23]

This supernova$_g$ was made famous by Tycho. The star flared up more brilliantly than the planet Venus in November 1572. By December it began to fade; by May of the following year it had dimmed to second magnitude, and in 1574 it disappeared. Tycho was not the first to discover it. Priority went to a Schuler of Wittenberg who saw it on November 6; and it went to Hainzel at Augsburg and Lindauer in Winterthur of Switzerland who observed it on November 7. But because Tycho studied it closely and published his findings it is always referred to as Tycho's Star. He measured its distance from the North Star, both when the nearby stars Cassiopeia were near the zenith and twelve hours later when it stood low. Since the distances from the nearby stars, at high and low altitude, were always exactly the same, the supernova had no parallax$_g$ and this was proof that it was not as close as the Moon or any of the five planets but as far distant as the stars. It demonstrated that contrary to Aristotle's doctrine of fixed stars to all eternity, changes did occur among them. The stars were not permanently rivetted to the firmament.[24]

Tycho was so excited he blazed ahead with renewed zeal in astronomy. He put aside the widespread notion that it was below the dignity of a nobleman to write a book. He published his account *Of the*

*New Star (De Stella Nova)* in May 1573.[25] He wrote about his measurements, the supernova's distance from Earth, his deductions and opinions on the formation of the new star, about its nature, and even its astrological implications.[26]

Tycho's discovery created an immediate sensation among astronomers. Maestlin of Tuebingen in Germany, Thomas Digges in England, and others agreed with Tycho that it did not have a sublunar parallax. Therefore, it could not be an object of the sublunar$_g$ sphere. Nor could it be a planet in motion. No, the new star stood perfectly still, remaining in the same position among the fixed stars. Not all astronomers agreed with this conclusion. Some believed it was a comet that moved on a straight-line course and gradually grew dimmer as it retreated from Earth. This, however, did not change Tycho's view. While he could not explain why the intensity of light should diminish, he was convinced that it was a new star. Although the supernova disappeared from sight after 20 months, its remnant has been detected and identified as radio image 3C10 by D.A. Green of the Cavendish Laboratory of Cambridge, England.[27]

More than any other empirical finding, the precise description of Tycho's observations obliterated the Aristotelian, Platonic, and Christian doctrines that the stars were permanent, immutable, and incorruptible since the time of creation and forever after to all eternity. Whether other astronomers agreed or disagreed with him, the publicity surrounding the discovery made Tycho the best-known astronomer of his time.[28]

*More Travel*

Three years after his discovery, Tycho travelled Europe again. He did it in grand style, visiting his friends in Frankfurt, Augsburg, Wittenberg, and Venice. On his way back he called on Count Wilhelm IV at the town of Kassel. They got along famously. The Count was devoted to the study of astronomy. His father, Count Philip, had already built him an observatory with a movable roof to observe the skies. When governmental affairs preoccupied him, he hired an astronomer and a mechanic to continue with celestial observations. From Wilhelm's observatory in Kassel came the first West-European star catalogue with new measurements.

After Tycho left, Count Wilhelm urged King Frederick of Denmark to provide funds to Tycho for the construction of an observatory. On Tycho's return to Denmark the king offered him the choice of several castles. Tycho declined because he had decided to make his home in the charming Swiss town of Basel, the northern gateway of Switzerland. He packed up and went on his way. When the news reached King Frederick, he ordered him back to Denmark.

Surprisingly, Tycho obeyed. The king rewarded him by promising to build, at Denmark's expense, a splendid observatory equipped with the best astronomical instruments money could buy and a residence on the three-mile island of Hveen, not far from Copenhagen. The island covered more than two thousand acres of land. Rising on sheer white cliffs out of the sea, it was as flat as a table, an ideal location for an observatory. In addition, the King promised Tycho an annual grant and a variety of benefits. Together, they added up to one of the highest incomes in Denmark. Tycho could not refuse the king's royal offer. He settled in Denmark, and started to build "Uraniborg," a palatial observatory after his own design.[29]

*Uraniborg*

Uraniborg, also called the "castle of the heavens," was built in a style true to Tycho's taste.[30] It has been described as a fortress-like monstrosity, a cross between an Italian palazzo and the Kremlin. It combined meticulous precision with wasteful extravagance. Cylindrical towers and onion-shaped domes with removable tops housed Tycho's astronomical instruments. The walls were covered with sundials, globes and clocks. A 14-foot quadrant was mounted to the wall in Tycho's study. In the library stood a five-foot diameter celestial globe, made of brass and with the positions of the fixed stars engraved on it. It was part of Tycho's precious collection of astronomical equipments. The globe alone had cost 5000 Thaler, an enormous sum of money. Kepler, his principal assistant and eventual successor, would not earn that much money in his whole lifetime (Figure 9.4).[31]

Tycho had carefully planned the layout of the observatory. The building had plumbing, had eight rooms for his assistants, and contained several kitchens. It included a library and a pharmacy. In the basement was his private printing press, his alchemist's laboratory, and even a prison cell. He had peasants work the land and take care of the fish ponds for him. In later years he added a second observatory. To protect his astronomical instruments from vibrations he had this second observatory, except for the observation domes, built totally underground.[32] Tycho's verses and epigrams filled the walls and hallways of his palatial mansion. Surrounded by his instruments and poetic output, he entertained many distinguished visitors, presided over lavish banquets, and talked about the strange orbit of Mars.

*Unequalled Precision*

All the while he kept records of his observations. He made and recorded them continually, night after night, for 20 years. They were of previously unequalled precision.[33] Tycho achieved this precision by designing and constructing his own instruments. He used vertical quadrants of dif-ferent sizes for measuring the angular altitudes of celestial objects. The smaller quadrants were of 1⅓ and 2 feet radii and were movable, while the larger quadrants were 5½ and 7 feet, and solidly mounted. For the most accurate measurements he used a 6¾ foot quadrant attached to a wall. To work this quadrant he had one assistant pointing it, a second recording the readings, and he himself directing it. He also had sextants and armillary spheres. His nightly observations intensified as the number of instruments increased. He recognized that multiple observations, when averaged over several instruments, yielded better results. At times of lunar eclipses he employed three separate teams of observers.[34]

Tycho inserted thread-like pinnules in the sights of his instruments to ensure the utmost precision of his astronomical observations. Regularly spaced, the pinnules enabled the observer to focus on the center of the heavenly object and position it with greater accuracy.

At times Tycho went to extreme lengths to verify the validity of his own findings. When he detected a 3½ second difference between the solar altitude recorded by Copernicus and his own estimate, he had one of his assistants travel from Denmark along the Baltic Sea to Frauenburg (where Copernicus had done his work) to confirm the validity of his own observation.[35] He found that Copernicus' observations were less accurate than his own. And he discovered other differences between his own measurements and records of the past (such as an 11-second difference in the annual lunar motion, roughly equivalent to 1/330 of 1°.

Fascinated by the continuous motion of celestial objects, Tycho recorded his observations without interruption year after year. He ranked comets with other celestial bodies, moving their orbits beyond the sublunar regions where Aristotle had put them. He traced the ever-changing orbital positions of the five planets with painstaking accuracy.[36] In pursuing his goal of precision with singular obsession, he drove his assistants just as hard as he drove himself. Some of them did not endure their merciless taskmaster for very long. Tycho may have employed as many as 60 assistants over a period of 20 years.[37]

*The Tychonic System*

Tycho was convinced that by the precision of his observations he could lay down a foundation for a renewed astronomy. Yet, he did not integrate his principle of precision into his model of the universe. His image of the universe was intuitive, highlighted by some striking insights. For example, in describing the trajectory of the comet of 1577, he wrote:

> Modern philosophers agree with the almost universal belief of antiquity who hold it as certain and irrefutable that the heavens are divided into various orbs of hard and impervious matter, to some of which stars are attached so that they revolve with them. But even if there were no other evidence, the comets themselves would most lucidly convince us that this opinion does not correspond with the truth.[38]

Thus, in one fell swoop he demolished the classical notion of impenetrable spheres.

Having done away with the crystalline spheres of antiquity, Tycho went on to say that the solar system of the great Copernicus was even more difficult to accept. Mathematically elegant and beautiful as the Copernican theory appeared to him, he believed the Earth was far too large and massive to travel around the Sun. For Tycho, the whole idea contradicted not only the Holy Bible but also the physical principles of motion. He wrote:

> The Earth, large, sluggish, and inapt for motion, is not to be
> disturbed by movement ... anymore than the stars are to be shifted,
> so that such ideas are opposed both to physical principles and the
> authority of Holy Writ which many times confirms the stability of
> the Earth.

And so Tycho arrived at his own model. It was a compromise between
Ptolemy's geocentric system and Copernicus' heliocentric system.
Ironically, the superior precision of his astronomical observations played
no role in it. Tycho described his model in a chapter of a book he
published in 1588 under the title *Concerning Recent Phenomena of the Aetherial
World*. In the Ptolemaic tradition he stationed the Earth at the center of the
cosmos, with both Moon and Sun circling it. In contrast to tradition,
however, he let Mercury, Venus, Mars, Jupiter, and Saturn orbit the Sun
(Figure 9.5).[40] With his modified geocentric model Tycho avoided what in
his view was the physical incongruity of the Earth orbiting the Sun. With
his model, he steered clear of any inconsistency with the Bible. As later
astronomers found the Ptolemaic system less and less acceptable, they took
refuge in the "Tychonic System" or some variant of it. It put the Earth
back to where they thought it belonged, at the center of the universe.

## Move to Prague

When King Frederick died (of too much alcohol) in 1588, his son Christian
was only 11 years old. A regency of four nobles took over and ruled the
country for the next eight years. Then Christian assumed power. He was
a born leader. Full of energy, his people loved him. He was well educated
and interested in the arts and sciences. Despite what they may have
had in common, Christian disliked Tycho's overbearing arrogance.[41]

Rumours had it that Tycho kept a peasant family chained in the
prison cell in Uraniborg. The callous mistreatment of his tenants caused
an uproar in the country. Tycho ignored the king's letters of reprimands.
In turn, King Christian decided to curb some of Tycho's extravagant
expenditures. Tycho took this as a personal insult. He gathered up his
family and assistants, dismantled and packed his precious instruments,
had his furniture, books, and luggage loaded on wagons, and left Denmark

in 1597. For the next two years Tycho's lengthy caravan wound its way through Hamburg, Dresden, and Wittenberg. In 1599 he and his wagon train entered Prague where Emperor Rudolph II welcomed him. The Emperor appointed him the Imperial Mathematicus.[42]

The appointment made Tycho the successor of Ursus (the Latinized name of Bear). In his youth, Ursus had been a farm hand in Ditmarsch, at the lower part of the Jutland peninsula. His outstanding intellectual gifts quickly caught the eye of his teachers. Still a youth, he had published a Latin grammar book and a book on land surveying. Employed later by a Danish nobleman, he had the opportunity to visit Tycho on his island. When Ursus published a book on the *Fundaments of Astronomy*,[43] Tycho thought perhaps the former swineherd should know his place. He accused him of having stolen the ideas from him when on a visit to Uraniborg in 1584.

Supposedly, one of Tycho's assistants had searched Ursus' pockets while he slept and found incriminating papers that depicted an earlier version of Tycho's universe. Although the arrangements of the planets were the same under both systems, Tycho attributed the daily rotation to the revolving stars, whereas Ursus attributed it to the Earth's rotation around its own axis.[44]

A very similar system was independently developed by Helisaeus Roeslin, a German astronomer, astrologer, and physician opposed to the Copernican system. It was a compromise between the geocentric Aristotelian system and the solar system of Copernicus: the Earth was reinstated at the centre of the universe, the five planets circled the Sun, and the Sun, together with the planets, circled the Earth. Again this intermediate system appealed to all who did not wish to offend the "common sense" approach of traditional astronomy.[45]

Emperor Rudolph II gave Tycho the castle Benatek. A six-hour distance from Prague, Benatek was near the river Iser and may have reminded Tycho of his island in Denmark. Progress in setting up his observatory was slow. The Emperor had offered Tycho an income that surpassed that of counts and barons, but because the Emperor's finances were in terrible shape, the court's treasury officials did not rush to provide the funds to Tycho. Nevertheless, he decided to hire some assistants, among them a young astronomer named Johannes Kepler, whose ideas intrigued him.[46]

*Kepler, one of Tycho's Assistants*

In 1596 Johannes Kepler, Tycho's contemporary but 25 years younger, had conceived of five perfect solids that fit into the planetary spheres. He communicated his wonderful discovery to Ursus in Prague and to Tycho de Brahe in Denmark. In his letter to Ursus, Kepler wrote glowingly of the mathematician's fame "which makes thee rank first among the mathematici of our time like the sun among the minor stars."[47] In the letter to Tycho, Kepler referred to him as "the prince of mathematicians not only of our time but of all times."[48] Somehow Tycho found out about Kepler's letter to Ursus in which he had ranked him first among mathematicians of his day. Understandably, Tycho was upset since in his younger years a similar comparison had cost him part of his nose.

Nevertheless, he replied to Kepler very courteously, saying, among other things that he was willing to forget the whole affair. Later, in December 1599, Tycho sent a letter inviting Kepler to come to Prague "on your own will and desire for common study."[49] In fact, Kepler was already on his way to Prague. On Kepler's arrival, Tycho assigned him to analyse the orbit of Mars. At first glance Kepler thought he could figure out its precise orbit in a week or so. Not long after, Kepler wrote in a letter that Tycho's data "took such a hold of me that I nearly went out of my mind."[50] It was to take him eight years to geometrically define the orbit of Mars.

The first two years were very difficult for Kepler. Within two months of his arrival, a quarrel broke out. Kepler had put down in writing the conditions Tycho was to meet if Kepler and his family were to settle in Benatek. Somehow Tycho had gotten a hold of Kepler's notes. Since they were hardly flattering to Tycho, harsh words were exchanged. Kepler left Benatek the next day. However, within a week he wrote a long letter of apology to Tycho. Two weeks later they reconciled. Tycho went to Prague and drove Kepler back to Benatek in his luxurious coach. Both knew they needed each other; Kepler needed Tycho's data and Tycho needed Kepler to solve the puzzle of the planetary orbits.[51]

133

During the next 18 months Kepler twice went back to Gratz to settle his family's affairs. He had hoped to gain a leave of absence to save his teaching position in Gratz, or to be granted a position at the university of his native Wuerttemberg. Yet, it was not to be. On July 31, 1600 all Lutherans of Gratz had to appear before an ecclesiastical commission, declare their willingness to convert to Catholicism, or be expelled. Kepler refused to convert. He chose exile.[52]

*Tycho's Premature Death*
On October 24 of 1601, Tycho died unexpectedly. It happened within two weeks of a party he had attended in Prague. Tycho had dinner at the illustrious Rosenberg's table when he drank more than was good for him. Politeness prevented him from excusing himself from the table. After five sleepless nights, in constant pain because he could not pass water, in fever and delirium, he expired peacefully among people close to him. His celestial observations of 38 years had come to an end. As Tycho had written in his first letter to Kepler, and again in his last will[53] he expressed the wish that Kepler apply the theory of the five Platonic solids—described in the next chapter—to Tycho's own model of the universe.

Tycho was buried in a great state funeral, "his coffin carried by twelve imperial gentlemen-at-arms, preceded by his coat of arms, his golden spurs, and favorite horse."[54] Within days, Kepler was appointed Tycho's successor as Imperial Mathematicus. He remained in Prague until the death of King Rudolph II eleven years later. These were to become Kepler's most productive years.

FIGURES AND DIAGRAMS

CHAPTERS   1   TO 11

## Figure 1.1: Angles of Equal Size

Whenever two straight lines intersect, two pairs of angles are formed. The angles of each pair are of equal size. In Diagram 1, the straight line A crosses the parallel lines $B_1$ and $B_2$. At the intersections of A with $B_1$ and $B_2$, the alternate angles 1 and 2 (denoted by $\angle 1$ and $\angle 2$, respectively) are of equal size.

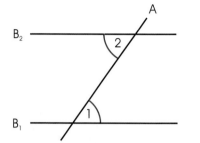

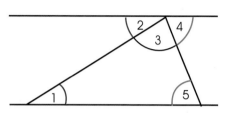

Diagram 1: When two parallel lines, $B_1$ and $B_2$, are crossed by the straight line A, the alternate interior angles are of equal size or, in short, $\angle 1 = \angle 2$.

Diagram 2: The three interior angles of a triangle add up to 180°. Note $\angle 1 = \angle 2$ and $\angle 4 = \angle 5$. It is also true that $\angle 2 + \angle 3 + \angle 4 = 180°$ and therefore: $\angle 1 + \angle 3 + \angle 5 = 180°$.

## Figure 1.2: Congruent Triangles

Congruent triangles are equal in all respects. When superimposed on each other, their sides and angles coincide exactly. They are congruent when:

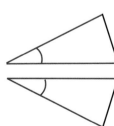
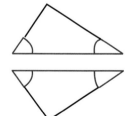

Diagram 1: the three sides of triangles are equal.

Diagram 2: two sides and the enclosed angles are equal.

Diagram 3: the base line and two adjacent angles are equal.

# Figure 1.3: The Two Angles at the Base of an Isosceles Triangle Equal Each Other in Size

By definition isosceles triangles have two sides of equal length. Thales demonstrated that the two base angles of such triangles will always be of equal size. The proof of this theorem is illustrated in Diagrams 2 to 6.

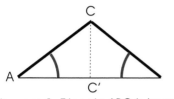

Diagram 1: Triangle ABC is isosceles because the sides AC and BC are of equal length. According to Thales, the two base angles of such triangles are of equal size.

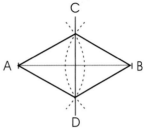

Diagram 2: To illustrate, an isosceles triangle is constructed by compass and straightedge.

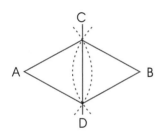

Diagram 3: Constructed in this fashion, triangles ACD and BCD are congruent because their three sides are equal in length.

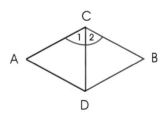

Diagram 4: Since the two triangles ACD and BCD are congruent, ∠1 and ∠2 are of the same size.

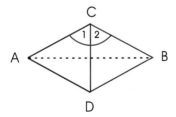

Diagram 5: From the congruence of triangles ACD and BCD, it also follows that the length of side AC equals the length of side BC.

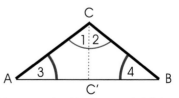

Diagram 6: Having established that ∠1 = ∠2, that AC=BC, and that C = C′ is common to both, the triangles ACC′ and BCC′ are congruent. Therefore, the base angles 3 and 4 are of equal size.

Q.E.D.[17]

# Figure 1.4: Thales' Theorem: A Triangle Inscribed in a Semi-circle Will Always be Rectangular

According to Thales, any triangle based on the diameter of a semicircle, with its endpoints connected by straight lines to the circumference, will be rectangular. The proof of his theorem went something like this:

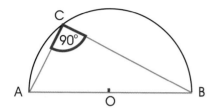
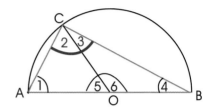

Diagram 1: A triangle inscribed in a semicircle forms a right angle at any point C of the circumference. As shown in Diagram 2, this triangle can be split into two isosceles triangles. Both are isosceles because the semicircle's radii OA, OB and OC make up two of their three sides.

Diagram 2: The two triangles ACO and BCO are isosceles so that:
∡1 = ∡2 and ∡3 = ∡4.
Adding the angles of triangle ABC:
∡1 + ∡2 + ∡3 + ∡4 = 180°.
This sum can be restated as:
2 (∡2) + 2 (∡3) = 180°.
Dividing both sides by 2, yields:
(∡2 + ∡3) = 90°.

Q.E.D.

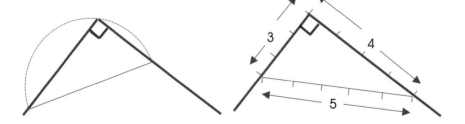

Diagram 3: Although geometers could have applied the theorem of Thales to form rectangular areas, it would have been impractical.

Diagram 4: The geometers used their own technique of creating right angles by forming a triangle with sides of 3, 4, and 5 units. It was simple and gave perfect results.

# Figure 2.1: Samples of Pythagorean Figurate Numbers

By expanding geometric figures Pythagoras created figurate numbers. When he enlarged the patterns of triangles he discovered that consecutive numbers such as 1, 3, 6, 10, 15 yielded a series of square numbers as in $1+3=4$, $3+6=9$, $6+10=16$, and $10+15=25$. Or, $1+3=4$, $4+5=9$, $9+7=16$ and $16+9=25$. Embedded in this series of square numbers ($3^2=9$, $4^2=16$, and $5^2=25$), was the set 3, 4, 5, the numbers needed to form a right angle.

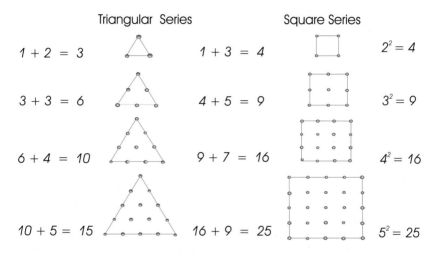

Triangular Series

$1 + 2 = 3$

$3 + 3 = 6$

$6 + 4 = 10$

$10 + 5 = 15$

Square Series

$1 + 3 = 4$       $2^2 = 4$

$4 + 5 = 9$       $3^2 = 9$

$9 + 7 = 16$      $4^2 = 16$

$16 + 9 = 25$     $5^2 = 25$

# Figure 2.2: Areas of Irregular Triangles

The area of an irregular triangle equals ½ the triangle's base times its height, i.e., $A = \frac{1}{2} b\, h$. For example:

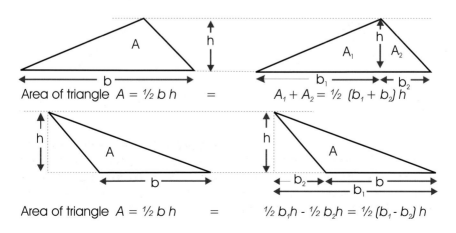

Area of triangle $A = \frac{1}{2} b\, h$ $\quad = \quad$ $A_1 + A_2 = \frac{1}{2} (b_1 + b_2) h$

Area of triangle $A = \frac{1}{2} b\, h$ $\quad = \quad$ $\frac{1}{2} b_1 h - \frac{1}{2} b_2 h = \frac{1}{2} (b_1 - b_2) h$

# Figure 2.3: The Great Pythagorean Theorem

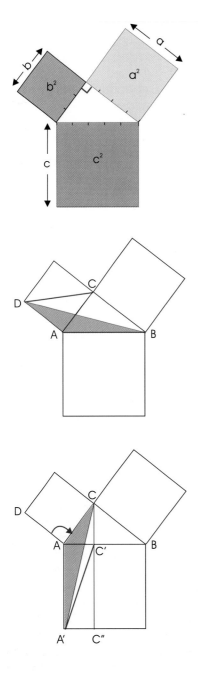

Diagram 1: The Pythagorean Theorem. In a rectangular (or right-angled) triangle, the area of the two squares on the shorter sides equals the area of the square on the longest side. Here, $a^2 + b^2 = c^2$. If, for example, $a = 3$ and $b = 4$, then $c = 5$ because
$$3^2 + 4^2 = 5^2 \text{ or } 9 + 16 = 25.$$

Diagram 2: The proof of the Pythagorean Theorem goes like this: the area of triangle *ACD* is half as large as the area $b^2$ in Diagram 1. As shown in Figure 2.2 the area of a triangle equals half its base times its height. Since triangles *ACD* and *ABD* share the same base, *AD,* and are both of equal height, *AC*, they are equal in size.

Diagram 3: Turning triangle *ABD* in Diagram 2 by 90° yields triangle *AA'C*. The two triangles are congruent because they match each other in two sides and the enclosed angle (i.e., *AA'=AB*, *AC=AD,* and angle *CAA' = DAB*). Triangle *AA'C* also equals the size of triangle *AA'C'* since they share the base *AA'* and are of equal height *AC'*. Just as triangle *ACD* in Diagram 2 was half as large as $b^2$ in Diagram 1, triangle *AA'C'* in Diagram 3 is half as large as rectangle *AA'C'C"*.

(Continued)

# Figure 2.3: The Great Pythagorean Theorem (continued)

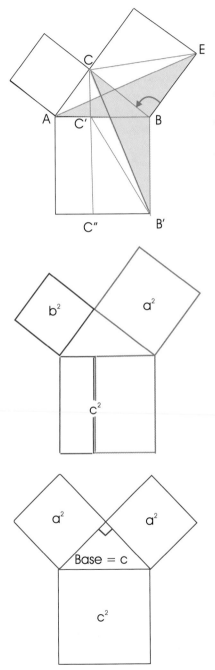

Diagram 4: The triangle BCE is half as large as $a^2$ in Diagram 1. It is equal in size to triangle ABE and congruent to triangle B'BC which, in turn, is of the same size as triangle B'BC'. But triangle B'BC' is half the size of the rectangle B'BC'C". It follows that the area $a^2$ of Diagram 1 is of the same size as that of the rectangle B'BC'C".

Diagram 5: Diagrams 3 and 4 illustrate that the areas of the squares on the two shorter sides of a right-angled triangle equal the two rectangular areas on its third side. Since together these two areas match the square on the third side, the squares on the two shorter sides of a right-angled triangle equal the square on its third side so that $a^2 + b^2 = c^2$.          Q.E.D.

Diagram 6: Pythagoras believed that whole numbers (i.e., integers and ratios of integers) made up all numbers. Yet, if the base of a right-angled isosceles triangle is an uneven number, it leads to a contradiction. By definition an uneven number multiplied by itself (i.e., squared) can never be an even number. But if $c^2 = 2\,a^2$, then $c^2$ is an even number. So, c cannot be an uneven number!          Q.E.D.

# Figure 3.1: The Lunes of Hippocrates

Adapted from William Dunham, *Journey Through Genius, p. 17 to 20.*

Hippocrates was the first mathematician to prove that a curvilinear figure could be converted into a rectilinear (or straight-line) figure of identical size. In his proof Hippocrates relied on the Pythagorean Theorem and on the proposition that the area of a circle is proportionate to a square whose sides are equal to the circle's diameter.

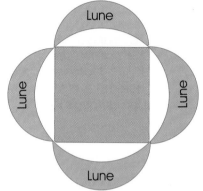

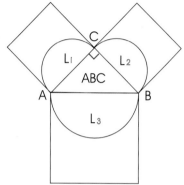

Diagram 1: Hippocrates' Theorem is also known as the Lunulae of Hippocrates because the four areas surrounding the circle look like a moon-shaped necklace. Together, the four areas match the area of the square inscribed in the circle.

Diagram 2: Knowing that the size of a semicircle is proportionate to that of a square, Hippocrates concluded that the two smaller semicircles $L_1 + L_2$ matched the area of the larger semicircle $L_3$.

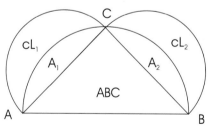

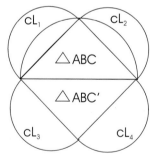

Diagram 3: By flipping the larger semicircle $L_3$ over its axis $AB$, the triangle remains unchanged, but it creates two crescent-shaped lunes $cL_1$ and $cL_2$. From

$$(L_1 - A_1) + (L_2 - A_2) = (L_3 - A_1 - A_2)$$ follows
$$(cL_1) + (cL_2) = ABC.$$

Diagram 4: Just as $cL_1 + cL_2 =$ triangle $ABC$, $cL_3 + cL_4 =$ triangle $ABC'$. It proves that the area of the crescent-shaped lunes equals the area of the square in the center. Q.E.D.

# Figure 3.2: Squaring a Rectangle
Adapted from Dunham, pp. 13 to 14.

A simpler, but equally important task was to convert a rectangle of arbitrary size into a square of an equal area. This example will be used later to illustrate the similarity between a rectangle within an ellipse and a corresponding square (see Figure 7.1).

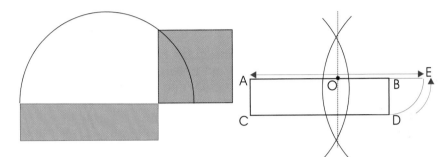

Diagram 1: The objective is to convert a rectangle of arbitrary size into a square of equal area by use of a compass and a straightedge.

Diagram 2: The side *AB* is extended by *BE* in a straight line to *AE*. After cutting the distance *AE* in half, the distance *OA* equals *OE*.

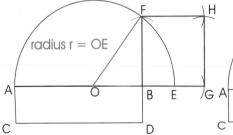

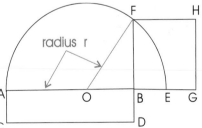

Diagram 3: The semicircle of radius OE intersects with the extension of BD at point F. The distance BF is the side of the square, constructed by extending line AB by FB to G, and by marking off the equidistant end-points around F and G, forming the intersection at H.

Diagram 4: The rectangle
$ABCD = (r + OB)(BD)$. Also
$$BD = (r - OB)$$
and, therefore,
$ABCD = (r + OB)(r - OB)$ and
$= r^2 - (OB)^2$. In line with the Pythagorean Theorem:
$$r^2 - (OB)^2 = (FB)^2$$ and, therefore, the rectangle
$$ABCD = (FB)^2. \qquad \text{Q.E.D.}$$

## Figure 3.3: The Five Platonic Solids
Adapted from Dunham, pp. 78 to 81.

The five solids are aesthetically pleasing because their plane faces are made up of congruent polygons symmetrically arranged on the surface.

*Fire*

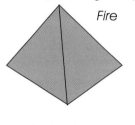

The **tetrahedron** is shaped like a pyramid. Its sides consist of four equilateral triangles. Plato asserted that fire is shaped like a tetrahedron because it is the smallest, sharpest and the most mobile element.

*Earth*

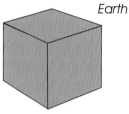

The **cube** has six squares as sides. Plato believed that the Earth is best represented by a cube because it is the most stable of the five solids. The solids would be in particle form and like other solids too small to be seen individually. They would only be visible when massed in large numbers.

*Air*

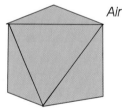

The **octahedron** has eight triangles as sides and ranks third among the five solids in the number of sides. Since Plato believed that air was intermediate in size, weight, and fluidity, he equated it with the solid that had the intermediate number of sides.

*Water*

The **icosahedron** has twenty triangles as sides. Among the regular solids it is the most spherical and rolls easily. As the most mobile of the fluid elements, Plato let it represent the element water.

*Constellations*

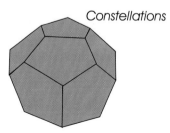

The **dodecahedron** has twelve sides. The Greek philosopher Empedocles had proposed that there were four elements: fire, earth, air and water. Since Plato was trying to match the five solids with the basic elements, he decided on the constellations in the heavens as a fifth.

# Figure 4.1: In Rectangular Triangles the Ratios of Their Corresponding Sides are Equal

Adapted from Lancelot Hogben, *Mathematics for the Million*, pp. 124 to 127.

By combining parallels with triangles Greek mathematicians discovered a new method of estimation. This method was a forerunner of trigonometry. To illustrate, similar but smaller triangles are fit into a rectangular triangle, ABC. This enables us to estimate from two sides of a smaller triangle, the length of the second side of a larger triangle.

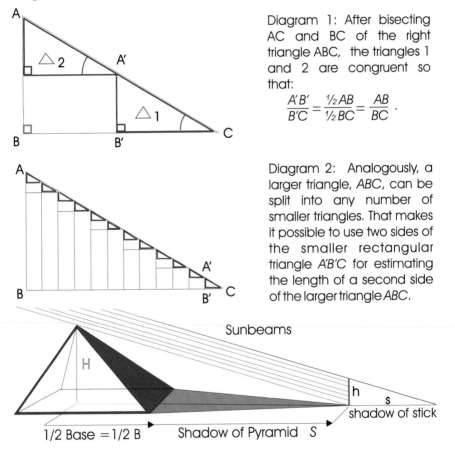

Diagram 1: After bisecting AC and BC of the right triangle ABC, the triangles 1 and 2 are congruent so that:

$$\frac{A'B'}{B'C} = \frac{\frac{1}{2}AB}{\frac{1}{2}BC} = \frac{AB}{BC}.$$

Diagram 2: Analogously, a larger triangle, *ABC*, can be split into any number of smaller triangles. That makes it possible to use two sides of the smaller rectangular triangle *A'B'C* for estimating the length of a second side of the larger triangle *ABC*.

Sunbeams

H

h    s
shadow of stick

1/2 Base = 1/2 B      Shadow of Pyramid  S

Diagram 3: Thales intuitively applied this technique long before Eudoxus and Euclid put it in writing. He used the "shadow stick" to obtain the answer. Given the height h of the shadow stick, the length of its shadow, and the distance from half the Pyramid's base to the end of its shadow , he could estimate its height *H* by solving:

$$\frac{h}{s} = \frac{H}{(\frac{1}{2}B + S)} \qquad \text{for} \qquad H = (\frac{1}{2}B + S)\frac{h}{s}.$$

# Figure 4.2: Approximating the Circumference of a Circle

Archimedes estimated the circumference of a circle by calculating the circumference of a many-sided polygon, once inscribing it and once circumscribing it, and then averaging the two estimates. To illustrate the method, let $p_1$ be the inscribed the perimeter and $p_2$ the circumscribed perimeter, then the value of $\pi$ can be approximated.

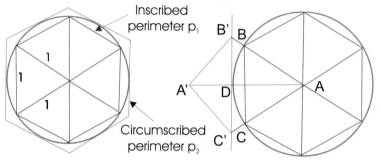

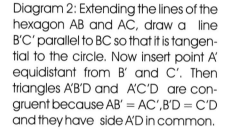

Inscribed perimeter $p_1$

Circumscribed perimeter $p_2$

Diagram 1: In an equilateral hexagon the radius and the sides are equal to 1, its perimeter is 6. Denoting the perimeter of the hexagon by 2 $p_1$, $r$, the lower bound is $p_1 = 3$. .

Diagram 2: Extending the lines of the hexagon AB and AC, draw a line B'C' parallel to BC so that it is tangential to the circle. Now insert point A' equidistant from B' and C'. Then triangles A'B'D and A'C'D are congruent because AB' = AC', B'D = C'D and they have side A'D in common.

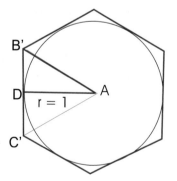

Diagram 3: Because triangles A'B'D and A'C'D are congruent, B'D = C'D. It is also true that AB' = B'C' and, therefore, B'D = ½ AB'. According to the Pythagorean theorem
$$r^2 + (B'D)^2 = (AB')^2 \text{ here } r = 1,$$
so that
$$1^2 + (B'D)^2 = (AB')^2.$$

Diagram 3 continued : This can be rewritten as
$$1 + (½ AB)^2 = (AB')^2 \qquad \text{or as} \qquad 1 = (AB')^2 - 1/4 (AB')^2.$$
From this follows that
$$1 = (AB')^2 (1 - 1/4) \quad \text{and} \quad (AB')^2 = 1/(1 - 1/4) = 1/0.75.$$
Recall that AB' = B'C'   so that   B'C' = 1/0.75 = 1.333 = 1.15.
Then   $2 p_2 r = 2(3.45) r$   ½ $(p_1 + p_2)$ = ½ (3.00 + 3.45) = 3.225 .
This last value can be taken as a first approximation of $\pi$. Better estimates can be derived trigonometrically (see Chapter 6, Table 6.1).

## Figure 4.3: The Five Conic Sections

Apollonius was the first to discover that all five conic sections could be generated by varying the angle of the cutting plane of a circular (single or double) cone.

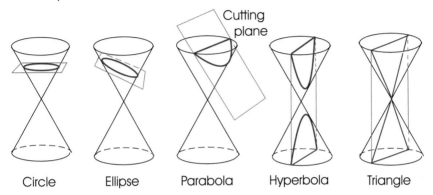

| Circle | Ellipse | Parabola | Hyperbola | Triangle |

## Figure 4.4: A Theorem of Apollonian Conics (later used by Isaac Newton) Adapted from Heinrich Dorrie, *100 Great Problems of Elementary Mathematics*, p. 32.

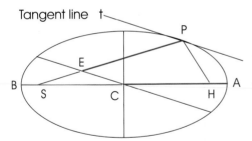

Diagram 1: Apollonian Theorem. The segments *EP* and *AC* are of equal length, that means that *EP* equals half of the major diameter *AC*. The proof is illustrated in Diagrams 2 to 6.

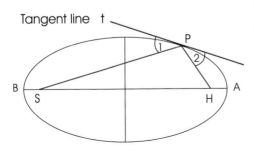

Diagram 2: An ellipse can be traced out by a string attached to two focal points, *S* and *H*. The length is: *SP+PH* = *constant*. The tangent line *t* forms angles 1 and 2, both equal in size. The tangent line reflects the rays, connecting *P* to *S* and *H* , like a mirror. This is also referred to as the "optical property" of an ellipse.

# Figure 4.4: A Theorem of Apollonian Conics (continued)

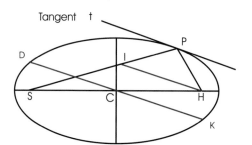

Diagram 3: For the proof of this Apollonian theorem, we draw two lines parallel to tangent $t$: the first from focal point $H$ to intersect with ray $PS$ at a point, call it $I$; the second through center $C$ to intersect with the perimeter and label the points of intersection D

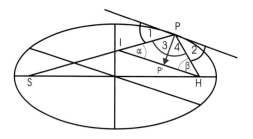

Diagram 4: Bisecting the angle at point $P$ into 3 and 4, and thereby splitting triangle $HIP$ in half, leads to two congruent triangles $HPP'$ and $IPP'$. They are congruent since angles $\alpha = 1$ and $\beta = 2$, angle $3 = 4$, and they share the side $PP'$. Therefore, $IP$ and $HP$ are equal in length.

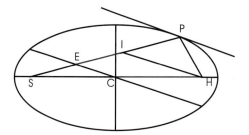

Diagram 5: According to definition $SC = CH$. Moreover,
$$SC / CH = SE / EI.$$
Since $CE$ and $HI$ are parallel, $SI = SE + EI = 2(EI)$. Noting that $SP = 2(EI) + IP$ and $IP = HP$, It follows that:
$$PS + HP = 2(EI) + 2(IP).$$

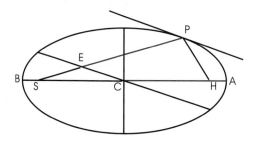

Diagram 6: The lines $PS$ and $HP$ equal the length of the diameter $AB$. But $AC = 1/2\ AB$. Having shown in Diagram 5 that $PS + HP = 2(EI) + 2(IP)$, it follows that:
$$EI + IP = \tfrac{1}{2}(PS + PH) = EP$$
and, therefore, $EP = AC$.

Q.E.D.

## Figure 5.1: The Universe of Aristarchus, ca. 250 B.C.

The geocentric universe
of the Greek philosophers

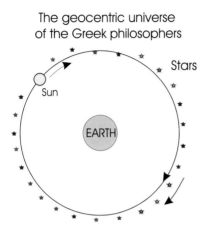

The heliocentric Universe
of Aristarchus

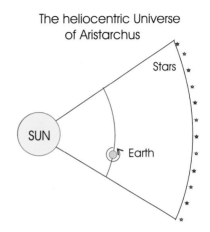

Diagram 1: The traditional view of the Greek philosophers was that the Earth was at the center of the universe and that the Sun, the planets and the stars revolved around the Earth.

Diagram 2: Aristarchus' revolutionary view was that the Earth revolved around its own axis while circling the Sun at the center of the solar system.

## Figure 5.2: The Zodiac Circle

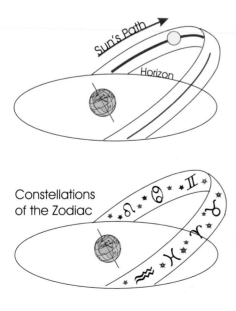

Diagram 1: Zodiac is the name of an imaginary belt on which the Moon and the planets seem to travel. This belt extends 8° on each side of the Sun's apparent path around the sky, also called the ecliptic.

Diagram 2: The Zodiac is a key element of astrology. Astrologers believe that the motions of the Sun, the Moon, the five planets, and their positions relative to the stars determine the destinies of people on Earth. In ancient times it was the most important method of predicting the future.

Figure 5.2 : The Zodiac Circle (continued)

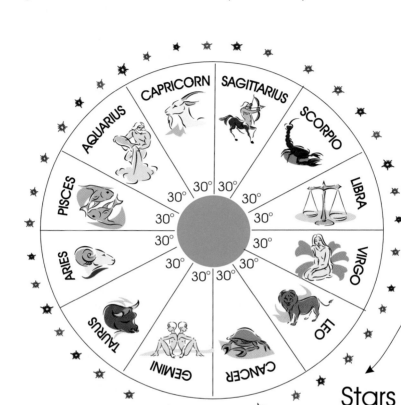

Diagram 3: From the earliest times astrologers divided the Zodiac into 12 houses, the houses of heaven. Each house covers one twelfth of the Zodiac or 30°. Each is named for an easily identifiable constellation, usually after an animal because of some recognizable characteristic.

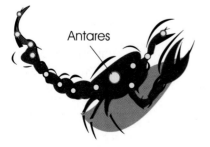

Diagram 4: The Scorpion is one of the signs of the Zodiac. This constellation appears in the southern part of the sky. It contains the bright star Antares. Long before Hellenistic times the scorpion was known as a constellation. It appeared in the mythology of the Sumerians.

## Figure 5.3: How Aristarchus Estimated the Distances of Moon and Sun from Earth[8]

Aristarchus was the first astronomer to compute astronomical distances. In estimating how far it was to the Moon he started with the proposition that the diameter of the Moon measured 180th of the Zodiac Circle, the great band of stellar constellations encircling the Earth at night. As seen from Earth, this amounted to a width of $\frac{360°}{180} = 2°$.

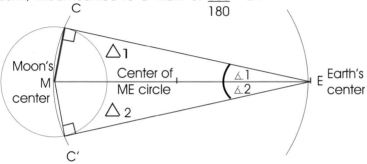

By connecting the tangents' points $C$ and $C'$ to the center $M$ of the Moon, he constructed two right triangles $\triangle 1$ and $\triangle 2$. The two are congruent because they have three matching sides: $EC$ and $EC'$, $MC$ and $MC'$, and $ME$ is common to both triangles. Therefore, the angles $\triangle 1$ and $\triangle 2$ are equal in size, measuring $1°$ each. Knowing the size of the angles, Aristarchus estimated the ratio of the two sides $MC/ME$ to be between $1/45$ and $1/60$ (i.e., $1/45 > MC/ME > 1/60$ where $>$ denotes "greater than.") Since he wanted to know how many lunar diameters made up the Moon-to-Earth distance he turned the ratio $ME/MC$ upside down so that $45 < ME/MC < 60$ where $<$ denotes "smaller than." Knowing that the Moon's diameter was $MC+MC' = 2MC$, Aristarchus estimated the Moon-to-Earth distance to be between $45/2 = 22.5$ and $60/2 = 30$ Moon diameters.

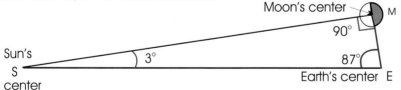

Aristarchus computed the Earth-to-Sun distance. When at half-Moon the dark side cut the Moon's sphere in half and the angle at $M$ appeared to be exactly $90°$. Since at that point the Earth-to-Sun angle at $E$ appeared to be $87°$, he concluded that the angle at the Sun was $180 - 90 - 87 = 3°$. From this he deduced the Earth-to-Sun distance to be $18 < MS/ME < 20$ or $19$ times the Earth-to-Moon distance. How he knew the relation between angles and sides of a rectangular triangle is not known.

## Figure 5.4: How Aristarchus Estimated the Diameter of the Sun

Aristarchus based his estimate on two assumptions or "facts" as they appeared to him: 1. the visual angles of the Sun and the Moon were of equal size, and 2. the diameter of the Moon was half as large as that of the Earth. Since the visual angles were equal, the triangles *EMA* and *ESC* were similar. Aristarchus had estimated the distance of the Sun to be 19 times that of the Moon. It followed that the Sun's diameter was 19 times that of the Moon (i.e., *ES=19 EM* and, therefore, *SC = 19 MA* ). Since he believed the Moon to be half the size of the Earth, he concluded the Sun to be roughly 10 times (19/2=9.5) as large as the Earth.

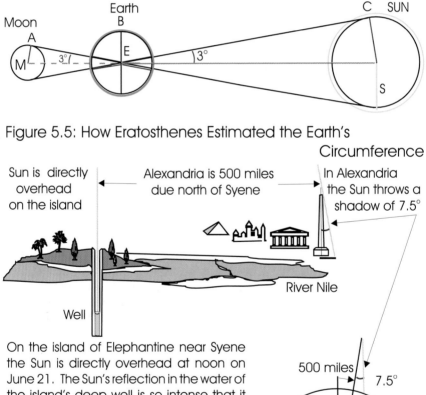

## Figure 5.5: How Eratosthenes Estimated the Earth's Circumference

Sun is directly overhead on the island

Alexandria is 500 miles due north of Syene

In Alexandria the Sun throws a shadow of 7.5°

River Nile

Well

On the island of Elephantine near Syene the Sun is directly overhead at noon on June 21. The Sun's reflection in the water of the island's deep well is so intense that it lights it up to its full depth. In Alexandria, 500 miles to the north, the Sun throws a shadow of 7.5°. From this Eratosthenes deduced that the circumference of the Earth is (360°/7.5°)(500) = 24,000 miles.

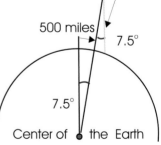

500 miles

7.5°

7.5°

Center of the Earth

# Figure 6.1: Babylonian Astronomy

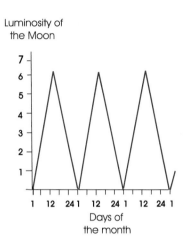

Luminosity of
the Moon

Days of
the month

Diagram 1: Babylonian astrologers kept track of the recurring celestial events by zig-zag functions. More interested in the timing of religious rites, they did not develop a three-dimensional geometric structure of the universe. Instead, they recorded the motions of their luminary deities. To summarize their findings they kept time schedules of lunar and planetary events by days, months, and years. Converted to charts, their observational data formed zig-zag lines, alternating between upper and lower limits. The lunar charts, for example, followed on a day-by-day basis the waxing and waning of the Moon's luminosity.

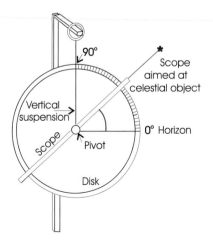

Diagram 2: For observing of the motions of the Moon and planets, ancient astronomers used mechanical instruments, among them an early version of an astrolabe. It consisted of a metal disk vertically suspended from a pole. Fixed to the disk was a movable scope for observing a celestial body and gradations for measuring the elevation of a star or planet above the horizon.

# Figure 6.2: Geographic Longitudes and Latitudes

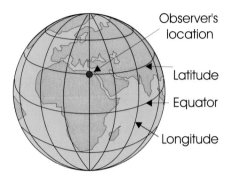

Observer's
location

Latitude

Equator

Longitude

Diagram 1: Today, geographic coordinates are commonly used in designating the locations of places on Earth. The longitude indicates the location of a place east or west of a north-south line called the prime meridian. The latitude gives the location north or south of the equator.

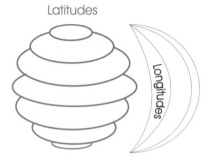

Latitudes

Longitudes

Diagram 2: Latitudes run parallel to the equator, forming circles above and below that are smaller than the great circle of the equator. Longitudes form semicircles, running from north to south. All of them are of the same length, i.e., half the size of the great circle of the plane passing through north and south pole.

# Figure 6.3: Hipparchus' Coordinates of the Celestial Sphere

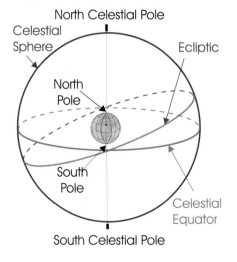

North Celestial Pole

Celestial
Sphere

Ecliptic

North
Pole

South
Pole

Celestial
Equator

South Celestial Pole

Diagram 1: The celestial sphere is an extension of the Earth's sphere. The celestial equator extends the Earth's equator to the stars. The north and south celestial poles are projections of the Earth's North and South Poles, the Earth's axis pointing at the star Polaris. The great circle of the ecliptic traces the path of the Sun against the back ground of the stars. It matches the center of the Zodiac Circle (Chapter 5).

## Figre 6.3: Hipparchus' Coordinates of the Celestial Sphere
(continued)

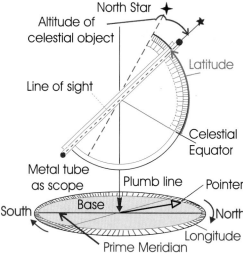

North Star

Altitude of celestial object

Line of sight

Latitude

Metal tube as scope

Celestial Equator

South

Base

Plumb line

North

Longitude

Pointer

Prime Meridian

Diagram 2: Hipparchus improved on the Babylonian astrolabe. From the base of it he could read off the longitude in terms of the angular deviation from the meridian. From the scale on the quadrant he could determine the latitude and measure the altitude of celestial objects.

AO and BC are both pointing in the direction of the North Star. Note: they are parallel to each other but they meet at the North Star.

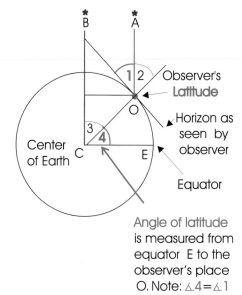

B    A

1 2    Observer's Latitude

O

Horizon as seen by observer

Center of Earth    C    3    4    E

Equator

Angle of latitude is measured from equator E to the observer's place O. Note: $\angle 4 = \angle 1$

Diagram 3: Hipparchus proved that $\angle 1$ (angle 1) is the observer's latitude at O. By an ingenious diagram he showed that this angle varied precisely with the latitude as an observer travels in the north-south direction: At the ob-server's location, $\angle 2 = \angle 3$ because the line of sight to the North Star AO is parallel to the imaginary line BC from the North Star to the Earth's center. The imaginary line C to the observer's location O cuts the line of sight to the horizon H at a right angle. Also the imaginary line BC intersects with the line from the Earth's center C to the equator E at a right angle. So that angles $\angle 1 + \angle 2 = 90°$ and $\angle 3 + \angle 4 = 90.°$ But since $\angle 2 = \angle 3$, it follows that $\angle 1 = \angle 4$. This proves that $\angle 1$ formed at O between the

# Figre 6.3: Hipparchus' Coordinates of the Celestial Sphere
(continued)

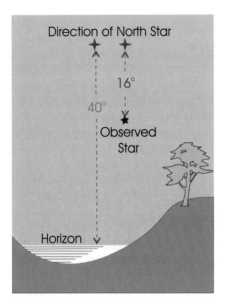

Direction of North Star

16°

40°

Observed
Star

Horizon

Diagram 4: Babylonian astrologers measured the elevation of a planet or star by the angle between the horizon and the object in the sky. Hipparchus invented a new and better method. As explained in Diagram 3, he estimated a star's or planet's longitude as marked by the angle formed between the meridian and the line of sight set by the pointer. He obtained the latitude of the observer's location by the angle between the horizon and the North Star. He derived the elevation of the star or planet by the angle between the North Star and the line of his scope aimed at the celestial object.

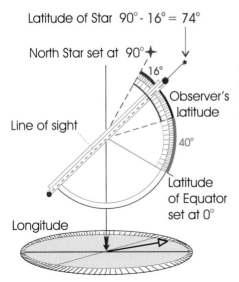

Latitude of Star 90° - 16° = 74°

North Star set at 90°

16°

Observer's latitude

Line of sight

40°

Latitude
of Equator
set at 0°

Longitude

Diagram 5: To illustrate the mechanics of Hipparchus' astrolabe, Diagram 4 features three elements of the night sky: the North Star, another star, and the horizon. After the pointer at the base is adjusted for the longitude, the observer's latitude is measured by the angle between the horizon and the North Star, i.e., at 40°. The elevation of the other star is read as the angle between the North Star and the line of sight, i.e., at 16°. So that the star's latitude equals : $90° - 16° = 74°$.

# Figure 6.4: How Hipparchus Estimated Trigonometric Ratios

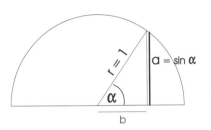

Diagram 1: In Diagram 5.3 of Chapter 5 it was shown how Aristarchus estimated the Moon-to-Earth distance by use of the ratio of two sides and an angle. In principle, trigonometry is based on the same idea. The ratio of two sides is related to the size of an angle. Here, for example, the ratio a/r is related to angle α (alpha). Trigonometrically, this is stated as $\sin \alpha = a/r = a/1 = a$.

Diagram 2: The perimeter of a regular hexagon can be computed by geometry. Inscribed in a circle, each of its six sides simply equals the length of the radius. In trigonometry, we would note that each side is the base of an equilateral (equal-sided) triangle. Split in half, the 6 triangles are converted into 12 congruent triangles. If the radius $r = 1.0$ then $\sin 30° = (1/2) / r = (1/2)/1 = 1/2$ and the size of the perimeter is:

$$12 (\sin \alpha) = 12 (1/2) = 6.0.$$

Diagram 3: Hipparchus used the half-angle theorem to derive an angle of half the size. Here, ∡1 and ∡2 are half the size of ∡4. That is because the triangle is isosceles, so ∡1 = ∡2. Since ∡1+∡2+∡3 = 180° and also

$$∡3+∡4 = 180,°$$
$$∡1+∡2+∡3 = ∡3+∡4, \text{ it}$$

follows that ∡1+∡2 = ∡4 and that
$$∡1 = ∡2 = 1/2∡4.$$

From the sine of ∡4, Hipparchus derived the sine of ½∡4. This involves the side b in Diagram 1 above (also see Figure 6.4 A).

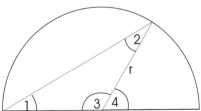

# Appendix Figure A6.4: Trigonometric Half-Angle Formula

Adapted from Hogben, *Mathematics for the Million*, p. 147.

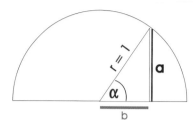

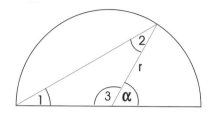

**Diagram 1:** The sine and cosine ratios are $\sin \alpha = \dfrac{a}{r} = \dfrac{a}{1} = a$

and $\cos \alpha = \dfrac{b}{r} = \dfrac{b}{1} = b$

**Diagram 2:** Diagram 3 of Figure 6.4 showed why angle

$$\angle 1 = \angle 2 = \tfrac{1}{2} \alpha$$

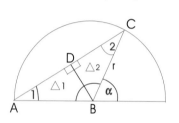

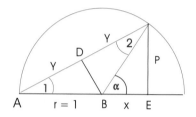

**Diagram 3:** After drawing the perpendicular BD, $\angle 1 = \angle 2$ because $AB = BC$, $DB = DB$, $\angle 1 = \angle 2$, and angle at $D = 90°$.

**Diagram 4:** It yields the ratios:
$\sin \alpha = p / r = p$ ; $\cos \alpha = x/r = x$
$\sin \tfrac{1}{2} \alpha = p / 2y$
$\cos \tfrac{1}{2} \alpha = \cos \angle 1 = (1 + x) / 2y$
$\cos \tfrac{1}{2} \alpha = y / 1 = y$

## Half-angle formula for cosines

The following cosine values come from Diagram 4:
(1) $\cos \alpha = x$
(2) $\cos \tfrac{1}{2} \alpha = (1+x) / 2y$
(3) $\cos \tfrac{1}{2} \alpha = y$
Substituting *(1)* into *(2)* gives:
(4) $\cos \tfrac{1}{2} \alpha = (1 + \cos \alpha) / 2y$
and substituting (3) into (4) yields:
(5). $\cos \tfrac{1}{2} \alpha =$
$\quad (1 + \cos \alpha) / (2 \cos \tfrac{1}{2} \alpha)$ or
(6) $2 (\cos \tfrac{1}{2} \alpha)^2 = (1 + \cos \alpha)$
(7) $(\cos \tfrac{1}{2} \alpha)^2 = \tfrac{1}{2} (1 + \cos \alpha)$
and, therefore:
**(8)** $\cos \tfrac{1}{2} \alpha = [\tfrac{1}{2}(1 + \cos \alpha)]^{1/2}$

## Half-angle formula for sines

Also the following sine ratios come from Diagram 4:
(1) $\sin \alpha = p$
(2) $\sin \tfrac{1}{2} \alpha = p / 2y$
(3) $\cos \tfrac{1}{2} \alpha = y$
Substituting *(1)* into *(2)* yields:
(4) $\sin \tfrac{1}{2} \alpha = (\sin \alpha) / 2y$ and
Substituting *(3)* into *(4)* results in:
(5) $\sin \tfrac{1}{2} \alpha =$
$\quad (\sin \alpha) \div (2 \cos \tfrac{1}{2} \alpha)$

Combining *(5)* and *(8)* yields:
$\sin \tfrac{1}{2} \alpha =$
$\quad (\sin \alpha) / 2 (\tfrac{1}{2} (1 + \cos \alpha))^{1/2}$

## Figure 6.5: How Hipparchus Estimated the Distance of the Moon from the Earth

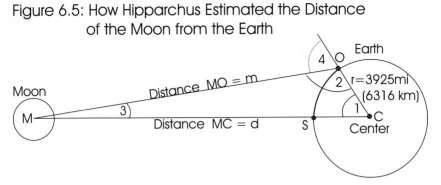

Hipparchus measured the angles of the Moon from two stations on Earth. At station S the Moon appeared directly overhead so that the line of sight MS coincided with the plumb line SC. At station O, at latitudinal ∡1, the line of sight formed ∡4 with the plumb line OC. By subtracting ∡4 from 180°, and then ∡1 and ∡2 from 180°, he found ∡2 and ∡3. From the ∡1, ∡2, ∡3 and the radius OC of the Earth, he estimated the distance MC from Moon to Earth by trigonometry and by his knowledge of latitudes. (For detail see Appendix B of this Chapter.)

## Figure 6.6: Hipparchus' Solar Theory
Adapted from Michael J. Crow, *Theories of the World*, p. 41.

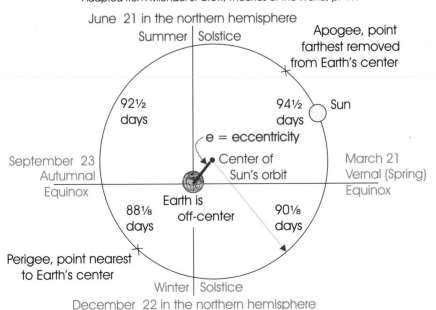

Hipparchus devised an eccentric circular orbit that mathematically evened out the Sun's variations in its orbital speed around the Earth.

## Figure 6.7: Hipparchus' Lunar Epicycle and Deferent, Simplified

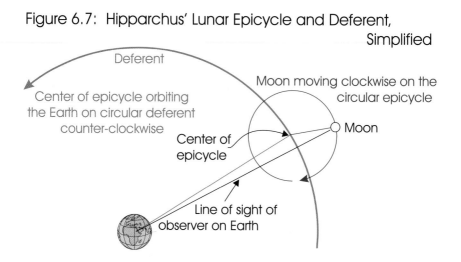

To make his lunar model fit the observations, Hipparchus had the Moon revolve on an epicycle. The center of the epicyle circled the Earth.

## Figure 6.8: Ptolemy's Model of Planetary Motion, Simplified

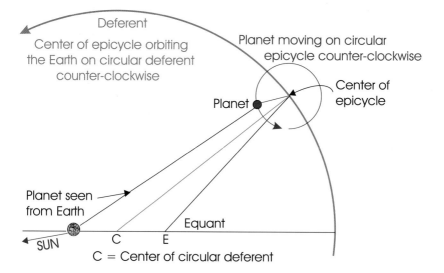

Diagram 1: Ptolemy refined and applied Hipparchus' ideas to the five planets. Based on circular deferents, epicycles, and equants, astronomers adopted and used his superior model of planetary motion for the next 1000 years.

# Figure 6.8: Ptolemy's Model of Planetary Motion (continued)

Diagram 2: Ptolemy built an innovative model of the heavens. Hipparchus had discovered that the revolving spheres of Eudoxus and Aristotle did not fit very well the actual planetary orbits. Based on more accurate obserrvations, Ptolemy's model allowed for the planetary aberrations.

Counter-clockwise motion of planet on its orbit

Planet thought to move clockwise on its epicycle

Direction of planet's orbit

Earth

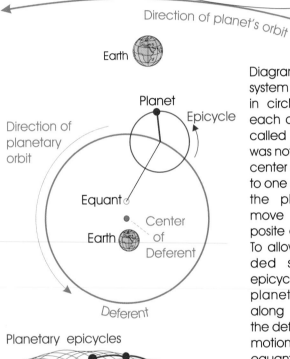

Direction of planetary orbit

Planet

Epicycle

Equant

Center of Deferent

Earth

Deferent

Planetary epicycles

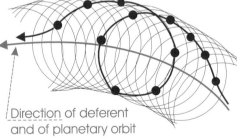

Direction of deferent and of planetary orbit

Diagram 3: In the Ptolemaic system the five planets moved in circles around the Earth, each on its own great circle, called a "deferent." The Earth was not located exactly at the center of the deferents but off to one side. From time to time the planets appeared to move back-ward in the op-posite direction to their orbits. To allow for this, Ptolemy ad-ded smaller circles, the epicycles. The center of each planet's epicycle moved along the circumference of the deferent and their angular motion was directed from the equant situated off center and opposite the Earth. It did make for equal angular motion of the epicycle.

Diagram 4: According to the astronomer Ptolemy (ca. 100--70 A.D.) Apollonius (292--190 B.C.) was the first to dis-cover a relation between the speed of the planet moving on the epicycle and the speed of it moving on the deferent. Hipparchus (ca. 180--100 B.C.) was the first to fit a model to a substantial set of recorded astronomical data.[31]

# Figure 7.1: A Characteristic Property of an Ellipse

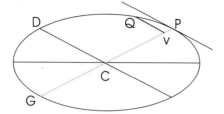

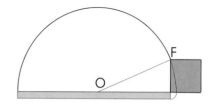

Diagram 1: This theorem states that two ratios are equal:

$$(Gv)(Pv) / (Qv)^2 = (CP)^2 / (CD)^2.$$

Think of this equality as the ratio of a rectangle *(Gv)(Pv)* over a square *(Qv)*² that equals another ratio *(CP)*² / *(CD)*².

Diagram 2: Recall from Chapter 3 (Figure 3.2) how a rectangle can be converted into a square of equal size. As shown earlier, the proof of this proposition involved a circle of radius *OF*.

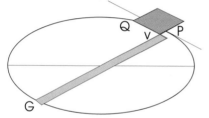

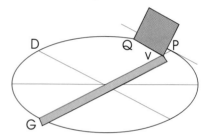

Diagram 3: If the same two figures are inscribed in an ellipse, it is as if the perspective had changed from an overhead view in Diagram 2 to a view at an angle here. Both figures are still equal in size.

Diagram 4: After converting the two figures of Diagram 3 back into a rectangle and square again, they still equal each other in size. Therefore, it can be concluded, that in an ellipse $(Gv)(Pv) = (Qv)^2$

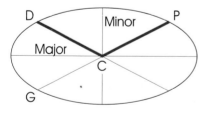

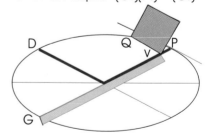

Diagram 5: An ellipse is symmetrical around its minor and major axes. A line drawn from center *C* to point *P* is mirrored, therefore, by line *CD* forming two "conjugate" diameters of equal length. So that: *CD=CP.*

Diagram 6: From the equalities in Diagrams 4 and 5, it follows that $(Qv)(Pv) / (Qv)^2 = 1.0$ and that $CD/CP = 1.0$. Therefore, It can an be concluded that $(Gv)(Pv) / (Qv)^2 = (CP)^2 / (CD)^2$ which is a theorem of Apollonius.

## Figure 7.2: Two More Theorems of Apollonius

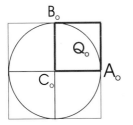

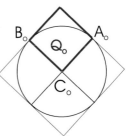

Diagram 1: A circle and an ellipse have certain features in common. Just as the area of the quadrant $Q_o$ of a circle is $Q_o = (A_oC_o)(B_oC_o)$,

Diagram 2: the area of this quadrant is the same as in Diagram 1, i.e., $Q_o = (A_oC_o)(B_oC_o)$, only the angle of view has changed.

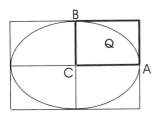

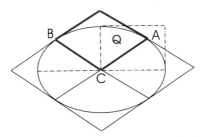

Diagram 3: Similar to the quadrant $Q_o$ of the circle in Diagram 1, the area of the quadrant $Q$ of the ellipse is:
$$Q = (AC)(BC).$$

Diagram 4: The area of this quadrant equals that in Diagram 3 even though its perspective has changed (A formal proof is given in Heath, vol. II, p. 168-174).

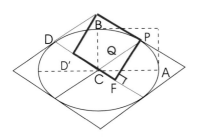

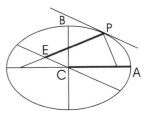

Diagram 5: The area
$(FD')(FP) = (CD)(FP)$ and it also equals that of Diagram 4 so that the area of the quadrant
$Q = (AC)(BC) = (CD)(FP)$. As shown later in Chapter 12, Newton uses this theorem in his analysis.

Diagram 6: In Diagram 3 it was noted that quadrant Q's area is $(AC)(BC)$. In Chapter 4, Figure 4.4, Diagram 6, it was shown that $EP = AC$. It implies that the area of quadrant $Q = (AC)(BC) = (EP)(BC)$. This theorem will also reappear in Newton's analysis.

## Figure 7.3: Symmetry Found On Spanish Tiles

Islam does not allow the worship of any statue of any mortal, be it a person or animal. Only God deserves worship. It was a law against idolatry, taken over from the Christians and Jews. Not permitted to incorporate figures in their religious art, the Muslims decided in favor of strict geometric forms. They strove for perfection in ever more complicated geometrical patterns. Decorating whole walls with tiles, they found beauty and infinity in these patterns. In shape they were square, rectangular, interlocking crosses or stars each carrying a small part of the total design. This art form has been highly developed and is still found today on decorative tiles in Spain.

# Figure 8.6: How Ptolemy and Copernicus Explained the Apparent Epicycles

Apparent reversals

Earth

Apparent positions of Mars

Diagram1: Greek astronomers of antiquity discovered that the planets did not revolve around the Earth in perfect circles. From time to time, each planet on its own, reversed course, made a full turn and then continued on as before. Hence, they were called "planets" (Greek for "wanderers").

Ptolemaic model

Earth

Deferent

Epicyclical motion

Diagram 2: To model this strange phenomenon, the Greek astronomer Ptolemy modified the universe of Aristotle. He added small epicycles that moved along the circumference of the greater circle, the so-called deferent. (For more detail of epicycles see Figure 6.8).

Circular planetary orbit

Copernican Model

SUN

Earth

Mars orbiting the Sun slower than the Earth does.

Diagram 3: Copernicus placed the Sun at the center of the universe and let the Earth and the other five planets revolve around it. He explained how the difference in orbital speeds made the planets appear to wander off their circular orbits. With his heliocentric theory he eliminated most of the epicycles and also accounted for the variations in brightness of the planets. The Copernican model was simpler and more elegant than the Ptolemaic model. It made for a revolution in science because it proved that visual impressions do not necessarily represent reality.

## Figure 8.5: How Copernicus Estimated the Tilt or Inclination of the Earth's Axis (Part 2: Summer Solstice)

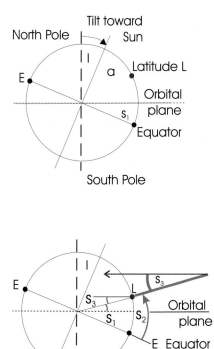

Diagram 4: At summer solstice (June 21) the Earth's axis is tilted toward the Sun (Figure 8.3). The angles $\angle l$ and $\angle s_1$ are of equal size because:

$$\angle l + \angle a = 90° = \angle s_1 + \angle a$$

so that $\quad \angle l = \angle s_1$

Although the observation point is still at exactly the same latitude $L$ as before, the angle between the orbital plane and $L$ changed.

Diagram 5: At the time of summer solstice (June 21) the Earth's axis is tilted toward the Sun as was shown in Figure 8.4 . At latitude $L$

$$\angle s_3 = (\angle s_2 - \angle s_1)$$

because $\angle s_3$ and $(\angle s_2 - \angle s_1)$ are the interior angles of the parallel lines formed by the orbital plane of the Earth and by the Sun's rays. Also note that $\angle s_2$ is the angle between

$L$ and $E$. As suggested in Diagram 1, Copernicus based his estimate of the inclination of the Earth's axis on the seasonal variations in the angles of the Sun's shadows. Diagrams 3 and 5 illustrate how he determined the angles of the shadows at the time of the winter and summer solstices. To estimate the angle of the Earth's inclination or tilt, he needed to find the difference. between the shadows' angles. He determined the inclination to equal the difference between the winter and summer angles as in:

$$\angle w_3 - \angle s_3 = (\angle w_1 + \angle w_2) - (\angle s_2 - \angle s_1) = \angle w_1 + (\angle w_2 - \angle s_2) + \angle s_1$$

Noting that $\angle w_2 = \angle s_2$ because both measure the same degrees from the Earth's equator to latitude $L$ of the observer's location, the equation reduces to $\angle w_3 - \angle s_3 = \angle w_1 + 0 + \angle s_1$ and since it was shown that $\qquad \angle w_1 = \angle l = \angle s_1$, $\qquad$ it follows that

$$\angle w_3 - \angle s_3 = 2(\angle l) \qquad \text{and, therefore:}$$
$$(\angle w_3 - \angle s_3)/2 = \angle l.$$

This result implies that average difference of the angles of the two seasonal shadows measures the angle of the Earth's inclination.

# Figure 8.5: How Copernicus Estimated the Tilt or Inclination of the Earth's Axis (Part 1: Winter Solstice)

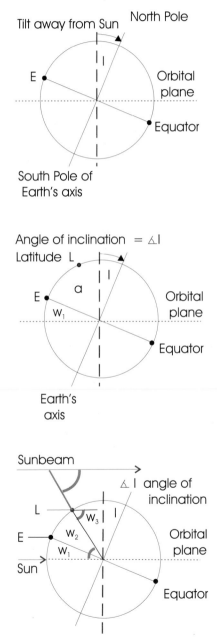

Tilt away from Sun

North Pole

E

Orbital plane

Equator

South Pole of Earth's axis

Angle of inclination = $\triangle$l

Latitude L

E

a

$w_1$

Orbital plane

Equator

Earth's axis

Sunbeam

$\triangle$l angle of inclination

L

$w_3$ l

E

$w_2$

$w_1$

Orbital plane

Sun

Equator

Diagram 1: The tilt of the Earth's axis relative to the orbital plane of the earth was pictured in diagram 1 of figure 8.3. at the time of the winter solstice (December 22) the Earth's axis is tilted away from the Sun. In Figure 8.4, the same angle of tilt or inclination is schematically shown by $\triangle$l Copernicus measured this angle by the seasonal variation in the length of shadows as shown below.

Diagram 2: At the time of the winter solstice the angles $\triangle$ and $\triangle w_1$ are of the same size . That is b ecause:

$$\triangle l + \triangle a = 90° = \triangle w_1 + \triangle a$$

and after subtracting $\triangle a$ from each:

$$\triangle l = 90° - \triangle a = \triangle w_1 .$$

Copernicus observed the variations of the Sun's shadows at a latitude of $L = 54.°$ His method was general and could be applied at any latitude.

Diagram 3: On December 22 the Sun's mid-winter shadow reaches its maximum length and the angle $w_3$ its maximum width (also shown in Diagram 2 of Figure 8.3). Note that:

$$\triangle w_3 = \triangle w_1 + \triangle w_2$$

Because the line of latitude L intersects the parallel lines of the sunbeams. In turn, the sunbeams are parallel to the orbital plane. Also note that $\triangle w_2$ is defined by the lines of latitude L and equator E .

## Figure 8.4: The Earth's Tilt Matches the Angle of the Ecliptic

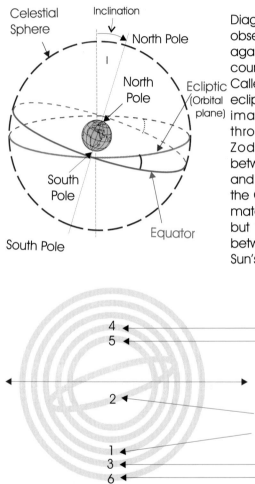

Diagram 1: Greek astronomers observed the Sun tracing a path against the sky. It was the same course the stars followed at night. Called the great circle of the ecliptic it corresponded to the imaginary line that traced through the middle of the Zodiac's band. The angle between the celestial equator and the ecliptic was recorded by the Greek astronomer Ptolemy. It matched the tilt of the Earth's axis, but was taken to be the angle between the horizon and the Sun's daily path.

4  Inner cirle
5  Little circle

Meridian line

2  Ecliptic
1  Circle through poles of ecliptic
3  Outer circle
6  Meridian circle

Diagram 2: Copernicus had his astrolabe constructed so that it matched Ptolemy's geocentric model of the universe. It was more elaborate than Hipparchus' astrolabe (Figure 6.3) and allowed tracking of more than one celestial object at a time. All circles of it were connected by pivots. Only circle 6 was permanently aligned with the meridian and with the Polar Star. Having his astrolabe match Ptolemy's model of the universe, helped Copernicus to verify and use Ptolemy's recorded observations.

## Figure 8.2: The Sun's Daily Path as it Appears During the Seasons

Diagram 1: The Sun appears to be highest above the horizon during the summer and lowest during the winter. The daylight hours vary with the seasons. For example, in Philadelphia, in midsummer, at a 40° latitude, the longest day has 14.5 hours of daylight and in midwinter the shortest day has 9.15 hours of daylight.

## Figure 8.3: The Tilt or Inclination of the Earth's Axis

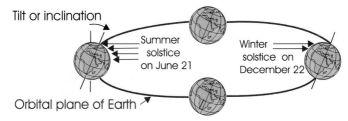

Diagram 1: The Earth's axis is not straight up from its orbital plane but tilted. During its orbital course, this tilt causes the change of seasons because the intensity of sunshine is greater during the summer months than during the winter months.

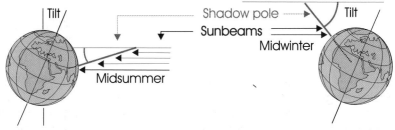

Diagram 2: If at a given latitude (say at 40°) a pole is positioned vertically, its shadow in mid-summer will be shorter than it will be in mid -winter. That is because the angle between pole and sunbeams is narrower in the summer and wider in the winter. Copernicus used this unique character-istic to determine the angle of the Earth's tilt or its inclination..

# Figure 8.1: The Geocentric and the Heliocentric Systems

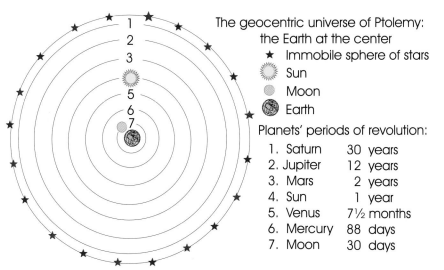

The geocentric universe of Ptolemy:
the Earth at the center

★   Immobile sphere of stars

  Sun

  Moon

  Earth

Planets' periods of revolution:

| | | |
|---|---|---|
| 1. Saturn | 30 | years |
| 2. Jupiter | 12 | years |
| 3. Mars | 2 | years |
| 4. Sun | 1 | year |
| 5. Venus | 7½ | months |
| 6. Mercury | 88 | days |
| 7. Moon | 30 | days |

Diagram 1: In Greek antiquity Aristotle, Hipparchus, and Ptolemy asserted that the Earth was the center of the universe. They believed that the Moon and the five planets circled the Earth and that their distance from Earth increased with the time period of their orbital revolution.

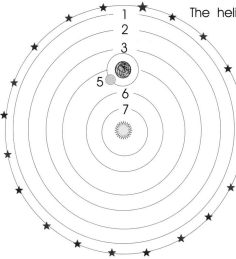

The heliocentric universe of Copernicus:
the Sun at the center

★   Immobile sphere of stars

  Earth

  Moon

  Sun

Planets' periods of revolution:

| | | |
|---|---|---|
| 1. Saturn | 30 | years |
| 2. Jupiter | 12 | years |
| 3. Mars | 2 | years |
| 4. Earth | 1 | year |
| 5. Moon | 30 | days |
| 6. Venus | 7½ | months |
| 7. Mercury | 88 | days |

Diasgram 2: Copernicus broke away from the classical tradition. Like Aristarchus of antiquity he believed that the Sun was at the center of the universe. Unlike Aristarchus he substantiated his proposition by demonstrating that his geometric model of the universe fit with astronomical observations better than did the Ptolemaic model.

## Figure 8.7: How Copernicus Estimated Distances to
### the Outer Planets
Adapted from Pasachoff and Kutner, pp. 351-353.

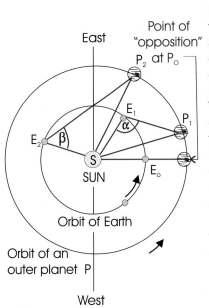

Diagram 1: At the point of opposi-tion the Earth is perfectly aligned with the Sun and the exterior planet. While the outer planet and the Earth continue on their orbits, the Earth is passing the planet since it is orbiting the Sun faster. Viewed from the Earth, this creates an angle $\alpha$ between Sun and planet. As the Earth pulls farther ahead the angle narrows. Here, for example, the Earth advances from position $E_1$ to $E_2$, the planet moves from $P_1$ to $P_2$ and the angle narrows from $\alpha$ to $\beta$. As the planet advances along its orbit from the point of opposition $P_o$ the angle changes from more than 90° $(\alpha > 90°)$ to less than 90° $(\beta < 90°)$.

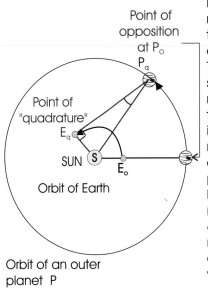

Diagram 2: The point of quadrature is reached when the angle between the lines of sight from Earth-to-planet and from Earth-to-Sun reaches 90°. This angle can be measured by the sidereal movement. The sidereal motion is measured by reference to the stars. Long be before the invention of clocks, time could measured very accurately by observing the siderial motion of the planets (on the astrolabe). This was known since the time of Hipparchus (ca. 180-100 B.C.). Figures 6.6 to 6.8 illustrate the precision of his measurement technique. For example, he dis-covered that there was an eastward shift of the fixed stars, the precession, by about 1° in 75 years.

# Figure 8.7: How Copernicus Estimated the Solar Distances of the Outer Planets Mars, Jupiter, and Saturn.

### Adapted from Pasachoff and Kutner, pp. 351-353.

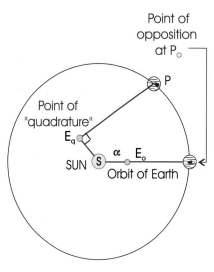

**Diagram 3:** His objective was to find the distance of the planet from the Sun, that is the radius r of the planet's orbit. Since the sidereal movement of planets was known, it was possible to determine the angle $\alpha$ which the planet swept out between the time of opposition and that of quadrature. Having estimated the angle the Earth swept out during that period (or $E_o$ to $E_q$ in Diagram 2), the angle $\beta$ can be found by subtraction. As well angle $\gamma$ can be derived as in

$$\gamma = 180 - 90 - \beta$$

Now that the angles are determined, the distance of the planet from the Sun can be estimated by trigonometry.

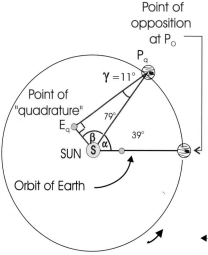

**Diagram 4:** At the point of quadrature the angle is $90°$ exactly. The sine ratio of the planet is

$$\sin \gamma = SE_q / SP_{q'}$$ and the distance of the planet from the Sun is $Sp_q = SE_q / \sin \beta$. In the case of Jupiter, for example, $\alpha = 39°$ and $\beta = 79°$, so that

$$\gamma = 180° - 90° - 79° = 11.°$$

And the ratio:

$$\sin \gamma = 1.0 / 0.1908 = 5.24$$

where the Sun-to-Earth distance is one astronomical unit (A.U.). It implies that Jupiter's distance from the Sun is 5.24 times the Earth's distance from the Sun or 5.24 astronomical units.

# Figure 8.8: How Copernicus Estimated the Solar Distances of the Inner Planets Venus and Mercury.

Adapted from Pasachoff and Kutner, pp. 352,353.

Angle between "inferior conjunction" and east-erly elongation

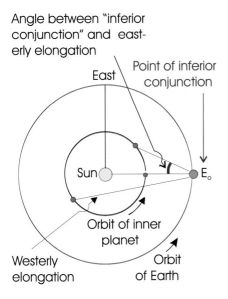

Diagram 1: The inner planets are closer to the Sun than the Earth. To measure their distance from the Sun Copernicus applied the concept of the greatest angular elongatlon. It is based on the angular distance of the planet's orbital position from the line-up of Sun and Earth at the point of the planet's inferior conjunction. Similar to the point of opposition of the outer planets, the inferior conjunction occurs when the inner planet, seen from Earth, is per-fectly lined up with the Sun and the Earth as in Diagram 1 at point $E_o$. (The location of the Sun is set on the astrolabe!)

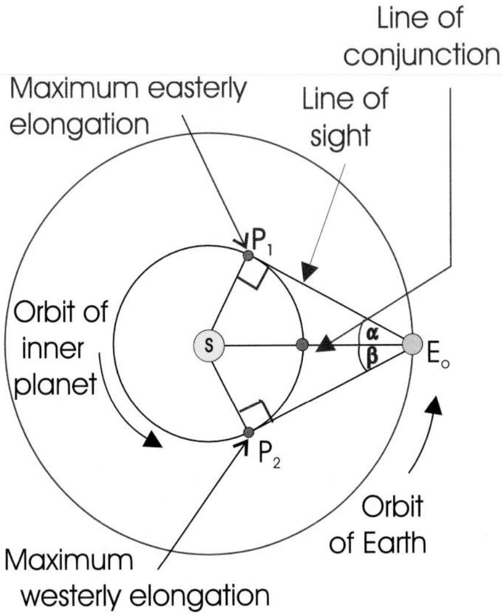

Diagram 2: An inner planet moving east along its orbit forms an angle of $90°$ at point $P_1$. This is the point of maximum easterly elongation where $\alpha$ between line of sight and line of conjunction reaches its maximum. From there it moves on to point $P_2$ of maximum westerly elongation. Copernicus estimated angles $\alpha$ and $\beta$ of maximum elongation for Venus to range from $44.8°$ to $47.3°$ and the cor-responding **sine values** from $0.7046$ to $0.7346$. To allow for the eccentric orbit of Venus he averaged them to $0.7193$. It implied that the mean solar distance of Venus was $0.7193$ times that of the Earth, an estimate within 1% of today's value.

## Figure 9.1: Use of the Cross-Staff for Measuring Latitude

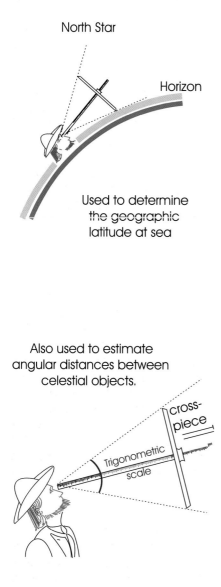

North Star

Horizon

Used to determine
the geographic
latitude at sea

Also used to estimate
angular distances between
celestial objects.

cross-
piece

Trigonometric
scale

Diagram 1: Portuguese seamen determined the geographical latitude at sea by observing the angle between the Polar Star and the horizon. The first instrument for finding the latitude in this fashion went back to Hipparchus, who used his astrolabe for finding this angle (for more detail, see Chapter 6, Figure 6.3). In the six-teenth century navigators used the astrolabe, however, less widely than its successor, the mariner's cross-staff. The cross-staff was first described in 1328 A.D. by Rabbi Levi ben Gerson, an astronomer and mathematician of France.

Diagram 2: The cross-staff was a simple device. It consisted of a staff about three feet long fitted with a sliding cross-piece. The staff was graduated trigonometrically so that the angle could be read off the staff. At sea, the navigator would hold the staff to one eye and move the cross-piece until its lower end coincided with the horizon and its upper end with the North Star. For several centuries the cross-staff was the most common instrument of navigators. On land it could also be used, as Tycho did, to measure the angular distances between stars and planets, or the length of a comet's tail. It was light, easy to construct, and could be readily dismantled and carried.

## Figure 9.2: Measuring Angles in Minutes and Seconds

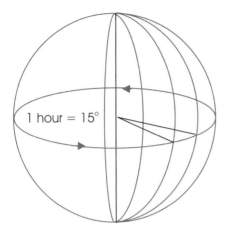

1 hour = 15°

Diagram 1: A minute is used to measure both time and angle. Ancient civilizations—the Babylonians, the Egyptians, and the Chaldeans—divided the circle into 360°. They also divided the day into 24 hours so that one hour corresponded to a star's apparent motion of *360 / 24 =15°* along the great circle of the ecliptic. Since they were accustomed to a sexagesimal number system (based on 6 and 60, see Glossary), the numbers 24 and 360 were natural to them.

15° Angle

Diagram 2: They arrived at a 1° angle by sub-dividing the 15° into 15 parts. Then, each degree was subdivided into 60 parts and each of these again into 60. The Romans called the first division (partes minutae primae) and the second (partes minutae secondae). Based on these divisions and shortened later to minutes and seconds, angles were measured in degrees, minutes and seconds. Eventually, time was measured in minutes and seconds too.

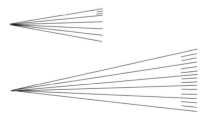

Diagram 3: Subdividing an angle of 1° into 60 minutes and then each into 60 seconds seems to be impossible. It can be done, however, if the 360° base is enlarged. Tycho's instruments were large enough to measure astronomically small angles.

# Figure 9.3: Tycho's Supernova of 1572

Based on Raymo, p. 187, 188.

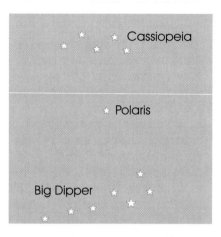

Diagram 1: Chinese astronomers had recorded a Supernova as early as 1054 A.D., but it was not known to Tycho. The Chinese described the appearance as a "guest star." It is likely that a supernova occurs in a galaxy every few hundred years. Novas are more frequent but less brilliant than supernovas. Astronomers observe about two novas a year in the Milky Way Galaxy.

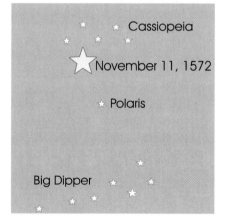

Diagram 2: What Tycho described was a supernova, the violent self-destruction of a star. At its brightest, Tycho's Star was more brilliant than the planet Venus. It was so bright that it could be seen in broad daylight. Tycho correctly described it as a distant star, far removed from Earth. Modern studies suggest that the star was about 7000 light years from Earth.

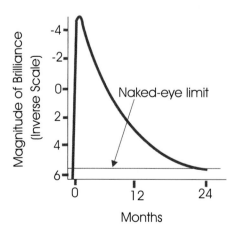

Diagram 3: When Tycho discovered the new star, it was already several days old and was just reaching its peak-brilliance. It could be seen with the naked eye for the next 20 months before it vanished from sight. Although Tycho could not have known, today it is believed that supernovas come from stars that are at least 8 times as big as the Sun and throw off 10% or more of their mass during the explosion.

# Figure 9.4: Tycho's Astronomical Instruments

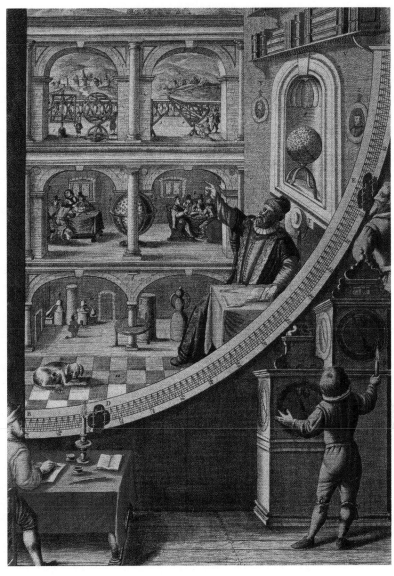

Source: By permission of the British Library

Tycho's great mural quadrant in Uraniborg, Denmark. The un-precedented accuracy was achieved by the enormous size of the quadrant and by the  precise  subdivision of its scale

## Figure 9.5: The Tychonic System of the Universe

In Tycho de Brahe's planetary system, the Earth was at the center of the universe. The Moon and the Sun circled the Earth and the five planets orbited the Sun following the Sun's course around the Earth. The stars surrounded the system and the comets came from regions beyond. Putting the Earth at the center of the universe accommodated the dogma of the Church and positioning the Sun at the center of the planetary orbits allowed for the Copernican view. With concessions to both sides, Tycho's compromise made for a faulty solution.

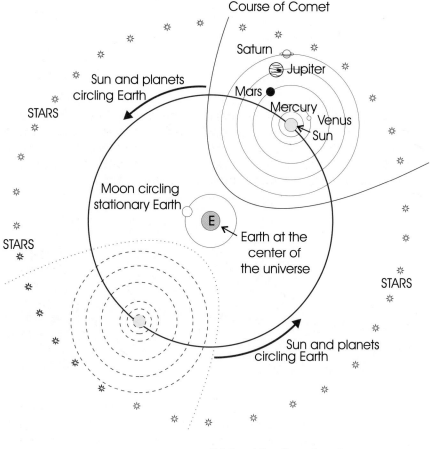

Orbits of the five planets ——————

Orbit of Sun, followed by five planets, around stationary Earth ██████████

## Figure 10.1: Kepler's Search for Geometric Relations
### Among Planetary Orbits

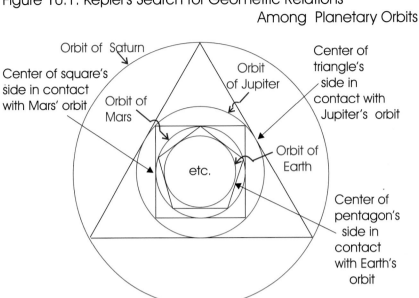

Diagram 1: While teaching a class in geometry it suddenly occurred to Kepler that an equilateral triangle could be fit in between two circles and that the ratio of the two matched the ratio of the orbits of Saturn and Jupiter. When he next inscribed a square between two circles it matched the ratio of the orbits of Jupiter and Mars, and when he next ..... etc.

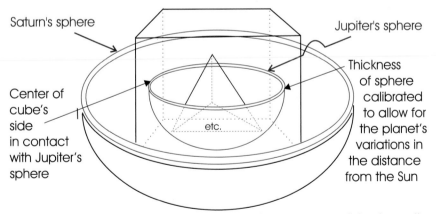

Diagram 2: Yet, Kepler soon discovered that the polygons did not exactly fit into the circular orbits. He then tried to inscribe the five regularly shaped solids, i.e., The cube (6 sides), pyramid (4 sides), octahedron (8 sides), dodecahedron (12 sides), and the icosahedron (20 sides), each into its own sphere. The ratio of the planet-to-Sun distances were to match the ratios of two adjacent planetary orbits. To his delight they made for a nearly perfect fit.

# Figure 10.2: Kepler's Initial Attempt of Estimating
## the Martian Orbit

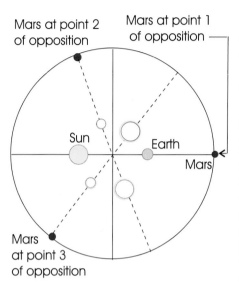

Mars at point 2 of opposition

Mars at point 1 of opposition

Sun

Earth

Mars

Mars at point 3 of opposition

Diagram 1: Knowing that it takes only three points on the circumference to derive a circle, Kepler chose 3 out of 10 observations of "oppositions" when Mars, Earth, and Sun were perfectly aligned. From the three he derived the center of the Martian orbit, its radius, and the points closest to (perihelion$_g$) and farthest away (aphelion$_g$) from the Sun. Since in his day a method for finding a precise solution did not exist, Kepler approximated it. Finding the answer to the problem by gradual approximation was a tedious and time-consuming task, but it worked.

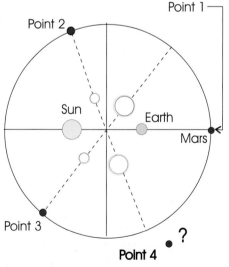

Point 1

Point 2

Sun

Earth

Mars

Point 3

Point 4 • ?

Diagram 2: Nevertheless, disaster struck. One day he compared his newly arrived at estimates with some of Tycho de Brahe's other observations of the planet Mars (e.g., point 4 in Diagram 2). He was shocked to find that they differed by as much as 8 minutes or by roughly 1/8 of one degree. Being fully aware of the precision of Tycho's observations, Kepler found this to be well beyond a permissible range of a 2-minute error. He decided to start all over again. The correction of this error was Kepler's turning point away from the classical dogma of circular planetary orbits.

# Figure 10.3: Kepler's New Method of Estimating the Mars-to-Sun Distance (still Assuming a Circular Orbit)

Based on Pasachoff and Kutner, pp. 353, 354

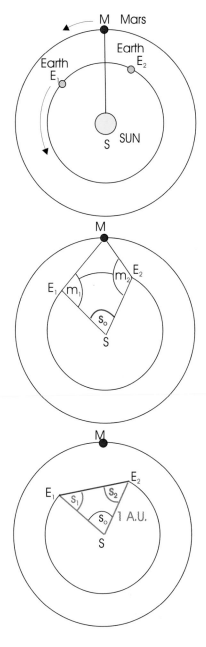

Diagram 1: From Chapter 8 we know that the outer planets orbit the Sun more slowly than the Earth. For example, it takes Mars 687 Earth days to complete one orbit. During the same period the Earth travels from point $E_1$ to point $E_2$, falling short of two full revolutions (i.e., 2 x 365.25 days, by 730.5 - 687.0 = 43.5) by 43.5 Earth days. From this observation and from Tycho de Brahe's data base, Kepler computed the solar distances of the planets by trigonometry.

Diagram 2: From the shortfall of 43.5 Earth days Kepler derived the size of angle $s_o$ at the Sun as a proportion of the full 360° circle. In the case of the planet Mars this angle amounted to

$$s_o = (43.5 \text{ days} / 365.25 \text{ days})(360°)$$
$$= (0.11910)(360°) = 42.87°.$$

From Tycho's records he also knew the size of two more angles between the Sun and Mars (i.e., $m_1$ and $m_2$). Going from there to determine the distance from Mars to the Sun required some intermediate steps.

Diagram 3: Still believing that the Earth orbited the Sun on a perfect circle, Kepler deduced that the triangle $E_2 E_1 S$ was isosceles so that the Sun-to-Earth distance $SE_1 = SE_2$ and $s_1 = s_2$ each measuring $(1/2)(180° - s_o) = 68.56°$. According to the "Sine Rule" ( Chapter 10, Appendix A ) the sine-to-side ratio $\sin s_o / E_1 E_2 = \sin s_1 / Se_2$ and

$$E_1 E_2 = SE_2 (\sin s_o / \sin s_1).$$

The Earth-to-Sun distance $Se_2 = SE_1$ is often called "one astro-nomical unit$_g$" or, in short, "1 A.U."

# Figure 10.3: Kepler's New Method of Estimating the Mars-to-Sun Distance (continued)

Based on Pasachoff and Kutner, p. 353.

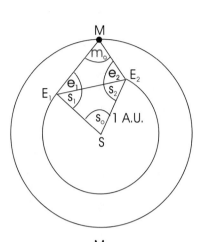

Diagram 4: Diagram 2 showed the angles $m_1$ and $m_2$ that Tycho had recorded. Diagram 3 described how Kepler determined that $s_1 = 68.56° = s_2$. He could now compute the size of angles $e_1$ and $e_2$ of triangle $ME_1E_2$ as $e_1 = m_1 - s_1$ and $e_2 = m_2 - s_2$. The size of the third angle $m_0$ could then be deduced as in
$$m_0 = 180° - e_1 - e_2.$$
Thus, Kepler found the size of all six angles of the two triangles.

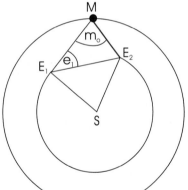

Diagram 5: This enabled Kepler to compute the distance from Earth to Mars by applying the "Sine Rule" (Chapter 10, Appendix A) to triangle $ME_1E_2$. According to this sine rule
$$(\sin e_1 / ME_2) = (\sin m_0 / E_1E_2),$$
And, therefore,
$$ME_2 = E_1E_2 (\sin e_1 / \sin m_0).$$
At this point Kepler had estimated the sizes of the six angles as well as the distances $E_1 E_2$ and $ME_2$.

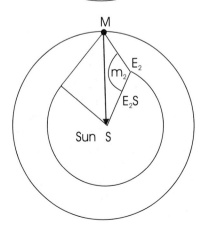

Diagram 6: He now had all the information needed for estimating the distance from the planet Mars to the Sun. Given the lengths of the two sides $SE_2$ and $ME_2$, the size of the enclosed angle $m_2$, the distance from Mars to the Sun could now be computed by the "Cosine Rule" (Chapter 10, Appendix A). This rule implies that
$$(MS)^2 = (ME_2)^2 + (1 \text{ A.U.})^2 - 2 (ME_2)(1 \text{ A.U.})$$
Finally, the square root of this expression yielded $MS$, the distance from Mars to the Sun.

# Figure 10.4: Kepler's Discovery of the Area Law: Planets Orbiting the Sun Sweep Out Equal Areas in Equal Times

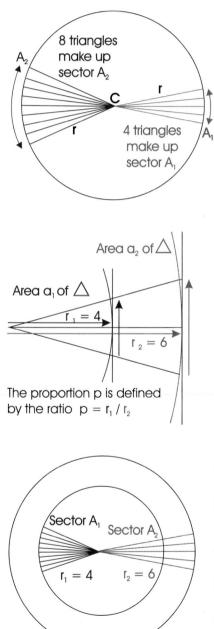

Diagram 1: Kepler estimated sectors of different sizes inscribed in a circle by "summing up the distances." For example, the areas $A_1$ and $A_2$ of two sectors of a circle are matched by two sets of triangles, 4 for $A_1$ and 8 for $A_2$. All 12 are congruent because their angles at the vertex C are equal, their bases along the circumference are of the same width, and their height equals the radius r. Therefore, the ratio $A_1/A_2 = 4r/8r$ matches that of the distances $4/8$.

Diagram 2: But now suppose that there are two circles, one larger than the other. Then the triangles will no longer be congruent but similar, matching in angles but differing in height by ratio $p = r_1/r_2$. If, for example, the ratio $p = 4/6$ then
$$a_1/a_2 = 4^2/6^2 = 16/36 = 4/9.$$
It follows that the two sectors $a_1$ and $a_2$ are of equal size if the numbers of triangles, $n_1$ and $n_2$, are adjusted so that $a_1/a_2 = (r_1^2/r_2^2)(n_2/n_1)$. More detail in Chapter 10, Appendix B.

Diagram 3: For example, if the ratio of the squared radii is $p = (r_1^2/r_2^2) = 4^2/6^2 = 16/36$ and the relative number of similar triangles is $(n_2/n_1) = 9/4$, then $A_1/A_2 = (16/36)(9/4) = 144/144 = 1.0$. Or, in general, the two areas will be of equal size when their number of similar triangles is inversely related to the squared radii. This implies that sectors of different circles can be compared in area provided their squared radii are taken into account.

# Figure 10.4: Kepler's Discovery of the Area Law (continued)

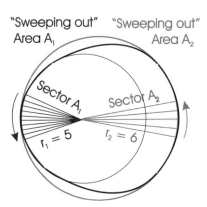

"Sweeping out" Area $A_1$    "Sweeping out" Area $A_2$

Sector $A_1$    Sector $A_2$

$r_1 = 5$    $r_2 = 6$

Diagram 4: When Kepler first abandoned the idea of a perfect circular orbit of Mars, he compared the sector closest to the Sun (near the perihelion) with that farthest away from it (near the aphelion). He discovered that Mars "swept out" equal areas in equal times (e.g., $A_1 = A_2$). If, for example, the initial ratio of the two distances was

$$r_1 / r_2 = 5/6 \qquad \text{and}$$
$$(r_1)^2/(r_2)^2 = 25/36 \qquad n_1/n_2 = 6/4,$$

then the estimated ratio of the two areas was

$$A_1/A_2 = (25/36)(6/4) = 150/144 .$$

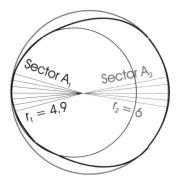

Sector $A_1$    Sector $A_2$

$r_1 = 4.9$    $r_2 = 6$

Diagram 5: To improve on the initial estimates Kepler could have adjusted the numbers of similar triangles, say, from $n_1/n_2 = 6/4$ to $13/9$ so that:

$$A_1/A_2 = (25/36)(13/9) = 325/324 = 1.0.$$

Or he could have adjusted the distances, say, from

$$(r_1/r_2) = 5/6 \text{ to } 4.9/6.0 \qquad \text{so that}$$
$$(r_1)^2/(r_2)^2 = 24.01/36 \qquad \text{and}$$
$$A_1/A_2 = (24/36)(6/4) = 144/144 = 1.0.$$

In either case it confirmed that $A_1/A_2 = 1.0$, which is equivalent to $A_1 = A_2$.

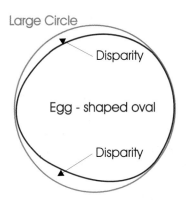

Large Circle

Disparity

Egg - shaped oval

Disparity

Diagram 6: Kepler was delighted with his discovery of the "Area Law," which implies that planets sweep out equal areas in equal times. Yet, the strange shape of the orbit of Mars puzzled him. Why should the orbit be such an egg-shaped oval? It lacked symmetry and elegance. To remedy it, Kepler now focused on the "sickle-shaped disparities" of the Martian orbit.

# Figure 10.5: Kepler's Discovery of Elliptical Planetary Orbits

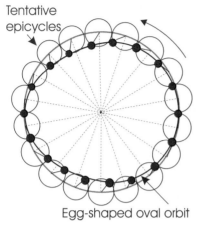

Tentative epicycles

Egg-shaped oval orbit

Diagram 1: Kepler was puzzled by the egg-shaped appearance of the orbit of Mars. He found it impossible to fit epicycles to the asymmetric oval so as to have a point revolving on the epicycles move smoothly and precisely match Tycho de Brahe's orbital observations of the planet. It was an extraordinary coincidence that he stumbled on a particular trigonometric ratio he recognized to be a characteristic of an ellipse.

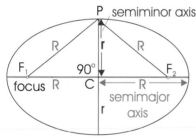

Diagram 2: An ellipse can be drawn by stretching a loose string over two fixed points $F_1$, $F_2$, and over a third movable point P, marking the circumference. The length $R + R = 2R$ spans the major axis and $r + r = 2r$ spans the minor axis of the ellipse. At the intersection C the angle equals $90°$, the distance $F_1P = F_2P = R$, so that each equals the length of the semi-major axis R. As well, at point C, the angle at P reaches its maximum size.

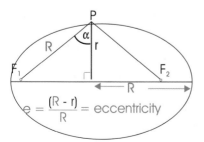

Diagram 3: The "eccentricity (e)" describes the oblate shape of the ellipse. It is defined by the relation between the semi-major axis R and the semi-minor axis r, as in
$$e = (R-r)/R.$$
When the two are of equal length, $R = r$, the eccentricity $e = 0.0$, and the ellipse assumes the shape of a circle. When R increases relative to r, the ellipse gets flatter. The ratio $R/r$ is the secant of the angle $\alpha$ at P. It is another measure of the eccentricity of the ellipse.

# Figure 10.5: Kepler's Discovery of Elliptical Planetary Orbits

Adapted from Walker, p. 226.

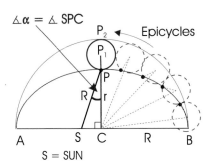

$\measuredangle \alpha = \measuredangle SPC$

Epicycles

$S = SUN$

Diagram 4: Kepler noticed that at point P , half-way between A and B , the breadth of the "sickle" was 0.000429 times the radius r. This was half the size of the diameter of the epicycle (i.e., $(0.5)\ PP_2 = PP_1$). It suddenly dawned on him that 1.000429 was the numerical value of the secant $\alpha$ of an ellipse. Here it meant that the ratio of the distances $CP_1/CP$ equaled the secant ratio $R/r$ of angle SPC, in short, secant of $\measuredangle SPC = \sec \measuredangle \alpha = 1.000429$.

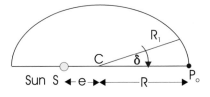

Sun S $\leftarrow$ e $\blacktriangleright\blacktriangleleft$ ——R—— $P_0$

Diagram 5: As soon as Kepler found that the angle $\measuredangle SPC$ characterized the eccentricity of an ellipse, he searched for a mathematical link between the eccentricity e and any point on the orbit. Kepler defined the distance between the Sun and Mars by the equation

$SP = R + e(\cos \delta)$. It implies that the orbital distance of a planet from the Sun equals the semimajor radius R augmented by the term e $(\cos \delta )$.

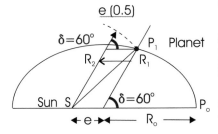

e (0.5)

$\delta = 60°$ $\qquad$ $P_1$ Planet

$R_2$ $\qquad$ $R_1$

Sun S $\qquad$ $\delta = 60°$ $P_0$

$\leftarrow$ e $\blacktriangleright\blacktriangleleft$ —— $R_0$ ——$\rightarrow$

Diagram 6: Since the proof of Kepler's equation is not easy we only verify it for two selected points. When $\delta = 0°$, $\cos 0° = R_0/R_1 = 1.0$ so that $SP_0 = R_0 + e (1.0) = R_0 + e$ which is the correct distance from planet to Sun. Or, when $\delta = 60°$ then

$\cos 60° = 0.5$ and Kepler's equation yields $SP_1 = R_1 + e\ (0.5)$. This is shown here by letting $R_2 = R_1$ and by turning $SP_1$ around point S so that

$Sp_1 = R_2 + e\ (0.5)$.

Kepler's equation works!

# Figure 10.6: Kepler's Three Laws of Planetary Orbits

Kepler's First Law : The planetary orbit is an ellipse with the Sun located at one focus of it.

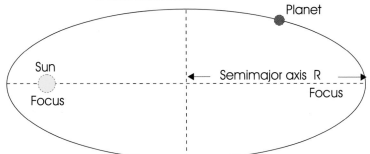

Kepler's Second Law: The imaginary line joining the centers of the Sun and of a planet sweeps out equal areas in equal times.

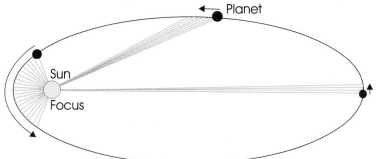

Kepler's Third Law: The Square of a planet's orbital period is proportional to the cube of its semimajor axis as in $P^2 = k R^3$, where $P$ is the planet's (sidereal) period in years, $k$ is a constant, and $R$ is the semimajor axis.

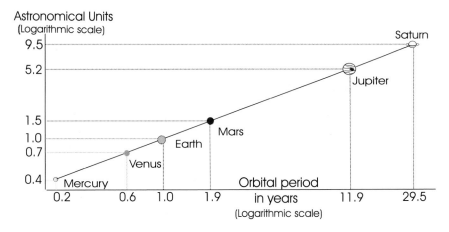

# Figure 11.1: How Galileo Analyzed the Rate of Acceleration

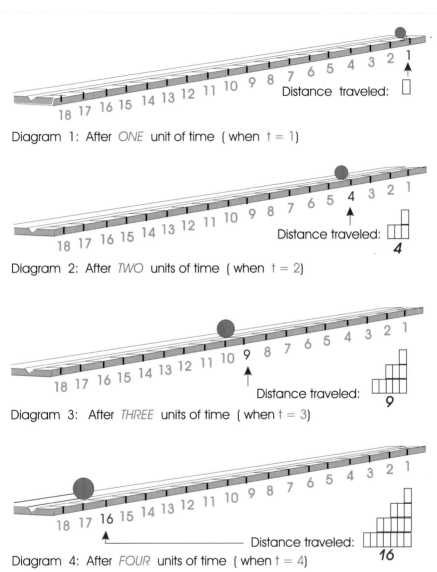

Diagram 1: After *ONE* unit of time ( when t = 1)

Diagram 2: After *TWO* units of time ( when t = 2)

Diagram 3: After *THREE* units of time ( when t = 3)

Diagram 4: After *FOUR* units of time ( when t = 4)

Galileo geometrically analyzed accelerated motion by representing distance as rectangular boxes piled on top of each other, each box measuring one unit of distance a metal ball traveled along the inclined plane. Thus, the area formed by the boxes corresponded to the cumulative distance the ball had covered after each unit of time.

# Figure 11.2: Galilean Analysis of Uniformly Accelerated Motion

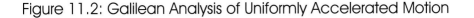

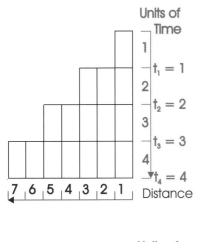

**Diagram 1:** As shown in Figure 11.1, Galileo described accelerated motion by relating units of time to distance. He pictured the distance a metal ball traveled down an inclined plane by rectangular boxes. He found that at the end of the first time interval $t = 1$ the ball rolled down a distance of one unit, at $t = 2$ four units, at $t = 3$ nine units, and at $t = 4$ sixteen units.

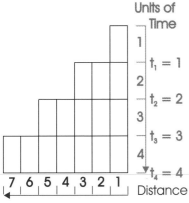

**Diagram 2:** To picture the total distance the ball traveled, Galileo arranged the boxes in a triangular pattern. Here, for example, the total distance the ball traveled is given by the sum of 16 rectangles. This figurative pattern corresponds to the series $1+3+5+7$, encountered earlier (in Chapter 2) as the "Square Series" of Pythagorean figurate numbers.

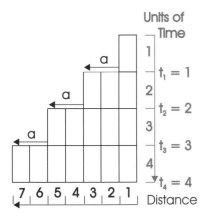

**Diagram 3:** In this fashion Galileo showed that the distance the ball went on the inclined plane during a specified time interval, matched the square series ( i.e., $1 = 1^2$, $1+3 = 2^2$, $1+3+5 = 3^2$, $1+3+5+7 = 4^2$, ... , etc.) . He also showed that at each successive time interval the ball accelerated by a constant number of units, as in : $3 - 1 = a$, $5 - 3 = a$, $7 - 5 = a$, ... , etc.

# Figure 11.2: Galilean Analysis of Uniformly Accelerated Motion (cont'd.)

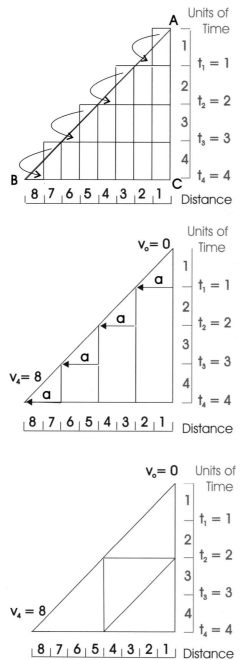

**Diagram 4:** In Diagrams 1 to 3, a set of rectangles illustrated the distance the ball traveled. In Diagram 4 the area of the rectangles is converted into triangle *ABC* of identical size where the triangle
$$ABC = 1/2\,(8)\,4 = 16.$$
It is another figurate measure of the same distance traveled.

**Diagram 5:** Alternatively, the same distance can be described as a function of the acceleration (*a*) and the time (*t*), as in
$$d_4 = \tfrac{1}{2}\,(a\,t_4)\,t_4$$
$$= \tfrac{1}{2}\,((2)\,4)\,4 = 16.$$
In general, the distance covered in *n* time intervals is defined by $d_n = \tfrac{1}{2}\,(a\,t_n)\,t_n$ or simply by $d = \tfrac{1}{2}\,a t^2$.

**Diagram 6:** The average speed or mean velocity (*v*) can be computed as the distance covered (*d*) per unit of time (*t*). After four time intervals, for example,
$$v_4 = d_4\,/\,t_4 = 16\,/\,4 = 4.$$
When the distance is computed as in:
$$d = \tfrac{1}{2}\,a t^2, \quad v = \tfrac{1}{2}\,a t^2 / t.$$
$$v_4 = \tfrac{1}{2}\,(2)\,16/4 = 4.$$
In general, the mean velocity is $v = d/t = \tfrac{1}{2}\,a t$.

Chapter 10

# KEPLER (1571–1630),
# THREE LAWS OF PLANETARY ORBITS

*It was the immortal achievement of Kepler (1618) to discover the simple and striking laws of the planetary orbits and hence save the Copernican system at a critical period. The orbits are not circles about the Sun but curves closely related to circles, namely ellipses, in one focus of which the Sun is situated.*

Max Born[1]

Weil-der-Stadt is located in Swabia, a wine region of southern Germany that is fringed to the west by the Black Forest, to the east by Bavaria, and to the south by Switzerland. From the south, the river Neckar meanders north past Swabia's hilly vineyards, through Heidelberg, and merges with the Rhine River.

To this day, Weil-der-Stadt with its narrow, cobbled streets is a small town.[2] In the town center is a spacious marketplace surrounded by gabled houses. During the summer months red geraniums seem to overflow the flower boxes of the windows. The people of the town revere Kepler like a patron saint. His statue, positioned on a huge pedestal of red sandstone and showing him looking upward to the sky, dominates the marketplace. Nearby, and visible from afar, rises the mighty tower of the Gothic church of St. Peter and Paul, built before 1200 A.D. The Church was to throw a long shadow over Kepler's life.

## Kepler's Early Years

Next to the marketplace in Weil-der-Stadt is the small, half-timbered house where Johannes Kepler was born on December 27 of 1571, almost 100 years after the birth of Copernicus. He was the first-born child of Heinrich Kepler and Katharina, née Guldenmann. His parents named him after the Apostle John, the saint of the day.[3] According to Kepler's astrologically tainted notes, his father was "vicious, inflexible, quarrelsome, and doomed to come to a bad end." In the family horoscope Kepler characterized his mother, the daughter of an innkeeper, as "small, thin, swarthy, gossiping, and quarrelsome, and of a bad disposition."[4] It appears that she not only collected herbs and concocted powerful potions, but also believed in magic and witchcraft. She had been raised by an aunt who was eventually burned at the stake, and she herself nearly shared the same horrible fate later in life. His parents quarreled often and made their children's lives miserable.[5]

While Johannes' achievements would eventually earn undying fame for the family name, the talents among his siblings varied. His younger brother, Heinrich, apprenticed as a baker, got into fights, ran away from home, served with soldiers in Hungary, earned a meager living by singing in Vienna, and then begged his way home. Later he became an imperial guardsman in Prague, returned home poor, and died a beaten man at age 42. By contrast his sister Margarete was gentle and kind. She married a clergyman. Johannes's youngest brother, Christopher, became a respectable craftsman who also took pride in being a part-time army drill master.[6]

### Kepler's Grandparents

Johannes was the first-born, a two-months' premature baby of rather delicate constitution. He was small, of graceful build, dark-eyed and black-haired. He was barely three years old when his father left for The Netherlands to serve as a mercenary in the army in the fight against the protestant insurgents in this foreign country. A year later his mother followed him. She left little Johannes behind in the care of his grandparents, the Sebald Keplers. Johannes became so sick with smallpox that he nearly died.

Grandfather Sebald was one of the town's prominent citizens. A strong advocate of Lutheran teachings, he was the leader of the co-religionists who advocated peaceful co-existence. Highly regarded among his fellow citizens, he became Weil-der-Stadt's mayor.[7] Later in life Johannes described his grandfather as proud and arrogant, hot-tempered and impetuous, stubborn and sensual. Johannes thought that the beard lent his grandfather's red face an air of importance. Yet, without being eloquent, his grandfather could give wise instructions and follow up on their observance.[8]

Inclined towards astrology, Johannes interpreted his grandmother's horoscope in less complimentary terms. He characterized her as "restless, clever, and lying, but devoted to religion; slim and of fiery nature; vivacious, an inveterate troublemaker; jealous, extreme in her hatreds; violent, a bearer of grudges. And all her children have something like this."[9] This is how Kepler pictured the Sebald grandparents in his private notes. Obviously it was a complex family environment and young Johannes did not have an easy time at it. Yet, he was known to revere his grandparents. At least, that was the impression of his relatives and friends.

## *Sporadic Schooling*

Having fought on the side of a foreign government that oppressed religious freedom, his parents were disgraced upon their return from The Netherlands. Forced to renounce their right of citizenship in Weil-der-Stadt, they moved to a nearby town where his father opened a tavern. They did not stay long, however, and fell into a pattern of wandering from town to town. Kepler attended school only sporadically; he worked as a farmhand to help earn a living. Aside from the hardships of his youth, he remembered that in the year 1577 his mother took him up a hill at night and showed him the great comet that became known as Tycho's Comet; and in 1580 his father went out with him after dark to have him see a lunar eclipse. Both events left a deep impression on Johannes.[10]

Before Johannes reached his teens, his father left home again to fight in yet another war. He never came back. He is said to have died on the way home in the vicinity of the city of Augsburg. Very likely, because of sporadic school attendance and family hardship, it took Johannes twice as long as it took other children to complete the first three classes of elementary Latin school. Finally, at age 13, he was allowed to enter the lower theological seminary.[11]

## Education

Yet, for all of young Kepler's family hardships, life had its compensations, too. The school system was excellent. The Lutheran Dukes of Wuerttemberg had confiscated the monasteries and convents for their new system of elementary and secondary schools. They had hired protestant clergymen who could hold their own in the religious controversy with the Catholics. Bright young people were given the opportunity to enter the universities of Tuebingen and Wittenberg to prepare for the clergy and for administrative positions in the government's chancellory. Scholarships and grants were available for the children of the poor. Kepler, precocious and brilliant, went from semenary to university.[12]

Latin was a prerequisite for careers in the clergy, government, and education. It was taught at the elementary level and at the seminary, all courses were given in Latin. With his formidable intellect and interest in religion, Kepler advanced quickly. Apart from theology the curriculum included the study of the Greek classics, mathematics, music, rhetoric, and dialectics. Discipline was strict. During the summer months classes started at four o'clock in the morning and in winter months at five o'clock in the morning.[13]

### *Convent School and Seminary*

At age 13, Kepler passed the state examinations that allowed him to enter the convent school at Adelberg near Mt. Hohenstaufen. Two years later he successfully moved on to the higher seminary at a monastery in Maulbronn. Although he gained high praise from his teachers, he tortured himself with introspection, self-examination, religious anxiety, conscience, and confessional conflicts.[14] He kept notes of real and imaginary conflicts as he encountered them. He wrote:

> I suffered dreadfully and nearly died of my troubles. I often incensed
> everyone against me through my own fault: at Tuebingen [it was] my

violent request for silence. Lendlinus I alienated by foolish writings, Spangenberg in correcting him when he was my teacher; Kleberus hated me as a rival, the reputation of my talent annoyed Rebstock, and also my frivolousness, my friend Jaeger lied to me and squandered much of my money. I turned to hatred and exercised it in angry letters during the course of two years.[15]

Yet, Kepler's anxieties did not overwhelm him. He still made good use of his time. Aside from studying for his obligatory courses he found time for some extracurricular activities, not to participate in sports and other outdoor activities, but to write lyrical poems imitating ancient poetical forms or to exercise his memory by learning the longest psalms by heart.[16]

*Graduation From University*

At age 20 Kepler graduated from the faculty of arts at the University of Tuebingen. He went on to study at the theological faculty for four more years. In the city of Tuebingen, situated alongside the picturesque Neckar valley, no one could have been better accommodated and provided for than a theologian. The students' progress in rhetoric, dialectics, ethics, Greek, Hebrew, astronomy, and physics was closely monitored; grades were given every quarter. It was here that Kepler attended the stimulating lectures on astronomy by the famous astronomer Michael Maestlin. Although Maestlin had no choice but to teach the traditional Ptolemaic system, he often referred to the alternative Copernican system. Kepler was so intrigued that he immediately sat down to make a careful analysis of all the advantages the Copernican system had over the Ptolemaic system. It was the start of Kepler's lifelong fascination with astronomy.[17]

*Teaching Position in Gratz*

At age 23, before passing his final examination, he was offered the post of teacher in mathematics and astronomy in Gratz, a city in the southeastern part of Austria. He had been selected because of his outstanding knowledge in mathematics and astronomy. Kepler hesitated. He had cherished the study of theology and counted on becoming a priest. It was an unexpected offer for a lowly position compared with that of a priest. After consulting with his grandfather Sebald Kepler and his mother, he accepted, while explicitly reserving the right to return to enter the clerical profession. He left the university of Tuebingen for Gratz on March 13, 1594. Although his pay would not be very generous, for him the move meant financial independence.[18]

During the first year of teaching Kepler had a handful of students, but in his second year, not one. Kepler described himself as a poor teacher because he felt that his "enthusiasm and eagerness is harmful, leads me into digressions, new ways of expressing or proving my point."[19] The head of the school did not blame the lack of students on Kepler but simply said that mathematics was not for everybody. The school's board asked him to teach a course in rhetoric and lecture on Virgil so that they could justify his salary until the public was ready to profit from mathematics. In the board's opinion Kepler was a learned and modest professor and they lauded his intellect and character.

Kepler was unhappy, not only because of his teaching post but also because religious tension was on the rise. While in Tuebingen, the Duke of Wuerttemberg and the people of the area were totally dedicated to Martin Luther's protestant teachings–not so in Gratz. As early as 1573 Archduke Charles had summoned Jesuits to the city to teach at a Latin school. In 1586 he had founded a university with Jesuit faculties of philosophy and theology. After his death in 1590 his widow, Archduchess Maria, continued efforts to regain the land for the Catholic faith. She strengthened the influence of the learning institutions in the city and the country.[20]

During his four-year stay in Gratz, Kepler was also obligated to publish annual astrological forecasts. Traditionally, that was the task of the provincial mathematician. His first calender was a great success. Based on his astrological analysis he predicted a very cold winter and an invasion by Turkish forces. That winter was so cold that people in the Alps died of the cold and the Turks burned down the country from Vienna to Neustadt, raped the women, carried off the men, and plundered their farms. His prophesies did not go unnoticed. His annual forecasts were in high demand and so were the individual horoscopes that he cast.

Together, they added significantly to his meager salary and helped him make a living.[21]

Even though Kepler secretly had his reservations regarding astrology, he enjoyed doing it. He wrote: "A mind accustomed to mathematical deduction, when confronted with the faulty foundations [of astrology] resists a long, long time, like an obstinate mule, until compelled by beating and curses to put its foot into that dirty puddle."[22] Kepler may have prepared some horoscopes with tongue in cheek and thought of them as "monkey play,"[23] yet he considered it conceivable that an individual's soul reacted to the light coming at different angles from the planets, which created geometric harmonies and disharmonies and, in turn, set a pattern for life. This was a Pythagorean vision of the impact of the spheres on life.

**Kepler's Search for a Celestial Geometry**

Perhaps the frustrations of teaching drove Kepler further into cosmological speculations. One day, while instructing a class in geometry, he fit an equilateral triangle between two circles on the blackboard. As he looked at it, he noticed that the ratio of the two circles was the same as that of the orbits of Saturn and Jupiter. Saturn and Jupiter being the first of the exterior planets, he remembered that the triangle is the first figure in geometry. He was suddenly inspired: "Immediately I tried to inscribe a square into the next interval between Jupiter and Mars, a pentagon between Mars and Earth, a hexagon between Earth and Venus." Later he wrote: "The delight that I took in my discovery I shall never be able to describe in words."[24] Had he, Kepler, finally uncovered the secret of heavenly order and beautiful proportions? Had the Greek philosopher Plato not seen the world as a divine work of art and based the distances of the planets on geometrical progressions? Had Plato not said that the beautiful never lacks proportion? Had the philosopher Aristotle not insisted that the universe was arranged in crystalline spheres? And had Plato not challenged the astronomers to find the underlying cause of the perfect order in the universe? (See Chapter 3.)

One question had puzzled Kepler since his student days at Tuebingen. Why did the solar system have only six planets, neither more nor less? For a moment he thought he had found the answer to his question. Yet, on closer examination, the geometrical ratios of the figures did not precisely match the orbital ratios (Figure 10.1, Diagram 1).

Kepler did not give up but pressed on. If the two-dimensional figures of plane geometry did not match the six circular orbits, why not try a three-dimensional model. Some 2000 years earlier Euclid of Alexandria had demonstrated that only five regularly shaped solids had matching (congruent) sides all around:

1. The pyramid (a tetrahedron) with 4 sides of equilateral triangles,
2. The cube with 6 sides of squares,
3. The octahedron with 8 sides of equilateral triangles,
4. The dodecahedron with 12 sides of pentagons, and
5. The icosahedron with 20 sides of equilateral triangles.

Being perfectly symmetrical, each solid could be inscribed in a sphere, its corners just touching it from the inside. If done properly, each sphere would fit into another of greater size and the center of the each surface of each solid would touch the next smaller sphere from the outside. If the design worked for all five solids, surely it could not be pure chance! It would have to be the divine design of perfect proportions.

### *Mysterium Cosmographicum (1596)*

At once Kepler decided to space the five solids so that they fit perfectly into the six spheres of the planets. He inscribed a cube in the orbital sphere of Saturn so that its corners just touched the sphere from inside. He inserted a sphere for Jupiter, so that it just touched the cube at the center of its six surfaces (Figure 10.1, Diagram 2). Next he inserted the pyramid and inscribed in it the orbital sphere of Mars. Between Mars and Earth he fit the dodecahedron, between Earth and Venus the icosahedron and, finally, between Venus and Mercury the octahedron. It worked. Kepler was thrilled:

> It is amazing! Although I had as yet no clear idea of the order in which the perfect solids had to be arranged, I nevertheless succeeded. Day and night I spent with calculations to see whether the proposition that I had formulated fitted the Copernican orbits or whether my joy would be carried away by the winds. Within a few days everything fell into its place.[25]

Kepler described the newly discovered three-dimensional model in the first half of his book *Mysterium Cosmographicum* (1596). In it he explained to his readers why our solar system contained three exterior and two interior planets, why the orbits were spaced as they were, and why the five solids were distributed among the planets in this fashion and no other. His reasoning was quite mysterious if not fantastic at times.[26]

Had Kepler been a true Aristotelian, he would have left it at that. His model was a geometric construct of perfect order, its beauty of design was esthetically pleasing. Yet, Kepler went on and took the next crucial step: empirical verification. In the second half of his book he switched from his speculative reasoning and divine inspiration of the earlier chapters to testing his theory. In the opening statement he wrote:

> What we have so far said served merely to support our thesis by arguments of probability. Now we shall proceed to the astronomical determination of the orbits and to geometrical considerations. If these do not confirm the thesis, then all our previous efforts have doubtless been in vain.[27]

In attempting to account for discrepancies between the planetary orbits and his geometric construct, it suddenly occurred to him that Copernicus had based the planetary intervals on the planet-to-Earth distances and not on the planet-to-Sun distances. When Kepler tried to adjust for this difference, it only accentuated the size of the errors. It seemed to him that the geometric model was right but the observational data on which Copernicus had based his analysis were at fault.[28]

Kepler was first attracted to astronomy for metaphysical reasons—the search for the ultimate nature of existence. The Copernican idea of a heliocentric cosmos appealed to him because he believed the Sun was a symbol of God, the source of light and heat, and the generator of the force that drove the planets around their orbits. For Kepler the Sun had all the mystic attributes it had held for Pythagoras. He wrote: "The Sun in the middle of the moving stars, himself at rest and yet the source of motion, carries the image of God, the Father and Creator. He distributes his motive force through a medium which contains the moving bodies."[29] And further: "Geometry existed before the Creation, is coeternal in the mind of God, geometry provided God with a model for the creation."[30] In the closing chapter of the *Mysterium* Kepler could not resist casting a professional horoscope for the Earth. He deduced that the Earth was created on April 27, 4977 B.C., but found it impossible to predict when the world would end.

Kepler wrote the *Mysterium* at age 24. He finished it within six months from the day the inspiration of the five solids had struck him. During this time he often wrote to his former professor Michael Maestlin in Tuebingen to ask for help. Kepler's writings have been described as a mixture of flights of fancy, painstaking research, paradoxical theorizing carried to extremes verging on insanity, all peppered with recklessness and pedantic caution, naïveté and philosophical depth, audacity and foolishness. These character traits enabled him to ask questions nobody had dared to ask before. If Kepler had not gone any further than that one work, we might never have heard of him. But Kepler the scientist would emerge later.[31]

When Kepler had finished his book, he asked his superiors in Gratz for an eight-week leave of absence to take care of the publication of his book. He stayed away for seven months. Not because of the publication—Maestlin took care of that—but because he had persuaded Frederick, the Duke of Württemberg, to have a drinking fountain modeled after his "five-solids" universe. The fountain would serve seven different beverages pouring from the celestial spheres through concealed pipes. When the Duke finally agreed to have it done, the silversmiths were unable to build it. It did not take Kepler very long to entice the Duke with another project, a planetarium. Yet, after two years of correspondence it, too, was dropped.[32]

*Kepler Marries*

Before his departure for Württemberg, Kepler's friends had found a prospective bride for him. She was the daughter of a rich mill owner and already twice widowed. She was willing to marry him but it took some time convincing her father. Kepler's friends relentlessly kept up the pressure and eventually the mill owner gave in. According to Kepler's horoscope the wedding (April 27, 1597) took place "under a calamitous sky." Their marriage lasted fourteen years. After a serious illness his wife died at age

37, with a distraught mind. Kepler described their marriage in depressing terms. His horoscope had predicted disaster when he married her and in predicting disasters Kepler was nearly infallible.[33]

When the *Mysterium* appeared in the spring of 1597, Kepler sent copies to the leading scholars of Europe, including Galileo and Tycho de Brahe. By this time printing had become widely adopted and, on average, more than a thousand scientific books were published every year in Germany alone. His book created a stir but it was not in the mainstream of astronomy. The response to it was not all favorable. Galileo of Padua was among the "moderns" who rejected it because of its mystic speculations, which reminded him of the numerology of Pythagoras.[34]

Tycho de Brahe of Denmark—the best known astronomer of his day—was the only scientist who rejected Kepler's wild speculations but immediately recognized the genius of the young man. The two would not meet for another three years. Meanwhile, between 1597 and 1599 Kepler got down to serious study of mathematics and astronomy. As a first step he wanted to find out if the apparent position of the stars shifted as the Earth orbited the Sun. They did not. Blaming it on his primitive observatory, he wrote to other astronomers for help. No one reported a successful observation of a shift of the stars.

In creating his theory of celestial spheres separated by geometric solids (Figure 10.1, Diagram 2), Kepler had allowed for variations in the planetary orbits. The Greek astronomers of antiquity, Ptolemy and Hipparchus, had observed periodic variations in the Sun's distance from the Earth and from other planets. They adjusted for them by adding off-center equants to their circular deferent orbits (Chapter 6, Figure 6.8). Copernicus retained the planetary eccentricities of Ptolemy's model. Kepler allowed for them by carefully calibrating the thickness of each sphere between successive planets. He let the inner wall represent the interior planet's maximum distance and the outer wall the exterior planet's minimum distance from the Sun. By this kind of calibration his results agreed with the orbits of Mars, Venus, and Earth but not with the others.

Not being very happy with the orbital fit of his five solids he searched for a musical harmony of the spheres. As he expanded on his computations, he ran into new problems. The planets did not move at uniform speeds but faster when near the Sun and slower when away from it. Because of their variations in orbital speed they could not hum at a steady pitch or produce a harmonious melody. Yet, he did not know with any precision the orbits of the planets. The only astronomer who had collected precise data on their orbital positions was Tycho de Brahe, but he had not released his records.[35]

Kepler expressed his deep frustrations in a letter to Maestlin: "For Tycho alone do I wait; he shall explain to me the order and arrangement of orbits. Any single instrument of his cost more than my whole family's fortune put together. My opinion of Tycho is this: he is superlatively rich, but he knows not how to make use of it, as is the case with most rich people." [36]

*Expelled from Gratz*

At the time that Kepler met him, Tycho had only 18 months to live. Their meeting was caused by a turn in political events. The young Archduke Ferdinand of Hapsburg, the Jesuit-educated son of the Archduchesse Maria, was determined to wipe out the Lutheran heresy in the Austrian provinces. In the summer of 1598 Ferdinand had closed down the school where Kepler had taught. By fall of that year all Lutheran school teachers were ordered, at the threat of death penalty, to leave the province. Kepler's exile did not last very long. By October 1599 he was permitted to return. Among all the teachers, Kepler was the only one allowed to resettle.

Kepler believed that the Archduke favoured him because he was so pleased with his astronomical discoveries. But Kepler had some influential allies. He had been befriended by the Catholic chancellor of Bavaria (Herwart von Hohenburg). An amateur philosopher and supporter of the arts, he let it be known that scholars of Kepler's calibre and reputation deserved protection. Jesuits were interested in astronomical forecasts of eclipses and other celestial events because such knowledge helped them greatly in their missionary work. Finally, Kepler himself did not agree wholeheartedly with the Lutheran doctrine, and the Catholics may have counted on his conversion to their faith.[37]

Kepler's return to Gratz was short-lived. Disease and pestilence was sweeping through Hungary, not far east of the town of Gratz. His child had died of meningitis and dysentery was killing people of all ages. At the same time heretics were being tortured. Fortunately, Tycho de Brahe was not very far away. He had left Denmark for Prague, where Emperor Rudolph II had appointed him "Imperial Mathematicus." Kepler's opportunity came when a councillor to the emperor, a certain Baron Hoffman, was returning to Prague. He offered Kepler the chance to escape and arranged for him to meet Tycho de Brahe. It gave Kepler, the theoretical astronomer, the opportunity to interact with Tycho de Brahe, the empirical astronomer. Kepler needed Tycho's observational data and Tycho wanted Kepler to incorporate them in his theoretical framework. The date was January 1, 1600.[38]

## Kepler's New Approach to Planetary Motion

Tycho's superb database—built on observations of unprecedented precision and painstakingly assembled during the preceding thirty years—would enable Kepler to develop a perfect picture of the planetary orbits. Over the course of the next three decades Kepler discovered "Three Laws" of planetary motion. They were new and different from all earlier efforts in astronomy. Independent of the planetary spheres of Eudoxus and Aristotle, they no longer relied on the circles and epicycles of Hipparchus, Ptolemy, and Copernicus.

Unlike the Euclidean textbook exposition of Copernicus, Kepler's treatise did not follow the academic format. Kepler wrote it more as a diary describing all the errors and traps he had fallen into during his search. In the preface to his book *A New Astronomy (Astronomia Nova)*[39] he explains why he chose this style:

> What matters to me is not merely to impart to the reader what I have to say, but above all to convey to him the reasons, subterfuges, and lucky hazards which led me to my discoveries. When Christopher Columbus, Magellan, and the Portuguese relate how they went astray on their journeys, we not only forgive them, but would regret to miss their narration because without it the whole, grand entertainment would be lost. Hence I shall not be

blamed if, prompted by the same affection for the reader, I follow the same method .[40]

Here, we can only catch a glimpse of Kepler's frustrating trials and his joys of triumph. Recall from the preceding chapter that on his arrival in Benatek, Tycho assigned Kepler to the study of Mars. He gave the task to him because the strange orbit of this planet had not yielded its secret to Tycho or his loyal and proficient assistant Christian Sørensen Longomontanus. Kepler wrote:

> I believe it was an act of Divine Providence that I arrived just at the time when Longomontanus was occupied with Mars. For Mars alone enables us to penetrate the secrets of astronomy which otherwise would remain forever hidden from us.[41]

At first Kepler tackled the orbit of Mars along the classical doctrine of cycles and epicycles. When that failed, he decided to put the Sun at the center of the system. However, once he did that, he could no longer fit his computed values to Tycho's recorded observations. This perplexed him. If the planets moved around the Sun, shouldn't the Sun be precisely at the center of the planetary orbits? Kepler simplified the system further. Copernicus had upheld the axiom of perfectly uniform planetary motion—Kepler abolished it.[42] By accepting variations in the speed of the planets as real, Kepler would eventually eliminate the need for the remaining epicycles, which the Greek astronomers of antiquity had first imposed. It was a radical innovation and an abandonment of classical axioms.

In short, Kepler began the study of the Martian orbit by dropping two key axioms that had cluttered up the planetary landscape since the days of Ptolemy:

1. Instead of making the center of the Earth's orbit the focal point, Kepler positioned the Sun at the center; and
2. Instead of assuming that the planets moved at constant speeds Kepler accepted that they moved along their orbits at varying speeds.

Additionally, Kepler showed that the planets did not move along orbits that oscillated up and down about the Earth, but that they orbited the Sun on nearly the same plane at narrow invariant angles to each other. Nevertheless, as Kepler was soon to find out, his innovative changes were not sufficient for a perfect fit to Tycho's recorded observations.

When Kepler first tried to figure out the orbit of Mars, he chose those dates out of Tycho's observations on which Mars was "in opposition" to the Sun, (i.e., when Mars was perfectly aligned with the Earth and the Sun). From these observations he wanted to deduce:

- The radius of the orbit of Mars,
- The direction of the axis connecting the points when Mars was nearest to (perihelion) and farthest away (aphelion) from the Sun, and
- The three positions on this axis: Sun, the orbital center, and the distance from the center (Figure 10.2, Diagram 1).[43]

Since a circle is defined by three points on the circumference, Kepler needed three observations on the planetary orbit. Copernicus had pointed out that at the time of the planet's opposition it is immaterial whether one assumes a stationary Sun or a stationary Earth. That is because at opposition the planet, the Earth, and the Sun lie on a straight line. Between 1580 and 1600 Tycho de Brahe had observations for 10 such Mars oppositions. Assuming that Mars orbited the Sun on a circle, any three of the 10 observations should have yielded the same circular orbit. Since the mathematical problem of finding the circle whose circumference intersected all three points could not yet be solved by rigorous mathematics, Kepler instead arrived at a solution by a method of gradual approximation.[44]

When he completed the long and time-consuming approximations he checked the orbit of Mars so calculated against the other orbital positions at conjunction in the other years. He found that the results of his calculation came within two minutes of the Tychonic observations. At the end of Chapter XVI of his book, *The New Astronomy*, Kepler asks the reader who might have been bored by his calculations, to take pity on him who had to go through at least 70 iterations.[45]

## The Turning Point

After this conclusion the opening lines of the Kepler's next chapter may have startled the diligent reader but not nearly as much as it must have shocked Kepler. He wrote: "Who would have thought it possible? This hypothesis, which so closely agrees with the observed oppositions, is nevertheless false."[46] In the next two chapters Kepler describes how he discovered the disparities between observed and calculated positions of Mars. He had added some additional but rare observations from Tycho's data base and found that they did not fit his calculated points. Further adjustments made the fit even worse. Instead of disparities of two minutes they now reached up to eight minutes (Figure 10.2, Diagram 2).

Ptolemy and Copernicus could readily ignore discrepancies of that size because their observations had a 10-minute margin of error. For Kepler an 8-minute error was catastrophic. Where others might have despaired, it spurred Kepler on to renewed effort. He wrote:

> But for us, who, by divine kindness were given an accurate observer such as Tycho Brahe, for us it is fitting that we acknowledge this divine gift and put it to use. Henceforth I shall lead the way toward that goal according to my own ideas. For, if I had believed that we could ignore these eight minutes, I would have patched up my hypothesis accordingly. But since it was not possible to ignore them, those eight minutes point the road to a complete reformation of astronomy. They have become the building material for a large part of this work.

And he writes further:

> And thus the edifice which we erected on the foundation of Tycho's observations, we have now again destroyed. This was our punishment for having followed some plausible, but in reality false, axioms of the great men of the past.[47]

It was not only a turning point in Kepler's search for a better mathematical model of the universe, but it also signaled the point of departure from ancient dogma. Precise empirical observations had imposed a new rigor and discipline on scientific research.

Undaunted, Kepler started from scratch again. Evidently his circular orbit did not fit all of Tycho's planetary observations. He now decided to reverse the procedure. Although three points ought to have been sufficient for specifying the size of a circular orbit, he now tried to incorporate more than three points of observation.[48]

*The View from Mars*

While considering this problem, Kepler thought of a radically new approach. Up to then he had followed the method of Copernicus and examined the planetary motions as seen from Earth. Now he looked at it as seen from Mars. Tycho had gathered the data of the celestial motions on a continuing basis. To translate the actual points of observation from Earth into imaginary points of observation from Mars, Kepler devised an ingenious method of calculating the orbital positions.

A simplified version of his method is illustrated in Figure 10.3.[49] First he found the angles and then the distances. As shown in Chapter 8 (Figure 8.1), the outer planets (Mars, Jupiter, and Saturn) move more slowly than the inner planets (Venus and Mercury). For example, a Mars year takes 687.98 days compared with an Earth year of 365.25 days.[50] During the course of one year the angles between Mars, Earth, and the Sun change continuously. After one orbital revolution Mars returns to the same position. In 687 days the Earth travels beyond its initial point to a second point, falling short of two full revolutions by 43.5 Earth days.[51] From the shortfall of 43.5 days Kepler computed the angle between Sun, Earth, and Mars.

However, more information was needed to find the critical distance from the Sun to Mars. Kepler derived the sizes of other angles by geometric reasoning, estimated certain relationships between angles and orbital points by trigonometry, and after massive computations obtained a new set of estimates.[52] Thus Kepler was able to compute the distances of Mars to the Sun for any of the observations recorded by Tycho de Brahe (Figure 10.3).

Copernicus could estimate the distance of a planet at only one point of its orbit by comparing the point of opposition to that of its maximum elongation. In contrast, Kepler could now examine the shape of the Martian orbit by estimating Mars-to-Sun distances from many more observations by applying his novel trigonometric method. Although he had freed himself from any of the earlier preconceived notions of the planetary orbits, he nevertheless worked with a trigonometric method that relied on circular orbits. It had taken him many pages of calculations and nearly five years since the day he took on Mars. Not surprisingly, perhaps, he encountered some new surprises.

*Puzzling Variations in Orbital Speeds*
When Kepler decided on a fundamental change in perspective—from an Earth-oriented to a planet-oriented view—he had hoped to eliminate the orbital "misfits," estimates with a greater than permissible error (Figure 10.2, Diagram 2, point 4). After all his painstaking computations he had expected to see them fall on a neatly defined circular orbit. They did not. By then, Kepler had written 51 chapters of his book on *The New Astronomy*. It was mainly a commentary on the orbital characteristics of the planet Mars. Yet, he was still not certain of the exact shape of its orbit.[53] While mulling over the strange results, he noticed for the first time that, according to his calculations, Mars did not revolve at a uniform speed around the Sun. When approaching the Sun it accelerated, and when moving away from the Sun, Mars slowed down. Kepler was puzzled.

To examine the variations in the orbital speed more closely, Kepler divided the Martian orbit into 360 parts. Still in the belief that the planetary orbits could somehow be represented by circles, he recalled how Archimedes had arrived at a measure of the area of the circle. Kepler wrote:

> Since I was aware that there exists an infinite number of points in the orbit and accordingly an infinite number of distances [from the Sun] the idea occurred to me that the sum of these distances is contained in the area of the orbit. For I remembered that in the same manner Archimedes too divided the area of a circle into an infinite number of triangles.[54]

At first glance, comparing areas of different size by "summing the distances" seems farfetched. Indeed, the validity of the method was questioned because of doubt that the size of an oval-shaped sector could be measured by adding distances. Like Copernicus, Kepler still believed that the planets orbited the Sun in circles. This was not an unreasonable assumption since the orbits of most planets are nearly circular. Computationally, summing the distances from center to circumference in a circular orbit would have given him perfect results.

*Comparing the Size of Orbital Sectors*

Kepler derived Mars's orbital course from Tycho's astronomical observations. His geometric method of measuring parts of a circle is of interest. Figure 10.4 shows two sectors of different sizes inscribed in a circle and demonstrates how their areas can be geometrically measured. It follows from the diagrams that the areas of the two orbital sectors can be found by "summing the distances" from the center to the base of the triangles.

From Tycho's observations and his own computations Kepler had concluded, however, that the Sun was not at the center of a circular orbit of Mars. Recall that Kepler had followed the method of Copernicus and examined the planetary motions as seen from Earth. But then he changed his approach and translated all Mars-to-Earth distances into Mars-to-Sun distances. To translate the actual points of observation from Earth into imaginary points of observation from Mars, Kepler had devised the ingenious method of calculating the orbital positions (Figure 10.3).

Having adjusted his estimates, Kepler was disappointed that his newly computed results still did not fit a circular orbit. He found it hard to believe that the Sun was off-centre. Yet, if true, could it not explain why the orbital distance of Mars varied by as much as ±10 percent?[55] With variations of this size he wondered whether it was possible to represent the Martian orbit by merging two circles of different size, a smaller circle connected to a larger one?

Kepler decided to find out. Since his computations suggested that the speed of the angular sweep of Mars varied as it traveled along its orbit, he wanted to see how long it takes Mars to complete different sectors of its orbit.[56] Therefore, he subdivided the Martian orbit into 360 narrow triangular segments and proceeded by intricate geometric arguments.[57] Kepler noticed that Mars moved fastest when closest to the Sun (perihelion$_g$) and slowest when farthest away from it (aphelion$_g$). Although it clashed with his sense of geometric harmony, Kepler reluctantly assumed that Mars orbited the Sun along an egg-shaped oval course, best represented by connecting two circles, a smaller and a larger one. We have seen already how he could compare two areas within the same circle. When two circles differed in size, however, he had to modify the method of comparison (Figure 10.4, Diagrams 2 and 3, and Appendix B). Awkward as this geometric construct must have appeared to him, he was convinced that Tycho's recorded astronomical observations could not be ignored. Undeterred, he pursued the mystery of the Martian orbit further.

## Discovery of the First Two Laws of Planetary Motion

Like Aristotle, Kepler believed that it takes force to keep the planets moving. However, unlike Aristotle, Kepler thought that the Sun exerted a "magnetic" force that pushed and pulled the planets along their orbital path. Since a magnetic force weakens with distance, he expected the force acting on the planets to weaken too. He expected the Sun's force to diminish inversely with the square of its distance.[58] This did not agree with Aristotle's concept of the mover's force but it did agree with Kepler's comparison of areas.

### *Kepler's Law of Areas*

When Kepler first abandoned the notion of a perfect circular orbit of Mars, he compared two sectors, one for the shortest distance from the Sun and the other for the longest. On comparing the two sector areas he discovered to his amazement that Mars swept out equal areas in equal intervals of time. (The concept of "*sweeping out*" is illustrated in Figure 10.4, Diagram 4.) This did hold true for area comparisons at the two extreme distances, the apsides$_g$ of the Martian orbit that lie closest to or farthest away from the Sun. But he was not yet certain whether it held true for other points of the orbit. Yet, he could not believe that such a wonderful law would not apply all along the orbit of Mars.[59] Although he was delighted with his discovery, he felt compelled to search for further proof.

Kepler now focussed his energies on the shape of the Martian orbit. If it was not a perfect circle, what geometric shape could it be? As shown Figure 10.4, Diagrams 4 and 5, it created an egg-shaped oval embedded in the larger circle. Kepler did not know what to make of this strange orbit. The sickle-shaped disparities between the oval and the larger circle puzzled him (Diagram 6).

It bothered him considerably that he had not been able to match the Martian orbit with an aesthetically pleasing figure. He described his agonizing attempts of computing equations for the oval in ten chapters and 50 pages. Always being in search of harmony, he refused to accept this odd-shaped oval as the true orbit of Mars.[60]

To make matters worse, times were difficult for him. Kepler had no money, he was plagued by gall bladder troubles, and his wife became very ill after giving birth to a son. Yet, he could not tear himself away from the problematic shape of the Martian orbit. How could an asymmetric figure be a divine creation? He had searched for the area of the oval by splitting it in half, had calculated Sun-to-Mars distances for many orbital points, had tested many circular and oval orbits against Tycho's observations, had accumulated 900 pages of calculations, and still he had not found a pleasing solution.[61]

Kepler concentrated all his attention on the sickle-shaped disparity between the oval and the circle. He had already discovered that the Martian orbit was not a perfect circle, but he still adhered to the traditional belief that the odd-shaped orbit could somehow be explained by an epicyclical motion on its circumference. With seemingly never-ending computations, he explored this possibility. No matter how he tried he could not fit the epicycles to the asymmetric oval so that a point revolving on the epicycle moved smoothly and precisely matched Tycho de Brahe's orbital observations of the planet Mars (Figure 10.5, Diagram 1). All his attempts of finding a solution to the problem had failed.[62]

*Kepler's Law of Elliptical Orbit*
While Kepler was still trying to fit epicycles, he noticed that half-way along the Martian orbit between perihelion and aphelion, "the maximal breadth of the deficient sickle [was] 0.00429 times the radius."[63] Endowed with a

prodigious memory for numbers, it suddenly dawned on him that this number was also a measure of the eccentricity of an ellipse he had encountered years before in his work on optics. At that moment it became perfectly clear to him, although not to anyone else, that the correct curve for the orbit of the planet Mars was an ellipse.[64] In his own words:

> I was wondering why and how a sickle of just this thickness (0.00429) came into being. While this thought was driving me around, while I was considering again and again that, my apparent triumph of Mars had been in vain, I stumbled entirely by chance on the secant of the angle 5°18', which is the measure of the greatest optical equation. When I realized that this secant equals 1.00429, I felt as if I had awakened from a sleep.[65]

Kepler recalled from his earlier work on optics that at maximal width of the ellipse the difference between the semimajor and semiminor axis was 0.00429.[66] Now, when the angle at the center of the ellipse was 90° and the breadth of the sickle at its maximum–the "deficient" sickle was exactly 0.00429 times the radius. At once he realized that a clearly defined mathematical relationship existed between the angle at Mars and the distance to the Sun. Kepler had just recognized a unique characteristic of an ellipse. This mysterious explanation can be briefly simplified.[67]

An ellipse can be drawn by slipping a string loosely over two pins, stretching it to its full length and by drawing a closed curve all around (Figure 10.5, Diagram 2). The eccentricity defines the oblate shape of an ellipse. It is linked to the two diameters of the ellipse, its major and minor axes. When the two are of equal length, the ellipse assumes the shape of a circle. When the eccentricity is very large, the ellipse becomes very long and narrow and the measure of eccentricity approaches unity. For example, the eccentricity $e$ of the long and narrow orbit of Halley's Comet is estimated at $e = 0.967$.[68] (Figure 10.5, Diagrams 2 and 3 illustrate how the eccentricity of an ellipse is measured.).

*Kepler's Equation for the Elliptical Orbit*
Once Kepler was aware that the angle at the midpoint of the Martian orbit was a measure of the orbit's eccentricity, he searched for a link between the eccentricity and the numerical value of 0.00429 (Figure 10.5, Dia-

grams 4 and 5).[69] By geometric reasoning he discovered a trigonometric function, which allowed him to find any point on a planet's orbit. Since the proof of Kepler's equation is not easy, it is verified here for only two selected points of an elliptical orbit (Figure 10.5, Diagram 6).[70]

*Kepler's "First Two Laws"*

Kepler's orbital points, newly derived from his equation, matched Tycho's observations of Mars with great precision.[71] Later, Kepler could show that the other planets, including the planet Earth, revolved around the Sun on elliptical orbits too. In each case the Sun was positioned at one focus of the ellipse. Since the eccentricity of the planetary orbits is quite small and their path around the Sun nearly circular, it took Kepler many years of painstaking calculations to arrive at this conclusion.

It would take several decades before the idea was accepted and recognized by other astronomers. Even though Kepler had discovered it after his Law of Areas, the elliptical planetary orbits became known as Kepler's First Law: "The planets move about the Sun in elliptical orbits, the Sun being at one focus of the ellipse."[72]

So finally, after 2000 years, the great mental block of circular planetary orbits and circular epicycles had been pushed aside by an immense effort of observation and empirical analysis. Tycho de Brahe had recorded 30 years of observation and Kepler discovered the true shape of the planetary orbits. It was a great moment in the history of astronomy.

Now that Kepler had hit on the elliptical shape he became very concerned that his earlier sector estimates had lost some precision. He described the problem in his book at some length but concluded that the errors canceled each other. The fact that they canceled, was to him like a miracle. Although he intended to prove this cancellation, he admitted himself his arguments were almost impossible to follow. In time the Law of Areas became known as Kepler's Second Law: "The straight line joining a planet and the Sun sweeps out equal areas in the orbital plane in equal intervals of time."[73]

*The New Astronomy (1609)*

Kepler wrote his *New Astronomy* over a period of six years, but from start to publication it spanned ten years. All too often his work was interrupted and he was also occupied with his work on *Optics*, which was published in 1604. As the mathematician of the Imperial Court, Kepler was obligated to publish annual calenders with astrological predictions. He had to cast horoscopes for visitors to the court and write comments on eclipses and comets. Above all, he had to lobby for funding. He never did receive his full salary and barely managed to cover his household expenses and the cost of printing.

All the while the heirs of Tycho's estate harassed him about Tycho's astronomical records. On his appointment to Imperial Mathematicus, as Tycho's successor, Kepler had secured these records. Had he not done so they could well have been lost forever just as Tycho's precious instruments ended up as scrap metal. By demanding that he be listed as co-author of the *New Astronomy*, Tycho's son-in-law held up the printing. Eventually he settled for writing the Preface to the book.[74] Finally, in 1609, the beautifully printed book on the *New Astronomy* was published.[75]

Kepler's *New Astronomy* was not enthusiastically received. When Kepler first discovered the true orbit of Mars, he wrote to his astronomer friend David Fabricius: "I have the answer, the orbit of the planet is a true ellipse."[76] His friend replied he thought Kepler's theory was absurd because only the circle, and no other geometric shape, was perfectly symmetric and worthy of the heavens. Kepler's former Professor Maestlin reminded him that astronomical questions should be treated astronomically, based on geometry and arithmetic, not on physical conjectures, which disturb the reader rather than informing him.[77] Galileo, in Italy, was not impressed. He ignored Kepler's discoveries and continued to believe in celestial circles and epicycles for the rest of his life. The first to recognise the significance of Kepler's Laws were the British, among them Edmund Bruce (a traveler), Thomas Harriot (a mathematician), John Donne (a poet and reverend), Jeremiah Horrocks (an astronomer) and much later, Sir Isaac Newton.[78]

## Dissonance and Harmony of the World

Through his writings on astrology, optics, and astronomy, Kepler had become well known in circles of higher social status. Official visitors

Kepler finished his book on the *Harmony of the World* on May 27, 1618. In the Introduction he wrote:

> The thing which dawned on me before I had yet discovered the five regular bodies between the Heavenly orbits, which caused me to devote the best years of my life to astronomical studies, to join Tycho Brahe and to choose Prague as my residence, I have now at long last brought to light. Yes, I give myself up to holy raving. I mockingly defy all mortals with this open confession: I have robbed the golden vessels of the Egyptians to make out of them a tabernacle for my God, far from the frontiers of Egypt. If you forgive me, I shall rejoice. If you are angry, I shall bear it. Behold, I have cast the dice, and I am writing a book either for my contemporaries, or for posterity.[93]

Kepler was thrilled. His harmonic ratios were intimately linked to perfect polygons by a complex set of rules. The rules only allowed for equilateral polygons inscribed in a circle and only for those that could be constructed by compass and ruler. From this set he derived harmonics in politics, metaphysics, physiognomy, and whatever else came to his imaginative mind.

## The Epitome (1620)

Two years after he completed his book, the *Harmony of the World*, Kepler wrote the *Epitome*, the most systematic exposition of the cosmos since Ptolemy's *Almagest*. In it he refined some of his earlier views and explained how the magnetic force of the Sun interacts with the planets. He suggested that the Sun's magnetic force sweeps the planets along their orbits acting like the center of a vortex with "a raging current which tears all the planets, and perhaps all the celestial ether, from West to East." [94]

The tidal force of magnetism was only one of Kepler's many ideas which did not survive. That is not to deny that Kepler had some of the right ideas. For example, he defined gravity as "the mutual bodily tendency toward unity or contact, so that the Earth draws a stone much more than the stone draws the Earth." Extrapolating to celestial bodies, he wrote: "If the attractive force of the Moon reaches down to the Earth, it follows that the attractive force of the Earth, all the more, extends to the Moon and even farther."[95]Not only that, but he defined gravity even more precisely as being proportionate to the mass of the body. And he correctly attributed the ocean tides to the gravitational force of the Moon. Yet, when he elaborated on the impact of the Sun on the planets he chose to ignore the force of gravity.

Kepler's imaginative mind produced many ideas. He embedded them with all his other findings in flowery descriptions of intricate detail. He tested some of his key hypotheses with extraordinary care against Tycho's precise astronomical observations. Others he did not. Among all of them, three survived as Kepler's Laws (Figure 10.6). The three formed the foundation on which the new structure of the cosmos was to be built.

*Rudolphine Tables (1627)*

Despite his contemporaries' criticisms of his work, Kepler ignored them and went on. He finished the long-awaited *Rudolphine Tables (Tabulae Rudolphinae)*. He was fortunate enough to have heard of John Napier's invention of logarithms. Not having access to them he constructed his own by a somewhat different method. It very much lightened his computational burden. In the case of Mars, where errors of earlier tables of astronomy approached 5°, Kepler's were down to one half of 1°.[96]

The *Rudolphine Tables* contained Tycho's atlas of 777 stars expanded by Kepler to 1005, tables of optical refraction and logarithms, and the longitudes of major urban centers. Since the *Tables* were named after Emperor Rudolph II, Kepler tried to recoup the printing costs from the Imperial Court, now in Vienna. The Crown still owed him 6299 florins, but he only received enough to cover the cost of the paper. Having lost a whole year on horseback and on foot in search of funding, he had to pay for the printing out of his own pocket.[97]

Further delays followed. All protestants in Linz were ordered to convert to the Catholic faith. Kepler refused to convert, was excommunicated but allowed to stay. The Lutherans rose in revolt and soldiers laid siege to Linz. The peasantry set fire to the town, burning down 70 houses. Printed pages of the *Tables* went up in flames, but Kepler managed to save the manuscript. He escaped from Linz to Ulm on the Danube and had the *Tables* printed there. They were finally completed in

1627. He left Ulm with the first copies for the book market in Frankfurt.[98] Attractive teaching positions were offered to him in Italy and France, and Sir Henry Wotton invited him to England but Kepler did not accept.[99]

*His Last Days*

Instead of traveling to England Kepler contributed to the *Ephemerides*, an annual publication that provided information on the position of the planets. It was useful and in great demand by astronomers and astrologers of his day. When time allowed, he worked on a science fiction story about a journey to the Moon. He entitled it *Somnium (A Dream)*. The story was published posthumously in 1634. It was incomplete.

In 1630, Kepler took ill with fever. Health practitioners bled him. His fever continued to rise and preachers administered the last rites. He died on November 15, 1630. The epitaph on his tombstone read:

> I measured the skies, now the shadows I measure
> Sky-bound was the mind, earth-bound the body rests.[100]

Kepler's burying place was destroyed during the 30-year war and his bones were scattered. Only the epitaph on the tombstone, which he had written for himself, remained.[101]

Tycho de Brahe had brought unprecedented precision to astronomical observation. Kepler discovered the Three Laws that described the planetary orbits, the motion of the planets, and their distances from the Sun with unequaled accuracy. For the first time and forever, the principle of Aristotelian circular orbits, accepted by astronomers for over a thousand years, had been replaced by elliptical orbits. It was the beginning of the new science, founded on careful observation and exacting quantitative analysis. With his Three Laws, Kepler had shown how the planets moved around the Sun, what needed to be done was to explain why they moved according to these Laws. As revealed in Chapter 12, this challenge was met by Sir Isaac Newton.[102]

## Appendix A

To determine the Mars-to-Sun distance Kepler applied two trigonometric rules: the Sine-to-Side Rule and the Cosine Rule.[103] The Sine-to-Side Rule enabled him to find the length of a third side when the length of two sides and three angles were known. In Diagram 5 of Figure 3, for example, Kepler found the Earth-to-Mars distance by this method. The Cosine Rule is an extension of the Theorem of Pythagoras (Chapter 3, Figure 2.3). It states that in a rectangular triangle the squares over the two shorter sides equal the square over the longest side. The Cosine Rule generalizes this by extending it from rectangular triangles to all triangles. This allowed Kepler to determine the Mars-to-Sun distance as in Diagram 6 of Figure 10.3. In this appendix the proof of both rules is illustrated in Equations A10.1 and A10.2.

## Appendix B

In his attempt to find the areas "swept out by planets orbiting the Sun" Kepler summed up their distances from the Sun. As shown here in the text and illustrated in Figure 10.4, this method is valid for areas within the same circle. It can be also be extended, with some modifications, to circles of different size.

*Size of Sectors Within a Circle*

When two sectors are inscribed in a circle, their relative size can be compared by the sum of their distances measured from the center to the circumference, provided the distances intersect the circle at equally spaced intervals (Figure 10.4, Diagram 1). In Equation B10.1, the areas of two sectors $A_1$ and $A_2$ are determined by their ratio $A_1/A_2$. The two sectors are composed of $n$ and $m$ smaller triangular areas, each of them having the same base ($b$) and the same height. For example, in Equation B10.1, Area $A_1$ has two triangles ($n=2$) and Area $A_2$ has eight triangles ($m = 8$). The equation shows that the ratio of their areas $A_1/A_2$ equals the ratio of the sums of their distances $n_1/n_2$ from center to circumference.

Equation A10.1: The Sine Rule

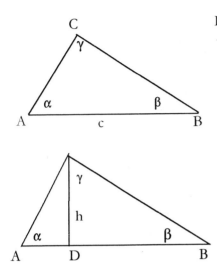

Diagram 1: The Sine Rule links the three sides a, b, c of triangles ABC to the corresponding sine values sin α, sin β , sin γ as in

$$\frac{a}{\sin\ \alpha} = \frac{b}{\sin\beta} = \frac{c}{\sin\ \gamma}$$

Diagram 2: To prove, subdivide the triangle ABC into two rectangular triangles ADC and BDC so that the distance CD = h. Then form the ratios

$$\sin\alpha\ =\ h/b, \quad h\ =\ b\ \sin\beta\ ; \quad \sin\beta\ =\ h/a, \quad h\ =\ \alpha\ \sin\ \alpha$$

*so that* $\dfrac{\sin\ \alpha}{a} = \dfrac{h}{a\ b} = \dfrac{\sin\beta}{b}$ *and* $\dfrac{\sin\ \alpha}{a} = \dfrac{\sin\beta}{b} = \dfrac{\sin\ \gamma}{c}$

*and, therefore,* $\dfrac{a}{\sin\ \alpha} = \dfrac{b}{\sin\beta} = \dfrac{c}{\sin\ \gamma}\ .$

*Applying the Sine Rule to* $SE_1E_2$ *in Diagram 4 of Figure* 10.3 *yields*

$$\frac{\sin s_0}{E_1\ E_2} = \frac{\sin\ s_1}{1\ A.U.} \quad \textit{and, therefore,} \quad E_1E_2\ =\ 1\ A.U.\ \frac{\sin\ s_0}{\sin\ s_1}.$$

*Next, applying, the Sine Rule to* $ME_1E_2$ *in Figure* 10.3, *Diagram* 5 *yields*

$$\frac{\sin e_1}{ME_2} = \frac{\sin m_o}{E_1\ E_2} \quad \textit{and, therefore,} \quad ME_2\ =\ E_1E_2\ \frac{\sin e_1}{\sin m_o}.$$

Equation A10.2: The Cosine Rule

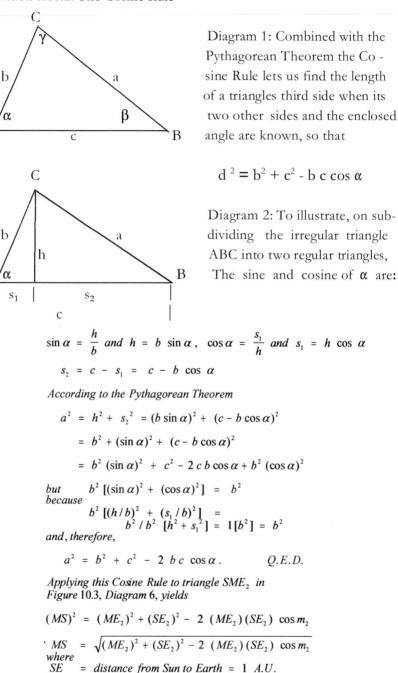

Diagram 1: Combined with the Pythagorean Theorem the Co - sine Rule lets us find the length of a triangles third side when its two other sides and the enclosed angle are known, so that

$$d^2 = b^2 + c^2 - b\,c\cos\alpha$$

Diagram 2: To illustrate, on sub-dividing the irregular triangle ABC into two regular triangles, The sine and cosine of $\alpha$ are:

$$\sin\alpha = \frac{h}{b} \ \text{and} \ h = b\sin\alpha, \quad \cos\alpha = \frac{s_1}{h} \ \text{and} \ s_1 = h\cos\alpha$$

$$s_2 = c - s_1 = c - b\cos\alpha$$

*According to the Pythagorean Theorem*

$$a^2 = h^2 + s_2{}^2 = (b\sin\alpha)^2 + (c - b\cos\alpha)^2$$

$$= b^2 + (\sin\alpha)^2 + (c - b\cos\alpha)^2$$

$$= b^2(\sin\alpha)^2 + c^2 - 2cb\cos\alpha + b^2(\cos\alpha)^2$$

*but because*   $b^2[(\sin\alpha)^2 + (\cos\alpha)^2] = b^2$

$$b^2[(h/b)^2 + (s_1/b)^2] =$$
$$b^2/b^2\,[h^2 + s_1{}^2] = 1[b^2] = b^2$$

*and, therefore,*

$$a^2 = b^2 + c^2 - 2bc\cos\alpha. \qquad Q.E.D.$$

*Applying this Cosine Rule to triangle $SME_2$ in Figure 10.3, Diagram 6, yields*

$$(MS)^2 = (ME_2)^2 + (SE_2)^2 - 2(ME_2)(SE_2)\cos m_2$$

$$MS = \sqrt{(ME_2)^2 + (SE_2)^2 - 2(ME_2)(SE_2)\cos m_2}$$

*where*
SE  = *distance from Sun to Earth* = 1 *A.U.*

Equation B10.1: Size of Sectors Within a Circle

$$\frac{A_1}{A_2} = \frac{\sum\limits_{1}^{n} a_{1i}}{\sum\limits_{1}^{m} a_{2j}} = \frac{n(\frac{1}{2} r h)}{m(\frac{1}{2} r h)} = \frac{n r}{m r} = \frac{\sum\limits_{1}^{n} r}{\sum\limits_{1}^{m} r}$$

$$i = 1,2 \qquad j = 1, \dots ,8$$

$$n = 2 \qquad m = 8 \quad r = 5 \quad h = 0.01$$

$$\frac{2 \ (\frac{1}{2}) \ 5 \ (0.01)}{8 \ (\frac{1}{2}) \ 5 \ (0.01)} = \frac{10}{40}$$

Equation B10.2: Relative Size of Sectors in Two Different Circles

$$\frac{A_1}{A_2} = \frac{n_1 \, a_1}{n_2 \, a_2} = \frac{n_1 \, \frac{1}{2} b_1 \, r_1}{n_2 \, \frac{1}{2} b_2 \, r_2} = \frac{n_1 \, b_1 \, r_1}{n_2 \, b_2 \, r_2}$$

$$\frac{n_1}{n_2} = 1 \qquad \frac{b_2}{b_1} = \frac{r_2}{r_1} = p$$

$$\frac{A_1}{A_2} = \frac{b_1 \, r_1}{p \, b_1 \, p \, r_1} = \frac{1}{p^2} = \frac{r_1^2}{r_2^2} \text{ but if } n_1 \neq n_2 \text{, then}$$

$$n_2 \, r_1 = n_1 \, r_2 \text{, so that } A_1 = A_2 \text{.}$$

*Size of Sectors Within Circles of Different Size*

Kepler estimated sectors of different sizes inscribed in a circle by adding the radiuses or, as he put it, by "summing up the distances." This works as long as all triangels are congruent, i.e., have identical base and height. In Equation B10.1, for example, the area $A_1$ consists of two triangles and area $A_2$ of 8 triangles, being all of the same size, and their areas are found by " summing the distances."

But if radius $r_1$ differs from $r_2$, the two areas differ by ratio of their radii squared $r_1^2/r_2^2$ provided $n_1 = n_2$. If they should differ they squared radii must be multiplied by the inverse ratio of their numbers so that $n_2 r_1^2 = n_1 r_2^2$ because only then $A_1 = A_2$ as shown in Equation B10.2.

Chapter 11

## GALILEO (1564–1642)

*Kepler's contemporary, Galileo (1610), directed the recently invented telescope at the sky and discovered the moons of Jupiter. In them he recognized a model of the planetary system in a smaller scale and saw Copernicus' ideas as optical realities. But it is Galileo's greater merit to have developed the principles of mechanics, which were applied by Newton (1687) to planetary orbits, thus bringing about the completion of the Copernican world system.*

Max Born[1]

Galileo was an Italian physicist, an astronomer, and a mathematician. Although he did not invent the telescope, he is probably best known as the first man to study the skies with a telescope. He agreed with Copernicus that the Sun is at the center of the universe. Galileo's popularisation of the Copernican views brought him into conflict with academicians of his day and, later in life, with the Church. Eventually the Inquisition of the Church in Rome ordered him to recant his views.

Galileo is also recognized as the founder of modern mechanics and experimental physics. He broke away from Aristotelian verbal logic and reestablished mathematics as the logical base of the study of nature. By combining mathematics with physical experimentation Galileo formally derived the principles of the laws of motion. They were later embedded in Sir Isaac Newton's first two laws of motion.[2]

170

## Renaissance on the Wane in Italy

In Italy freedom of thought still prevailed. The arts flourished. Education was more advanced than in other European countries. Students from all over Europe came to Italy to study law, medicine, literature, and astronomy. Copernicus himself had taught mathematics at the University of Rome and astronomy at the University of Bologna. Nevertheless, science was slow to advance. The Renaissance had produced many outstanding artists but very few scientists.

In Galileo's lifetime the Renaissance was already on the wane. Political control of the continent had passed from Italy to Spain. Some Italian states had kept their own rulers, others came under the rule of Spanish viceroys or became Spanish protectorates. High taxes threatened industry and commerce. More seriously, the overland trade routes from the Far East to Europe had shifted to the sea, around the Cape of Good Hope and on to Spain. The freedom of thought of the previous centuries came to an end as the Church of Rome reacted nervously to the German Reformation, the religious movement that led to the establishment of the Protestant churches.[3]

## Galileo's Youth

Galileo was born in Pisa, Italy in 1564, the oldest of seven children. As was customary among the natives of Tuscany, his parents duplicated the family name for their first-born by naming him Galileo Galilei.[4] Little is known of his mother Giulia Ammannati and, what has become known through her letters, is not very flattering. His father, Vincensio Galileo, was a musician of originality who combined practice with theory. While Italy was still flourishing in arts, he was a musician and composer at the Court of Tuscany. Having studied music theory at Venice, he became interested in the revival of classical Greek music. He tried to shift away from the ornate choir music of the day to a combination of instrument and voice. This aroused a controversy over the abstract mathematical theory of music. Theory had stifled progress, the change in musical practice led to the creation of opera. It was a victory of practice over theory.[5]

As a youngster Galileo watched his father experiment. Studying the sounds produced by vibrating strings of different length and tension, his father had discovered a mathematical law that contradicted the traditional classical theory. Later in life Galileo recalled what his father had impressed on him in his youth: "To search for truth, no matter what others believe." In *A Dialogue on Ancient and Modern Music* his father had written: "I, on the contrary, wish to be allowed to raise questions freely and to answer without any adulation [of authorities] as becomes those who are truly in search of the truth."[6] Vincenzio's son Galileo had never forgotten and he lived by this credo.

*At the Jesuit Monastery*

When Galileo was 10 years old, his family moved from Pisa to Florence. At age 12, his father arranged for him to attend school at Santa Maria di Vallombrosa, a monastery run by Jesuit friars a few miles outside of Florence.[7] Surrounded by meadows, trees, and hills, it was safe from the dreadful plague that often struck people in the city during the first hot summer days. Life at the monastery followed a strict routine. Students rose at 5 a.m. After washing, dressing, morning prayers, and breakfast at 6:30 a.m., they went to classes. Prayers followed at midday, lunch at half past noon, rest until 2 p.m., back to afternoon lessons until 5 p.m., then evening prayers, supper, study until 9 p.m., then candles out, to bed and to sleep.[8]

It was an intensive training. Galileo learned to speak Latin fluently. He could read and write Greek, studied rhetoric, and wrote good poetry. His father was very proud that he did so well in school. Galileo enjoyed the quiet and studious life. He liked it so much that he wanted to join the monks as a novice, but his father was opposed to it. He wanted him to study medicine and had scraped together enough money to let Galileo enrol at the faculty of medicine of the University of Pisa.[9]

*University*

Galileo entered university at age 17 and, following his father's wish, studied medicine and philosophy. In 1583 Galileo attended some lectures on geometry that inspired him to study *Euclid's Elements* on his own. While at the university, Ostilio Ricci, the court mathematician, happened to recognize Galileo's talents and urged Vincenzio to let his son study mathematics. Concerned about the meager prospects of ever earning a decent living as a mathematician, his father insisted that Galileo complete his medical courses first. Although medicine was a lucrative field, Galileo neglected the study of medicine and, instead, concentrated on mathematics and philosophy.[10] In 1585 he left the university without having fulfilled the requirements for an advanced degree.[11] He had already distinguished himself in pure and applied mathematics. Admittedly, mathematics would never make him rich but he found it much more rewarding than medicine.

*Teaching Positions*

To earn a living, Galileo privately instructed students in mathematics. He wrote copious lecture notes dealing with conventional physics and cosmology. At the time his notes contained no trace of originality. The Copernican system was mentioned but rejected. As yet, he did not quarrel with Aristotle's physics. During this time he wrote his first original treatise on hydrostatic balance, a characteristic feature of fluid mechanics. It was a mixture of Archimedean theory and practical application. He also began his first writings on motion, which he was to follow up in later years and which would become his most important contribution to physics.[12]

*Finding Centers of Gravity*

Toward the end of 1587, at age 23, Galileo discovered how to detect the centers of gravity of solids. Going beyond Archimedes, that earned him his first international recognition. He had hoped that, on the strength of this achievement, he would be given the chair of mathematics at the University of Bologna, but it was awarded to someone else who already had several books to his credit. Among those who had read Galileo's treatise was the Marquis Guidobaldo del Monte, who himself had written a book on mechanics. He found Galileo's discovery most interesting and became his lifelong friend and patron. So did Christopher Clavius, a mathematician and astronomer of the Jesuit college in Rome.[13]

By 1588, leaders of the literary circles of Florence had become aware of Galileo's mathematical talents. They invited him to address the Academy of Florence on the *Divine Comedy* of Dante Alighieri. Considered by some as one of the greatest epics, Dante described heaven and hell. He envisioned heaven as a paradise with the glory of God glowing throughout the universe and the sounds of celestial music accompanying the light from the revolving spheres of the planets and stars. He saw hell as an inferno where the damned were exposed to the evils and horrors of devilish forces. Dante cleverly wove into his narrative certain aspects of nature, astronomy, alchemy, and medicine that reflected the state of science of the day. Asked to elaborate on the geography and mathematics of location, size, and arrangement of Dante's hell, Galileo impressed the audience so much that the head of the literary academy later helped him to secure professorships at the universities of Pisa and Padua.[14]

The chair of mathematics at the University of Pisa was given to Galileo in 1589. It was a minor and poorly paid position. As a newcomer he received only 60 florins per year, less than most other professors were paid.[15]

## Rebellion

While at Pisa he completed the manuscript *On Motion (De motu)*. It was a commentary on Ptolemy's *Almagest*. Although he was already acquainted with the work of Copernicus, he still accepted the Earth as the center of the universe. However, in several chapters *On Motion* he attacked Aristotle's physics.

Specifically, he questioned the validity of the statement that the speed of falling bodies (made of the same material) varied with their weight. If Aristotle was right a 10-pound weight should fall to the ground 10 times faster than a 1-pound weight: the greater the weight the faster the fall. Aristotle was wrong and so were all the professors who perpetuated such misconceptions. High-spirited as he was, Galileo got himself into arguments with members of his faculty.[16] And , being popular with his students he could not resist publicly displaying his discoveries. With a flair for dramatics he invited those who doubted his word, professors and students alike, to see for themselves. To show that Aristotle's idea about free fall was wrong, Galileo dropped cannon balls of different weights off the Leaning Tower of Pisa. Released simultaneously from high up, the balls hit the ground at the same time. Some biographers claim that this event is merely myth and that it never happened,[17] others present evidence in support of it.[18] However, all agree that Galileo showed by experiment that an object's weight did not affect its rate of fall.

Galileo was not the first to suggest that Aristotle was wrong. In 1533, Benedetti, a student of the famous mathematician Tartaglia, had asserted that all falling bodies dropped at the same speed. Some 50 years later, in 1586, the Flemish engineer Stevin published the results of his experiments confirming it too. Galileo did not publish *On Motion* but circulated it privately. Yet, despite this evidence academic philosophers still considered Aristotle to be the divine guide.

Galileo could not resist making fun of the academicians. Once he had started, he went further. He joked about the administration's directive that academic gowns should be worn at all times, asking whether it really added anything to the university's prestige. Would it not be more honest to walk nakedly and judge the professors by their achievements? And what about the clergy? Did their long cassocks make it easier for them to kick others before they saw them move a leg? Galileo did not write in Latin but in a Florentine dialect. Use of the everyday language of the people made his scathing satire even more popular among the students. Inevitably, these breaches of etiquette undermined the presumptuous arrogance of the academicians and the noble bearing of the clergy and made those who suffered at his ridicule look for revenge.[19]

### Appointment at Pisa Not Renewed

Galileo had found a few close friends among his colleagues at the University of Pisa but he had antagonized many others. His attack on Aristotle did not endear him to the Aristotelians or the clergy. Moreover, he had criticized a scheme to improve the harbor of Livorno and thereby had created some powerful enemies at the Court of Tuscany. When his appointment at the university came to a close, he had good reason to believe that he would not be granted a second term. He was right. Having little choice, he went home, nearly penniless.

## Change of Course

Then one day, after a long wait, a special messenger arrived with a letter from the Marquis del Monte letting him know that the chair of mathematics at the University of Padua was vacant. The Marquis had recommended him to the board of governors. Although a professor of the University of Bologna had also applied for the chair, the Marquis was certain that if Galileo hastened at once for a personal interview the position would be his. Within hours Galileo was in the saddle and on his way. After two days of a fast ride, he could see the rooftops of Padua. From Padua a friend took him by carriage to Venice.

Friends of the Marquis had arranged for an interview with the members of the board. Three learned members dressed in velvet robes questioned Galileo for an hour. On the strength of this interview, his impressive knowledge, and on the recommendation of the Marquis, they appointed him professor of mathematics and astronomy of the University of Padua. In 1592, at age 28, Galileo left for Padua a happy man.[20]

Padua was governed by the State of Venice. It surpassed all other Italian states in tolerance. The university benefitted from its enlightened government, at times enrolling as many as 8000 students. It was re-nowned throughout Europe for its school of medicine and in Italy it was second only to Bologna in mathematics.

The campus was surrounded by a literary community. Visiting dignitaries, scholars, and men of letters gathered at the home of an erudite businessman, Pinelli, who owned an astonishing collection of some 80,000 books and manuscripts. For a time Galileo lodged with Pinelli. Very likely it was at Pinelli's home that Galileo first met Friar Paolo Sarpi and Cardinal Roberto Bellarmino. Both were to play important roles later in his life. Although they did not share Galileo's views, both highly respected him. Apart from newly-found friends and admirers, the appointment at the University of Padua had another beneficial effect. His salary was now 180 florins, triple what he had made at the University of Pisa.[21]

At the University of Padua, Galileo delivered lectures on geometry, astronomy, military engineering, and fortification. He published treatises on mechanics, spherical geometry, and military fortifications.[22] On *Questions of Mechanics* he wrote:

> The science of mechanics is that faculty which teaches the reasons and gives us the causes of marvelous effects that we see made by various instruments, moving, and raising very great weights with little force. We shall begin by theorizing on the nature of the primary and simplest instruments. There are five, that is, lever, capstan, pulley, screw and wedge, which are in a way all reducible to one only, the balance.[23]

It was a novel idea to reduce various aspects of mechanics to one axiom. Galileo added to it his newly discovered quantifiable relations between force, weight, distance, speed, and time.

### Invention of the Thermoscope

A year after his arrival in Padua (in 1593) he invented a new medical device. As a student of medicine, he had learned that for the diagnosis of illness, changes in the patient's temperature and pulse were important indicators of a patient's status of health. Yet, how was it possible to get accurate readings on either? Should there not be a way of measuring temperature on a scale accurate enough to detect small changes?

Knowing that air expanded when heated, he asked a glass blower at the university to draw out a very thin glass tube and then weld it onto a hollow glass bulb at one end. While still warm, he had him dip the open end of the tube into a bowl of water. As the glass cooled off, the air in the bulb contracted, and the water rose up in the tube. He then had the thin end of the tube quickly welded shut. When holding the glass bulb in hand, the air inside the bulb warmed up, expanded, and made the water rise in the glass tube. Marking off equal intervals with a file, small changes in temperature could now be observed.

Galileo called the appliance a *thermoscope* from the Greek *thermae* (θέρμη), meaning heat, fever; and from *skopain* (σκοπεῖν), meaning to watch, observe). In principle it worked like a modern-day mercury thermometer, but since neither the diameter of the glass tube nor the temperature at the time of welding was tightly controlled, it did not give very accurate readings. Surprisingly, Galileo did not refine his thermoscope. It was not widely used as a thermometer in everyday medicine until Santorio of the Paduan Medical School improved on it in later years. Perhaps Galileo lost interest or something else attracted his attention.[24]

Galileo was an entertaining professor with many novel ideas. His classes were well attended. Still, his salary was not generous enough to take care of all his expenses. In 1591 his father died and Galileo felt duty-bound to support his siblings, paying for his sisters' dowries and helping his financially irresponsible brother.[25] The University of Padua attracted young noblemen from other Italian states and from foreign countries. Galileo privately tutored some of them. Their fees augmented his salary and helped cover the expenses that family relatives piled on him. Like Kepler, Galileo cast horoscopes to make extra money.[26]

*Invention of the Computing Compass*
During his fourth year at the University of Padua, Galileo invented an instrument that functioned like a circular slide rule. The engravings on the disc could be used to compute proportions, square roots and cube roots. Applicable to military uses, business transactions, and currency exchange, many calculations could be performed with great ease. Galileo's computing gadget won great acclaim. Orders for it came in great numbers, some from foreign countries. He hired an instrument maker to meet the demand. Overall, as many as a 300 may have been marketed, a few of them made of silver and gold. As money came in, it eased Galileo's financial difficulties and enabled him to move into a larger home with a beautiful garden. [27]

*Contact with Kepler*
Galileo's lecture notes indicated almost no interest in astronomy before 1595. It was not until Galileo attempted an explanation of the ocean tides that he first showed an interest in planetary motions.[28] Around this time he acquainted himself with Copernican theory, published in Germany as a

treatise on the "*Revolutions of the Celestial Orbs*" in 1543 (see Chapter 8). Dedicated to Pope Paul III, it countered Aristotelian theory and the astronomy of Ptolemy.[29]

When Kepler, who had thoroughly studied the Copernican system, sent him a copy of his latest book in 1597, Galileo responded:

> I promise to read your book in tranquility, certain to find the most admirable things in it, and this I shall do the more gladly as I adopted the teaching of Copernicus many years ago, and his point of view enables me to explain many phenomena of nature which certainly remain inexplicable according to the more current hypotheses. I have written many arguments in support of him and in refutation of the opposite view—which, however, so far I have not dared to bring into the public light, frightened by the fate of Copernicus himself, our teacher, who, though he acquired immortal fame with some, is yet to an infinite multitude of others (for such is the number of fools) an object of ridicule and derision. I would certainly dare to publish my reflections at once if more people like you existed; as they don't, I shall refrain from doing so. [30]

Kepler responded: "With your clever secretive manner you underline, by your example, the warning that one should retreat before the ignorance of the world. Have faith, Galilei, and come forward."[31] Kepler did not ask what phenomena of nature Galileo was exploring but guessed correctly that it must be the ocean tides.

### Economic, Social, and Spiritual Changes

By the year 1600 the world had changed. Spain had been the greatest military power in Europe, but in 1588 it lost its entire navy in the war against England. England and Holland became the great sea powers. Ships sailed across the Atlantic to the New World. Dutch vessels sailed to India and the East Indies and brought home spices.

The rest of Europe split into small states. Kings and dukes had been subservient to the Pope until many of them joined the Lutheran Protestant movement. By the turn of the century they had become a powerful political and spiritual force. To the Catholic Church, Protestantism was heresy. The rise of monarchical powers, Protestants' opposition to the Catholic

Church, exploration of new continents; the inflow of gold, monetary inflation, higher prices and impoverishment; and political and religious wars, were all part of a social and spiritual upheaval. To prevent the disintegration of its spiritual and economic powers, the Church of Rome reinforced the Inquisition. In every state faithful to the Pope, the Vatican in Rome appointed Inquisitors. They searched out, questioned, put on trial, and often tortured the suspected, accused infidels.[32]

### *Church and University Against the New Astronomy*

In astronomy it was as if the writings of Aristotle had become part of the holy scriptures. To say that Aristotle was wrong was like asserting that the Bible was wrong. In this respect the Lutherans were as adamant as the Roman Catholics. They objected strongly to the Copernican system which cast doubt on the truth of biblical scriptures. When Martin Luther first heard of the Copernican system, he publically ridiculed it. Referring to Copernicus, he said: "That fool will reverse the entire Ars Astronomiae; but according to the scripture Joshua bade the Sun and not the Earth to stand still."[33] Luther and his followers believed in the scriptures verbatim, whereas the Catholic Church reserved the right to interpretation. It seemed as if a solid Earth and a permanent celestial sphere offered the only safe refuge to humanity, faith, and Church.[34]

At the universities, philosophers did not object to the opposition of the Church. On the contrary, most of them were in favor of the Aristotelian philosophy. Not versed in mathematics they dismissed the Copernican theory as cosmic speculation. Nor did the official astronomers endorse the Copernican theory. They favored the geocentric system, not necessarily the Ptolemaic system of antiquity, but the modified system of the great astronomer Tycho de Brahe. Following Copernicus, Tycho had the five planets circle the Sun but unlike Copernicus he had the Sun together with the planets orbit the Earth (see Chapter 9). His system was a compromise between the old and the new.[35]

Throughout these times of change, Galileo remained at Padua and continued with his teaching. Although he never married, he lived with Marina Gamba, a Venetian woman who bore him two daughters and a son between 1600 and 1606. Apart from this liaison, his financial situation was made difficult because he had promised to provide a generous dowry for his younger sister who had married in 1602. His brother continued to borrow money from him but never repaid it. Eventually Galileo also supported his brother's family. To cope with these financial demands Galileo increased his private teaching, borrowed against his salaries, and obtained advances. During these years he spent much of his time on solving practical problems and dedicated very little of it to theory.[36]

*Invention of the Pulsilogium*

In 1602, Galileo revised his earlier treatise on mechanics and motion. His new work produced new insights that became the cornerstone of further developments. As part of the revisions he elaborated on the pendulum, leading to the invention of the pulsilogium, a new medical device.[37]

Years earlier Galileo had discovered that a pendulum takes equal time from one swing to the next. The story is told that Galileo observed this "isochronous" (from the Greek *isos* (ἴσος) meaning equal and *chronos* (χρόνος) meaning duration) movement of the pendulum in the cathedral of Pisa in 1582. He noticed that as the sexton of the cathedral lit the oil lamps of the huge chandelier, it started swinging gently back and forth. Not being captivated by the priest's sermon of the day Galileo timed the duration of the swings against the beats of his own pulse. Whether the swings of the chandelier extended over a longer arc at the beginning or a shorter arc towards the end, each swing accounted for the same number of heart beats. For Galileo it was an exciting discovery.[38]

Timing the swings of the pendulum against his own pulse was the next best thing to a stopwatch. In his day mechanical clocks were not only cumbersome and very expensive but also unreliable. He knew from his university courses in medicine that sickness and fever accelerated the heartbeat of the patient. Convinced that the movements of the pendulum were regular, even more regular than his own heartbeat, he decided to apply the inverse: instead of timing the swings of the pendulum against his pulse, he timed his pulse against the motion of the pendulum. He attached a metal bob to a string, fastened the string to the end of a stick, and let it swing. By unwinding the string he could lengthen the pendulum and make it swing slower. Marking off on the stick the length of string that matched the normal pulse he could time a patient's heart beat with greater precision than ever before. The medical profession quickly adopted Galileo's "pulsilogium." It was a boon to the diagnosis of disease.[39]

*The Supernova of 1604*

Out of no where, suddenly in October 1604, a new star appeared in the heavens. Night after night people could see the bright new star. Everyone was puzzled by it. Some were afraid it was a sign from God that a terrible war was coming, others feared that it was the foreboding of another plague. Astrologers predicted the end of the world was near.[40] However, Galileo reasoned that it was a repeat of an earlier event, a new star, similar to the rare supernova the astronomer Tycho de Brahe had seen some 30 years earlier and described as a Stella Nova (new star).

Galileo decided to give a public lecture on the new star in the Aula, the largest hall of the university. People crowded in until no standing room was left. Galileo claimed that this star had always been in the same spot though it had not been visible before. He confidently predicted that it would burn itself out and within the next two years become invisible again.

His lecture caused a scandal on campus. The Aristotelians disagreed with him. Professor Cremonini was the leading advocate among them. He quoted from the books of classical astronomy that the heavens were perfect and immutable. Stars could never come and go. Others joined the chorus of opposition. How dare Galileo call them liars? Yet, 18 months later the new star, having remained in precisely the same spot, disappeared, not to be seen again. The people calmed down. For them it did not mean the end of the world, it was just one less worry.[41]

## Galileo's New Theory of Motion

After this event Galileo was preoccupied with examining the phenomenon of accelerating motion in a systematic way. He decided to analyze it by combining the experimental approach with the logic of mathematics, a novel idea that had never been tried before. Timing the acceleration of falling bodies seemed impossible because the timing devices of his day were simply not accurate enough to measure variations in speed.[42]

Galileo believed that Pythagoras was right in his claim that mathematics could best explain nature. For centuries astronomers had managed to predict the course of the planets in the heavens; should it not be possible to discover the mathematical laws of motion on Earth? It was intuitively obvious to Galileo that the constant duration of a pendulum's swings could be mathematically explained. And if he could tell how fast a projectile moved and how its speed changed along its course, he could predict the path of a cannonball. That knowledge could revolutionize military battle tactics.[43]

Yet, it had been impossible to observe if and how an object, dropped from high-up to the ground, changed speed on its way down. Galileo succeeded with an ingenious experimental set up. He "diluted the force of gravity."[44] Instead of timing the acceleration of bodies in free fall he studied their motion along an inclined plane. This enabled him to measure the distance a ball traversed during consecutive time intervals. Historically, it was the crucial first step in the direction of experimental physics.

Galileo discovered the "Law of Free Fall" by letting polished brass balls run down a straight channel of a gently sloping wooden beam. Casual observation was not good enough for him. He was looking for greater precision. To attain it, he marked off the progress of the brass balls down the runway at evenly spaced intervals. He may have timed the motion by use of a water clock, in his day perhaps the most accurate timing device, or even with the pulsilogium of his own design. By measuring the distances from the starting point at successive time intervals, he found that if during the 1st time interval the ball advanced by one unit, then it advanced during the 2nd by three units, during the 3rd by five units, and during the 4th by seven (Figure 11.1, Diagrams 1 to 4).

When he added the successive distances they produced the series *1, 1+3=4, 1+3+5=9,* and *1+3+5+7=16.* Galileo concluded that at successive time intervals the speeds of a uniformly accelerating object were represented by the uneven numbers, and the cumulative distances were represented by the squares of the corresponding time intervals.[45] It must have delighted him that the law of uniformly accelerated motion matched the figurate$_g$ square numbers of Pythagoras (see Chapter 2). Clearly, mathematics did apply to motion.

Galileo's experimental results contradicted Aristotle's theorem that the distance of falling bodies increased in direct proportion with time. Galileo repeated the experiment, varied it, and verified his findings. In his own words:

> This operation being precisely established, we made the same ball descend only one-quarter the length of this channel, and the time of its descent being measured, this was found always to be precisely one half the other. Next making the experiment for other lengths, [he] repeated [it] a full hundred times, the spaces were always found to be to one another as the squares of time.[46]

Galileo observed that as long as the ball descended on the inclined plane, it accelerated. He understood that the speed of a body in motion changed only if acted on by a force. Rolling down the inclined plane, the force of gravity continually accelerated its speed. If he lowered or raised the plane, he reduced or increased the rate of acceleration, but it did not alter the basic laws he derived from the experiments.

Once the ball reached the level plane it continued at a nearly constant speed. Galileo realized it would continue at a constant speed, without any additional force, if the surface was perfectly smooth and frictionless. As he saw it, a body maintained its course at constant speed, without the addition of force.[47] This idea also clearly contradicted Aristotle's contention that force is needed to keep an object moving.

*Geometric Representation*

Galileo analyzed this accelerated motion by geometrically interpreting his experimental results. His diagrams incorporated time, speed, and distance.[48] They consisted of rectangular boxes, piled on top of each other in a triangular pattern, each box representing one unit of distance measured along the inclined plane. From the area fashioned in this way, Galileo deduced how time, acceleration, and distance are linked together (Figure 11.2).

From his experiments and analysis Galileo formulated the Laws of Motion:

1. The velocity[49] of a falling and uniformly accelerating object is pro
   portionate to the time of the fall, and
2. The distance of the fall is proportionate to time of the fall
   squared.[50]

In his research on motion, Galileo went further. He also demonstrated that projectiles followed a compound trajectory of two motions, a uniform forward motion and an accelerated downward motion.[51]

## Astronomical Discoveries

Apart from his teaching obligations Galileo kept working on his treatise of natural motions. In July of 1609 he took a trip in Venice to visit his friend Sarpi, who told him about a most remarkable Dutch invention—an instrument that made distant objects appear close. As Galileo reported it:

> About ten months ago (May 1609) a report reached my ears that a certain Fleming had constructed a spyglass by means of which visible objects, though very distant from the eye of the observer, were distinctly seen as if nearby. Of this truly remarkable effect several stories were related, which some believed and others denied. A few days later the report was confirmed to me in a letter.[52]

Galileo was very excited. He immediately hurried back to Padua to see if he could build one himself. Familiar with the theory of refraction, Galileo had two lenses ground, both flat on one side but one being spherically convex and the other concave. He then mounted them on both ends of a tube made of lead, and found that the objects appeared three times closer and nine times larger.

### Use of the Telescope

When Galileo heard that a foreigner had just come through town who intended to offer such a "spyglass" at a very high price to the Venetian government, his friend Sarpi advised the government against buying it because Galileo was currently constructing a superior one. By changing the curvature of the lenses, Galileo was able to bring the distant objects nearly thirty times closer and enlarging them even more than ever before possible. Not only did he achieve this enormous increase in magnification power, but he managed to turn the image right-side up. Also he had the first tube fitted into a second so that he could adjust the distance between the lenses and thereby sharpen the focus. It made an excellent spyglass. He gave his new improved spyglass the scholarly name "telescope" (from the Greek words *tele* (τῆλε) for distant and *skopein* (σκοπεῖν) for peering, watching).[53]

The following month, in August, Galileo arrived with his new and more powerful telescope at the chief magistrate's palace in Venice, prepared for a demonstration. Curious crowds gathered in St. Mark's Square as rumors of the event spread. Soldiers in dress uniform opened a passageway from the palace to the Campanile of St. Mark. The Doge (chief magistrate) and the Dogessa Donato, followed by Galileo, his friends Sarpi and Pinelli carrying the telescope, the Doge's six councilors, ten judges and sixty senators slowly made their way to the Campanile. They climbed the 322 foot (98 m) bell tower. From the top they could overlook the harbor. While the official lookout reported no ships in sight, looking through the telescope the Doge himself could clearly see a far-out merchant ship approaching the Venetian harbor. It took nearly all afternoon for his Excellency and all the nobles to have their turn at the telescope. Hearing of their enthusiastic reports, the excited crowds slowly dispersed. The demonstration had been a splendid success. In one of his rare gestures of diplomacy, Galileo presented the telescope as a gift to the Doge.[54]

Following this event, the chief administrator of the university informed him that from this day on Galileo would be paid an annual salary of 1000 florins.[55] Moreover, he offered him a lifelong tenure as a professor at the University of Padua.

*Searching the Sky*

Pointing his telescope at the Moon, Galileo detected mountains and craters. Judging by the length of the shadows of the Moon's mountains, he estimated some of them reached heights of four to five miles (6.4-8 km). Where the Aristotelian philosophers believed to see a perfectly polished sphere, Galileo saw a sphere marred by enormous mountains and craters, quite similar to that of Earth.[56]

When he turned his telescope to the stars it struck him immediately that he had never seen so many stars. Where the ancient Greeks had identified the six stars of the Pleiades, he could see at least 30 others.[57] Where before the Milky Way was like a veil floating across the sky he saw an enormous multitude of individual stars crowded closely together. They all differed from the planets, however. Where the stars appeared brighter but no larger than seen with the naked eye, the planets emerged as perfectly formed little globes.

## Discovery of Jupiter's Satellites

What surprised Galileo even more was what he discovered when in January 1610, he directed his telescope at the planet Jupiter. He noticed several tiny stars close by. At first they appeared to be merely tiny stars but then he discovered that they followed the path of Jupiter from one day to the next. Directing his telescope at Jupiter night after night, he kept track of their motion. They followed the planet's path just like the Moon followed that of the Earth. Their light disappeared when they moved into Jupiter's shadow. They actually orbited the planet Jupiter like four satellites. Clearly, his latest discovery contradicted the age-old belief that all celestial bodies revolved around the Earth. If four satellites circled the planet Jupiter, then the Moon circling the Earth did not make the Earth the center of the universe. For Galileo this was the ultimate vindication of the Copernican system.[58]

## The Starry Messenger

By March of the same year, Galileo published his new discoveries in the *Starry Messenger*. He dedicated it to Cosimo de Medici, the Grand Duke of Tuscany, calling Jupiter's planets the Medicean stars. Again it was a good move. Soon after, he was invited to the Tuscan court by the Grand Duke Cosimo and appointed chief mathematician.[59] Although Padua had offered Galileo a generous increase in salary he accepted the offer of the grand duke and left for Florence. At heart, Galileo was still a Florentine.

Publication of the *Starry Messenger* created tremendous excitement among the literate public.[60] In his book Galileo not only described his astronomical discoveries but also the telescope that had never before been used for astronomical observations. He explained how the new instrument had the potential to revolutionize science. The English ambassador to Venice bought a copy of the book on the day of publication, read it and sent it off to the king of England with the promise to send him a telescope as well.[61] Overnight, the book made Galileo the best known astronomer in Italy and spread the fame of Italian science across Europe.

Among the public the *Starry Messenger* was an immediate success. Everyone wanted to look through a telescope. Galileo could have made a fortune if he had set up a workshop. Nobody could grind lenses with his precision. He did oversee the manufacture of telescopes he sent on to a few princes and powerful men who might help him advance his career, but he did not expand the enterprise.

However, not all of the reaction to his book was enthusiastic. Most of Italy's professional astronomers and professors of philosophy at the universities were not at all thrilled. They even belittled his findings. Some alleged Galileo's observations had to be optical illusions. Others sneered that it was all a fraud. In particular, Professor Cremonini quoted book after book to demonstrate that Galileo was not only wrong but that he was an outright liar.[62]

Galileo defended his discoveries against the slurs of his opponents. He delivered lectures at the universities and the time came when he believed he had convinced his audience and that he had even brought the enemies on his side. In a letter to the Tuscan secretary of state Galileo reported:

> The whole university turned out, and I so convinced and satisfied everyone that in the end those very leaders who at first were my sharpest critics and the most stubborn opponents of the things I had written, seeing their case to be desperate and in fact lost, stated publicly that they are not only persuaded but are ready to defend and support my teachings against any philosopher who dares to attack them.[63]

Galileo received further support from the Jesuit astronomers in Rome after they had gained access to a telescope. They even confirmed Galileo's telescopic observations.

*Discovery of Sunspots and Eclipses of Jupiter's Moons*

In 1613 Galileo published three "*Letters on Sunspots.*" He had discovered the sunspots two years earlier while on a visit to Rome. In these letters Galileo also referred to his discovery of eclipses of Jupiter's moons. He described them and predicted their occurrence. The timing of the eclipses of the moons of Jupiter, and his observations of the phases of the planet Venus, clinched for him the proof that the Copernican system was for real. Galileo did not give the full details of his findings. He kept his method of calculation secret, partly because he was reluctant to ruffle feathers in the Catholic Church.[64]

## The Opposition and Galileo's Defence

The silencing of Galileo toward the end of his career has often been interpreted as the inevitable conflict between religious belief and scientific fact. The Catholic pope and his counselors have been blamed for their confrontation with Galileo. In reality, it was the confrontation between the traditional opinion of the majority and the newly emerging views of a select minority, between Aristotelian tradition and scientific inquiry. Superstition and reluctance to accept new ideas, and not the opposition of the Church, hampered the progress of science. To gain a better understanding of the historical outcome of events around the conflict between new science and old ideas, we need to look at what went on behind the scenes.[65]

In 1614 a young, ambitious Dominican, Thomas Caccini, openly denounced Galileo and his followers. He asked how the Galileans could possibly teach that the Earth was moving and the Sun was standing still. Was it not one of God's great miracles to have halted the Sun in its daily orbit? How could they deny it? Aiming for a promotion to a better position in Rome, Caccini believed his attack against the Galileans would help him advance. His sermon created quite a stir. Although a Dominican Father at Rome apologized to Galileo for Caccini's behaviour, word of the incident was passed on to the Inquisition for further investigation. Caccini was called to testify but the case against Galileo was summarily dismissed for lack of evidence.[66]

Then a Carmelite theologian, Father Foscarini, tried to reconcile the Copernican astronomy with the Bible. He submitted his book to Cardinal Bellarmi. In a courteous reply the Cardinal recommended that the motions of the Sun and Earth should be treated by Father Foscarini and Galileo as a hypothetical system, not as reality. If that was done, the word of the Bible would not need to be reinterpreted, it would leave the astronomers free to advance their science, and would not lead to any further confrontation. Galileo adamantly refused to accept this compromise. He wrote back that it was not a religious but a scientific matter and that the word of the Bible should not be invoked in favour of one astronomy over another.[67]

What the Church found intolerable was that Galileo claimed the Earth revolved around the Sun. For more than a thousand years it had been taught that the Earth was at rest in the center of the universe while the Sun revolved around it. The philosophical school of thought that had dominated the middle ages went back to St. Anselm, a Benedictine Abbot. Born in Italy, he became the founder of Scholasticism. In 1077 he had written a theological treatise *Monologium*. Contrary to the custom of the day, when writing the *Monologium* he had not relied on the authority of the scriptures, but based his philosophy on logical deduction. In his proof of God's existence he asserted that God was perfection. He took the fact of the idea of perfection as the demonstration of God's existence and made it the standard of all comparisons.

To philosophers, especially those opposed to Galileo's Copernican views, it was obvious that removing the Earth from the center of the universe was not just imperfection but a wilful distortion of truth. Inevitably, they found the picture the poet Dante had painted of the universe far more convincing. As Dante in the *Divine Comedy* (published in 1320) had so aptly described it, the stars in heaven were closest to God, beyond a crystalline sphere was paradise, and all was perfect. Imperfection prevailed on Earth, sinners were condemned to the fires of hell, deep inside the Earth, farthest removed from God. Followers of modern science may look at Dante's *Divine Comedy* as a quaint model of the universe, yet its astronomy was based on the Ptolemaic *Almagest*, which had served them so well for many centuries.

*Arguments Against the Motion of the Earth*

More plausible arguments could be raised against Galileo's claims. If the Earth really moved, why was nobody aware of it? Spinning around its axis once a day, its velocity at the equator would be more than 1000 miles per hour (1609 km per hour). And if, in addition, it orbited the Sun once a year, it raced through space at an enormous velocity (67,000 miles per hour or 108,000 km). If it were really true, should the winds on Earth not blow continuously? Should not everybody be blown off their feet? Would not everything be swept away? Yet as anyone could plainly see, all is at rest. The grains grow upright in the fields and the trees stand tall in the forests. If an arrow is shot straight up in the air, it comes down close by. If a rock is dropped from a great height, it hits the ground below and does not land miles away or never even hit the ground.[68] Does not common sense tell that it must be so because the Earth is at rest? [69]

The arguments against Galileo's claims raised a much more in-triguing and broader question, still valid today, of how anyone knows when a scientific model describes reality or when it is an abstract mathematical construct?[70] While today no astronomer would doubt for a minute that the Sun is really at the center of the solar system, one must not rule out the possibility that a new and better description of the cosmos will be discovered in the future. Scientific theories can capture some element of reality, but it is questionable whether they can ever deliver the full truth. To quote a modern scientist, Niels Bohr, "Physics is not about how the world is, it is about what we can say about the world."[71]

*The Reaction of the Catholic Church*

Galileo was convinced that he only needed to elaborate on his views to persuade sceptics of the reality of the Copernican solar system. He circulated a manuscript and visited officials of the Church of Rome. Pope Paul V (reigned from 1605–1621) was not in the mood to see Galileo and to argue with him about the motions of the Sun, Moon, or Earth. He had no wish to give the Lutheran Protestants more ground to claim that the Church of Rome deliberately misinterpreted the Bible. Instead, he turned to Cardinal Bellarmino for advice.

Cardinal Bellarmino, a Jesuit, was one of the Cardinals who had, at an earlier Inquisition, condemned Giordano Bruno to death at the stake.

Bruno had zealously supported the Copernican view, but it was only a marginal issue at the Inquisition. He was condemned by the Catholic Church because he advocated that Rome adopt an all-new philosophy of universal harmony. To the Church, this was heresy. Bruno was repeatedly denied his right of appeal. When the Inquisition sentenced him to death, Bruno challenged the Cardinals. Defiantly he said to them, "You must feel more fear in pronouncing this sentence than I do upon hearing it."[72] Did the Cardinals sense that the Church was losing its grip? Not letting Bruno defend himself at trial had harmed the reputation of the Church in the public's mind.

With Galileo, Cardinal Bellarmino proceeded cautiously. He advised Pope Paul to submit Galileo's propositions to the official "Qualifiers" of the Church. They favored censuring anyone who claimed the Sun to be the center of the world and the Earth moving around it. Following their advice, Pope Paul asked the Cardinal to inform Galileo that he could no longer defend or teach the Copernican propositions as reality. Should Galileo disobey he would be imprisoned.

Early in 1616 Cardinal Ballarmino summoned Galileo to his residence. The Cardinal stated that the writings of Copernicus had been banned by the Church until the errors had been corrected. Galileo could no longer lecture on the Copernican system. Rather than rot away in prison, Galileo agreed to abide by the newly imposed restriction. A notary public, present at this meeting, recorded the proceedings. At the next assembly of the Inquisition the Cardinal informed the other members that Galileo had acceded to the ruling of the Church.[73]

Galileo refrained from teaching astronomy. The election of a new Pope in 1623, however, raised his hopes anew. Cardinal Maffeo Barbarini had been elected to become Pope Urban VIII (reigned from 1623–1644). Years earlier he had defended and praised Galileo's ideas publicly. Galileo believed, erroneously, that the winds of the Vatican had changed.

In 1624 he visited Rome to pay his respects to Pope Urban VIII. Pope Urban was a Florentine, an intellectual, and an admirer of Galileo. In several audiences with him Galileo received permission to publish a book on his new theory of the oceans' tides, a theory linked to the Copernican motion of the Earth. The Pope's permission was conditional, however. Galileo was to make it clear that the motions of the Earth were hypothetical and not real.[74]

### Galileo's Defense of the Copernican System

Galileo worked on his new book between 1624 and 1630. He dropped the original title of a *Dialogue on the Tides* when told that it could convey the impression that the motion of the Earth was for real. He changed the title to a *Dialogue Concerning the Two Chief Systems of the World—Ptolemaic and Copernican* and wrote it in the form of a discussion exploring the two systems. Having assigned the role of the defender of the Aristotelian system to Simplicio,[75] a simpleton, he demolished Simplicio's arguments with biting satire, wit, and logic. Assuming the Sun to be at the center of circular planetary orbits he opted for a theory of the tides that was plausible but only partially correct.[76]

Galileo defended the Copernican System. He believed in celestial spheres, circular orbits, and epicycles. Kepler's elliptical planetary orbits did not impress him. He did not accept Kepler's belief that the Sun was the central force that moved the Earth and the other planets. Also, he rejected Kepler's suggestion that a force emanating from the Moon caused the oceans' tides on Earth. Galileo wrote:

> But among all the great men who have philosophized about this remarkable effect, I am more astonished at Kepler than at any other. Despite his open and acute mind, and though he has at his fingertips the motions attributed to the Earth, he has nevertheless lent his ear and his assent to the Moon's dominion over the waters, and to occult properties, and to such puerilities.[77]

Kepler himself admitted that he enjoyed formulating hypotheses and that he was searching for a mathematical harmony in the skies. In attributing the tides of the oceans to a force of the Moon, Kepler had been right. He was also right in his three laws of planetary motion. However, Galileo and others thought of it as number-juggling rather than science.

Galileo's discourse on the two world systems and the tides was published in March 1632. In August, the order came from the Inquisition to stop all sales of the book at once. Pope Urban was furious. He had just been shown the notary's memorandum of Galileo's agreement of acquiescence of 1616. When he had come to Rome for his first audience

Galileo had agreed to Cardinal Ballarmino's request. Galileo had never mentioned it to Pope Urban. Now the Pope had no choice but to act.[78]

Galileo's trial began on April 12, 1633. The ruling of the Qualifiers of the Inquisition was read to him. Galileo countered that he had not intended to disobey the Church. When the members of the Inquisition condemned him to indefinite imprisonment, Galileo was crushed. Yet, his sentence was commuted shortly after. Toward the end of the year he was permitted to return to his own villa. Already in poor health, the death of his daughter, Sister Maria Celeste, at a Franciscan Convent, struck a further blow. Nevertheless, Galileo carried on.[79]

**Galileo's Last Years**

Five years later Galileo published his last and greatest book *Two New Sciences, Including Centers of Gravity and Force of Percussion.* Galileo wrote it in the form of a dialogue using three characters: Salviati, modeled after his friend Filippo Salviati who had passed away in 1614, as a Copernican speaking for Galileo; Simplicius, modeled after the university professors of Pisa, obstinately adhering to Artistotles's theories; and Sacredo, an open-minded intellectual, needing to be convinced of the truth of the cause.[80]

He had written most of *Two New Sciences* between 1633 and 1635. Not allowed to publish in Italy, he had it printed in the Dutch town of Leyden in 1638. Referring to his treatise on motion, Galileo wrote:

> My purpose is to set forth a very new science dealing with a very ancient subject. There is, in nature, perhaps nothing older than motion concerning which the books written by philosophers are neither few nor small; nevertheless I have discovered by experiment some properties of it which are worth knowing and which have not hitherto been either observed or demonstrated. Some superficial observations have been made as, for instance, that the free motion of a heavy falling body is continuously accelerated; but to just what extent this acceleration occurs has not yet been announced; for so far as I know no one has yet pointed out that the distances traversed, during equal intervals of time, by a body falling from rest, stand to one another in the same ratio as the odd numbers of unity.
>
> It has been observed that missiles and projectiles describe a curved path of some sort; however no one has pointed out the fact

that this path is a parabola. But this and other facts, not few in number or less worth knowing, I have succeeded in proving; and what I consider more important, there have been opened up this vast and most excellent science, of which my work is merely the beginning, ways by which other minds will explore its remote corners.[81]

*Two New Sciences* is generally recognized as his greatest scientific achievement. Galileo himself considered it the most important of his studies and superior to anything else he had published. In applying his new scientific method, he combined experimental physics with mathematics to derive, in Euclidean fashion, scientific theorems of acceleration and other aspects of motion.

### Failing Health

By the time his latest book was published, Galileo was blind and no longer able to read or write. With the help of assistants he managed to correspond. In one of his last letters to a friend he described his predicament:

Your friend and servant has for the last month been irremediably blind, so that this heaven, this earth, this universe which I, by my remarkable discoveries and clear demonstrations had enlarged a hundred times beyond what has been believed by wise men of past ages, for me is from this time forth shrunk into so small a space as to be filled by my own sensations.[82]

The Church of Rome allowed him, after lengthy negotiations, to live with his son in Florence so that he could visit his physician, but he was not permitted to speak with others.

Galileo died in January of 1642. Luke Holste, a member of Cardinal Barbarini's household (Barbarini was one of three Cardinals who, among ten members of the Inquisition, did not sign Galileo's condemnation) wrote to a friend in Florence:

Today news has come of the loss of Signor Galilei, which touches not just Florence but the whole world, and our whole century which from this divine man has received more splendor than from almost all other ordinary philosophers. Now, envy ceasing, the sublimity of that intellect will begin to be known which will serve all posterity as guide in the search for truth.[83]

Chapter 12

# NEWTON (1642–1727), UNLOCKED THE HIDDEN TREASURES OF TRUTH[1]

*Newton's demonstration of the law of ellipses is a watershed that separates the ancient world from the modern world—the culmination of the Scientific Revolution. It is one of the crowning achievements of the human mind, comparable to Beethoven's symphonies, Shakespeare's plays, or Michelangelo's Sistine Chapel. Aside from its immense importance in the history of physics, it is a conclusive demonstration of the astonishing fact that has mystified and intrigued all deep thinkers since Newton's time: nature obeys mathematics.*

D. L. and J. R. Goodstein[2]

After the lost millennium (Chapter 7), the Renaissance produced scientific thinkers who advanced the study of astronomy by great strides. Books were written, printed, and distributed throughout the scientific communities of Europe. The Renaissance's recovery of classical manuscripts paved the way for the appearance of new revolutionary scientific systems and philosophic theories. It was the revival of the Pythagorean philosophy—God is Number—that started this revolution. Sir Isaac Newton inherited these advances and was a scientist of such mettle as to push the thinking to yet another level.

Copernicus (1473–1543) had demonstrated by geometric analysis that the heliocentric theory was superior to Ptolemy's geocentric theory (Chapter 8). With Tycho de Brahe's (1546–1601) accurate observations on hand, Johannes Kepler (1571–1630) uncovered the three laws of elliptical orbits and thereby overthrew Ptolemy's age-old theory of circular orbits (Chapters 9 and 10).

Galileo Galilei (1564–1642) formulated the laws of the dynamics of motion (Chapter 11). He deduced from his own experiments that the Earth attracted all objects equally. On the strength of his careful observations he rejected the ancient Aristotelian belief that heavier objects dropped faster to the ground than lighter objects. He concluded that without any kind of friction an object would continue on its course at a constant speed. Yet, in cosmology he adhered to the circular planetary orbits of Copernicus. He believed that Kepler's Laws were some sort of Pythagorean numerology and disputed that the Moon caused the ocean tides. Ignoring Kepler's elliptical orbits, he did not search for the dynamic forces that kept the planets in their orbits but attributed them to God, the almighty "Aristotelian Mover."

In Galileo's day, younger scientists came up with new ideas. Torricelli (1608–1647) and Cavaliery, at about the same time, were the first to give a modern definition of inertia. They asserted that motion is straight-linear and of constant speed, unless acted upon by some force.[3] In 1665 Berelli described the motions of the satellites of Jupiter and differentiated between two forces, a centrifugal force that pulled outward along the tangent line of their orbits, and an attractive force that pulled them inward. He pictured how, in equilibrium, the orbiting satellites balanced their centrifugal force of motion exactly against the attractive force of Jupiter.[4]

These novel ideas were like pieces of a puzzle. They could be fitted here and there but they did not reveal the complete picture. This task fell to an Englishman, Isaac Newton (1642–1727). He met the challenge and ultimately found the key to the universe. His theory dominated the next two centuries until Einstein opened a door to an even greater perspective.

**The Newtons**

Isaac Newton was born in 1642, in the same year that Galileo died, and one hundred years after Copernicus' death.[5]

Newton's ancestors were farmers. The Newtons farmed in Lincolnshire and had accumulated land and wealth. They had worked diligently, were intelligent, and had managed to improve their economic status over several generations. It had taken careful husbandry because the soil was thin and the land was poor. A hundred years earlier a John Newton had advanced to taxpayer status, his son had moved up to the status of husbandman, and a third John Newton had become a yeoman, another rung up on the socioeconomic ladder.

Robert Newton, Isaac's grandfather, expanded the family estate further by purchasing the manor of Woolsthorpe in 1623. It entitled him to conduct court and to levy fines for minor offenses. The farm's combined acreage afforded the family a comfortable living. On his death in 1641, Robert Newton left the farm to his eldest son, Isaac and Isaac's wife Hanna. Isaac's marriage to Hanna had been another step up. She was born an Ayscough (or Askew) and brought additional wealth and some education into Newton's family. Her brother had graduated from Cambridge University's Trinity College.[6]

Then suddenly, six months into their marriage, Isaac Newton died. He left behind an estate of more than 200 sheep, close to 50 head of cattle, an inventory of cash crops, feed, equipment, farm buildings, and a fully furnished house. Their assets were five times those of the average farm. He also left behind his pregnant wife Hanna. She gave birth to a son in the manor house of Woolsthorpe on Christmas morning of 1642. She named him after his father, Isaac. Born prematurely, the newborn was so tiny that "he could have fit into a quart bottle."[7] He was not expected to live.[8]

### Isaac Newton's Youth

Three years later Hanna married Barnabas Smith, a vigorous 63 year-old widower. Barnabas Smith was the reverend of North Witham, the nearby village. Her marriage to him added to the family's wealth but for little Isaac it meant the loss of his mother. Reverend Smith did not want three-year-old Isaac around the house and so he was sent to live with his grandparents Ayscough.

The separation from his mother was a traumatic experience for the three-year-old.[9] Young Isaac's diary reveals that he threatened to burn his parents' house down over their heads. After his stepfather died, his

He also wanted to relate the forces of planetary motion to Kepler's Laws. The story—one of several versions—that, while in his mother's garden, an apple fell from the tree and hit Newton on the head while he was musing about the force of gravity, created the myth that the apple's impact triggered the sudden inspiration he needed. In reality it took Newton years to find an acceptable solution to the puzzle of gravity.[27]

While Newton was occupied with the mechanics of celestial motion, he also delved into optics. The philosopher and mathematician René Descartes, the physicist Robert Hooke (1635–1703), and chemist and physicist Robert Boyle (1627–1691) had discussed the problem of chromatic aberration (i.e., the problematic coloring that spoiled the focus of regular telescopes) and tried to explain it.[28] Hooke believed that the contrast between blue and red left the impression of a confused pulse of light on the retina. Newton disagreed. By experiment he could show that blue light rays were reflected in a prism more sharply than red rays and that the coloring resulted from the angular modification of light. Descartes had suggested that hyperbolic and elliptical lenses gave a better focus than spherical lenses. Newton had found that spherical aberrations in the lenses were far less important than chromatic aberrations caused by the different colors being refracted at different angles.[29] Later he would apply his newly gained knowledge by constructing a new reflective telescope and thereby minimizing the annoying chromatic aberrations.

*Graduation*

Newton returned to Cambridge in April 1667. His scholarship of three years earlier was coming to the end and his future depended on being "elected to the fellowship." If successful, he could stay on at Cambridge, if not he had to return home either to manage the farm or to become a vicar. The election of fellows was up to the master and eight senior fellows. Newton had ignored his curricular studies for the last four years. Yet, as scheduled, he became a fellow at the College of Holy and Undivided Trinity in October 1667 and nine months later he was promoted to Master of Arts.[30]

## At Trinity College

Having obtained his degree, Newton lived at Trinity College for the next 28 years. It was not a congenial atmosphere but that bothered him very little. On the contrary it allowed him to be totally absorbed by his studies. Absent-minded, he could be seen walking on campus with his shoes down at the heels, stockings untied, hair uncombed, designing diagrams on the gravel paths. His colleagues, in awe of him, walked cautiously around his drawings. Instead of going for dinner he would find himself in church. He rarely left his rooms; not a genial companion, he preferred to eat alone.[31]

When Nicholas Mercator, contemporary of Newton, published a book on the simplified derivation of logarithms by evaluating a series,[32] John Collins (1625–1683), sent a copy of it to Dr. Isaac Barrow (1630–1677), Newton's former teacher and then colleague of Isaac Newton. Barrow wrote back that a friend of his had recently written a paper that gave a general method of computing such series. When Collins received Newton's paper "On Analysis by Infinite Series," he was enthusiastic. The paper dealt with the application of a series to the size of areas. Newton was upset when Collins showed a copy of it to other mathematicians. He did not want the paper to be published. His refusal to publish was the first of similar refusals that would create conflicts for him in later years.[33]

*Lucasian Professor of Mathematics*

Newton's long relationship with Dr. Barrow would eventually benefit him. From 1663 to 1669 Barrow was the Lucasian Professor of Mathematics at Cambridge University.[34] He resigned so that he could devote himself to his true calling, theology. It did not take Barrow long to be appointed chaplain to the king. Three years later he became master of the college. Barrow effected Newton's appointment to the richly endowed Lucasian chair. In his new position Newton was required to lecture on geometry, astronomy, geography, optics, statics, and philosophy. Newton lectured only one term per year. Although obligated to deposit his lecture notes, he rarely did so. His lectures were not popular, usually lasting for only half an hour. Beyond the comprehension of most, few students attended them and when nobody came, Newton cut his lecture down to 15 minutes speaking to the walls to meet his teaching requirements.[35]

*Newton's Reflecting Telescope*

During the first few years he lectured mostly on optics, with an emphasis on colors. Early in 1669 he built a reflecting telescope with his own hands. It magnified up to 150 times. Invited to show it to the members of the Royal Society, his new powerful telescope created a sensation. Shortly after this he sent the Society his paper on colors of light.

*The Royal Society*

As early as 1645, London scientists were holding weekly meetings to discuss scientific ideas of the day. In 1660 the British government, with the approval of King Charles II, officially recognized these gatherings. Incorporated by royal charter in 1662 as the Royal Society of London for Improving Natural Knowledge, the government financially supported some of its scientific investigations. Founded to promote knowledge of the physical sciences, members of the Royal Society met and discussed their findings. To keep the Society informed of scientific matters, it began publishing its *Philosophical Transactions* in 1665.

Among the original founding members were scientists like Boyle and Hooke, Wren the architect, several bishops, and poets. Under the auspices of the Royal Society John Evelyne improved English husbandry, Sir William Patty established the science of statistics, John Wallis advanced mathematics, and John Flamsteed authored the star catalogue. Foreigners were included too, among them: Christiaan Huygens and Anton van Leeuwenhoek of Holland, Gottfried Wilhelm Leibniz of Germany, and the Bernoullis of Switzerland. The Society elected Newton to their membership in 1672. In later years Isaac Newton would become the luminary of the Royal Society.

*Calculus*

Meanwhile, astronomers everywhere admired Newton's reflecting telescope. They commented on his theory of colors of light. Within a week Robert Hooke, sent a critique of Newton's corpuscular theory of light.

Newton did not like Hooke's patronizing tone. Christiaan Huygens, a Dutch mathematician, physicist, and astronomer (1629–1695), wrote him several letters too. Newton responded to them, but in a less insulting tone than he had used in his reply to Hooke. Newton hated any criticism of his work. It first upset him and then drove him back into seclusion.[36] Eventually he did publish his findings but only after friends and colleagues urged him to do so.

He also did some more work on mathematics. Barrow gave him free access to his library on mathematics and urged him to expand on his earlier work. Newton started a treatise of his method of calculus which he called "fluxionals" but did not finish it. He had become interested in other things.[37]

Newton could not completely shield himself from the learned world outside. In the early months of 1673 a young German philosopher, Wilhelm Leibniz (1646–1716) contacted Oldenburg and Collins, members of the Royal Society. Leibniz had heard of some of Newton's results on infinite series. In 1676, when Leibniz asked Oldenburg for some information on specific series, Oldenburg and Collins asked Newton to respond. Newton sent his responses to Oldenburg who passed them on to Leibniz. Upon receiving them, Leibniz wrote back to Oldenburg to express his admiration for Newton's remarkable ideas, and to share his own ideas on infinite series.[38] In October of that year, Leibniz visited London for 10 days and met Collins. Collins showed him Newton's files but did not inform Newton of this indiscretion. Instead, Collins wrote to Newton that he believed Leibniz's method of calculus was more general than Newton's method of fluxions and urged Newton to publish his version. Newton replied that his method had a very wide range of applications. He followed it up with a letter to Leibniz sent again through Oldenburg. In it he described his discovery of the binomial theorem, coded his method of fluxions in unintelligible anagrams, and revealed more of his mathematical series. Newton thought of calculus in terms of kinematics, a method of analyzing motion. His approach followed the route Wallis had taken earlier. Newton had extended it to calculus via a generalization of the binomial theorem. Reluctant to publish his method, he asked Oldenburg not to release any of his mathematical papers without his prior permission.[39]

Leibniz did not receive Newton's letter until the following year, in June.In response, Leibniz gave generous praise and described the essence of his own version of differential calculus. Again the letter was forwarded to Newton. Leibniz had hoped for further exchanges but Oldenburg died in September and communication lapsed.[40]

*Optics*

Newton was occupied with optics. His recent paper to the Royal Society on his findings in optics caused more controversy with Dr. Hooke, whose personality was as prickly as Newton's. Their exchange heated up. They accused each other of plagiarism. Quite possibly Oldenburg, Newton's middle man, added fuel to the fire.[41] Suspicious of a sinister plot Hooke contacted Newton directly to tell him how highly he valued his new findings and suggested communicating with him directly rather than by go-between. Newton agreed. Acknowledging Hooke's contributions to optics, he replied in a conciliatory mood: "What Descartes did was a good step. You have added much in several ways, especially in taking the colors of thin plates into consideration."[42] Following that, no personal corre-spondence emerged and the antagonism between them persisted.

Newton invited other members of the Royal Society for a discus-sion of their findings in optics. That led to some problematic incidents. When they failed to obtain the same results as he did, Newton convinced himself that they were out to discredit him. To counteract their criticisms Newton had planned to write another book on optics. Then misfortune struck. Going to chapel one morning in the winter of 1677–78, Newton had left a candle burning among the papers on his desk and they caught fire. The flames destroyed his nearly completed manuscript and many of his other writings. Newton was terribly upset and possibly experienced a nervous breakdown. He wrote some paranoid letters accusing others of trying to lure him into disputes. He withdrew further from the society of his peers and from then on his correspondence sharply diminished.[43]

*Spiritual Projects*

Throughout the 1670s Newton was deeply involved with two other subjects, chemistry and religion. In his day chemistry was still very much alchemy, a strange mix of science, magic, and religion. Newton started from the side of science and gradually become attracted to the more clandestine side of alchemy. He was not in it to discover how to make gold, but rather to explore the spiritual side of nature.[44]

Newton had received his Master of Arts degree in 1672. It was necessary for him to be ordained within three years or be expelled from Trinity College. So, theology preoccupied him, especially the belief that God embodied the Trinity of Father, Son, and Holy Spirit. He became obsessed with the idea that, toward the end of the fourth century, Bishop Athanasius of Alexandria (ca. 296–373 A.D.) had imposed a false doctrine of Trinity on Christianity over the opposition of Arius (ca. 250–336 A.D.), a priest and moral leader of the Christian community of Alexandria. To Arius this was a corruption of the Bible, a massive fraud.[45]

Newton took the side of Arius. Where Athanasius claimed that all three were equal, Arius asserted that God ranked higher than Jesus Christ and that both ranked above the Holy Spirit. Newton went further and blamed the Trinitarians for the idolatry of relics. By doing so he faced a crisis of heresy.

Had it become known, it could have meant the end of Newton's career at Trinity College. Fortunately, His Majesty Charles II intervened, possibly at the recommendation of Dr. Barrow. The king exempted Newton from taking holy orders unless he wanted to himself. This left Newton free to pursue his work without conditions.[46]

In 1679 Newton left Cambridge to comfort his dying mother. He cared for her, dressed her blisters, and sat up all night by her bedside. Although he had visited her only three times during the previous twelve years, his dedication was remarkable. After she passed away, he became heir and executor of his mother's substantial estate. The settlement of the estate took him a full six months.[47]

*On the Dynamics of Planetary Motion*

Shortly after returning to Cambridge Newton received a letter from Robert Hooke. He asked what Newton thought of his idea (first stated in 1674) that the planetary motions were composed of two forces, a tangential force along the planetary orbit and an attractive force toward the center.

It was the first time anyone had correctly described the dynamic forces directing the planetary motions. Newton had only referred to the balancing centripetal and centrifugal forces, the one directed toward and the other away from the center. Writing to him from the Royal Society where he had succeeded Oldenburg as secretary, Dr. Hooke invited Newton to resume their earlier communication. Newton declined. Still, he could not resist following it up by suggesting a hypothesis of his own.[48]

In a 1679 letter to the Royal Society Newton proposed an experiment. The classical argument against the daily rotation of the Earth was that objects falling from a great height would be left behind because of the Earth's rotation from west to east, and therefore would land to the west of the release point. Newton claimed that the tangential velocity at the top of a high tower was greater than at the bottom of it and that, therefore, an object dropped from such height would land to the east of the point. Assuming no resistance from the air, Newton claimed its trajectory would approach the center of the earth in a spiral. Hooke countered that it would not fall to the center but forever follow an elliptical trajectory.[49] Newton's subsequent analysis cleared up this puzzle. The path of the object depends on Earth's gravity, the distance from Earth, and the velocity of the object. At lower velocity the object could follow a spiral trajectory and at higher velocity it could follow an orbital trajectory. So, both were right, but under different assumptions.

Hooke was eager to pursue the experiment and wrote several letters to Newton. Enraged at Hooke's disagreement, Newton did not respond at all. Years later, after his more rigorous analysis had specified the underlying assumptions, Newton tried to explain the disagreement away as "a negligent stroke with his pen."[50] Actually, the affair had a beneficial side effect. It made Newton go back to his earlier notes. While verifying his calculations he found how he could prove mathematically that the force of the Earth's gravity extended to the Moon.[51]

## The Comet of 1680

In early November of 1680 a comet appeared in the sky. First seen just before sunrise, it vanished in the direction of the Sun. In late December a much bigger comet, with a tail four times as long as the Moon is wide, flamed across the sky. On successive evenings it streaked in the opposite direction of the first, away from the Sun. Most astronomers believed they had seen two different comets. However, John Flamsteed of the British Royal Observatory (the first Astromomer Royal, from 1675–1719) claimed that the second comet was the same as the first. He believed it had turned around before it reached the Sun.[52]

Newton did not support Flamsteed's theory. He wrote long letters to Flamsteed criticizing it. Like most astronomers of his day Newton believed that the planetary laws did not apply to comets because they came from outside the solar system. Halley's comet appeared in 1682. These appearances encouraged Newton to collect more information on comets for further study, reawakening his excitement of earlier years.[53]

### *Halley's Visit to Newton in 1684*

In 1669 Huygens, the Dutch mathematician, physicist, and astronomer gave a lecture at the Paris Academy "On the Cause of Gravity." Like Kepler and Descartes before him, he believed that a rotational force coming from the axis of the Earth carried the Moon along its path a-round the Earth. In 1673 Huygens completed his theory of centrifugal force. In his book *Horologium oscillatorium* he described the centrifugal force as directly proportional to the square of the velocity of an orbital object and inversely proportional to the object's distance from the center.[54]

In England, at about the same time (around 1675), some outstanding physicists and their friends gathered regularly to exchange information on the results of their own experiments. During their meetings members of the Royal Society reported on the problems they encountered in their research. They also discussed the findings of other researchers. By then the validity of Kepler's Laws had been confirmed. It was clear to them that Kepler's laws of "equal areas" and "harmonic distances" from the Sun were somehow conditioned by a forceful interaction between the Sun and the planets. However, this understanding raised a new problem: how could scientists determine the amount of force the Sun had to exert on the planets to account for their elliptical orbits. They could not see how the size of this force could be mathematically deduced. How could it be proven that a force emanating from the Sun resulted in the planets' elliptical orbits?[55]

Among the members of the Royal Society was England's brilliant architect, Sir Christopher Wren (1632–1723). He had redesigned many (55 of 87) churches that had burned down during the Great Fire of London in 1666. The most famous of the structures was London's monumental St. Paul's Cathedral. A keen student of mathematics and science, he was so fascinated by the mathematical problem of the elliptical planetary orbits that he offered a generous prize to anyone who could solve the celestial puzzle.[56]

Members of the Royal Society repeatedly discussed the problem at their meetings. They considered it the most intriguing problem of natural philosophy of the day. Halley, of Halley's Comet fame, conceded that he had tried to solve it but had not succeeded. At a meeting in January 1684 Robert Hooke (of the earlier Hooke-Newton controversy) claimed that he could deduce all the laws of celestial motion from the inverse-square relation of Huygen's theory. Wren doubted Hooke's claim. After Halley urged him to provide the proof, Hooke failed to do so. On hearing a rumour that Newton of Cambridge University had solved the problem, Halley decided to visit Newton and find out for himself.[57]

For years Newton had devoted his time to other interests. Neither his search in theology nor his studies in alchemy had yielded coherent sets of significant contributions. By 1684 his study was littered with notes and unpublished manuscripts. If Newton had done no more than this, his name might have become just a footnote in the annals of science. Still, he had not completely ignored mathematics.

When Dr. Halley visited Newton in 1684 to find out how far Newton had progressed on the problem of the Sun's force on the planets, he arrived at the right time. Halley explained the situation. Dr. Hooke had claimed that all the laws of planetary motion could be deduced from their attraction to the Sun, but had failed to prove it. Could Newton tell him how far he had advanced? Newton promptly replied that the planets would follow an elliptical path.

Many years later the mathematician Abraham de Moivre (1667–1754) gave an account based on Newton's recollections of this meeting:

After they had been some time together, the Dr. [Halley] asked him what he thought the curve would be that would be described by the planets supposing the force of attraction towards the Sun to be reciprocal to the square of their distance from it. Sir Isaac replied immediately that it would be an ellipsis. The Doctor, struck with joy and amazement, asked him how he knew it. Why saith he, I have calculated it. Whereupon Dr. Halley asked him for his calculation without any further delay. Sir Isaac looked among his papers but could not find it, but he promised him to renew it and then to send it to him. Sir Isaac, in order to make good his promise, fell to work again, but he could not come to that conclusion which he thought he had before examined with care. However, he attempted a new way which, though longer, than the first, brought him again to his former conclusion. Then he examined carefully what might be the reason why the calculation he had undertaken before did not prove right he found that, having drawn an ellipsis coarsely with his own hand, he had drawn the two axes of the curve, instead of drawing two diameters somewhat inclined to one another, whereby he might have fixed his imagination to any conjugate diameters, which was requisite he should do. That being perceived, he made both calculations agree together.[58]

Halley realized at once that Newton's novel theory of the celestial motions and cosmic structure went far beyond anything known on the European continent. It appeared that Newton was in possession of the solution to the problem but did not want to release it prematurely. Newton agreed to send Halley a more detailed description of his model. A few months later a nine-page manuscript entitled *De Motu Corporum in Gyrum* (*On the Motion of Bodies in Orbit*), arrived on Halley's desk. He read it and immediately urged Newton to let him publish it for him, but Newton asked for a delay so that he could improve on it. Elaboration and clarification took him another three years.[59]

### Newton's Laws of Celestial Dynamics

With Halley's visit, the problem of celestial dynamics now captured Newton's imagination. This kind of fascination had seized him once before. While still a student at Cambridge he had derived the inverse square law from Kepler's first law of elliptical orbits. Yet, this time the challenge took a hold of him as never before. He became so obsessed with it that his behavior appeared even more erratic.[60] A colleague of his reported:

> So intent, so serious upon his studies that he ate very sparingly, no, oftentimes he forgot to eat at all, so that going into his chamber, I found his meal untouched and when I reminded him, [he] would reply, have I?; and then going to the table, would eat a bite or two standing. Sometimes when he intended to dine in the Hall, he would turn to the left, and go out on the street, making a stop when he noticed his mistake, would hastily turn back, and then instead of going into the Hall, would return to his chamber again. Sometimes when he a took a turn or two [in the garden], he made a sudden stop, turned around, ran up the stairs, like another Archimedes with an εὕρηκα [Greek for eureka meaning "I have found it"], stop to write on his desk standing, without allowing himself the leisure to draw up a chair to sit down[61]

In his search for the celestial forces Newton wanted to get to the bottom of Kepler's Laws. In response to a request, Newton had also sent a copy of his earlier nine-page treatise to Flamsteed. Subsequently, Newton wrote several letters to him asking for data on the satellites of Jupiter and Saturn, on the periods and size of their orbits, on the mutual disturbances of Jupiter and Saturn on their orbits, on the course of the comets, and on the tides of the lower part of the Thames River.

In an earlier paper of the 1660s Newton had tried to determine by how much the centrifugal force of the rotation of the Earth reduced its centripetal gravitational force. He had not touched on this issue in his short treatise *On the Motion of Bodies in Orbit*. Now he conveyed to Halley how difficult it was to integrate the many aspects into a coherent framework.[62]

### Newton's Principia

In April of 1686 Halley reported to the Royal Society that Newton's long awaited treatise was nearly ready for publication. The minutes of the meeting read:

Dr. Vincent presented to the Society a manuscript treatise entitled "Philosophiae Naturalis Principia Mathematica" (Mathematical Principles of Natural Philosophy), and dedicated to the Society by Mr. Isaac Newton, wherein he gives a mathematical demonstration of the Copernican hypothesis as proposed by Kepler, and makes out all the phenomena of the celestial motions by the only supposition of a gravitation towards the center of the Sun decreasing as the squares of the distances there from reciprocally.

It was ordered that a letter of thanks be written to Mr. Newton; and that the printing of the book be referred to the consideration of the council; and that in the meantime the book be put in the hands of Mr. Halley, to make a report thereof to the council.[63] By the middle of May Halley reported back to Newton that the Society had voted to publish his book forthwith.

Halley also reported that Dr. Hooke claimed to have first given the rule for the decrease in gravity as proportionate to the reciprocal of the square of the distance from the center.[64] By the time Halley sent back the proof of the first page of the book for approval of the type, Newton fired back that Hooke had little right to lay such claims. He went on to say:

> Now is this not very fine? Mathematicians that find out, settle and do all the business must content themselves with being nothing but dry calculators and drudges and another that does nothing but pretends and grasps at all things must carry away all the invention as well as those that were to follow him as of those that went before.[65]

In response, Halley very diplomatically asked Newton not to let his resentments run so high as to withhold his third book from publication. In the end, Newton did not hold back his manuscript and he did parenthetically acknowledge the contribution of Hooke and others in a hidden corner of the *Principia*.[66]

The publication of Newton's book posed an unprecedented problem. For all practical purposes the Royal Society was bankrupt. In his enthusiasm, Halley, the secretary of the Society, had ordered its publication. Now the members of the Society asked him to foot the bill of publication. Although Halley came from a wealthy family, the death of his father in 1684 had made it difficult for him to support his young wife and family. As secretary of the Society his livelihood depended on the measly salary of £50 per year. But Halley recognized the significance of Newton's treatise. He obtained some funding, carried part of the financial burden himself, and took on the task of publication.[67]

Newton's *Principia* was published in 1687. In Britain, Newton's fame and influence spread like wildfire. On the European continent the reception of his ideas was more subdued though his achievement was greatly admired. Huygens and Leibniz were reluctant to adapt to the principle of gravitational attraction without an explanation of the underlying cause. Nevertheless, the *Principia* dominated meetings, talks, and correspondence of natural philosophers on both sides of the Channel. With one great leap Newton had vaulted to the forefront of natural science.[68]

In creating his new cosmology Newton had used geometry. His goal had been to derive all laws for planetary orbits by use of exact mathematics. He had brought together Galileo's laws of earthly motion and Kepler's laws of celestial motion in one unified grand design.[69] Newton chose geometry for all of his demonstrations. He explains:

> It is the glory of geometry that from those few principles, brought from without, it is able to produce so many things. Therefore geometry is founded in mechanical practice, and is nothing but that part of universal mechanics which accurately proposes and demonstrates the art of measuring.[70]

Newton not only used geometry for his analysis but patterned his presentation after Euclid. He based it on a set of definitions and axioms followed by postulates and propositions, all ordered and interconnected by logic. He imposed a very important constraint: the number of axioms (i.e., the number of self–evident principles) must be limited. It must be neither too small nor too large. If too small in number, not all theorems can be derived from them or, if too large, one axiom can be derived from another. This tightly structured presentation gives Newton's *Principia* an authority that rivals Euclid's *Elements*.[71]

*Newton's Three Axiomatic Laws*

In the *Principia* Newton starts with a set of eight definitions. He defines his measures of matter, motion, innate force, impressed force, centripetal force, centrifugal force, accelerative force, gravitational force.[72] He follows them up with three essential "axiomatic" laws. The First Law states, "Every body continues in its state of rest, or of uniform motion in a straight line, unless it is compelled to change that state by forces impressed on it."[73] This law is often called the Law of Inertia. It says that if no force is applied, a body continues in its present state of rest or it keeps on moving in a straight line at the same uniform velocity.[74] It is a generalization of Galileo's uniform horizontal motion. Some 50 years earlier Galileo had written (in 1638):

> Motion in the horizontal plane is uniform, as there is no cause of acceleration or retardation, whatever degree of speed is found in the object this is by its nature indelibly impressed on it when external causes of acceleration or retardationare removed, which occurs only in the horizontal plane; for on declining planes there is cause for more acceleration, and on rising planes, of retardation. From this it likewise follows that motion in the horizontal is also eternal, since if it is indeed uniform it is not weakened or remitted, much less removed.[75]

While Galileo wrote of "earthly" motion, a term that was more restrictive than Newton's First Law, Descartes had come up with a more radical formulation. He contended that uniform straight-line motion was a "state" just as rest was. Without the action of any external force, bodies would maintain that state. To him, uniform rectilinear motion was the dynamic equivalent of the state of rest. In his treatise on *The World (Le Monde)*, Descartes had set forth his theory but, living within the reach of the Church of Rome, did not publish it when he learned of Galileo's condemnation by the Inquisition. He published it later under the title *Principia Philosophiae*. Very likely, Newton's First Law had been "conditioned" by Descartes' laws of nature.[76]

Newton's First Law has also been described as a frame of reference in which an object has no acceleration. With no force acting on it, an object's acceleration is zero. More striking than this was Descartes' contention—because it is completely detached from our Earth-bound experience—of not differentiating between rest and uniform motion.

Newton adopted it but went further. He made a point of not distin—
guishing between the absence of all forces and forces that cancel each
other and have a zero net effect.[77]

Newton's Second Law could hardly be attributed to Galileo's
concept of *"impressed force."* Nevertheless, it does contain some aspects
that are common to both. Newton's Second Law reads: "A change in
motion is proportional to the motive force impressed; and is made in the
direction of the straight line in which that force is impressed."[78]

Galileo had described the *"force of impact"* as an obscure concept.
To illustrate how difficult it was to make sense out of first impressions,
Galileo gave some practical examples:

- If a blow was being struck with a lead hammer, for instance, it was
  the hammer and not the anvil that flattened.

- Or, if a sculptor used a mallet of iron to hit a chisel of steel, it was
  the mallet and not the chisel that dented.

- If an inflated ball hit the hard pavement, it yielded to the impact
  and bounced. But if a ball was made of metal, it bounced back
  when it hit the skin of a drum.

- If pressure is applied to an olive press, it differs from striking the
  crossbars of the lid of the press with a sledge hammer, even
  though pressures have the same end effect.[79]

Newton clarified the idea of force by relating it directly to motion.
His Second Law consists of two parts. The first refers to the change in
motion that is proportionate to the force of impact: the greater the force
that impresses on an object, the greater the effect on its motion. If the
force is doubled, it will cause twice the change in motion. The second part
relates to the change in direction of motion. Newton says the force of
impact causes a change of speed "in the direction of the straight line in
which that force is impressed."[80] This conforms to Galileo's analysis
of the projectile motion. Were it not for the gravitational force, the initial
impact would continue to propel the object in a straight line.

Newton's Third Law may be intuitively obvious but it is subtle. It
reads: "To every action there is always opposed an equal reaction: or, the
mutual actions of two bodies upon each other are always equal, and

directed to contrary parts."[81] Newton illustrates it by giving several examples, among them the following:

> If you press a stone with your finger, the finger is also pressed by the stone. If a horse draws a stone tied to a rope, the horse (if I may so say) will be equally drawn back towards the stone; for the distended rope will draw the horse as much towards the stone as it does the stone towards the horse, and will obstruct the progress of one as much as it advances the other. The changes made by these actions are equal, not in the velocities but in the motions of bodies; that is to say, if the motions are not hindered by any other impediments.[82]

Newton amplified this law by adding corollaries that describe the interactions of motions in greater detail.

At their first meeting in 1684, Halley had asked Newton what kind of curves the planets trace out if the force of the Sun were to diminish as the inverse square of the distance from the planets. Newton answered Halley's question by first sending him a nine-page explanation and, three years later, by supplying him with the manuscript of the *Principia*.

In the *Principia* Newton focussed on the mathematical analysis of the motion of bodies. After the introductory definitions and the three axiomatic laws, Newton proceeded with his analysis of the dynamics of motion. Having invented some of the more advanced mathematical techniques himself, Newton could have described his approach by applying calculus and vector analysis. Yet he preferred to do it by basing his proofs and demonstrations on geometry.

### Newton's Deduction of Kepler's Laws

Newton deduced Kepler's laws of elliptical planetary orbits from Kepler's two other laws: that planets sweep out equal areas in equal time, and that the time they need for completing their orbits is inversely related to their distance from the Sun. It has been called one of Newton's most dramatic discoveries that he demonstrated how Kepler's law of elliptical orbits was the consequence of Kepler's other two laws, it meant three laws could be understood in terms of two.[83]

Newton tackled Kepler's Second Law first. Kepler had derived it from Tycho de Brahe's precise astronomical observations. Going through a vast amount of painstaking computations, Kepler had discovered that the imaginary line joining a planet to the Sun sweeps out equal areas in equal times. Eventually, this discovery became known as Kepler's Second Law, though he uncovered it as the first of his three laws. Whereas Kepler had been searching for and found the mathematical relationship that best described *how* the planets moved around the Sun, Newton was determined to find out *why* the planets orbited the Sun in this fashion. This required proof.

Newton couched his analysis in geometry. In elaborating on his findings a bit of algebra is added here, but only to interpret the original text.[84] To make it less cumbersome a good part of it is put in Appendixes A12 and B12 of this Chapter.

*Why do Planets Sweep Out Equal Areas in Equal Times?*

Generally known as Keplers's First Law, it takes us to Newton's "Theorem I: The areas which revolving bodies describe by radii drawn to an immovable centre of force, are proportional to the times in which they are described." [85] To show why this must be so he illustrates it geometrically as in Figure 12.1, Diagram 1. In this Diagram the points *A, B, C, D, E, F* represent successive positions a planet takes during its path around the Sun. Newton attributes the shape of planetary orbits to two forces: one is the inertial force that would, if unimpeded, let the planet continue to move in a straight line; and the other is the gravitational force that emanates from the Sun and attracts the planet to it. Together, the two produce a smooth orbit.[86]

Newton shows how the inertial and gravitational forces of the Sun affect a planet's course. Without this force, a planet would follow a straight line as dictated by inertia or the inertial force. He explains by geometric analysis why, in equal time intervals, a planet sweeps out areas of equal size. According to him the triangular areas formed by two successive orbital positions of a planet and the Sun must always be of the same size if spaced at equal time intervals. While the shape of the triangles changes from one interval to the next, they retain their size (Figure 12.1, Diagrams 2 to 7).[87]

Newton's geometric analysis illustrates how the gravitational force of the Sun impresses on the planet and bends its straight-line path. The stronger the force the more the path is bent (Figure 12.1, Diagrams 8 and 9). Augmenting the number of triangles reduces the width of each, so that with ever greater numbers the orbital perimeter becomes a smooth curve. Newton concludes: planets attracted by a central gravitational force sweep out equal areas in equal times. It was the first time that Kepler's Second Law had been confirmed on purely theoretical grounds.

Newton's *Principia* do not make easy reading. Readers who feel they have been sufficiently exposed to Newton's geometric reasoning may wish to skip the geometry of the next two sections. They deal with Kepler's Laws of the elliptical orbits of the planets and the periods of revolution. Newton himself advised his readers not to read every proposition as it " might cost too much time, even of readers of good mathematical learning."[88] Of course, Newton was referring to the great many and complex propositions he put forth in the *Principia*. Only a selected few are considered here. Although each element is easy enough, taken together it can still be somewhat of a challenge. Newton's key results are illustrated in diagrams here. The underlying reasoning is given in Appendices A12 and B12 of this Chapter.

*Why is the Force of Gravity Inversely Related to Distance From the Sun?*
Much of what follows was not a direct response to the question Dr. Halley had posed at his meeting with Newton. He had asked him what orbit a planet would follow if the force of attraction toward the Sun was inverse to the square of its distance from it. The problem Newton addresses here is not quite the same. Newton asks what the law of the force would be if the planet orbited the Sun along an ellipse. Similarly, Newton does not ask from which of the two focal points of an ellipse will gravity exert its force. He asks how to find the center to which the force is directed if a body describes an ellipse at particular speeds.[89] This is because Newton's analysis is much broader. He articulates the laws of force not only for

ellipses but also for other curves of conic sections, such as circles, parabolas, and hyperbolas (for conic sections see Chapter 4 Figure 4.3).

With regard to elliptical orbits and in a space of less than two pages, Newton concludes that the centripetal force is inversely related to the square of the distance from one focus of the ellipse.[90] He proves it with the aid of a complex geometric model (described in Appendix A12, p. 232 and in Figure 12.2) and by invoking some of the Apollonian theorems, illustrated earlier in chapters 4 and 7.

In Section III, Proposition XI, Problem VI, Newton specifically defines the problem: "If a body revolves in an ellipse; it is required to find the law of the centripetal force tending to the focus of the ellipse."[91] Newton deduces from his model (Appendix A12 ) that the gravitational force F varies inversely with the distance from planet to Sun as in:

$$F \propto k \ (PS)^{-2}$$

It implies the force $F$ that keeps a planet on an elliptic orbit is directed toward the Sun $S$, located at one focus of the ellipse, and is inversely related to the squared distance $(PS)^2$ of the planet from the Sun.

*Why do Planets Orbit the Sun in Harmonic Ratios?*
Kepler discovered that the time it takes planets to revolve in different orbits around the Sun is proportionate to the 3/2th (or 1.5th) power of the planet's distance from the focal point of the Sun.

Newton demonstrates that this follows from his earlier findings. He infers that the area of the ellipse varies with the size of the triangles summed over the periodic orbital time of the planet. He proves, as Kepler had predicted, that:

$$t = k \ (AC)^{3/2} = (AC)^{1.5},$$

where

$t$ = the orbital period of a planet,
$AC$ = semimajor axis of ellipse, and
$k$ = some constant.

Kepler described his Third Law in harmony of the world. He devoted a whole book to this Law because it was his attempt to bring together geometry, music, mathematics, harmony, astrology, and even politics in one unified framework. Newton's style was very different. He presented his material with a sharp focus and concise commentary. He answered questions that related to each of the conic sections. It took him no more than a single page to deduce the proof of Kepler's Third Law (a more detailed explanation of Newton's derivation of Kepler's Third Law is given in Appendix B12, p. 240 and Figure 12.3).[92]

*Summary*

Newton's basic geometric model (Figure 12.1) illustrates how the Sun's gravitational force interacts with a planet's inertial force to produce the planetary orbit. This geometric interpretation proved why planets sweep out equal areas in equal times, confirming Kepler's Second Law. Newton combined the characteristics of the ellipse with the inverse-square law of the centripetal force. He showed that a planet's period of revolution around the Sun is proportional to the 3/2th power of the length of the semi–major axis of the planet's elliptical orbit.

Actually, Newton's proof was the answer to the converse of Halley's question. Newton showed that *if* the planet's orbit was an ellipse, *then* the force of attraction would be inversely proportional to the planet's distance from the Sun. But Newton even went far beyond that.

*Only Five of Nearly 200 Propositions*

Only five propositions of Newton's monumental treatise are illustrated here. In the three books of the *Principia* Newton treats the reader to nearly 200 propositions surrounded by many explanatory notes (scholia), subsidiary propositions (lemmas), and problems. With classic geometric rigor he examines a great variety of orbital motions and forces, many of them very complex. It is noticeable that aspects of vector analysis and differential and integral calculus form a background to his geometric examination of planetary motion.

In the *Principia, Book I, The Motion of Bodies*, for example, Newton analyses circular, parabolic and hyperbolic orbits, the motion of bodies in movable orbits, and the attractive forces of bodies that are not spherical. In *Book II, The Motion of Bodies in Resisting Mediums*, he addresses questions of the circular motion of bodies, the resistance to projected bodies, and the motion propagated through fluids. ( *Book I* and *Book II* make up volume I and *Book III* volume II.) In *Book III, The System of the World,* he devotes a large part of the book to the motions of the Moon, a subject that caused him many headaches because of the perturbations of the Moon's orbital motions. While his presentation is couched in geometry, the treatment often reflects his mastery of higher mathematics.

By July 1687 Halley had succeeded in publishing Newton's *Principia.* He sent printed copies of it to Newton who in turn presented copies to his colleagues at Cambridge and to others. The material overwhelmed them. One Trinity colleague, Dr. Babington, said they might have to study it for seven years before they would understand any of it. A student, passing Newton on the street, conveyed his feeling more irreverently by saying: "There goes the man that writt a book that neither he nor anybody else understands."[93]

Not only did the *Principia* take British universities by storm, but the brilliance of its author was also quickly recognized on the continent. Many learned journals gave reviews of Newton's masterpiece. Although greatly admired by the leading philosophers of the day, Huygens and Leibniz were wondering why Newton had not explained the underlying cause of gravity. What was the source of the gravitational attraction? Kepler had attributed the Sun's force to an interaction of the planets with a magnetic field of the Sun, and Descartes' had assigned the force to the whirl of the Sun's vortex.[94] Without searching for the underlying cause, Newton simply defined the gravitational force as that by which bodies are drawn toward a central point, and went on from there.[95]

Newton believed in absolute space that is without relation to anything external. Leibniz and Huygens argued that nothing happens without sufficient cause and asked why material bodies should have been arranged in a certain order and no other. Sometimes referred to as the philosophical principle of sufficient reason, it is a principle that is behind modern-day particle physics, relativity and quantum theory.[96] Newton did not address questions of this kind.

## Newton's Remaining Years

After publishing the *Principia* Newton was thinking of putting his mathematical advances in print. Leibniz had begun publishing his differential calculus in 1684. At the time Newton was still an unknown for most European mathematicians and Leibniz had not mentioned Newton in his articles. While Newton's *Principia* established him as a brilliant physicist and mathematician, he had not based his analysis on differential and integral calculus. Yet in *Book II* of the *Principia*, Newton stated Lemma II dealing with the motion of bodies that clearly showed the author knew about the basics of calculus.[97]

*Priority Dispute With Leibniz Over Calculus*

By today's standards, priority of the discovery of calculus would have gone to the author who published first, and that was Leibniz. Nevertheless, even if Leibniz pursued an independent course in developing calculus, neglecting to mention his earlier contact with Newton was a mistake. Eventually it lead to an unfortunate priority dispute.

Leibniz was interested in many things. His philosophy dealt with history, theology, biology, geology, mathematics, politics, and invention. He constructed a computing machine, studied Chinese philosophy, promoted unity in Germany, and searched for a universal method of inventing and transmitting new knowledge. In mathematics his search led him to permutations, combinations, and symbolic logic. He developed his ideas on calculus while in Paris between 1673 and 1676, where he had met and befriended the Dutch physicist Christiaan Huygens. Through him he became acquainted with the works of Descartes and Blaise Pascal (French philosopher and mathematician, 1623–1662).

Leibniz approached his calculus geometrically in terms of the characteristic triangle of the differentials $(dx, dy, dz)$. In a 1684 article he introduced the principal operational rules of differential calculus, and in a 1686 article he stated those of integral calculus. He invented a powerful mathematical notation for both. Superior to alternative notations, it facilitated the application of the concepts and is predominantly used in textbooks today. Leibniz's publications marked the beginning of a grand period of growth of mathematics on the European continent.[98]

In 1691 Newton wrote a treatise on his methods of differentiation and integration and circulated it among his supporters and younger disciples. Yet shortly after he had picked up on the topic, he lost interest. Perhaps he anticipated annoyances he may have liked to avoid. Instead he went back to his earlier studies of optics and alchemy. But his friends were adamant that he continue with calculus. One of Newton's friends, Fatio, referred Huygens to Lemma II of the *Principia*. A further exposition of his method appeared in 1694 in a book published by Wallis, a colleague and friend of Newton's.

Leibniz had published an article of his method 10 years earlier. His presentation was more explicit than Newton's, and to Leibniz and his friends, clearer. Johann Bernoulli (Swiss mathematician, 1667–1748) went even further and questioned whether Newton had not plundered the ideas from Leibniz. Newton's supporters could not leave it there. Fatio wrote that a comparison between the two methods "is like that of a perfected original and a botched and very imperfect copy." The dispute over priority of who discovered calculus first had started.[99]

## After Trinity

The year 1693 was a black period for Newton. He suffered from acute depression and some thought he had lost his sanity.[100] Perhaps the strain from the intense intellectual effort of his earlier years had totally exhausted him and he likely suffered a nervous breakdown. It marked the end of his intellectual pursuits. Now past the age of 50, he never regained his earlier creativity.

### *Appointment to the Mint*

Newton needed to escape from demanding intellectual activities. His friend Montague, who was England's Chancellor of the Exchequer, appointed him as Warden of the Mint in 1696. Newton decided to leave academia, and within a month of his appointment notice he departed for London. Uncertain about the future, Newton continued to hold the Lucasian Chair of Mathematics and received income from the university for another five years. As it turned out, Newton had an immediate grasp of the Mint's accounting system and was respected as a very talented and able administrator. He also assumed responsibility for the re-coinage, although it was outside the traditional domain of the Warden. By the time it was done, Newton had fully mastered the operation of the Mint.[101]

Newton's daily life had changed. He lived very comfortably, was hospitable, and on occasion entertained quite generously. Frequently he received visitors from abroad. Honors were bestowed on him. Newton's niece, Catherine, lived with him for many years, before and again during her marriage to John Conduit. She was a woman of great charm and wit. When Voltaire (French philosopher, 1694–1778) dropped by for a visit, he was so enchanted by her he confessed that until then he had believed that Newton was appointed to the Mint on his own merit but changed his mind when he met her. As Voltaire put it, neither the theory of gravitation nor the calculus of fluxions could have done as much for Newton as his charming niece. Not all of it was Voltaire's imagination. When Montague died he bequeathed on Catherine a magnificent fortune as a token of his appreciation "for her excellent conversation."[102]

In 1697 Newton received a letter from Bernoulli—the same Bernoulli who had earlier expressed some strong reservations about Newton's priority claim—describing two mathematical problems that could not be solved by classical geometry. Although still in the midst of his work with the re-coinage at the Mint, Newton accepted the challenge. Coming home from a heavy day's work at the Mint, Newton sat down and had the problems solved by four o'clock the next morning. When Bernoulli received the response without a note from the author, he readily identified him by the way he had tackled the problem. He said he recognized him just as easily "as the lion is recognized from his paw."[103]

Newton was appointed Master of the Mint in 1699 after his predecessor passed away. He greatly improved the operating efficiency of the Mint and it became more profitable than it had been for many years. Also, it was very profitable for Newton. Over the next 27 years his annual income averaged £994, much higher than his salary of £150, because of management bonuses. Although his income varied with the volume of coinage, it was a splendid remuneration by the standards of the day. It ensured for him a life of plenty. As Master of the Mint he was obliged to lend his support to the government in power. When Queen Anne visited

Cambridge University in 1705, Newton was knighted. He was the first scientist of England to receive this honor.[104] Perhaps it was not so much for his achievement in science but for the glory of the party.[105]

With the outbreak of the War of the Spanish Succession in 1701, the demand for new coinage dropped off sharply. It meant a substantial loss in Newton's income but it also freed him from the burden of the office. After Hooke's death in 1703, Newton was elected President of the Royal Society. Not all members supported his nomination. Nevertheless, he quickly imposed his leadership through more effective administration. He arranged for meetings of greater scientific interest.[106]

With one of his greatest critics no longer alive (Hooke), Newton decided to publish his treatise on *Opticks*. This 1704 edition was largely based on his earlier work of the 1680s. It was a welcome addition as no one else had made a major contribution to optics in the intervening years. Newton had also added two appendices, "A Treatise on the Quadrature of Curves," and the "Enumeration of Lines of the Third Order," which included calculus. These additions did not make for a major event in the annals of mathematics because by then Leibniz and his followers had already written and published a variety of journal articles on infinitesimal calculus during the previous two decades.[107]

*Dispute With Flamsteed*

Newton was also thinking of a second edition of the *Principia*. He was still agonizing over his inability to explain the aberrations of the lunar orbit. Convinced that inadequate empirical data were the cause of his problem, he used his authority as the President of the Royal Society to extract more data from Flamsteed, the Astronomer Royal of the Royal Observatory at Greenwich. In order to find a more reliable method of determining longitudes at sea, Flamsteed had obtained more accurate measurements of the stars and the motions of the Moon than had previously been recorded.

During their first meeting Newton was all charm. Flamsteed was trying to finish his own book, a *British History of the Heavens*. Publication of the *History* would have been the proper tribute to his life's work. But Newton needed Flamsteed's observational data of his as yet unpublished book and somehow he managed to get a hold them. Ignoring Flamsteed's wishes, he published the data without the historical background. The referees of the Royal Society, including Newton, rewarded a profit to the publisher but did not allow Flamsteed a recompense for his own expenses and work. Newton refused to consider it.[108]

Still, Newton did not have all the data he wanted. Once again using his position as President of the Royal Society, he decided to gain access to the data by imposing force. In 1710, a warrant was produced appointing Newton and others to be constant visitors to the Royal Observatory. Effectively, this put the Greenwich Observatory under the control of the Royal Society. Flamsteed was ordered to complete the publication of the *History*. Having discovered how far the positions of the stars differed from those of the published tables, Flamsteed had started to correct for the disparities. It caused another delay and Newton was furious. Newton had all the observations of the fixed stars (for which he had no need) eliminated from the yet unpublished *British History of the Heavens*, and had the second revised edition of the *Principia* published. In the process he removed every source reference to Flamsteed from this version.[109]

Yet, Flamsteed would have the last word. When Queen Anne died, the government fell, and the opposition came to power. Newton lost his chief contact and Flamsteed gained one. Now Flamsteed arranged to have a warrant issued to Newton and the other referees, demanding the immediate release of the remaining 300 copies of the Royal Society's publication of the *History*. Once in his hands, he burned them. Eventually, Flamsteed had his *History* (it was completed by his wife and two assistants after his own death) published in three volumes as planned. Newton had failed to have Flamsteed surrender to his will.[110]

While engaged in this feud, Newton was also fighting on other fronts. He was preparing the second edition of the *Principia*. To be published under the auspices of Trinity College, the president of the university had put Roger Cotes, a gifted young mathematician, in charge of editing. He encountered little problems in *Book I*, but found more significant problems in *Book II*. Newton was not used to such editing. When Cotes came back to him on a particular point, Newton replied that re-examining all the computations was unnecessary because errors in computation were not very important since the reasoning was right. The amendments Newton had made to the lunar theory did not meet Cotes' expectations.

Then another revision was required. During a visit to London Nicolaus Bernoulli had told Newton that his uncle (Johann Bernoulli) had noticed an error (in 1710) in Proposition X. The error suggested that Newton had not understood the meaning of second derivatives (of differential calculus), a point that was important in the Newton-Leibniz priority dispute. Newton immediately sensed that more was at stake. He informed Cotes of the error but did not send him his revised proposition for another three months. In 1713 the second edition of the *Principia* was published. Cotes received neither money nor thanks for his efforts. Newton had suppressed the Preface, in which Cotes was credited, and eliminated a reference to him from the text.[111]

### End of the Priority Dispute With Leibniz

A letter arrived from Leibniz. He had been made aware that Fatio, a former friend of Newton, claimed to have invented his own calculus in 1687. Newton decided it was time to respond. Insinuations went back and forth. Newton contended that he had invented his method of fluxions in 1665–66 and that whoever came after had no right to lay claim. Yet he had communicated very little and had not published anything before Leibniz did in 1684. On the other side of the Channel, Leibniz did not mention his correspondence with Newton of 1676. He had not referenced it in his article of 1684, and had never indicated what he knew of Newton's work through his earlier contact with Collins.[112]

When Leibniz received a strong letter from Keill, a spokesman for Newton, he turned to the Royal Society to clarify the situation. Newton presided over the meeting when the letter was read and subsequently explained the issues for the members of the Society. A letter of response was drafted, read, approved by him and sent off. Leibniz complained that the jurors acted without having had him provide his own evidence. Had they done so, he too could have shown that he invented his calculus before his contacts in 1676. When Newton heard of this claim he rejected it outright declaring righteously that "no Man is a Witness in his own Cause." [113]

The controversy over priority claims continued. Patriotic sentiments in Britain and Germany kept the coals glowing.[114] The intensity of the debate prevailed for a time but eventually diminished after Leibniz passed away in 1716.

After a meteoric rise in his younger years—Leibniz had received his doctorate at age 22—he entered the service of the Archbishop of Mainz as a political advisor, traveled to Paris as a diplomat, met Huygens, engaged in mathematical studies, invented a calculating machine, and at age 27 became a Fellow of the Royal Society of England. Leibniz entered and remained in the service of successive dukes of Hannover and Brunswick. This career move was a strategic error on his part because much of his time was wasted on genealogical searches for the Electors. In 1714 the Duke of Hanover ascended to the throne of England to become King George I. To avoid any further priority quarrels and to alleviate hostility he left Leibniz behind. Living in poverty, Leibniz died two years later. Only his loyal servant attended the funeral.[115]

Newton could not let go of the priority issue, even after the death of his antagonist. It took him another six years before he let it rest. By then he was busy with another edition of his *Opticks* and after that with a third publication of the *Principia*. Also, he returned to theology again. He wrote a book on it, but he did not reveal his real views and the book caused hardly a stir.

Today it is generally agreed that both Newton and Leibniz, building on the advances made by earlier mathematicians, independently discovered the basic features of differential and integral calculus.[116] If Newton was by far the greater master of mathematics and physics, his towering achievements threw a long shadow over the field of mathematics in Britain. He had based the concepts of calculus on the expansion of the binomial theorem. The application of his technique to other mathematical series was very difficult and slowed down any further advance. Leibniz aligned the concepts of calculus with the basic rules of arithmetic, that is addition, subtraction, multiplication, and division. These rules of operation could be systematically applied and were readily understood. The more attractive interpretation and advantageous symbolism of Leibniz's calculus lit up the field in continental Europe.[117]

## Two Assessments

Shortly before his death in 1727, Newton summed up his life's work very modestly:

> I don't know what I may seem to the world, but, as to myself, I seem to have been only like a boy playing on the seashore, and diverting myself in now and then finding a smoother pebble or a prettier shell than ordinary, whilst the great ocean of truth lay all undiscovered before me.

Richard Westfall, in his definitive biography of *The Life of Isaac Newton* (1993), wrote:

> The more I have studied him, the more Newton has receded from me. It has been my privilege at various times to know a number of brilliant men, men whom I acknowledge without hesitation to be my intellectual superiors. I have never, however, met one against whom I was unwilling to measure myself, so that it seemed reasonable to say that I was half as able as the person in question, or a third or a fourth, but in every case a fraction. The end result of my study of Newton has served to convince me that with him there is no measure. He has become wholly other, one of the tiny handful of supreme geniuses who have shaped the categories of the human intellect, a man not finally reducible to the criteria by which we comprehend our fellow beings.[118]

Honoured during his lifetime, Newton was buried in the Jerusalem Chamber of the Westminister Abbey. His heirs, whom he had richly endowed, built a lavish monument in his honor. Located in a space that had been refused to nobility on earlier occasions,[119] it carried the inscription "Let Mortals rejoice that there existed such and so great an Ornament to the Human Race."[120]

## Conclusion

Isaac Newton laid down the foundations of physics that form the base of much of science today. He is credited with the clarification of inertia and force, proof of the composite nature of light, insistence on experimental verification, construction of the reflecting telescope, the universal existence of gravity, deduction and integration of physical laws in his revolutionary system of the universe, and the creation of the science of mechanics.

His predecessors and contemporaries achieved a partial under-standing, but Newton coupled physics with mathematics and created a new comprehensive quantitative system of nature. Kepler discovered the three laws of planetary motion in the heavens. Galileo formulated the laws of dynamics of motion on Earth. But Newton created a comprehensive system of all of physics. His work deeply affected science and the learned people of culture for the next three centuries and beyond. In the public mind his creative genius was never approached by anyone other than Einstein.[121]

## APPENDIXES

These appendixes provide the mathematical background to Newton's proof of Kepler's second and third laws. Newton demonstrates why the gravitational force is inversely related to the squared distance of the planets from the Sun, and why the planets orbit the Sun in harmonic ratios. Following Newton's line of reasoning the proof of the two laws is given in Appendices A and B below. Although mathematically not difficult, the argumentation is lengthy and requires attention.

### Appendix A12: Why Gravity is Inversely Related to Distance

Newton begins with an intricate drawing reproduced here in Figure A12, Diagram 1. In preparation for further analysis, he refers to **Four Sets** of Properties that can be deduced from it. [122]

**Set One:** Newton notes that the length of $EP$ equals the length of the major semi-axis $AC$, i.e., $EP = AC$, as in Figure 12.2, Diagram 2. The proof of this theorem was given earlier (Chapter 4, Figure 4.4). Dividing both sides of $EP = AC$ by CP yields $EP/CP = AC/CP$ (Figure 12.2, Diagram 2). Newton also notes that $EP/CP = Px/Pv$. The two ratios $EP/CP$ and $Px/Pv$ are equal because they are based on similar triangles, i.e., the larger triangle $EPC$ is similar to the smaller triangle $xPv$, so that $EP/CP = Px/Pv$ as in Diagram 3. Moreover, since $Px$ equals $QR$, $EP/CP$ is also equal to $QR/Pv$. From this and Figure 12.2, Diagrams 2 and 3, follow the first set of properties: $EP/CP = AC/CP = QR/Pv$.

**Set Two:** Newton points out that $(Gv)(Pv)/(Qv)^2 = (CP)^2/(CD)^2$. Both ratios are equal because each equals 1.0 (i.e., unity). This theorem was also described (Chapter 7, Figure 7.1). Excerpts of it are illustrated here in Figure 12.2, Diagrams 4 and 5.

**Set Three:** Newton equates the two ratios: $AC/FP = CD/BC$ with the comment:"All parallelograms circumscribed about any conjugate diameters of a given ellipse or hyperbola are equal among themselves," and he continues,"this is demonstrated by the writers on the conic sections." [124]

Conjugate diameters of an ellipse are symmetrically arranged around its center. They have certain properties in common. For example, in Figure 12.2, Diagram 6, the points $D$, $G$, $K$ and $P$ are symmetrically arranged around the center $C$ so that $DK$ equals $GP$. Similarly the endpoints of the minor and major axes are symmetrically arranged along the perimeter of the ellipse. Again, this concept was introduced earlier (Chapter 7, Figure 7.2).

As illustrated here in Figure 12.2, Diagram 7, it tells us that $(AC)(BC) = (FP)(CD)$. After dividing both sides by $(FP)(BC)$, we obtain the ratios $AC/FP = CD/BC$. Since $AC$ also equals $EP$ (as in Figure 12.2, Diagram 2), the ratio $AC/FP = EP/FP$ holds true as well. Combining these ratios we have $EP/FP = AC/FP = CD/BC$.

**Set Four:** Newton makes use of another property, namely that: $L = 2(BC)^2/AC$. The letter $L$ refers to the straight line, the *Latus Rectum*, that passes through one focus of the ellipse and is perpendicular to the major axis (Figure 12.2, Diagram 8). Distances $d_1$, $d_2$, and $d_3$ match the length of the major axis. They can be related to the Latus Rectum $L = DG$ as is shown in Equation A12.1. [125]

Equation A12.1: The Relation Between the Latus Rectum and the
                Diameters of an Ellipse

To prove that $L = 2 (BC)^2 / AC$ proceed as follows:

$L = 2 (BC)^2 / AC$ where          $AC$ = Larger Semi-Diameter
$L$ = Latus Rectum                 $BC$ = Smaller Semi-Diameter
$L/2$ = Latus Rectum / 2

$$d_1 = d_2 = d_3$$

$$d_1 = 2 \sqrt{(BC)^2 + (CS)^2}$$

$$d_2 = \tfrac{L}{2} + \sqrt{(2CS)^2 + (\tfrac{L}{2})^2} \quad where \quad L = DG$$

$$d_3 = 2\,AC$$

*Squaring both sides of* $d_1 = d_2$ *, yields*

$$d_1^2 = 4\left[(BC)^2 + (CS)^2\right]$$

$$d_2^2 = \left[(\tfrac{L}{2})^2\right] + \left[2(\tfrac{L}{2})\sqrt{(2\,CS)^2 + (\tfrac{L}{2})^2}\,\right] + \left[(2\,CS)^2 + (\tfrac{L}{2})^2\right]$$

*and equating* $d_1^2$ *to* $d_2^2$ *, results in*

$$4\left[(BC)^2 + (CS)^2\right] = \left[(\tfrac{L}{2})^2\right] + \left[2(\tfrac{L}{2})\sqrt{(2\,CS)^2 + (\tfrac{L}{2})^2}\,\right] + \left[(2\,CS)^2 + (\tfrac{L}{2})^2\right]$$

$$4\,(BC)^2 = \left[(\tfrac{L}{2})^2\right] + \left[2(\tfrac{L}{2})\sqrt{(2\,CS)^2 + (\tfrac{L}{2})^2}\,\right] + 4\,CS^2 - 4\,CS^2 + (\tfrac{L}{2})^2$$

$$4\,(BC)^2 = 2(\tfrac{L}{2})^2 + \left[2(\tfrac{L}{2})\sqrt{(2\,CS)^2 + (\tfrac{L}{2})^2}\,\right]$$

$$= 2\,\tfrac{1}{4}\,L^2 + \left[(L)\sqrt{(2\,CS)^2 + (\tfrac{L}{2})^2}\,\right]$$

$$= L\left[\tfrac{L}{2} + \sqrt{(2\,CS)^2 + (\tfrac{L}{2})^2}\,\right]$$

*substituting for the term in brackets (which equals* $d_2$ *above), the value* $d_3 = 2\,AC$, *this becomes*

$$4\,(BC)^2 = 2\,L\left[\,AC\,\right] \quad so\ that \quad L = \frac{2\,(BC)^2}{AC}\,.$$

In this fashion the Latus Rectum $L$ defines the size and shape of an ellipse. To summarize the above, based on Figure 12.2, Diagram 1, Newton defined **Four Sets of Properties** of an ellipse as:

Equations A12.2: Four Sets of Properties of an Ellipse

**Set One:** $EP/CP = AC/CP = QR/Pv$
**Set Two:** $(Gv)(Pv)/(Qv)^2 = (CP)^2/(CD)^2$
**Set Three:** $EP/FP = AC/FP = CD/BC$
**Set Four:** $L = 2 (BC)^2/AC$

He then develops the Four Sets of Properties a bit further and arrives at a set of **Four Equalities.**[126]

**Four Equalities**

    **Equality I** is the same as **Set One** of the Properties above although Newton augments it by adding the factor $L$ for the Latus Rectum in the numerator and denominator of the first term.

$$I. \quad \frac{[L]\ QR}{[L]\ Pv} = \frac{QR}{Pv} = \frac{EP}{CP} = \frac{AC}{CP}$$

    **Equality II** is new. It is an identity because the terms $Pv$ cancel.

$$II. \quad \frac{[Pv]\ L}{[Pv]\ Gv} = \frac{L}{Gv}$$

    **Equality III** is identical to **Set Two** of the properties above.

$$III. \quad \frac{Gv\ Pv}{Qv^2} = \frac{CP^2}{CD^2}$$

    **Equality IV** enlarges on **Set Three** above as Newton adds the (squared) ratios of $Qx$ and $Qv$ over $QT$ (since Qx becomes Qv as R approaches P) and equates them to the (squared) ratios of $EP/EF$ and the others (Figure 12.2, Diagram 9).

$$IV. \quad \frac{[Qx]}{[QT]} \ \text{ or } \ \frac{[Qv]}{[QT]} = \frac{EP}{FP} = \frac{AC}{FP} = \frac{CD}{BC}$$

$$\frac{[Qv]^2}{[QT]^2} = \frac{EP^2}{FP^2} = \frac{AC^2}{FP^2} = \frac{CD^2}{BC^2}$$

As shown in Figure 12.2, Diagram 9, the additional ratio $Qx/Qt$ can be deduced from the similarity of triangles $QxT$ and $PFE$.

For any point $P$ on the circumference of an ellipse, the two triangles $QxT$ and $EPF$ are similar because they agree in all three angles, and consequently the ratios of their sides are equal so that

$$Qx/QT = Px/Py = EP/FP.$$

Since $Px$ equals $QR$, we can also say that

$$QR/Py = Px/Py = EP/FP.$$

If we let $R$ approach $P$, the equality of the ratios continues to hold. It proves that the $QR/Py$ keeps the value $EP/FP$ as $R$ comes to $P$ (Figure 12.2, Diagram 9).

Newton goes further, however, and concludes that the ratio of $QR/QT$ is constant too (Figure 12.2, Diagram 9). The two triangles $QxT$ and $Pxy$ being similar

$$Qx/QT = k\,Px/\,k\,Py = Px/\,Py$$

which implies that for any point $P$ the ratio $Px / Py$ will remain constant, no matter how small the distance between $Q$ and $P$ (Figure 12.2, Diagram 2). Yet, Newton does more. He not only shows the constancy of the ratio $QR/QT$ but in Equation A12.3 derives its value as

$$QR/QT^2 = 1 / L.$$

Equation A12.3: Algebraic Measure of the Centripetal Force

*The four Equalities were:*

$$\text{I.} \quad \frac{L\ QR}{L\ Pv} = \frac{QR}{Pv} = \frac{EP}{CP} = \frac{AC}{CP}$$

$$\text{II.} \quad \frac{L\ Pv}{Gv\ Pv} = \frac{L}{Gv}$$

$$\text{III.} \quad \frac{Gv\ Pv}{(Qv)^2} = \frac{CP^2}{CD^2}$$

$$\text{IV.} \quad \frac{Qx^2}{QT^2} \ \text{or} \ \frac{Qv^2}{QT^2} = \frac{EP^2}{FP^2} = \frac{AC^2}{FP^2} = \frac{CD^2}{BC^2}$$

*Newton multiplies the left – hand – side terms of Equalities I. to IV. and finds, after canceling the bracketed terms, that:*

$$\frac{L \ QR}{(L)(Pv)} \ \frac{(Pv)(L)}{(Pv)(Gv)} \ \frac{(Gv)(Pv)}{(Qv)^2} \ \frac{(Qv)^2}{QT^2} \ = \ \frac{L \ QR}{QT^{\ 2}} \ ;$$

*where the ratio* $\dfrac{QR}{QT^2} \ \neq \ \dfrac{0}{0}$ *as explained in the text and*

*in Diagram 9 of Figure 12.2 .*

*If the right – hand – side terms of the Equalities are multiplied together, as in*

$$\frac{AC}{CP} \ \frac{L}{Gv} \ \frac{CP^2}{CD^2} \ \frac{CD^2}{BC^2} \qquad and \ if$$

*L is equated to the last Property Set IV* $\left(top \ of \ page \ 235\right)$ *as in*

$$L \ = \ \left[\frac{2 \ BC^2}{AC}\right] \qquad it \ yields$$

$$\frac{AC}{CP} \left[\frac{2 \ BC^2}{AC}\right] \frac{1}{Gv} \ \frac{CP^2}{CD^2} \ \frac{CD^2}{BC^2} \ .$$

*If these terms are multiplied together and the bracketed terms canceled, then*

$$\frac{(AC)}{(CP)} \ \frac{2 \ (BC)^2}{(AC)} \ \frac{1}{Gv} \ \frac{CP \ (CP)}{(CD)^2} \ \frac{(CD)^2}{(BC)^2} \ = \ \frac{2 \ (CP)}{Gv} \ .$$

*But* $\qquad \qquad \dfrac{2 \ (CP)}{Gv} \ = \ 1 . 0$

*when R approaches P and coincides with P,* $Gv = GP$ *and* $Gv = 2\left(CP\right)$ *as shown in Diagram 11 and 12* $\left(of \ Figure \ 12.2\right)$.

*That implies that the righthand side of the equations above equals* 1.0 *, and since the lefthand side equalled*

$$\frac{L \ QR}{QT^2} \qquad it \ follows \ that \qquad \frac{L \ QR}{QT^2} \ = \ 1.0$$

$$and \ therefore, \qquad \frac{QR}{QT^2} \ = \ \frac{1.0}{L} \ .$$

*To interpret the significance of this result, i.e.,*

$$QR/QT^2 = 1/L \, ,$$

*Newton gives this constant as a measure of the centripetal force for any planetary orbit.*[127] *He rewrites the equation above as (in Proposition XI, problem VI),*

$$L \bullet QR = QT^2$$

*and elaborates further.*

## Centripetal Acceleration

We have already seen why a planet exposed to a gravitational force sweeps out equal areas in equal time intervals. In approximating the swept-out area by triangles, they retain their original size even though their shape changes (Figure 12.1, Diagrams 1 to 9).

Also, the force emanating from the Sun diverts a planet from its straight (rectlinear) course and the deflection toward the center of the force is proportionate to the size of the gravitational force (centripetal) force.

Under Proposition VI of the *Principia* Newton describes a planet's path by the curve $APQ$ (Figure 12.3, Diagram 1). Drawn from a neighbouring point, the red line $QR$ is parallel to $SP$, and $QT$ is perpendicular to it. The area $SPQ$ is proportional to the time it takes $P$ to reach R.

During that same time interval, say $t$, the planet is diverted from R to $Q$ (Figure 12.3, Diagram 1). The deflective centripetal force results in an acceleration toward the Sun. Without the centripetal force the planet's speed toward the Sun would be zero at point R. With the centripetal force the planet's speed toward the Sun goes from $v_o = 0$ at point R to $v_q$ at point Q, at an average speed of $(v_o + v_q)/2 = v$. Since this increase in speed occurs during the time interval $t$, the acceleration $a$ from 0 to $v_q$ is $a = (v_q/2)/t$. We also know that the average speed is the distance travelled per unit of time. In this case the planet travels the distance QR per unit of time at the average speed of $v = QR/t$. Substituting this value into acceleration $a$ results in

$$a = \tfrac{1}{2}\, QR/t^2 . \quad [128]$$

Since Newton defines the centripetal force $F$ as being proportional to the acceleration it imparts on the planet, $F$ is proportionate to $QR/t^2$ (i.e., $F = k_1\, QR/t^2$) for some constant $k_1$.

Equation A12.4: Algebraic Measure of the Centripetal Force

*According to the statements in the last lines of Equation A12.3 the characteristic constant of any ellipse is, that*

$$\frac{QR}{(QT)^2} = \frac{1.0}{L} \ .$$

*The centripetal acceleration is*

$$a = \frac{1}{2} \frac{QR}{t^2}$$

*and the corresponding Force F*

$$F \propto \frac{QR}{t^2}$$

*where the symbol $\propto$ means " proportional to " and $t$ is the time required, based on area,*

$$t = \frac{1}{2} (PS)(QT) \qquad and$$

$$t^2 = \frac{1}{4} (PS)^2 (QT)^2 \ .$$

*Sustituting $t^2$ into $F$ above*

$$F \propto \frac{1.0}{(PS)^2 (QT)^2} \qquad and\ after$$

*substituting $\dfrac{1.0}{L}$ for $\dfrac{QR}{(QT)^2}$ , this yields*

$$F \propto \frac{1.0}{(PS)^2 \ L} \ .$$

The expression $F \propto QR/t^2$ implies that the force $F$ varies concurrently with the distance $QR$ per unit of time squared. Even if the underlying functional relationship is multiplied by a constant, say $k = \frac{1}{2}$ or $\frac{1}{4}$ , the expression $F \propto QR/t^2$ still applies because $k$ is a constant so that $F$ varies only with $QR/t^2$. This, in turn, implies that $F \propto 1/(PS)^2$ where $(PS)^2$ is the squared distance of the planet $P$ from the Sun $S$.

With this remarkable proposition Newton proves that the motion of a planet in an elliptical orbit follows the inverse square law: the gravitational (centripetal) force $F$ is directed toward one focus of the ellipse. For any specific elliptical orbit the force $F$ is constant. It varies inversely with the squared distance $(PS)^2$ of the planet $P$ from the focus of the Sun $S$ and also, inversely, with the size of the elliptical orbit its characteristic Latus Rectum $L$ as in $F = 1.0 / (PS)^2 L$, the last equation of A12.4.

**Appendix B12: Why Do Planets Orbit the Sun in Harmonic Ratios?**
Newton restates Kepler's Third Law in Propositions 14 and 15 as Theorems 6 and 7:

> If several bodies revolve about one common center, and the centripetal force is inversely as the square of the distance of places from the center: I say that the principal Latera Recta of their orbits are as the squares of the areas, which the bodies by radii drawn to the centre describe in the same time. [And] the same things being supposed, I say, that the periodic times in ellipses are as 1.5th (i.e., 3/2th) power of their greater axes.[129]

In deducing this theorem, Newton first recalls some of his earlier results. He reminds the reader that when point $R$ approaches and (nearly) coincides with $P$ on an elliptical orbit, the Latus Rectum $L$ equals the ratio $(QT)^2/QR$ as shown in Equation A12.3 and A12.4, and restated in a) of Equation B12.1.

Since the Latus Rectum $L$ is a characteristic constant of any given ellipse, the force varies inversely with the distance from the center $PS$—inversely with the planet's distance PS from the Sun—as in b) of Equation B12.1. We can now rewrite $L$ in terms of $QT$ and $PS$. From it Newton concludes that the area of an ellipse varies with the square root of the Latus Rectum $L$ multiplied by the cumulative time period $t$ as in c) of Equation B12.1. Also he concludes in e) of Equation B12.1 that if the distances $(QT)$ and $(PS)$ in ellipse $A_2$ are $k$ times as great as in ellipse $A_1$, the area of the second will be $k^2$ times as great as that of the first (Figure 12.3, Diagram 1 to 3).

Equation B12.1: The Area of an Ellipse Varies With the Square Root of the Latus Rectum.

*At the end of Equation A 12.3 it was shown that*

a ) $\quad \dfrac{QR}{QT^2} = \dfrac{1}{L}\quad$ *and, therefore,* $\quad L = \dfrac{QT^2}{QR}$ .

*From Equation A 12.4 it is known that*

b ) $\quad F = \dfrac{1.0}{(PS)^2\, L}\; \propto\; \dfrac{1.0}{(PS)^2}$

Re *calling that Force* $F = QR$ *as in Figure 12.2, Diagrams 4 and 9, replace QR in a ) by* $F \propto \dfrac{1.0}{(PS)^2}$ *in b), as in c):*

c ) $\quad L = \dfrac{(QT)^2}{1.0/(PS)^2}\quad$ *so that*

$$L = (QT)^2\,(PS)^2 \quad and \quad \sqrt{L} = (QT)(PS)$$

*Newton concludes that the Area A of the ellipse var ies with the size of the triangle PSQ in Figure 12.3, Diagram 2, multplied by the cumulative time t, as in*

d ) $\quad A = \dfrac{1}{2}(QT)(PS)\,t\; \propto\; (QT)(PS)\,t\quad and$

*substituting from c) above* $\sqrt{L} = (QT)(PS)$ *the area var ies as in*

$$A = t\,\sqrt{L}\qquad and\; time\; var\,ies\; as\; in$$

$$t \;\propto\; A\,L^{-0.5}$$

*where t is the periodic orbital time of a planet. If, for example, in Figure 12.3, Diagram 2:*

e ) $\quad (PS)_2 = k\,(PS)_1 \quad and \quad (QT)_2 = k\,(QT)_1$
*then*
$$A_2 \propto k^2\, t\,(QT)_1\,(PS)_1 = k^2\, t\,\sqrt{L} = k^2\, A_1 .$$

All this was done in preparation for the next step: to show that the periodic times of planets in elliptical orbits are as 1.5th (i.e., 3/2th) power of their greater axis. Again, we need to recall an earlier item. As illustrated in Figure 12.1, Diagram 8, the Latus Rectum $L = DG$ passes through the focus $S$ of the ellipse. Earlier in Equation A12.1 it was shown in the last term that

$$L = 2(BC)^2/AC$$

and, therefore, varies in proportion with $(AC)(BC)$.

Equation B12.2: The Harmonic Law of Orbital Motion

*Starting with*

*a)* $\quad L \;=\; \dfrac{2\,(BC)^2}{AC}, \quad so\ that \quad (AC)\,L \;=\; 2\,(BC)^2$

*and* $\quad BC = \sqrt{AC\,\dfrac{L}{2}} = \sqrt{\dfrac{AC}{2}}\,\sqrt{L}$

*based on a)* $(AC)(BC)$ *can be rewritten as*

*b)* $\quad (AC)(BC) \;=\; AC\sqrt{AC\,\dfrac{L}{2}} \;=\; AC\sqrt{\dfrac{AC}{2}}\,\sqrt{\dfrac{2\,(BC)^2}{AC}}$

$$\qquad\qquad = \; AC\sqrt{\dfrac{AC}{2}}\,\sqrt{L} \;\propto\; AC\,\sqrt{AC}\,\sqrt{L}$$

*so that* $(AC)(BC)$ *varies with* $\sqrt{L}$ *as in c):*

*c)* $\quad (AC)(BC) \;\propto\; (AC)^{1.5}\,\sqrt{L} \qquad and\ if$

$\qquad (AC)_2 \;=\; k\,(AC)_1 \quad and \quad (BC)_2 \;=\; k\,(BC)_1\,,\,then$

$\qquad\qquad (AC)_2\,(BC)_2 \;=\; k^2\,(AC)_1\,(BC)_1\;.$

As suggested in e) of Equation B12.1 and c) of Equation B12.2, the two expressions vary proportionately by the same factor $k^2$ so that the condition is met.

Finally, this lets us conclude in b) of Equation B12.3 that the planets moving in elliptical orbits around the Sun, complete their revolution in orbital time periods that are proportionate to 3/2th power of the greater axis AC of the ellipse (Diagram 3 of Figure 12.3). Thus Newton confirms Kepler's Third Law.

Equation 12B.3: Newton's Proof of Kepler's Third Law

*Recall a ) from Equation B* 12.1

*a )*     $A \propto t\sqrt{L} = t\,(SP)(QT)$ , *and*

*and b ) from Equation B* 12.2

*b )*     $(AC)(BC) \propto (AC)^{1.5}\sqrt{L}$

*then, following Newton, let Area A*

$$A \propto (AC)(BC)$$

*so that*

$$t\sqrt{L} \propto (AC)^{1.5}$$

*and, therefore,*

$$t \propto (AC)^{1.5}$$

*which confirms Kepler's Third Law.*

Chapter 13

## ON THE NATURE AND SPEED OF LIGHT

*Scholars of ancient and medieval times were completely in the dark as to the nature of light. They speculated that it consisted of particles emitted by the glowing object or perhaps by the eye itself.*

Isaac Asimov [1]

Before Newton's time, physics and natural philosophy were interchangeably used. Although Johannes Kepler (1571–1630) derived the laws of motion from planetary data and Galileo (1564–1642) made some significant contributions to mechanics, it was Newton (1642–1727) who developed the first systematic theory of mechanics to explain the laws of motion. Newton's theory became the basis of "classical mechanics." Together, the three theories of Kepler, Galileo, and Newton were taken to be new natural philosophies.

Today, physics is defined as the science that deals with the fundamental principles of nature and the universe. Physicists are concerned with many phenomena: the principles of motion (mechanics), the reaction of particles to heat (thermodynamics$_g$), the theories of electromagnetic fields and light (electromagnetism$_g$), the theory of high-speed motion and the origin of the universe (relativity), and that of particle behavior at the submicroscopic level (quantum mechanics$_g$).[2]

244

These phenomena are interrelated. For example, in the twentieth century the phenomenon of light became a fundamental constant of nature that is tightly linked to the theory of relativity. This theory provides a new interpretation of Newton's laws of motion and energy which will be discussed in the next two chapters. But first, a look at light. Light is also tied to particle behavior and electromagnetic force. This link will come to the fore in the final chapters of this book.

The quest for a better understanding of the nature of light was not only relevant for optics, for the development of telescopes, for measuring the distances to the stars, and for advances in electromagnetic radiation, but also for a better understanding of the nature of space. Eventually, it would open the door to a radically new perception of the universe.

This chapter deals with the evolution of various theories of light and different techniques for measuring the speed of light. Many scientists contributed. Their work yielded results of great precision that formed the foundation for the scientific revolution of the twentieth century. Here only some of the major elements are briefly described and illustrated.

## Sound and Light

Since time immemorial people have treasured the light of the Sun and scorned the dark of the night. They saw light and dark locked in a never-ending battle. When, during the winter months, the days shortened or when a solar eclipse obscured the Sun, they feared that demons of the dark would take over the world and conquer all.

Millennia passed before abstract questions were raised about the properties of light. What is light made of? How does it enable us to see? The Pythagoreans of ancient Greece believed that the eyes emitted rays to see the world. Euclid believed rays from the eyes probed the surroundings just like a blind person probes the way by tapping with a cane. The astronomer Ptolemy added some refinements when he described the same idea in the *Almagest*. Plato also postulated an interaction between the observer and the observed. Yet, he believed that it was a two-way phenomenon, the open eye sending out an inner light and the object emitting rays in return.[3]

Attempts at measuring the speed of light followed from earlier experiments with sound. As far back as the sixth century B.C. the Greek philosopher Pythagoras experimented with vibrating strings to find out which intervals produced the most pleasing sounds. About two centuries later Aristotle correctly anticipated that sound was transmitted by the motion of the air. He also speculated that higher sounds were transmitted faster than lower sounds, an error that persisted over many centuries.[4]

Galileo Galilei studied acoustics by experiment. Inspired by his father, who was a court musician and had written a treatise on music, Galileo studied the vibrations of sound using the strings of musical instruments in combination with tuning forks. He discovered a correlation between pitch and vibratory frequency. Others followed up on his discovery. In Galileo's time people were well aware that sound was transmitted with some delay.

Marin Mersenne (1588–1648), a French mathematician, philosopher and theologian, perhaps best known for his discovery of the Mersenne Numbers,[5] was the first to conduct experiments in acoustics. In 1636 he published his findings in a treatise. By formulating three mathematical laws he showed how the frequency of sound is related to the length, tension, and thickness of the string.[6]

He was also the first to estimate the speed of sound. To do so, he had a military cannon positioned on a hilltop several miles away from him and had an assistant set it off. By counting the swings of a pendulum, Marsenne estimated the time it took the blast to reach him after he saw the flash. Since he knew the distance between himself and the cannon, he divided the distance by the number of swings to arrive at the lag between the flash and the blast. He concluded that sound traveled close to 700 miles per hour (1127 km per hour, a result that came close to today's estimate of 1206 km per hour).[7] In his day, it was an unheard-of speed.

## An Early Attempt to Measure the Speed of Light

Galileo was the first to try measuring the speed of light. The French mathematician Descartes (1596–1650) had claimed that light was transmitted instantaneously. Galileo decided to test this hypothesis. With an experimental design similar to Mersenne's, he tried to compute the velocity

246

of light by timing the delay in light signals from some distance away. In the dark of the night, he climbed to a nearby hilltop with one of his assistants while a second assistant clambered up another hill, not quite a mile away. When the first assistant opened the shutter of his lantern, the second did the same. Timing the delay—possibly with the pulsilogium he had invented earlier (see Chapter 11)—Galileo measured the time lapse between the two signals.

As expected, Galileo did observe a certain delay. Yet, being a careful investigator, he had rehearsed the routine with his assistants before climbing the hills. He had timed their natural response time while both were standing close together and knew that they did not react instantaneously to the signal. When he compared the time lag of the experiment with their natural response time, he found no significant difference.

Galileo was not convinced of the validity of the results.[8] He believed that the experiment was inconclusive and wanted to repeat it over greater distances.[9] If again no delay could be observed, he might have concluded that light was transmitted instantaneously. As it was, however, he never did pursue it any further. The issue remained unresolved.[10]

When Galileo first directed his newly-built telescope at the heavens, he not only saw innumerable stars but discovered several new moons.[11] By careful observation and punctilious records, he found that they circled the distant planet Jupiter at regular intervals. For him this was the decisive proof that the Earth with its nearby Moon was not unique among the planets of the solar system. It enticed him to declare that the Earth was not the center of the universe.

Publicly announcing his discovery and claiming that the Copernican system was not just an alternative geometric interpretation of celestial motions but for real, contradicted the philosophical and ecclesiastical doctrine of his day. Predictably, the prominent powers of the Church did not take kindly to it. What neither he nor they anticipated, was that several decades later the moons of Jupiter would play a key role in measuring the velocity of light.

## The Speed of Light and the Eclipse of Jupiter's Moon Io

*Olaus Roemer (1644–1710)*

Some sixty years after Galileo had discovered the moons of Jupiter, the Danish astronomer Olaus Roemer, while in Paris during the early 1670s, observed the motions of the moons of Jupiter. He aimed his telescope at them and kept meticulous records of the orbital positions of one of them in particular, Jupiter's moon Io. From his observations Roemer could predict the dates and times when Jupiter's shadow eclipsed Io.[12]

What puzzled him was that his predictions did not quite match the actual occurrences. What puzzled him even more was that he could predict the size of the deviations from the expected values. Presumably, if Io circled Jupiter at a constant speed, you would expect regularly timed eclipses but that was not what Roemer observed. He found that whenever both Jupiter and the Earth were on the same side of the Sun, Jupiter eclipsed Io nearly 10 minutes earlier than expected. Conversely, when Jupiter and Earth were on opposite sides of the Sun, Jupiter eclipsed Io nearly 10 minutes later than expected. (This he could ascertain by clocks[13] which by that time, thanks to Huygens, had become quite accurate and, of course, he could compare it with the "angular motion" of the stars.) Then one day it occurred to him that the variations in the timing of the eclipses must be linked to the orbital positions of the Earth.

His argument went like this: when the Earth and Jupiter are both on the same side of the Sun, they are closer together. When the Earth and Jupiter are on opposite sides of the Sun, they are farther apart. After an eclipse, Io reappears from behind Jupiter and the time it takes for it to be seen will vary with the distance the light has to travel to reach Earth. Since Jupiter changes its orbital position much more slowly than Earth—one orbital revolution of Jupiter around the Sun takes 4333 Earth-days—the changes in distance must come from the motion of the Earth. At times the orbital position of the Earth adds to, and at other times it subtracts from, the average distance of Jupiter from Earth. Consequently, he could fix the speed of light by dividing this difference in distance by the difference in time. To apply this idea, Roemer needed to know the exact distance of the Earth from the Sun (Figure 13.1, Diagram 1).

More than a century earlier, Johannes Kepler had deduced from Tycho de Brahe's excellent observations that the shape of planetary orbits is elliptical. Toward the end of his life he had discovered the formula that related the orbital periods of the planets to their distance from the Sun. According to his Harmonic Law the square of the orbital period of a planet is proportionate to the cube of its semi-major axis (See Chapter 12, Appendix B, Equation B12.3). From the orbital period he could deduce how distant a planet was from the Sun.

Although Kepler's formula was accurate and later confirmed by Newton's theory, both had expressed planetary distances in astronomical units$_g$ rather than miles or kilometers. One astronomical unit equaled the average distance of the Sun from the Earth. In the *Principia*, for example, Newton equated the mean distance of the Sun from the Earth to 100,000 parts and related the orbital distances of other planetary bodies to this base.[14] Roemer, too, expressed the velocity of light in astronomical units but that did not yield a very useful estimate of the speed of light. As yet no method had been devised whereby astronomical distances could be measured in miles (or kilometers). The work of Cassini and Richer, would eventually help Roemer to estimate the speed of light.

*Giovanni D. Cassini (1625–1712) and Jean Richer (1630–1696).*
Cassini and Richer obtained the first estimates of the distance of the planet Mars from Earth by method of parallax$_g$ in 1671. Richer led a scientific expedition to Cayenne, the capital of French Guiana in South America, and Cassini stayed behind in Paris, France. They agreed to observe the position of Mars from the two locations, and at the same point in time.[15]

Knowing the distance from Paris to Cayenne and having observed the position of Mars against the background of the stars, they estimated the distance from Earth to Mars by elementary trigonometry. Then, using Kepler's relative scale of the planetary orbits, Cassini computed the Sun's average distance from Earth at 87 million miles (140 million km). His estimate was only about 6 million miles (9.65 million km) short of the actual distance, or less than 10%. For his day, it was an excellent approximation (Figure 13.1, Diagram 2).

From Cassini's estimate of planetary distances and his own observations of the moon Io, Olaus Roemer estimated the velocity of light. He attributed the irregularities in Io's eclipses to variations in the delay of light transmission. After Io comes out of Jupiter's shadow, sunlight is reflected from it. To reach Earth, the reflected light has to travel an extra 186 million miles (300 million km) when Earth and Jupiter are not on the same side of the Sun. Since the gap between expected and actual times of the eclipses is close to 17 minutes (1020 seconds), light has to travel at $(186)(10)^6$ miles$/1020$ seconds $= 182,400$ miles, close to the actual speed of 186,282 miles (or 299,783 km) per second (Figure 13.1, Diagrams 3 and 4).

Roemer arrived at a speed of light of 130,000 to 150,000 miles per second or between 210,000 and 240,000 km/sec, an estimate that fell about one quarter short of the modern-day value of 299,783 km/sec. His estimates were on the low side, mainly because he had put the time lags as high as 22 minutes and the Earth/Sun distance nearly 7% below today's value.[16] Nevertheless, his values were based on sound theory. They gave a first indication of the enormous speed of light.[17]

Roemer's estimate did not meet with the approval of astronomers. Few accepted it. Instead, astronomers kept searching for better methods of determining the distance to the stars. Confirmation of Roemer's estimates only came 50 years later.

## Light Corpuscles or Waves?

*Isaac Newton (1642–1727)*

While Olaus Roemer deduced the speed of light from the motions of Jupiter's moon Io, Newton proposed a theory of light. During the early 1670s Newton lectured at Trinity College on the topic of optics. In 1672, after the Royal Society elected him to membership, he volunteered to present a paper on optics. Newton proposed a mechanical theory of light transmission.

In his research Newton accepted the ancient theory of light—going as far back as Aristotle—that light consisted of tiny corpuscles. But he did not accept the proposition of his contemporaries that colours were modifications of white light. Instead, he proposed that colours of light came from the light's basic components. In his treatise on optics Newton reported that ordinary white light could be spread out into a spectrum of many colours by passing it through a prism. He could show that the process was reversible. By passing the same colours through a second inverted prism of the same shape, he reconstituted them into white light. Individual light rays, he believed, were composed of tiny immutable particles that varied in size. On contact with the retina of the human eye, they would produce different colours.

From this theory of light corpuscles, Newton deduced an explanation of the reflection and refraction of light. Light corpuscles formed light rays emitted from a source of light in all direction (Figure 13.2, Diagram 1). Light rays are reflected when pointed at a dense solid such as a polished metal surface or mirror. Just like a ball is deflected from a solid surface, a lightbeam is deflected from a polished surface (Figure 13.2, Diagram 2). If the surface is of a transparent material such as glass or water, light rays are refracted (change direction) when they strike the surface (Figure 13.2, Diagram 3). Newton attributed this characteristic to differences in the density of the transparent materials. According to him, the same corpuscles of light were diverted more or less from their path depending on the greater or lesser density of the material.

Some natural crystals have the unique property of polarizing light. Calcite, for example, divides the light into polarized beams that are at right angles to each other. When the crystal is held at a certain angle a light beam passes through, when turned at a right angle it does not. Newton was aware of this polarizing property. He believed the light corpuscels were of elliptical shape so that the polarizing crystals would let the corpuscles through when aligned with the polarizing axis of the crystal, but blocked the light when turned at a right angle (Figure 13.2, Diagram 4).

## Christiaan Huygens (1629–1695)
Huygens, a Dutch mathematician, astronomer and physicist, had a knack for mechanical applications. He discovered a new method of grinding lenses, built more powerful telescopes, invented the micrometer for

measuring extremely small distances, and was the first to construct a pendulum clock, a kind of grandfather clock still in vogue today.[18]

Christiaan was born into a wealthy family near the Dutch city of The Hague.[19] Young Christiaan showed an early talent for drawing, geometry, and mathematics. He became a friend of René Descartes$_g$, mathematician and philosopher, who often visited his parents. At age 16 Christiaan entered the University of Leiden in Holland for the study of mathematics and law. Ten years later he visited Paris for the first time. His family's name, his wealth, and his pleasant disposition gained him entry to the highest social and intellectual circles. By the time he returned from his second visit, in 1660, he had already gained a reputation in astronomy and mathematics. With his improved telescope he had discovered the rings of the planet Saturn and its moon Titan. He had even identified some faint stars in the Great Nebula of Orion. As well, he had corresponded with Blaise Pascal (1623–1662), French philosopher and mathematician) on questions in mathematics.

In 1663 King Louis XIV honored Huygens for his invention of the pendulum clock. Three years later the king's minister, Colbert, requested that Huygens become the founder and first director of the French Academy of Sciences. He was granted a very generous salary and for the next 15 years Huygens lived in Paris. Throughout his life Huygens suffered from recurrent illnesses and, in 1681, poor health prompted him to return home. For a time he stayed in England and then spent his remaining years in Holland.

In 1690 Huygens published his *Treatise on Light* in which he gave an alternative explanation of reflection and refraction. It not only survived but proved—for the next two centuries—more popular than Newton's corpuscular theory. Although Newton's views differed from his, Huygens never engaged in a public controversy with him. He respected the brilliant genius of Newton as much as he admired the wide-ranging intellect of his lifelong friend, Leibniz (1646–1716). (See Chapter 12 for an account of the controversy between Newton and Leibniz.)

In his treatise Huygens related the wave theory to the reflection and refraction of light, basing his explanation on secondary wavefronts, which have since been named the Huygens' Principle.[20] A secondary wavefront can be derived from knowledge of an earlier wave front. "All points on a given wave front are taken as point sources for the production of spherical secondary waves, called wavelets, which propagate outward with speeds characteristic of waves on that medium."[21] Secondary wave fronts, one curvilinear and the other rectilinear, are illustrated in Figure 13.3, Diagrams 1 and 2.

From such wave fronts, Huygens derived the laws of reflection and refraction geometrically. He represented a new wave front along a tangent line, that touched a point on each semicircle at which the light ray was at a right angle to the new wave front. If all light rays traveled at the same speed, he could explain how light rays were reflected in a mirror or any other reflective surface (Figure 13.3, Diagram 3). He could also explain how light rays were refracted when they crossed from one medium to another. Just like one wing of a front line of soldiers falls behind when they encounter greater resistance, the wave front is refracted when light rays get into a medium that slows them down (Figure 13.3, Diagram 4).[22]

The wave theory of Huygens was in direct competition with Newton's corpuscular theory of light. Initially, the wave theory was in doubt because it was more complex than Newton's theory and the principles of reflection and refraction could be explained just as well by the corpuscular theory. At the time, no experimental evidence gave a clear advantage to the wave theory over Newton's theory.

As Newton's *Principia* rendered some of Huygens' views obsolete, Huygens felt he could no longer contribute to the advances of science. He returned to Holland and gradually lost contact with his former colleagues. Like Leibniz, Huygens spent the last years of his life in lonely isolation. Plagued by ill health and melancholy, he died after much suffering, in 1695. A first clear confirmation of his wave theory did not appear until about 100 years later.[23]

## The Speed of Light and the Angle of the Telescope
*James Bradley (1693–1762)*

James Bradley was the third Astronomer Royal successor at the Royal Observatory at Greenwich. He added many refinements to the construc tion of telescopes and improved on the techniques of astronomical observation.

In 1725, Bradley collaborated with Samuel Molyneux (1689–1728), a British astronomer and politician, in setting up a zenith telescope. They wanted to estimate the distance to the nearest star by method of parallax. Robert Hooke, of the Newton/Hooke controversy (see Chapter 12), had tried it at the turn of the century, but failed. To reduce optical distortions Bradley and Molyneux directed their telescope straight up at the sky. They installed it in the chimney of Molyneux's estate at Kew near London and pointed it at the star Gamma Draconis that passed through the zenith at London's latitude.[24] To allow for the rotation of the Earth they measured the deviation from the vertical by observing how much they had to adjust their aim to bring Gamma Draconis back into the crosshairs of their telescope.

Although this renewed bid for finding the distance to the nearest stars failed (the stars were too distant and telescopes of their day too weak for this task) their search was successful in a startling new way. In analyzing several months of data, Bradley noticed something very strange: the stars moved a tiny bit, all in the same direction and at the same rate. How could it be that the fixed stars moved all in unison? To be absolutely certain he installed a second telescope in his aunt's house, mounting it on the roof. Trying to prevent any distortions from variations in temperature and moisture, he put the measuring devices in the basement (his aunt had been kind enough to let him cut holes through the floors and the roof).[25]

By 1728 Bradley had carefully recorded the minute motions of some 200 stars. Their movement fascinated and puzzled him so much that he could not let go of the problem.[26] Then, on a day in September, it suddenly struck him. While relaxing in his sailboat on the river Thames he noticed a weather vane pointing in the direction of the wind and turning as the wind changed direction. Yet, the vane also appeared to turn whenever his boat changed course. It was then that the answer to the puzzle came to him in a flash: the Earth was like a boat adrift in a stream with the changes in its ccourse causing the apparent motion of the stars.[27]

Bradley reasoned that if the Earth were at rest in relation to the stars, light from the stars would strike the objective of the telescope from straight above and their nightly image would remain fixed in the same position.[28] The light of the stars would pass through the vertical tube of his telescope just like raindrops from straight above would fall through a tube without touching its walls. Yet, if the tube were moving' some rain drops would never make it all the way through but would hit the side of the tube's wall or fall outside of it. Bradley had discovered the principle of "aberration" of starlight.

Figure 13.4 illustrates the principle by using the example of four rain drops passing through a vertical tube. Assuming there is no wind and the rain comes straight down, all four drops will pass through the tube vertically (Figure 13.4, Diagram 1). If the tube is moved sideways, however, the four drops will clear the tube only if it is tilted at a proper angle so that they are not impeded by the walls of the tube (Figure 13.4, Diagram 2).[29] Similarly, the light of the stars would fall straight through the tube if the Earth stood still. Since it moves, the tube needs to be tilted. The proper degree of tilt depends on the speed and direction of the Earth's movements (Figure 13.4, Diagram 3).

Bradley knew that the Earth was not standing still but swinging back and forth on its annual course around the Sun. It was this orbital motion of the Earth that made it necessary to tilt the telescope. Adjusting it prevented the starlight from being blocked by the walls of the telescope's tube. The angle of tilt or aberration—the difference between the observed direction of a star and its true direction—was extremely small and barely noticeable over a six-month intervals.[30]

Bradley managed to adjust the angular aberration with extreme precision so that the tilt of the telescope matched the angle of the incoming light from the stars. He estimated the degree of aberration of starlight to be at an angle of 20 seconds, a very small angle. Consider that one degree is 1/90 of a right angle, each degree consists of 60 minutes, and each minute of 60 seconds, the angle of aberration amounted to 20/3600 or to 1/180th of 1°.

Quite unexpectedly and very ingeniously, based on this stellar aberration, Bradley derived an alternative estimate of the speed of light. It confirmed Roemer's earlier finding of the astonishing speed of light. Given the vertical length of the zenith telescope, the orbital speed of the Earth

(18.6 miles per second or roughly 30 km/sec),[31] and the angle of aberration, Bradley estimated the speed of light at 188,281 miles per second or 303,000 kilometers/second (Figure 13.5), a figure very close to the modern value of 186,272 miles/sec or 299,792 km/sec. His estimate of the enormous speed of light not only corroborated Roemer's earlier finding, but it was a great improvement over the earlier estimate because it was based on more precise information. He announced his discovery of the aberration of light at the Royal Society in 1729.[32]

Bradley greatly improved on the precision of telescopic observations but was unable to measure the distance to the nearest stars by method of parallax. It was still too formidable a task. In Bradley's time instrument makers were not equipped to meet this kind of challenge. It would take another hundred years before instruments of greater precision would enable astronomers to estimate the distance of nearby stars.

**Invisible Light**

While examining the characteristics of light, three scientists, Herschel, Wollaston and Ritter, discovered that the spectrum of light is bordered by invisible rays of energy.[33]

*William Herschel (1738–1822)*

Of the three scientists who discovered that the spectrum of light is bordered by invisible rays of energy, Herschel was the best known. Born in Hannover, Germany in 1738, he had followed in the footsteps of his father, an army musician. As a boy he played in the band of the Hannoverian Guards. When the French invaded Hannover in 1757, he escaped to England. First earning a living by copying music notes, he soon became a music teacher, a composer, and in 1766 was appointed organist of the chapel of Bath. From the practice of music he turned to the theory of music and from there to optics, the construction of telescopes, and then to astronomy. Searching ever deeper into the sky, he needed better telescopes. It was too costly to have them made by opticians, so he made them himself.

At age 43 he spotted the planet Uranus, the first new planet dis-covered since prehistoric times. Elected a fellow of the Royal Society of

London, he was appointed Astronomer Royal to King George III. In the dark of the night he studied the distant nebulas and postulated the existence of island universes. His sister Caroline recorded his observations during the day. Together they catalogued about 2500 nebulas. Before then only about 100 were known.

Herschel published some 70 scientific papers on astronomy and related subjects. Among them was the 1800 announcement of the discovery of infrared rays, the existence of rays beyond the range of visible light—he encountered them while measuring the temperature across the spectrum of colors dispersed by a prism. As he was moving the thermometer from violet to red he noticed a significant rise in temperature.[34]

## *William Hyde Wollaston (1766–1828)*

Wollaston studied independently the effects of light on silver chloride. He discovered modern methods of processing platinum, tungsten, and molybdenum. Born in Norfolk, England, he was formally trained as a physician. He authored 56 papers on chemistry, mineralogy, crystallography, physics, astronomy, botany, physiology, and pathology. The papers reflected his wide-ranging interests and brought about notable advances in science. While observing how quickly light darkened silver chloride he noticed that when the chemical was placed beyond the violet end of the spectrum of light it darkened even more rapidly.[35]

## *Johann Wilhelm Ritter (1776–1810)*

Ritter was a German physicist. Born near Haynau, Poland (formerly Germany), he worked as a pharmacist in Silesia. He studied medicine and later taught at the University of Jena. With a strong interest in electrochemistry, he succeeded in decomposing water into oxygen and hydrogen by electrolysis, discovered the process of electroplating, and experimented with silver chloride. In his experimental work he too observed the darkening of silver chloride beyond the violet range of the spectrum and was the first to discover thermal (heat) radiation.[36]

## Evidence of Light Waves

*Thomas Young (1773–1829)*

Advances during the nineteenth and twentieth centuries lent new support to the wave theory. In 1801 Young, an English physician and physicist, investigated the nature of light.[37] Thomas Young was a child prodigy. He could read at the age of two, pored over the Bible at age four, spoke Latin at six, knew French and Italian at 13, had mastered Newton's works at 19, had taught himself calculus, learned the languages of the Middle East, and then entered university to study medicine.[38] Yet, he became known as a physicist.

Thomas Young discovered the Principle of Interference of light and by that proved that light traveled in waves. Before elaborating on interference, however, it helps to first look at the Principle of Superposition.

Whether a strong wind churns up some white caps on a lake or variations in intensity of sound are produced by many instruments of an orchestra, it will be because two or more waves pass simultaneously through the same space. Peaks are produced when waves are superimposed on each other. To illustrate, we only need to let two pulses travel along a stretched rope in opposite directions, one from the left and the other from the right.[39] They peak as they pass through each other, superposing as the two coincide throughout their extent. Obeying the Principle of Superposition, their heights are additive.

The heights or amplitudes of waves (sound or water) are additive when they coincide. Waves interfere with each other when they run counter to each other, that is, when one is at a high and the other at a low. Then the amplitude of one is reduced by the other. They will offset each other if one happens to be the exact mirror image of the other.

In conducting his experiments Young was the first to show that light waves behave similarly to water waves. Water waves bend or diffract when they pass through narrow openings: the narrower the opening, the greater the diffraction (Figure 13.6, Diagram 1). Diffraction of light only becomes visible when the openings are extremely narrow. To detect patterns of interference, having waves of the same length and amplitude is crucial. In a classical experiment Young achieved this by letting a beam of light through a slot in a first barrier and letting it pass from there through two slots of a second barrier. In this fashion he created an interference pattern of light waves that could be seen as an "interference fringe" of variations in the intensity of light (Figure 13.6, Diagram 2).

More evidence in support of the wave theory was to come. All along it was believed that if light consisted of waves, they would have to be longitudinal waves. Such waves were a common occurrence. Sound waves had been successfully interpreted this way. Also, longitudinal waves were visible. They could be seen as crests and troughs when wind blew across the fields of grain. The undulations appeared as the stalks of grain swayed back and forth in the direction of the wind. Yet, there was just one major problem. If light waves were longitudinal, their property of polarization could not be explained.

Newton explained the polarization of light by assuming that the corpuscles of light were not globular but elongated so that they could slip through the sheet-like structure of a polarizing crystal of calcite or spar that blocked out any spherical particles.[40]

It occurred to Young that light waves would not have to move back and forth. They would not have to be longitudinal but could be transverse instead. Light could be transmitted by transverse waves just like the jerk of a rope transmits a pulse along its length. Light waves could vibrate up and down or from left to right, or anywhere between, if they vibrated at a right angle to the direction of the beam. That would allow some waves, say the up-and-down variety, to pass through the sheet-like structure of calcite, or any other polarizing material, while it would block waves of the left-to-right variety (Figure 13.6, Diagram 3). So finally, many years later, Huygens' wave theory of light was supported by Thomas Young's new experimental evidence.

## Terrestrial Estimates of the Speed of Light
*Armand Hippolyte Louis Fizeau (1819–1896)*
In 1849 Fizeau, a French physicist, made another attempt at measuring the velocity of light. He applied a different method, not based on celestial observations but on a novel terrestrial experiment. The first to measure the speed of light with a fair degree of accuracy by a non-astronomical method,

he succeeded where some 200 years earlier Galileo had failed. Fizeau conducted the experiment in the Parisian suburbs of Suresne and Montmatre.[41] Apart from other improvements, he modified Galileo's experimental design by lengthening the path of light from one to 10.75 miles (or 17.3 km) and by substituting a mirror for Galileo's second assistant.

Fizeau's experimental set-up consisted of a light source, a rotating twin-wheel, three mirrors, and several lenses. After the light-beam passed a toothed wheel, it split into two beams at a semi-transparent mirror, one beam going off in the direction of the observer and the other toward a second mirror set 5.3 miles (8.5 km) away from the first. The second mirror reflected the beam to a third mirror where it merged with the light that passed through the first (semi-transparent) mirror. This distance plus the distance between light source and observer added to a total distance of 10.75 miles (17.3 km).[42] A greatly simplified version of Fizeau's experimental design is shown in Figure 13.7, Diagram 1.[43]

Letting the toothed wheel spin, the light beam was either blocked by a tooth of the wheel or it freely passed through.[44] When it passed through, the observer saw it as a bright light, but when blocked it appeared dim because only the beam's partial reflection could be seen. On speeding up the wheel the observer did not see the light as switched on or off, but recognized only a brightening and dimming of the light as if turned up or down by a dimmer switch. It was brightest when, on consecutive turns, the light passed through the center of the openings and weakest when it was consistently blocked.[45]

Knowing the distance between light source and the speed of the rotation, Fizeau estimated the speed of light. The greater the speed of the wheel, the shorter the time to cover the distance. At any particular angular speed, the wheel rotated a measurable distance. By varying the speed of the wheel Fizeau estimated how far the wheel turned while the light made the 10.75 mile (17.3 km) trip from source to observer.[46] Figure 13.7 illustrates his experimental set-up for measuring the speed of light.

Since the precision of Fizeau's estimate hinged on the visual perception of variations in brightness of the light, it was difficult for him to precisely pinpoint maxima and minima of brightness. He computed the speed of light at 195,924 miles per second (or 315,300 km/sec).[47] This was higher and less accurate than Bradley's earlier estimate. Nevertheless, whether deduced from celestial observations or such terrestrial experimentation, the result made it clear that the speed of light was almost unbelievably high. It was incredibly high when compared with that of horse-drawn carriages or sailing ships, the most common means of transportation at the time.

*Jean Bernard Léon Foucault (1819–1868)*[48]

Foucault, friend and co-worker of Fizeau, improved on this method. By replacing the rotating toothed wheel with a revolving mirror he managed to eliminate the error-prone human element. Foucault could measure the speed of light more accurately than ever before.[49] With improvements in their experimental apparatus the two researchers eventually and convincingly showed that the velocity of light ranged from 185,795 to 187,038 miles per second (or 299,000 to 301,000 km/sec).[50]

Foucault's modification of Fizeau's original experiment led him to yet another important discovery. With his more sensitive instruments he explored how the speed of light varied when he let it pass through water and other media.[51] As well, he tested whether or not the speed of the light was affected by the direction of a current (Figure 13.7, Diagram 2). By 1850 he had discovered that light passed through water at a lower speed than through air. This new finding ran counter to Newton's contention—he had claimed that light went through water at a higher speed. Foucault's finding lent support to Huygens' wave theory of some 200 years earlier. Foucault also found that the current flow of a liquid affected the speed of light, although the observed change in speed was somewhat less than the variation in the speed of the water.[52]

## Measuring the Distance to the Stars

In his book on the *Harmony of the World (1618)*, Kepler described the formula for planetary orbits. As was customary in his day, he expressed their size in astronomical units, a unit of length based on the average distance of the Earth from the Sun (Chapter 10, Table 10.1). In 1671, Richer and Cassini were the first astronomers who approximated the size of the Earth's orbit around the Sun at 174 million miles (280 million km) (See Figure 13.1, Diagram 3.) Their estimate came within ten percent of the Earth's orbital diameter of roughly 186 million miles or 300 million km. Thus, the Earth's mean distance or one astronomical unit (1 A.U.) amounts to 93 million miles (150 million km).

*Friedrich Wilhelm Bessel (1784–1846)*
Measuring the distance to the stars defied the efforts of astronomers for over 150 years. The observational task was beyond the precision of available instruments. Using the diameter of Earth's orbit as a baseline of a triangle drawn to the nearest star, was like a one-foot baseline of a triangle drawn to a light 26 miles (42 km) away and finding the angle of convergence at the tip of the triangle. But the precision of optical instruments kept improving.

Bessel was the first astronomer to succeed in measuring the distance to the stars. Born in 1784, the son of a poor government em-ployee, he entered an import-export firm at age 15. Working at night, he wrote a paper on Halley's Comet in which he estimated its orbit based on the observations of 1607 and sent it to astronomer Wilhelm Olbers, who had calculated numerous comet orbits. Olbers was so impressed that he arranged to have Bessel's paper published and proposed that he be taken on as an assistant at the Lilienthal Observatory in Prussia. He later said that the greatest service he had rendered to astronomy was to have recognized the genius of Bessel.

With an offer of employment in hand, Bessel had to decide whether to opt for a future position of affluence with the import-export firm or for a future of potential poverty under the stars. He decided to switch. Within four years the Prussian government charged him with the construction of the first big German Observatory in Königsberg (now Kaliningrad). He had a precision telescope, constructed by the master optician Joseph Fraunhofer of Munich, installed. Appointed professor of astronomy in 1810, Bessel directed the Königsberg Observatory from the time of its completion in 1813, to the end of his life.[53]

After corrections for precession, aberration, nutation$_g$, and for errors due to disturbances in the atmosphere, he catalogued accurate measurements of the positions and motions of thousands of stars. Based on these observations he identified extremely small but highly significant differences in motion among them. From these, he deduced the angle created by the annual parallax caused by the orbital motion of the Earth around the Sun. In 1838 his calculations yielded an estimated distance to the Star 61 Cygnus of 10.3 light-years.

### Light-Years

Evidence of the size of the distance of stars was signified by the switch-over from a distance measure in astronomical units to light-years.

Setting the speed of light at approximately 186,400 miles per second (300 000 km/s), it takes the Sun's light 500 seconds or 8.3 minutes to reach Earth (i.e., 93 million miles at 186,400 miles/s ≈ 500 seconds). In astronomy one light-year equals the distance light travels in one year. It is equivalent to 63,240 Sun-to-Earth distances. To reach Earth the light of the star 60 Cygni has to travel through space for 10.3 years, for a distance close to 650,000 astronomical units or Sun-to-Earth distances. Thus, going from astronomical units to light-years was a giant step in the astronomical scale of distance measurement.

Olbers, when presented with the first measure to the stars on his 80th birthday, thanked Bessel for the gift and said that it "put our ideas about the universe for the first time on a sound basis." Bessel's achievement was recognized by the Royal Astronomical Society of London and honored by others.

With this breakthrough from planetary observations within our solar system to observation and distance measurement of a star, the stage was set for further exploration of the space beyond.

### Thomas Henderson (1798–1844)

Soon, two astronomers followed up on Bessel's discoveries. In 1839 Henderson, a Scottish astronomer working at the Cape of Good Hope in South Africa obtained the parallax for Alpha Centauri. Only seen in the southern hemisphere, it is the nearest Star to Earth. Although it has the largest parallax, it still measured no more than one ten-thousandth of 1°. He estimated its distance from the Earth at 4.3 light-years.

*Friedrich Georg Wilhelm Struve (1793–1864)*

Struve was born in Altona (Northern Germany, formerly Denmark) and worked in St. Petersburg, Russia. In 1840, he announced his estimate of the parallax of the bright star Vega in the western triangle of the constellation Lyra. Because of its bluish-white color it is often called the arc light of the sky. It was estimated to be about 26 light-years from Earth.

These astronomical observations signified a new age in instrumental precision and in exploration beyond the solar system. They made for an entirely new outlook in astronomy.[54]

## Luminiferous Ether?

According to these estimates of the nearest stars, light traveled enormous distances at an incredible speed. How was it possible? While a theory of light waves explained some aspects of the transmission of light, it left another unresolved. Newton's corpuscles of light could travel freely through space, but waves not. Already in Newton's time it had been shown that sound waves do not travel in a vacuum. They need air or some other medium suitable for transmission. So if a medium is required for the transmission of waves, how could light waves from the stars pass through outer space to Earth without the aid of a medium? Since no light-carrying medium was known to exist in space, physicists decided to invent one. They called it luminiferous ether (from the Latin *lumen* for light, *ferre* for carry, and *aether* for ether). Giving the unknown medium a Latin name may have added a touch of eloquence but it added little to scientific knowledge.

To make it plausible as to how light could move at such enormous speeds through the distance of interstellar space, the medium had to have some unique characteristics.[55] Physicists assumed the ether to be transparent, weightless, frictionless, chemically undetectable, and have the rigidity of a solid. If ether did fill all space, it raised the obvious and intriguing question of how the planets could move freely through this medium. If a rigid luminiferous ether was as essential for the transmission of light as air was essential for the transmission of sound, would ether not impede the motion of the planets?

Newton had distinguished between relative space and absolute space. He illustrated the two by examining the motion of a ship under sail.

According to him it was "relative motion" when a sailor walked about on board of a ship. But when the sailor slept in a cot, then the sailor's motion on board the ship could be traced to the ship's motion on the sea, from there to the current of the sea, on to the rotational motion of the Earth, and so on, until it reached the "absolute immovable space" and became "absolute motion."[56]

Physicists speculated that if an absolute space existed and if it was filled with luminiferous ether, it ought to affect a body moving through it. Detecting it should have been possible. Even if the Earth were moving together with the Sun within our galaxy and even if our galaxy were moving relative to other galaxies, it should still have been possible to measure the motion of the Earth relative to a luminiferous ether anchored in absolute space. Yet, it was not!

*Dominique François Jean Arago (1786–1853)*
The first to try his hand at measuring the motion of the Earth through space was Arago, a Frenchman of many talents. At the age of 23, he was appointed to the Chair of Analytic Geometry at the École Polytechnique in Paris. Later he became director of the Paris Observatory and then Permanent Secretary of the French Academy of Sciences. Eventually, he became involved in politics and after the Revolution of 1848 was appointed Minister of War.

Apart from research in electromagnetism, Arago conducted experiments on the speed of light. Letting light beams pass through air, water, and glass, he proved (after many refinements in his experimental apparatus) that light was slowed as it passed from the rarer to the denser medium. As light passed from air to glass, for example, its speed dropped by roughly one-third or from 186,000 to 124,000 miles per second (300,000 to 200,000 km/s).

Arago wanted to use his very sensitive experimental apparatus to find out by how much the luminiferous ether accelerated or lowered the speed of light. Although the speed at which the Earth traveled around the Sun was known, the speed at which the Sun carried the Earth and all its other planets with it through outer space, was not. By letting his apparatus revolve around a central axis Arago believed he could detect and measure the variations in the light's speed through ether.

If the Earth traveled in the same direction as the luminiferous ether, he expected the speed of light to increase. When it traveled against the stream of ether, he anticipated a reduction of the speed of light. He reckoned that such changes in speed would affect the refractive index. To his surprise, nothing happened. No matter how he turned his apparatus, the refractive index remained unchanged. One possible explanation was that any change in the refractive index was too small to measure with sufficient precision. At 18.6 miles per second (30 km/s) the orbital speed of the Earth was only 1/10 000th of the speed of light.

*Augustin Jean Fresnel (1788–1827)*

Arago's friend Fresnel came up with another explanation. When Arago told him about the negative outcome of his experiment, Fresnel suggested that the luminiferous ether flowed freely through all matter. It was always present, inside and outside any transparent matter. Furthermore, he believed the ether entrapped inside matter precisely compensated for the expected variation of the index of refraction.[57]

It was a curious theory. It was so strange that Foucault could not resist testing Fresnel's formula. In 1851 he verified Arago's finding that the speed of light was not affected by changes in the direction of the light beam. As described earlier he did it by an ingenious experiment that enabled him to measure the speed of light in rapidly circulating water with admirable precision. Yet, he could not detect any variation in the speed of light that could be attributed to a directional flow of the ether.

Fresnel's idea of "ether entrapment" contained a serious flaw. If, indeed, the ether entrapped in transparent material was directly linked to its refractive index, it led to an untenable conclusion. The size of the refractive index was known to vary with the color of light. It implied that ether entrapped in the material would have to vary with the different colors of light. Yet once entrapped in the material, the amount was fixed and could hardly increase or diminish in volume with changes in direction and color of light. It did not solve the ether puzzle.[58]

## Electromagnetism and Light

In the nineteenth century Michael Faraday was perhaps the greatest experimentalist. He explored the nature of electricity, with a focus on electromagnetic induction and electrochemistry. Translating Faraday's experimental results, physicist James Maxwell built a mathematical model of the electromagnetic theory. It synthesized all that was known at the time about magnetism and electricity. His mathematical model unified light with electromagnetism. To this day the integration of the two is considered the foremost achievement of classical optics.[59]

*Michael Faraday (1791–1867)*

Faraday was born in 1791, the son of a blacksmith. The family was poor, since his father was often ill and could not work steadily. Michael was one of four children, all of whom had barely enough to eat. He received a nominal education in a country school. To earn some money he delivered newspapers. At age 14 he started an apprenticeship with a bookbinder. He found the business not to his liking, because he thought it sterile and even vicious. Perhaps, by reading more books than he was binding, he educated himself very rapidly. Whenever he could, he also attended lectures at the Royal Institution in London. Attending a series of lectures on chemistry by Sir Humphrey Davy, Faraday took comprehensive notes, bound them up, and sent them to Davy with a request for employment at the Institution. Appointed as a laboratory assistant by Davy, he wrote his first research papers within three years of his appointment. Many more papers followed. Eventually he became the Director of the Royal Institution's laboratories.[60]

Faraday was first a chemist, being often called as an expert witness in legal trials. In 1820 he produced a new compound of carbon chlorides and in 1825 he isolated benzene. Having read that the flow of an electric current through a wire produced a magnetic field around the wire, Faraday managed to transform electrical energy into mechanical energy by building the first electric motor.

His friend Richard Phillips, editor of a journal of philosophy and fascinated by magnetism and electricity, asked Faraday to write an article of the history of ideas and experiments of magnetism and electricity. In his paper Faraday illustrated the equivalence of magnetism and electricity. He showed that bar magnets produced field lines linking the two poles, made visible by sprinkling some fine iron filings spread over a piece of paper resting on top of the magnet. He called them field lines because they reminded him of ploughed furrows of a farmer's field. He also showed that similar lines could be created by an electric current flowing through a wire coil (Figure 13.8).

### *James Clerk Maxwell (1831–1879)*

Modern physicists rank James Maxwell with Sir Isaac Newton and Albert Einstein. The concept of electromagnetic radiation originated with Maxwell. His field equations, based on Faraday's observations, paved the way for Einstein's special theory of relativity three decades later.

James was born in 1831 into a wealthy family. He had a lively curiosity and a phenomenal memory. His interests went far beyond the high school curriculum. At age 14 he published his first scientific paper. In it he described a generalized series of oval curves, a result of his fascination with geometry. At age 16 he entered the University of Edinburgh where he published two more scientific papers. Three years later he went to the University of Cambridge. His brilliance in mathematics was quickly recognized. In 1860 he was appointed professor of natural philosophy at King's College, London. The next five years were the most fruitful of Maxwell's career.[61]

During this period his two classical papers on the electromagnetic field were published. After his resignation from King's College, Maxwell devoted most of his energy to writing a *Treatise on Electricity and Magnetism* (1873). In the preface he stated that his objective was to convert Faraday's observational description into mathematical form. In four equations Maxwell integrated all the experimental characteristics of electrical currents and magnetism. Together, the four equations describe the way in which changing magnetic fields produce electric fields and, vice versa, the ways in which electric charges and currents produce electric and magnetic fields (Figure 13.8, Diagrams 1 to 4).[62] From his mathematical model Maxwell concluded that electric currents give rise to transverse waves and that they move at the same speed as light waves at about 186,000 miles per second (about 300,000 km/s).

In Maxwell's day visible light, infrared, and ultraviolet were the only electromagnetic radiations known. Driven on by Maxwell's predictions of a much wider spectrum of radiation Heinrich Rudolf Hertz (1857–1894) discovered radio waves and Guglielmo Marchese Marconi (1874–1937) invented wireless telegraphy. With his field equations Maxwell brought light wave s together with electromagnetism (Figure 13.8, Diagrams 5 to 7). Ultimately, this unification yielded unforeseen technological advances.

Maxwell also puzzled over the question of the luminiferous ether. Recall that it was Roemer who had arrived at some of the earliest estimates of the speed of light. He had done so by observing the delay in the reappearance of Jupiter's moon Io when the Earth was on the far side of the Sun. Maxwell suggested that a similar technique could be used to detect how the ether wind affected the rhythm of Io's eclipses. If the Earth traveled along its orbit in the same direction as the Sun and all its planets moved through the ether of the cosmos, it would shorten the periodicity of Io's emergence out of Jupiter's shadow. If the Earth traveled in the opposite direction of the Sun and the planets through the ether of the cosmos, it would lengthen the periodicity of Io.[63]

This caught the attention of D. P. Todd, an American astronomer who had painstakingly accumulated his observations of Io's eclipses. He promptly sent tables of his records to Maxwell. In response Maxwell wrote him a letter of thanks and noted that the detection of such variations in timing might be impossible. If light were sent back and forth in a laboratory setting, for example, the effect of the ether flow on the speed of light might amount to less than a billionth of a second. Shortly after this communication, in 1879, Maxwell died.

When Todd heard of it, he decided, for sentimental reasons, to pass Maxwell's letter on to the Royal Society of London. The Society published it in their *Proceedings*. Later, it reappeared in the widely distributed British scientific journal, *Nature*. This is where Albert Michelson first read it. Contrary to Maxwell's serious doubt, he was convinced that laboratory instruments could be designed that were sensitive enough to measure extremely small variations in the speed of light.

## Does the Earth's Motion Affect the Speed of Light?

*Albert Abraham Michelson (1852–1931)*

Michelson was born in Strelno, Prussia (now Poland) and came with his parents to the United States when he was two years old. Eventually, the family made its way to San Francisco where his father prospered as a merchant.[64]

At age 17, young Michelson entered the U.S. Naval Academy. Although his rating in seamanship was below average, he did well in science. At age 21 he graduated, taught science at the academy and began work on the precision measurement of the speed of light. It was to become the great passion of his life. In 1880 he took a leave of absence from the navy to pursue his studies in Berlin, Heidelberg, and Paris.

While in Berlin, he was associated with Herman von Helmholtz. He began work on the "interferometer," an apparatus designed to split a light beam in two and letting one part travel perpendicular to the other. If the two beams fell out of step on their return, changes in the interference pattern would show it. From changes in the width of the bands of the interference fringe, Michelson could detect any changes with unprecedented precision. His interferometer was so sensitive that the vibrations caused by street traffic spoiled the readings. To overcome this problem he moved to Potsdam, a suburb of Berlin, and put his apparatus in a room of the astronomical observatory. Even then, a pedestrian's steps could play havoc with the readings of the interference fringe.[65]

On his return to America he was determined to find out whether or not the velocity of light was affected by the light-carrying ether wind. The Earth was known to move around the Sun at an average orbital speed of 18.6 miles per second (30 km/s). If beamed in one direction, the light waves moved with the ether wind, if beamed in another direction they traveled against it. He was confident his interferometer was sensitive enough to capture such variations even if they were extremely small.

With that in mind Michelson resigned from the U.S. Navy. He set up his experimental apparatus and sent light-signals in two directions, one at 90° to the other. He let each be reflected by mirrors so that both arrived back at the point from which they were emitted. If an ether wind existed, the two light beams should have interfered with each other (Diagram 1 of

Figure 13.9).[66] Try as he might he could not detect any difference in the speed of the two beams. The negative outcome of the experiment came as a total surprise to him.

Michelson published his results in 1881. To his dismay an error in the theoretical analysis had led him to overestimate the effect of the Earth's orbital motion. Since the correct value was only half as large, the result of his experiment was considered inconclusive. Michelson did not give up. In collaboration with Edward Morley, of the Case School of Applied Science, he added some significant refinements to the interferometer and the experimental set-up (Diagram 2 of Figure 13.9). Published in 1887, the new results were beyond reproach. The luminiferous ether, if it existed, did not affect the speed of light. But this did not eliminate the original problem of how light was transmitted through space or what other factor could have accounted for the strange invariant experimental results.

At this point it is not self-evident by how much the speed of light was expected to vary. An analogy may help: consider the case of two canoeists, at right angle to each other, rowing their boats along side a square raft. If there is no current they both move at the same speed and travel the same distance in equal time (Figure 13.10, Diagram 1).

Now consider that the same raft is placed on a stream, with the same two canoeists, but now one is going with the current and the other cuts across the current. Based on their speeds of paddling and the flow of the current, calculations show that for the same distance it takes longer to go first with the current and then against it than it takes to go across the current and back (Figure 13.10, Diagram 2 and Appendix A to this Chapter).

From this analogy the differences in the speed of light, which Michelson and Morley could have expected, can be deduced. Letting the two canoeists travel at the speed of light we can estimate how the travel times ought to have varied with the direction of the light and the ether current (Equation B13.2 of Appendix B13.3).

Yet, no matter how Michelson and Morley tried, they did not detect any changes in the speed of light. Admittedly, they expected a very small difference in speeds. Yet, they had refined their apparatus to the point where they could have readily detected any ether flow. Even if the solar system had been at rest, standing perfectly still in space with only the planet Earth orbiting the Sun, they could have detected a difference in the speed of light reaching Earth.

Their negative experimental results could be interpreted in two ways: their apparatus was not accurate enough, or the Earth was not affected by the ether wind. Michelson and Morley ruled out the first. They tried to find an explanation for the second. Perhaps the Earth carried the ether along while circling the Sun. If so, the ether wind ought to have diminished at higher altitudes. To find out if there were any changes in the speed of light, they tested for variations in the speed at different altitudes. There were none. They concluded, therefore, that the motion of the ether was carried along by the Earth far above its surface at very great heights.[67]

*Sir Oliver Joseph Lodge (1851–1940)*
In 1892 Oliver Lodge tried to show by experiment that the ether could not be carried along. If the ether were to envelop the Earth and adhere to it while going around the Sun, the rapid orbital motion of the Earth ought to have affected the speed of light in its neighborhood. Yet, he experimentally showed that rapidly moving bodies passing a light beam did not change the speed of light at all. He also showed that a strong magnetic field or electric current near a beam of light did not alter the speed of light.[68] But, if the Earth did not drag the ether with it, an alternative and better explanation was needed.

**Does the Earth Contract?**
*George F. Fitzgerald (1851–1901)* and *Hendrik A. Lorentz (1853–1928)*
At this impasse the Irish physicist Fitzgerald came up with a novel idea. According to him the Earth contracted just enough to compensate for the effect of the ether wind. This strange notion was quickly picked up by the Dutch physicist Lorentz who derived the appropriate mathematical expression for it (Figure 13.11 and Appendix B13).[69]

Leaning on the earlier illustration of the two canoeists, the logic of the Lorentz-Fitzgerald contraction hypothesis can be followed again using an analogy. Consider now that the two canoeists represent light moving on alternative routes, both being exposed to the ether current.

Although the Earth orbits the Sun at the respectable speed of 67,000 miles per hour (108,000 km/h), this amounts to only 18.6 miles per second (30 km/s) and is, when compared to the speed of light at 186,000 miles per second (300 000 km/s), very slow. Based on the relative speeds of light and of the orbital motion of the Earth, the Lorentz-Fitzgerald contraction amounted to no more than half an inch.

Obviously, Figure 13.11 is a vast exaggeration. The orbital speed of the Earth would have to be far greater before the contraction could have any measurable effect. Even if the Earth were to move much faster, the effect of contraction would not be measurable because all measuring rods on Earth would contract in the direction of motion as well. Since Lorentz was concerned about the implication Michelson's results would have on his theory of electrons (subatomic particles), he concluded that a new measure of time was needed for systems moving at high speed, a measure free from contradictions. Although Sir Joseph Larmor (1857–1942), an Irish physicist, arrived at the same curious conclusion in 1900 and J. Henri Poincaré (1854–1912), a French mathematician, in 1905, neither Lorentz nor they arrived at a fully integrated theory.[70]

## The Meter Measured by Light

Michelson continued to measure the speed of light with ever greater precision. In his final experiment he used a mile-long (1.6093 km) sealed and evacuated steel tube, three-feet in diameter, letting light flash back and forth in it. The results of this experiment, a new and even more accurate estimate of the speed of light, reached him on his deathbed on May 7, 1931. Two days later he died.[71]

In more recent years a special (highly stabilized) laser has been used for measuring ultra-high optical frequencies. The estimate of the speed of light has become so accurate that any remaining uncertainties hinge on the definition of the meter as a standard unit of length. In 1983 it was decided, therefore, that the best measure of 299,792,458 meters per second become the new standard of distance by international convention. From that day forward, the meter was defined by the distance light travels in 1/299,792,458 of a second.[72]

## APPENDIXES

### Appendix A13:  The Effect of a Current on the Speed of Travel

Assume that two canoeists paddle their boats along the sides of a square raft that measures 240 feet. In still water, at a rowing speed of 15 feet per second, each canoeist covers the distance of 240 feet, going back and forth, in *240/15 = 16 seconds* (Figure 13.10, Diagram 1).

If the same raft is put on a stream with a current flowing at 9 feet per second, their travel times differ with the direction they take. As before, each keeps close to the side of the raft and paddles at a speed of 15 feet per second. The first canoeist goes with the flow of the current rowing 120 feet from point *A* to *B* of the raft and then back from *B* to *A* against the flow of the current. Going from *A* to *B* takes 5 seconds, i.e., *(120 feet)/(15 feet/sec + 9 feet/sec) = 5 seconds*; and going back from *B* to *A* takes 20 seconds, i.e., *(120 feet) at (15 feet/sec - 9 feet/sec) = 20 seconds*. So that the first canoeist makes the round trip from *A* to *B* and back in 25 seconds. (Figure 13.10, Diagram 2)

The second canoeist rows across the stream from point *A* to *C* of the raft, paddling at a speed of 15 feet per second while the current carries the boat downstream at 9 feet per second. After the first second, the boat arrives at point *D* in Diagram 2, that is 15 feet from *A* and 9 feet downstream. Applying the Pythagorean Theorem the distance *DE* is 12 feet, i.e.,

$$\sqrt{(15^2 - 9^2)} = \sqrt{(225 - 81)} = \sqrt{144} = 12$$

It follows that it takes the second canoeist 120 feet at 12 feet per second or 10 seconds to cover the 120 foot distance *AC* plus another 10 seconds to return to *A*, or 20 seconds for the round trip. Thus, in this example it takes 25 seconds going first with and then against the current, compared with 20 seconds to go across the current and back, a difference of 5 seconds. Evidently, paddling across the current is faster than first paddling with it and then against it.

The time difference can be generalized. Let *c* be the speed of the canoeists, *v* the velocity of the river's current and *l* the length and width of the (square) raft. Going with the current takes *l/(c - v)* seconds and going against it, takes *l/(c + v)* seconds.  Adding the two, gives time $t_1$. Paddling across the current takes $l/\sqrt{(c^2 - v^2)}$ seconds. Going back and forth, doubles it as in $t_2$. The difference between the expected times amounts to $t_1 - t_2$ as shown in the last line of Equation 13.A1.

Equation A13.1: Effects of Current on Travel Times of Canoeists

$$l = \textit{Distance traveled}$$
$$t_1 = \textit{Time for trip with and against river current}$$
$$t_2 = \textit{Time for trip across river current and back}$$
$$v = \textit{Speed of canoeists}$$
$$c = \textit{Velocity of current}$$

$$t_1 = \frac{distance}{speed} = \frac{l}{(c+v)} + \frac{l}{(c-v)}$$

$$= \frac{l(c-v) + l(c+v)}{c^2 - v^2}$$

$$= \frac{2\,l\,c}{c^2 - v^2} = \frac{2 \times 40 \times 5}{5^2 - 3^2} = \frac{400}{16} = 25$$

and

$$t_2 = \frac{2\,l}{\sqrt{c^2 - v^2}} = \frac{2 \times 40}{\sqrt{25 - 16}} = \frac{80}{\sqrt{16}} = 20$$

hence,

$$t_1 - t_2 = \frac{2\,l\,c}{c^2 - v^2} - \frac{2\,l}{\sqrt{c^2 - v^2}} = 25 - 20 = 5.$$

Now, assume the canoeists travel at the speed of light $c$ kilometers per second and the ether flows at $v$ kilometers per second. Going with the ether current takes the first canoeist $l/(c-v)$ seconds and going against it $l/(c+v)$ seconds. Adding the two gives the expected travel time $t_{1,\,exp}$. The corresponding time for light to travel across the ether wind would be $t_{2,\,exp}$. The difference between the two travel times is $t_{1,\,exp} - t_{2,\,exp}$ where $t_{2,\,exp}$ is shown to differ from $t_{1,\,exp}$ by a factor at the end of Equation A13.2 .

## Equation A13.2: Expected Time for Light to Travel Across Ether Wind

$t_{1,\,exp}$ = *Expected time for light to go with and against ether wind*

$t_{2,\,exp}$ = *Expected time for light to go across ether wind*

$v$ = *Speed of ether wind*

$c$ = *Speed of light*

*From Equation A13.1 it is known that*

$$t_{1,\text{exp}} = \frac{2\,l\,c}{c^2 - v^2} \quad , \textit{which can be}$$

*rewritten as*

$$= \frac{2\,l\,c}{c^2\,(1 - \frac{v^2}{c^2})} = \frac{2\,l}{c\,(1 - \frac{v^2}{c^2})}$$

*and abbreviated to*

$$= \frac{2\,l}{c\,(1 - \beta^2)} \quad \textit{where } \beta^2 = \frac{v^2}{c^2}\,.$$

*It was also shown in Equation A13.1 that*

$$t_{2,\text{exp}} = \frac{2\,l}{\sqrt{c^2 - v^2}} \quad , \textit{which}$$

*can be rewritten as*

$$= \frac{2\,l}{\sqrt{c^2\,(1 - \frac{v^2}{c^2})}} = \frac{2\,l}{c\,\sqrt{(1 - \beta^2)}}$$

*so that* $\quad t_{1,\text{exp}} - t_{2,\text{exp}} = \dfrac{2\,l}{c\,(1 - \beta^2)} - \dfrac{2\,l}{c\,\sqrt{(1 - \beta^2)}}$

*and the travel time across the ether wind is*

$$t_{2,\text{exp}} = \frac{2\,l}{c\,\sqrt{(1 - \beta^2)}} = \frac{2\,l}{c\,(1 - \beta^2)}\sqrt{(1 - \beta^2)}\,,$$

*which differs from*

$t_{1,\text{exp}}$ *by the factor* $r = \sqrt{1 - \beta^2}$

*as in*

$$t_{2,\text{exp}} = t_{1,\text{exp}}\,r\,, \textit{ where } r < 1\,.$$

**Appendix B13: Lorentz-Fitzgerald Contraction of Earth's Diameter**
In similar fashion expected changes can be deduced if light were to pass
through an ether current. First an analogy: suppose the two canoeists of
the previous illustration traveled at the speed of light on the ether current.
Let the expected time it would take them to go with and against the ether
current be denoted by $t_{1,exp}$, and the time to go across the ether and back
by $t_{2,exp}$.

As shown in Equation A13.2 the expected travel times differ.
Asssume the same laws of physics as applied before. It takes longer to go
with and against the ether current than going across it and back, that is, $t_{1,exp}$
should be greater than $t_{2,exp}$. Assume the canoeists travel at the speed of
light $c$ kilometers per second and the ether current flows at $v$ kilometers
per second. Now, going with the ether current takes the first canoeist $l/(c -
v)$ seconds and going against it $l/(c + v)$ seconds. Adding the two gives the
expected time $t_{1,exp}$. The corresponding time for light to travel across the
ether wind would be $t_{2,exp}$. The difference between the two expected travel
times is $t_{1,exp} - t_{2,exp}$ where $t_{2,exp}$ is shown to differ from $t_{1,exp}$ by a factor $r$, as
at the end of Equation B13.1.

According to this formulation, the ether flow would reduce the
Earth's diameter of 7926 miles (12,756 km) by about 1/2 of one inch
(Equation B13.1). This would be the reduction that could precisely
compensate for the difference in the expected time requirements of light,
when moving either in the direction of the ether current or crossing it at a
right angle. Even if the small contraction were measurable, it would be
impossible to observe because any conceivable measuring device on Earth
would be contracted by the same amount.

Equation B13.1: How Much Would the Ether Wind Cause the Earth to
Contract?

Let $t_{1,\,exp}$ = *Expected time for light to back and forth in ether wind*
$t_{2,\,exp}$ = *expected time for light to go across ether wind*
$l$ = *distance traveled*

$c$ = *speed of light*

$v$ = *speed of ether wind*

$r$ = *contraction factor*

*From Equation A13.2 above it follows that*

$$t_{1,\exp} = \frac{2\,l}{c\,(1-\beta^2\,)} \quad and \quad t_{2,\exp} = \frac{2\,l}{c\,\sqrt{(1\,-\,\beta^2\,)}}$$

*Setting the " Contraction Factor" at* $r = \sqrt{(1\,-\,\beta^2)}$
*where*

$$\beta = \frac{v}{c}$$

$$t_{2,\,\exp} = \frac{2\,l}{c\,(1\,-\,\beta^2\,)}\,\sqrt{(1\,-\,\beta^2\,)} = t_{1,\,\exp}\,(r\,)$$

*and the difference in time distance at:*

$$t_{diff} = t_{1,\exp}\,(1\,-\,r\,) \quad and \quad D_{diff} = c\,t_{1,\,\exp}\,(1\,-\,r\,)$$

*Applied to Earth, it implies that*

$$r_{Earth} = \sqrt{1\,-\,\frac{30^2}{300000}} = \sqrt{1\,-\,\frac{10^2}{10^{10}}}$$

*so that the Larentz – Fitzgerald Contraction amounts to*

$$D_{Earth} = 12\,756\,(1\,-\,r\,) = 12\,756\,(0.999\,999\,9)$$

$$= 1.2756 \quad centimeters\ or\ about\ 1/2\ inch.$$

FIGURES AND DIAGRAMS

CHAPTERS 12 TO 17

# Figure 12.1: Why Planets Sweep out Equal Areas in Equal Times

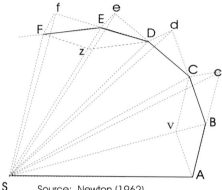

Source: Newton (1962),
*Principia*, Volume 1, p.40.

**Diagram 1:** Newton pictures the successive positions *A, B, C, ... F* of a planet on its orbit around the Sun. He attributes the changes in orbital positions to two straight-line forces. One, the inertial force that would, if unimpeded, let the planet continue its straight course. The other is the gravitational force that emanates from the Sun and attracts the planet to it.

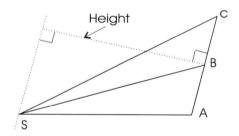

**Diagram 2:** If the inertial force was acting alone the planet would follow its unimpeded course, first from *A* to *B*, and then from *B* to *c*. The time it would take to go from *A* to *B* would be the same as the time it would take from *B* to *c*. Moreover, the area *SAB* would be of the same size as *SBc* because both triangles have the same base *AB = Bc* and height. ( See Figure 2.2 for a more detailed explanation. )

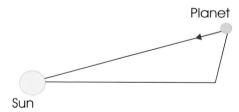

**Diagram 3:** The Sun's gravitational force is represented by the red arrow. It acts continually on the planet and pulls the planet toward it. The problem is how to combine the inertial and the gravitational forces and show how they make for a curvi-linear orbit.

# Figure 12.1: Why Planets Sweep out Equal Areas in Equal Times

Adapted from D. L. and J. R. Goodstein, pp. 87- 92.

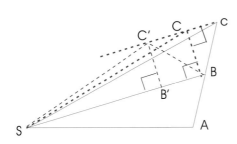

Diagram 4: The two forces, inertial and gravitational, cause curvilinear orbits by changing the shape of the triangle *SBc*. To illustrate, we extend the line *AB* to *Bc* so that *AB* = *Bc*. Now a line is drawn parallel to *SB* and a triangle *SBC* created. It equals triangle in size because it has the same base AB and is of equal height. The same goes for triangle SBC'. So that the equalities in Diagram 5 hold.

Diagram 5: To summarize, triangle *SAB* equals the area of triangle *SBc* because both have the same base line and height. But triangle *SBc* also equals triangle *SBC* because both share the same base *SB* and have the same height *BC*. And that goes for triangle SBC' too. (See Figure 2.2 for a more detailed explanation.)

$$\triangle 1 = S A B = \triangle 2$$
$$\triangle 2 = S B c = \triangle 3$$
$$\triangle 3 = S B C = \triangle 4$$
$$\triangle 4 = S B C'$$

Diagram 6: Now a new element is added: the force of gravity. Triangle *SAB* is the same as before. *AB* and *Bc* are also the same as before. But now the force of gravity Bc′ is added. Combined with the inertial force *Bc*, the resulting force is *BC*. Here, the area of triangle *SAB* equals *SBc*. The area *SBc* equals *SBC* because the two triangles share the same base *SB* and height, i.e, line Cc is parallel to the line C′c′.′ Therefore, triangle *SAB* equals triangle *SBC*.

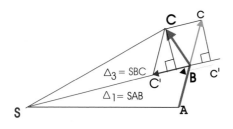

$\triangle_3$ = SBC

$\triangle_1$ = SAB

# Figure 12.1: Why Planets Sweep out Equal Areas in
## Equal Times

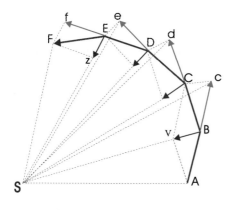

Diagram 7: In this diagram the force of gravity is shown in red and the force of inertia in blue. They work together to produce the resultant force in purple which determines the course of the planet. For example, gravity tugs at B and pulls it to v and inertia tugs at B and pulls it to C, and both together create the resultant force represented by the line BC. The two forces work continuously and determine the course of the

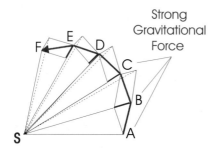

Strong Gravitational Force

Diagram 8: The stronger the gravitational force, the more sharply the curvature of orbit will be. Here, a strong gravitational force pulls the planet closer in, so that the successive orbital positions will make for a tighter course.

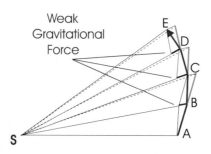

Weak Gravitational Force

Diagram 9: The weaker the gravitational force, the smaller will be the curvature of the planetary orbit. The force of gravity diminishes with distance. The curvature depends on the inter-action of the two forces (shown here in red and blue). So much for an introduction to the geometric interpretation of Newton's laws. In Equations A12 and B12 of Appendixes A and B of Chapter 12, more of Newton's geometric and algebraic details are given.

# Figure12.2: Why the Force ofGravity is Inversely Related to the Distance From the Sun

Newton's objective was to find the law of the centripetal force tending to one focus of the ellipse.

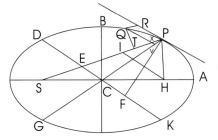

*Source: Newton, Principia, Volume I, p.56*

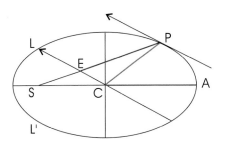

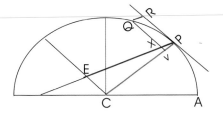

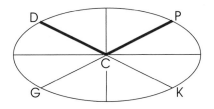

Diagram 1: Newton begins with an intricate drawing reproduced here. In preparation for the analysis he refers to FOUR SETS OF PROPERTIES that are embedded in it :

1. $EP / CP = AC / CP = QR / Pv$
2. $(Gv)(Pv) / (Qv)^2 = (CP)^2 / (CD)^2$
3. $EP / FP = AC / FP = CD / BC$
4. $L = 2 (BC)^2 / AC$.

Details on the FOUR SETS are given in the diagrams below.

Diagram 2: $EP = AP$ was shown to be one of the theorems on conics by Apollonius, proven earlier in Figure 4.4 of Chapter 4. If both sides of $EP = AC$ are divided by PC, the FIRST SET of the FOUR PROPERTIES is obtained:

$$EP/CP = AC/CP.$$

Diagram 3: Since $Qx$ and $RP$ are parallel, the large triangle $EPC$ is similar to the small triangle $xPv$ because their angles are equal so that $EP/CP = xP/Pv$.

It follows that $EP / CP = QR / Pv$. This confirms the FIRST SET:

$$EP / CP = AC / CP = QR / Pv.$$

Diagram 4: An ellipse is symmetrical around its minor and major axes. The conjugate diameters, here $GP$ and $KD$, are of equal length. It follows that half the diameters, here $CP$ and $CD$, are of equal length too and that

$$(CP)^2 = (CD)^2.$$

# Figure 12.2: Why the Force of Gravity is Inversely Related to the Distance From the Sun (continued)

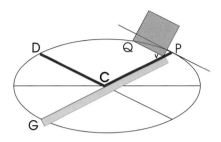

**Diagram 5:** As illustrated earlier in Figure 7.1 of Chapter 7,
$$(Gv)(Pv) = (Qv)^2 \text{ and}$$
$$(Gv)(Pv)/(Qv)^2 = 1.0.$$
According to Diagram 4, $(CP)^2 = (CD)^2$ so that $(CP)^2/(CD)^2 = 1.0$. This confirms the SECOND PROPERTY:
$$(Gv)(Pv)/(Qv)^2 = 1 = (CP)^2$$

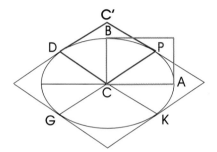

**Diagram 6:** Also as illustrated in Figure 7.2 of Chapter 7:
$$(AC)(BC) = \text{Area } CDC'P$$
Both are parallelograms circumscribed about conjugate diameters of the ellipse and therefore equal in size of areas.

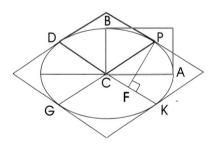

**Diagram 7:** Also, as illustrated in Figure 7.2 of Chapter 7:
$$(AC)(BC) = (CD)(FP)$$
On dividing both sides by $(FP)(BC)$, this yields
$$AC / FP = CD / BC.$$
According to Diagram 2 above $AC = EP$ so that
$$AC / FP = EP / FP.$$
*The combination of the ratios yields the THIRD PROPERTY:*
$$EP/FP = AC/FP = CD/BC$$

**Diagram 8:** The Latus Rectum, $L$ passes through one focus of the ellipse and is perpendicular to its major axis. It is linked to both semi-axes $AC$ and $BC$. As shown in this Chapter (Equation A12.1 of Appendix A) from this link Newton derives the FOURTH PROPERTY:
$$L = 2 (BC)^2/AC.$$

# Figure 12.2: Why the Force of Gravity is Inversely Related to the Distance From the Sun

From the FOUR PROPERTIES, pictured in Diagrams 1 to 8 , Newton develops a new set of FOUR EQUALITIES as described in Appendix A12. Here we elaborate only on the last of the FOUR EQUALITIES (Appendix Equation (A12.3), Equality IV :. $Qx^2/QT^2$ or $Qv^2/Qt^2 = EP^2/FP^2 = AC^2/FP^2 = CD^2/BC^2$

Diagram 9: This is a stripped-down version of Figure 12.1, Diagram 1. Point *P* is connected to one of the focal points, say *S*. Lines *DK* and *Qy* run parallel to the tangent line *tt*. Line *PF* is perpendicular to *DK* . Point R on the tangent *tt* connects with point Q and runs parallel to *PS*. The line *QT* is perpendicular to *PS*. All three contain a right angle *1*. Angles *2* are equal in size because lines *DK* and *Qy* are parallel. Consequently, the angles *3* are equal in size too. It means the three triangles *QTx*, *Pxy* and *EFP* are similar because they agree in all three angles. This proves that $Qx/QT = EP/FP$.

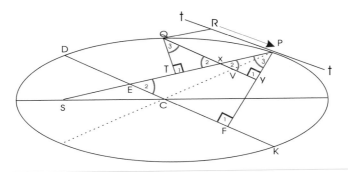

Diagram 10: When *R* moves closer to *P* these relationships are not altered. As *Qy* moves ever closer to *P,* the distances *Px* and *Py* get ever smaller, but the equality $Px/Py = EP/FP$ persists. *Therefore,*

$$Qx/QT \text{ or } Qv/QT = Px/Py = QR/Py = Qx/QT = EP/FP .$$

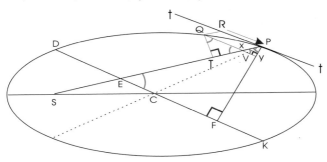

# Figure 12.2: Why the Force of Gravity is Inversely Related to the Distance From the Sun (continued)

From the FOUR PROPERTIES, pictured in Diagrams 1 to 8 , Newton develops a new set of FOUR EQUALITIES as described in Appendix A12. Here we elaborate only on the last of the FOUR EQUALITIES (Appendix Equation A12.3),

Equality IV : $Qx^2/QT^2$ or $Qv^2/QT^2 = EP^2/FP^2 = AC^2/FP^2 = CD^2/BC^2$.

Diagram 11: To demonstrate that

$$\frac{2\ (CP)}{Gv} = 1.0$$

the conjugate diameters of Diagram 4 (above) are superimposed on Diagram 11. Obviously they fit. Note that $CP = DP$ and that $CP + DP = 2\,(CP)$. This equality won't be affected as point $R$ moves to $P$.

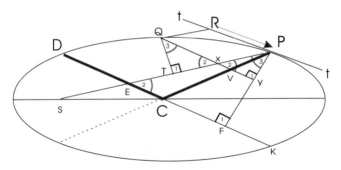

Diagram 12: Diagram 5 above shows that $Gv$ does not go all the way to $P$ but falls short by $Pv$. The distance $Pv$, however, shortens as $R$ moves closer to $P$. When $R$ coincides with $P$, then $Gv$ becomes $GP$. But $GP$ equals $2\,(CP)$ and therefore the ratio $2\,(CP)/Gv = 1.0$ .

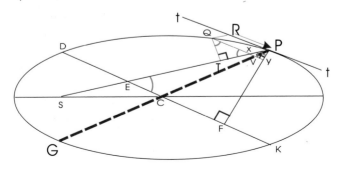

# Figure 12.3 : Why Planets Orbit the Sun in Harmonic-Ratios

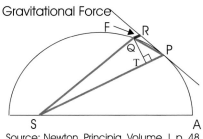

Gravitational Force

Source: Newton, Principia, Volume I, p. 48

Diagram 1: Under Proposition VI Newton describes a planet's orbital path by the curve $APQ$. As shown earlier (Figure 12.1,Diagrams 3 and 4) a planet sweeps out equal areas in equal times. During a given time interval, say $t$, the gravitational force $F$ accelerates the planet toward the Sun $S$ at $a = 1/2\, QT/t^2$. Newton defines the force $F$ as being proportional to $a$ so that $F = k\, QR/t^2$ where $k$ is a constant.

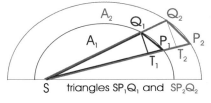

S      triangles $SP_1Q_1$ and $SP_2Q_2$

Diagram 2: As shown in Appendix Equation B12.1 Newton concludes that the areas of two ellipses $A_1$ and $A_2$ vary with the size of the triangles as in $SP_1Q_1 = 1/2\,(Q_1T_1)(P_1S)$ and in $SP_2Q_2 = 1/2\,(Q_2T_2)(P_2S)$ each multiplied by the cumulative time period $t$.

Diagram 3: According to Appendix Equation A12.1
$$L = 2\,(BC)^2/AC.$$
It follows that $(AC)\,(BC)$ varies with $(AC)^{1.5}\, L^{0.5}$ as in $(AC)\,(BC) = (AC)^{1.5}\, L^{0.5}$ of Equation B12.3. If two ellipses differ in size so that $AC$ and $BC$ are $k$ times bigger, the product $(AC)\,(BC)$ will be $k^2$ times bigger. From Equations B12.3 we know that the orbital Area $A$ varies with time as in $A \propto t\,(L)^{0.5}$. On combining the terms from above we get
$$A \propto (AC)(BC) \propto (AC)^{1.5}\, L^{0.5} \propto t\,(L)^{0.5}$$
so that
$$t \propto (AC)^{1.5} \text{ and } t^2 \propto (AC)^3.$$
And with this Newton confirms Kepler's Third Law of "harmonic" planetary motion.

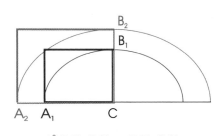

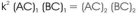
$A_2$   $A_1$              C

$k^2\,(AC)_1\,(BC)_1 = (AC)_2\,(BC)_2$

# Figure 13.1: Estimating the Speed of Light by Timing the Eclipse of Io

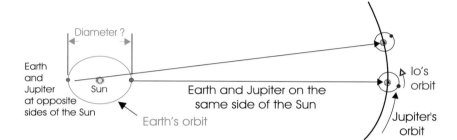

Diagram 1: To estimate the speed of light Roemer needed to know the diameter of the Earth's orbit in miles (or kilometers). Among astronomers the distance of the Earth from the Sun had been set at one astronomical unit (A.U.), but nobody had derived a measure of it in terms of miles. That is, not until Cassini and Richer determined it by method of parallax in 1671.

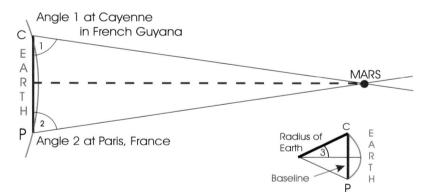

Diagram 2: The French government sent the French astronomer Richer to Cayenne, the capital and Atlantic port of French Guiana (located north of Brazil). While Richer measured the parallactic angle 1 at Cayenne, the French-Italian astronomer Cassini measured angle 2 at Paris. Knowing the surface distance between Cayenne and Paris and the circumference of the Earth, the angle 3 could be determined and from it the length of the baseline CP.

# Figure 13.1: Estimating the Speed of Light by Timing the Eclipse of Io (continued)

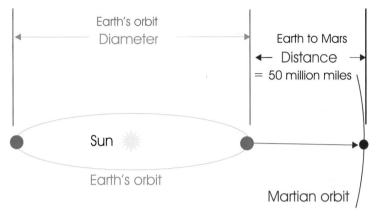

Diagram 3: Having trigonometrically estimated the distance of Mars from Earth, as indicated in Diagram 2, Cassini and Richer determined the size of the Earth's orbit by applying Kepler's harmonic ratios of the relative size of the planetary orbits. They computed the Earth's orbital distance at 174 million miles, an estimate less than 10 percent short of the actual distance.

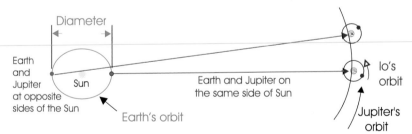

Diagram 4: From Cassini's and Richer's estimates of the Earth's orbit diameter of 174 million miles, Roemer estimated the speed of light. With Io's eclipses varying by as much as 22 minutes, i.e., *(22)(60) = 1320 seconds*) during the Earth's seasons, light had to travel at roughly 174 $(10)^6$ / 1320 = 132,000 miles per second ( 212,000 km/sec). Because of the underestimate of the diameter of the Earth's orbit and an over-estimate of the duration of Io's eclipse, Roemer's estimate of the speed of light was below the actual speed (approx. 186.000 miles per second (300,000 km/sec).

# Figure 13.2: Newton's Corpuscular Theory of Light

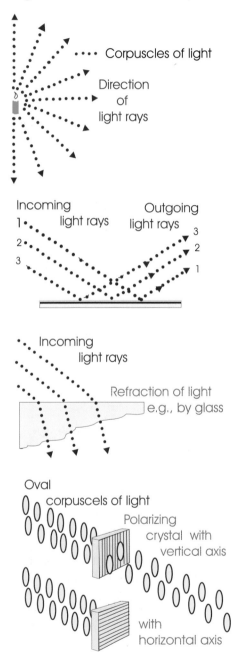

Corpuscles of light

Direction of light rays

Incoming light rays    Outgoing light rays

Incoming light rays

Refraction of light e.g., by glass

Oval corpuscels of light

Polarizing crystal with vertical axis

with horizontal axis

Diagram 1: Newton believed, as Aristotle and other Greek philosophers of antiquity before him, that light was transmitted in tiny particles which radiated from a source of light in all directions. Although the par-Ticles shown here are all of the same size, Newton attributed the different colors of light to particles of different size.

Diagram 2: According to Newton, light rays are reflected by polished metal surfaces because the light corpuscles bounce off the surface just like a ball rebounds from a plane hard surface.

Diagram 3: Rays of light are refracted when they leave one medium and enter another. Newton believed that some of the energy of corpuscles of light is transmitted into the new medium and that the corpuscles' energy loss caused the rays to refract.

Diagram 4: Newton knew that certain crystals, e.g., calcite, transmit light only if held in a certain way. He believed that the light corpuscles were oval-shaped and therefore slim enough to slip through when aligned with the crystal's axis but not in any other way.

# Figure 13.3: Huygens' Wave Theory of Light

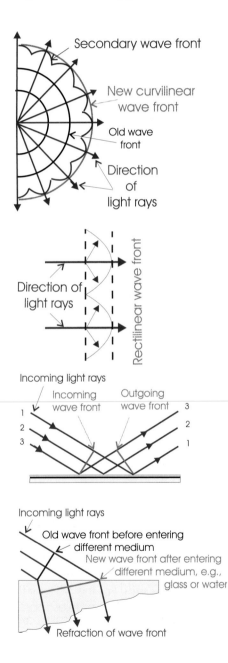

Diagram 1: Waves are caused when a medium is disturbed. A rock thrown into a still pond disturbs the water (the medium) and sets waves into motion. The waves cause the water to move up and down and this transverse motion spreads in all directions. Old wave fronts create secondary wave fronts, leading to new wave fronts, and so on.

Diagram 2: Light waves from the Sun are parallel. They, too, can be thought of as creating new wave fronts from secondary and earlier fronts. These wave fronts would advance at a right angle, or rectilinearly, to the direction of the sunbeams.

Diagram 3: Huygens used geometry to demonstrate how rectilinear wave fronts, created by parallel light beams, can be reflected by polished metal surfaces or mirrors.

Diagram 4: He also showed geometrically how such wave fronts refract on entering a transparent medium. The results were similar to Newton's. But Huygens could not explain why certain crystals polarized light. He assumed that light waves were longitudinal and behaved like sound waves.

## Figure 13.4: The Principle of Aberration

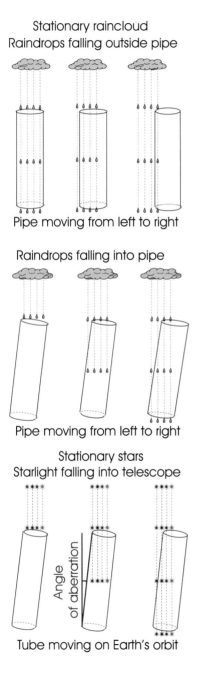

**Stationary raincloud**
Raindrops falling outside pipe

Pipe moving from left to right

Raindrops falling into pipe

Pipe moving from left to right

**Stationary stars**
Starlight falling into telescope

Angle of aberration

Tube moving on Earth's orbit

Diagram 1: Raindrops falling through a straight pipe may illustrate the principle. Assume the rain falls vertically and raindrops enter the pipe. If the pipe is at rest, all rain will pass through freely. But if the pipe is moved (from left to right) some raindrops may hit the wall of the pipe or fall outside.

Diagram 2: If the pipe is held at a slant while it is being moved, rain drops may pass through without touching the wall of the pipe or falling outside of it. For all the raindrops to freely pass through, requires that the angle of the pipe's slant is coordinated with the speed of the falling rain drops and the rate at which the pipe is moved.

Diagram 3: Assume that light from the stars comes straight down to Earth in the form of corpuscles. On entering the telescope they could freely pass through if the tube did not move. Yet the tube does move because the Earth is moving at an orbital speed of 18.6 miles per second (30 km /sec). For the starlight to freely pass through the telescope's tube it must be slanted to allow for the angle of aberration.

# Figure 13.5: Bradley's Estimate of the Speed of Light by Aberration

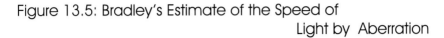

Diagram 1: As illustrated in Figure 13.4, light, like rain, will pass unimpeded through a pipe if the angle of tilt is aligned with the motion. The more rapid the motion, the greater the required angle. As well, the angle of aberration changes with the direction of motion. Bradley discovered that he needed to adjust his zenith telescope to allow for the orbital motion of the Earth.

Direction of the Earth's orbital motion

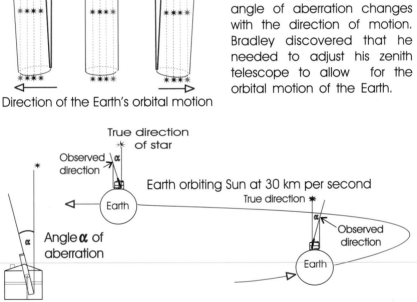

Diagram 2: Bradley had measured the angle $\alpha$ of aberration with great precision. He estimated it to be 20 seconds or 1/180th of $1°$ and from this, he trigonometrically calculated the speed of light as follows.

Let $c$ = Speed of light, $d_1$ = vertical length of telescopic tube, $v$ = orbital speed, $t_1$ = time it takes light to travel distance $d_1$,

Then $t_1 = \dfrac{d_1}{c} = \dfrac{d_E}{v}$ so $\dfrac{d_1}{d_E} = \dfrac{c}{v}$ and $\tan \alpha = \dfrac{d_E}{d_1} = \dfrac{v}{c} = \dfrac{30 \ km/second}{c}$

$c = \dfrac{30 \ km/second}{\tan \alpha} = \dfrac{30 \ km/second}{0.0001} = 300\,000 \ km/second$

# Figure 13.6: Young's Experiments Support
## Huygens' Wave Theory

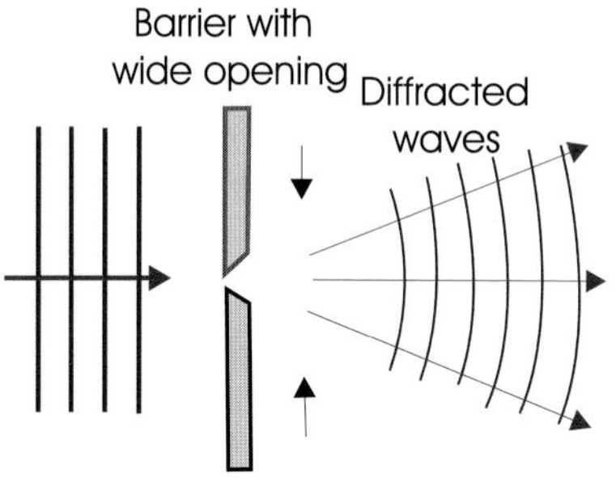

Barrier with wide opening  Diffracted waves

Barrier with 1 narrow slit    Barrier with 2 narrow slits    Min./ max. fringe

Diffracted waves    Waves' interference pattern

Transverse light waves    Waves aligned

Polarizing crystal

Diagram 1: When water waves pass through an opening, they ae diffracted. The smaller the opening, the more curved will be the wave fronts (Huygen's wave fronts were described in Figure 13.3).

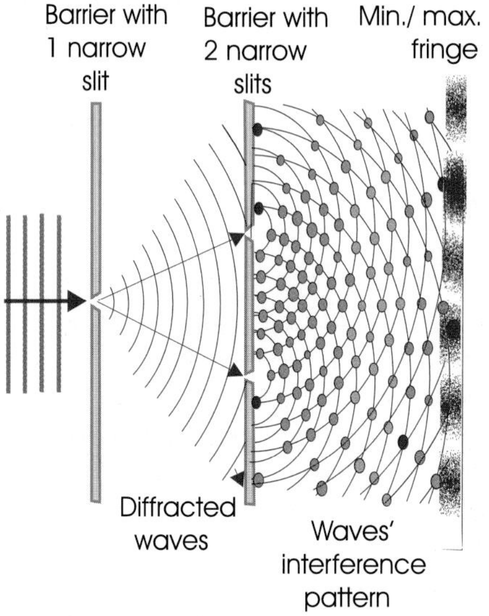

Diagram 2: The interference o Light waves was first demonstrated by Thomas Young. He let light waves fall on a screen that blocked them except for one narrow slit. The waves coming from this slit fell on a second screen with two such slits. Waves passing through these came from the same wave front and, therefore, were in the same phase relationship. That produced a pattern of interference which resulted in additive waves at the points of intersection creating a visible fringe of maximum alternating with minimum light intensities.

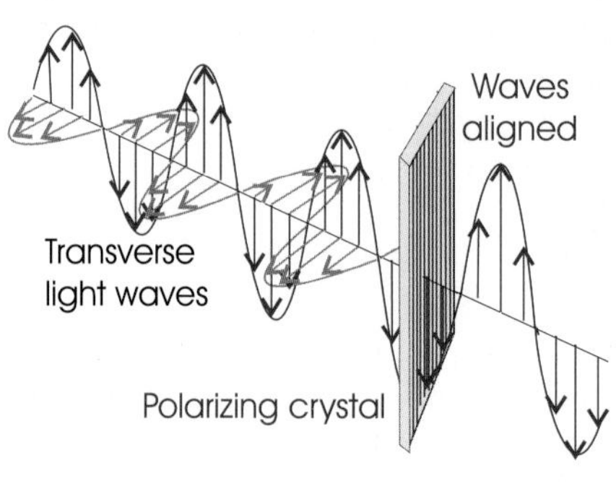

Diagram 3: Huygens had assumed that light waves were longitudinal. Young asserted they were transverse. This enabled him to explain why certain crystals polarized light – a polarizing crystal lets only light waves pass through that are aligned with the crystal's polarizing axis.

# Figure 13.7: Fitzeau's and Foucault's Estimates of the Speed of Light

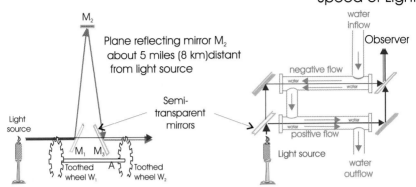

Diagram 1: Simplified version of Fizeau's experimental design for estimating the speed of light.

Diagram 2: Simplified version of Foucault's experiment of light passing through flowing water.

For his experiment, Fizeau used a light source, three mirrors, two toothed wheels joined by axis A. He directed a light beam at wheels $W_1$ and $W_2$. Beyond wheel $W_1$ he let the beam be split into two by a semi-transparent mirror $M_1$, one beam going off in the direction of reflecting mirror $M_2$ placed 5.4 miles (8.7 km) distant from $M_1$, and the second beam passing through the semi-transparent mirror $M_3$ and on toward another wheel $W_2$. At $M_3$ it merged with the first beam reflected from mirror $M_2$ and both together passed through wheel $W_2$ before reaching the eye of the observer. On letting the wheels spin, the light beam was either blocked by the tooth of a wheel or it passed through unimpeded. On speeding up the wheels, the light was brightest when, on consecutive turns, the light passed through the center of the openings and weakest when consistently blocked. Knowing the distance $\lambda$ between wheel openings 10.75 miles (17.3 km), the time $t$ for the wheel to rotate $d_1 = 0.7$ meters per revolution and the wheel's angular speed in revolutions per second. Fizeau estimated the speed of light by letting the time $t$ (Diagram 1):

$$t = \frac{D}{\alpha} = \frac{\lambda}{V} \text{ where the actual } t = \frac{0.7 \, meters}{12.1 \, rev/sec} = \frac{17.3 \, km/sec}{V} \text{ so that}$$

$$c = \frac{(17.3)(12.1) \, km/sec}{0.7 \, m} = \frac{209.33}{0.7m} = \frac{209.33}{0.0007 \, km} = 299\,043 \, km/sec$$

Foucault improved on Fizeau's method by replacing the toothed wheels with revolving mirrors, thereby eliminating the human error of observation, and found that light passed slower through water than air (Diagram 2).

# Figure 13.8: Faraday's and Maxwell's Field Lines

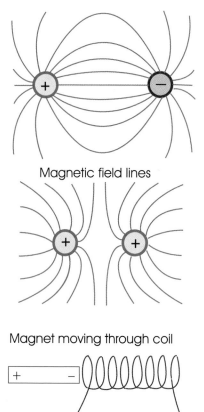

Magnetic field lines

Magnet moving through coil

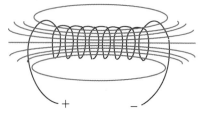

An electric current creates a magnetic field around a coil

Diagram 1: By sprinkling iron filings over a sheet of paper put on top of a magnet, Faraday made the field lines visible. Shown in this diagram schematically as individual lines, in reality the field lines cover the whole area surrounding a magnet. The strength of the magnetic force varies among individual field lines.

Diagram 2: Field lines extend away from the positive toward the negative charge. Field lines of two positive poles of two magnets, repel each other as if they were to meet negative poles somewhere in the opposite direction. In any magnetic field, size and direction of the force can be measured.

Diagram 3: Moving a magnet through a wire coil creates a current flow. As shown below the current creates a magnetic field. Faraday deduced that magnetism and electricity are closely related. Recognizing its practical potential, he constructed the first electrical motor.

Diagram 4: In 1865 Maxwell described the true nature of the relation between electric and magnetic fields. He summarized them in four field equations and predicted from them that visible light, and invisible forms of it at different wavelengths, were all electromagnetic waves moving at a speed of 186 000 miles per second (300 000 km/s).

## Figure 13.8: Faraday's and Maxwell's Field Lines (continued)

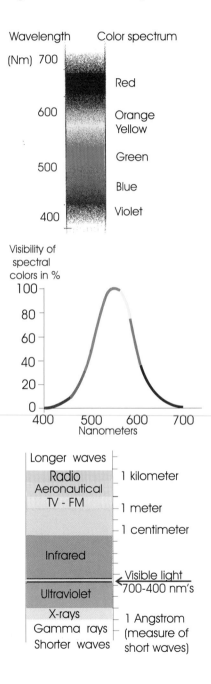

Wavelength   Color spectrum
(Nm) 700

Red

600
Orange
Yellow

Green
500

Blue

400   Violet

Visibility of
spectral
colors in %
100
80
60
40
20
0
400      500      600      700
Nanometers

Longer waves
Radio                1 kilometer
Aeronautical
TV - FM              1 meter
                     1 centimeter

Infrared
                     Visible light
                     700-400 nm's
Ultraviolet
X-rays               1 Angstrom
Gamma rays           (measure of
Shorter waves        short waves)

Diagram 5: Newton was the first to demonstrate that white light was composed of the colors of the rainbow. Herschel observed that the temperature increased from the violet end to the red end of the spectrum. Wollaston and Ritter discovered that ultra-vialet light, beyond the violet end of the spectrum, caused a chemical reaction. It darkened silver chloride.

Diagram 6: This diagram shows the region of the spectrum visible to the unaided eye. At the center the wave length is about 550 billionths of a meter (or 550 nanometers, i.e., nm). Bright yellow light is in the 560 to 580 nm range. Violet and red are toward the ends off the visible range, between 400 to 450 nm and between 625 to 700 nm. respectively.

Diagram 7: Maxwell's greatest achievement was to show that visible light is a branch of electromagnetism. His set of four equations identified light beams as electromagnetic fields that extended beyond the visible range. Maxwell's theory formed the basis for further research. Eventually, radio, television, and other appli-cations of the theory of electromagnetic fields would revolutionize every-day life.

## Figure 13.9: Michelson's and Morley's Estimates of the Speed of Light(Adapted from Leo Sartory, *Understanding Relativity*, p. 31)

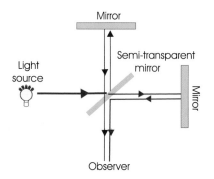

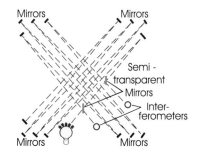

Diagram 1: Simplified version of Michelson's experimental design

Diagram 2: Michelson-Morley's design of multiple reflection and interferometers (simplified)

## Figure 13.10: Raft and Paddlers

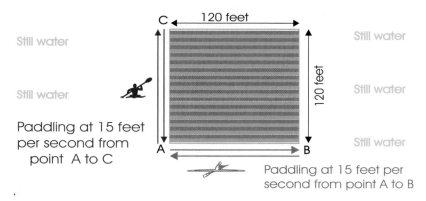

Diagram1: Imagine a log raft is sitting motionless in the midst of a still lake. Two canoeists paddle their boats along the sides of the raft, the first from point *A* to *B* and the se cond from *A* to *C*. Both move at a speed of 15 feet per second. For the first to get from *A* to *B* and back takes *240/ (15 feet per /sec) = 16 seconds*. For the second to paddle from *A* to *C*, takes 16 seconds as well. Both travel the same distance of 240 feet, at the same speed of 15 feet per second, during the same time interval of 16 seconds.

## Figure 13.10: Raft and Paddlers (continued)

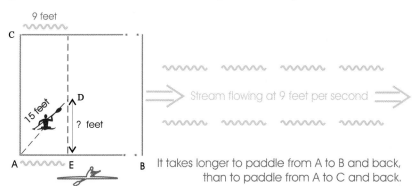

9 feet

C

15 feet

D

? feet

A E B

It takes longer to paddle from A to B and back, than to paddle from A to C and back.

Diagram 2: Now imagine a raft is positioned in a stream flowing at 9 feet per second. Suppose two canoeists paddle along the sides of the same square raft. Each rows at a speed of 15 feet per second. The first canoeist goes with the current of the stream from A to B and then back, against the current of the stream, from B to A. The second rows across the stream from A to C and then back from C to B but while doing so the current carries the canoeist diagonally across the stream in the direction A to D and back to B. It can be shown that paddling across the stream and back takes less time than going first with the current of the stream and then against it. A description of the underlying logic is given in Appendix Equation A13.1 at the end of this Chapter.

## Figure 13.11: Lorentz-Fitzgerald Contraction Hypothesis
### (vastly exaggerated!)

Ether stream

? ?

The speed of light is roughly 186,400 miles/sec (300,000 km/sec) and the orbital speed of the Earth some 18.6 miles/sec (30 km/sec). Physicists expected it would take light less time going across the "ether stream" than going first with it and then against it. Although the expected difference is extremely small, Michelson had fine-tuned his experimental setup to the point where even the slightest difference could have been detected. Yet, none was found. The alternative explanation was that the Earth contracted in the direction of the ether stream. A description of this idea is given in Appendix Equation B12.1.

# Figure 14.1: Perception of Motion

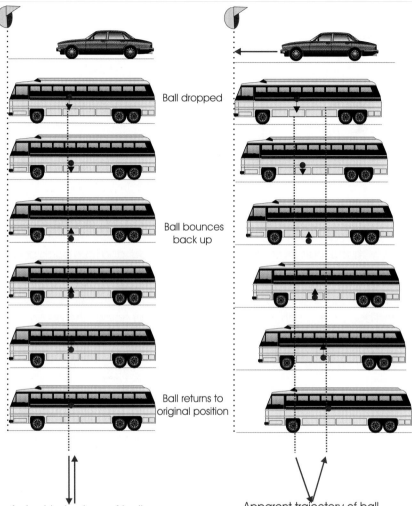

Ball dropped

Ball bounces back up

Ball returns to original position

Actual trajectory of ball

Apparent trajectory of ball

Diagram 1: A car and a bus are waiting at a stop sign. When the car and the bus are at rest, a ball hitting the road bounces straight back up. Seen from the car, the ball's trajectory is straight down and up.

Diagram 2: While the car is inching forward, it may look as if the bus is moving backward. In that case, the trajectory of the ball may appear to be V-shaped. This can happen when the car's motion cannot be visually checked against a stationary object. With no such a check, it is impossible to say which of the two is moving.

# Figure 14.2: Time Dilation Experienced on a Spacecraft

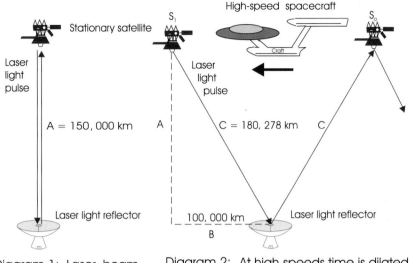

Diagram 1: Laser beam makes round trip in 1 sec. Intervals.

Diagram 2: At high speeds time is dilated at the rate gamma $\gamma = C/A$

The round trip of a laser light pulse from a stationary satellite 150,000 km up in space measures 300,000 km and, at 300,000 km/s, is completed in one second (Diagram 1). If a spacecraft passes the Earth at the speed of 200,000 km/s, a passenger on it sees the light pulse follow a zig-zag course. In one second the pulse crosses the distance from $S_o$ to $S_1$ which equals a distance of $2A = 300{,}000$ km or $2B = 200{,}000$ km on the ground (Diagram 2). From the Pythagorean Theorem we know that $A^2 + B^2 = C^2$. In this example:

$A = 150{,}000 \text{ km} = 15\,(10^4)\,km$ and $B = 100{,}000\,km = 10\,(10^4)\,km$.
It follows that
$$A^2 + B^2 = (15\,(10^4))^2 + (10\,(10^4))^2 = (225 + 100)\,(10)^8 = 325\,(10)^8 = C^2$$

so that $\qquad C = \sqrt{325\,(10)^8} = 18.0278\,(10)^4 = 180\,278\ km$.

Since light travels at 300,000 km/s it will take $2(180\,278)/\,300\,000 = 1.2$ seconds for the light pulse to reach the spacecraft.

This compares with the 1.0 second interval on the stationary satellite. If we accept the idea that the time interval between the two events (i.e., the sending and receiving of the light impulse) is stretched out on the spacecraft, we may conclude, as Einstein did, that time slows down at high speeds. In this example, one second is dilated to 1.2 seconds, a 20% dilation of time. For a more detailed description of this illustration, see Appendix A of this chapter.

# Figure 14.3: Relativistic Time Dilation and Space Contraction

Muons entering atmosphere

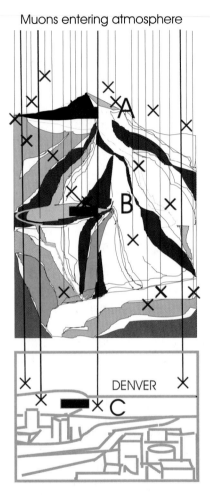

Diagram1:Muons are extremely high-energy particles of cosmic rays that enter the Earth's atmosphere. When physicists measured their frequency with muon counters they found a reduction in numbers with the increase in barometric pressure at lower altitudes. Rossi and Hall and others conducted an experiment in 1940 that yielded some strange results. They collected data at Mt. Evans in the vicinity of Denver, Colorado. As anticipated, their readings were highest at location *A* and lowest at *C*. Between Echo Lake at *B* and Denver at *C* the barometric pressure differed by 14.5 mm mercury. They submerged a second muon counter two meters under the surface of Echo Lake at *B* expecting the readings to be identical to those at *C*. To their surprise they found that the readings at *C* were consistently lower. Time dilation doubled the life-time of the fast muons but they were fewer in number than expected. Enrico Fermi was the first to propose that this was the result of relativistic time dilation at different speeds.

8848 meters

Diagram 2: While the time of the high-speed muons is dilated, space is contracted. Traveling alongside a muon, a person would not experience the muon's lifetime as, say, 20 micro-seconds but only as 1.0. Distance would shorten to 1/20. At the muon's speed the measured height of Mount Everest, for example, would be reduced from 29, 019 feet (8848m) to a mere 1450 feet (442m) (for detail see Appendix A, Equation A14.6).

442.4 meters

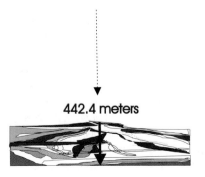

# Figure 14.3: Relativistic Time Dilation and Space Contraction

Based on Fritzsch, pp. 149,150, 152..

### 10 inch measuring stick at rest

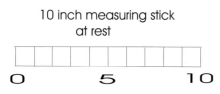

### Same measuring stick at 99.5 % of the speed of light

0 5 10    Direction of high-speed motion

Atom compressed into a spheroid when in straight-linear motion close to speed of light.

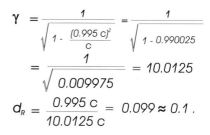

Diagram 3: Nuclear physicists have found that it takes 2.5 billion atoms, side by side, to account for a distance of 10 inches. If a ten-inch ruler were to move straight at a speed of 99.5 % of the speed of light, the ruler would shorten to one inch. In that case the gamma factor would be

$$\gamma = \frac{1}{\sqrt{1 - \frac{(0.995\,c)^2}{c}}} = \frac{1}{\sqrt{1 - 0.990025}}$$

$$= \frac{1}{\sqrt{0.009975}} = 10.0125$$

$$d_R = \frac{0.995\,c}{10.0125\,c} = 0.099 \approx 0.1 \,.$$

The corresponding relativistic space contraction would be $d_R$ = 0.1, which implies that the stick would be 1/10 the length it was at rest.

Diagram 4: How is it possible that at speeds close to light a measuring stick will shorten its length in the direction of motion? What happens to the 2.5 billion atoms that make up the length of the stick? In experiments at CERN (Conseil Européen pour la Recherche Nucléaire) nuclear research physicists have discovered that at speeds close to light the mass of atoms is no longer distributed in globe-shaped spheres but in ellipsoid spheroids. It implies that the individual atoms that make up the body are compressed in the direction of straight-line high-speed motion. Their shape depends on the observer's state of motion, which determines the structure of space.

# Figure 14.4: Distances in Two- and Three- Dimensions

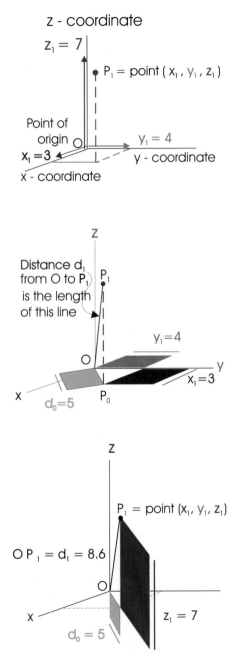

**z - coordinate**

$z_1 = 7$

$P_1$ = point $(x_1, y_1, z_1)$

Point of origin $O$

$x_1 = 3$

$y_1 = 4$

y - coordinate

x - coordinate

Distance $d_1$ from O to $P_1$ is the length of this line

$z$

$P_1$

$y_1 = 4$

O

$x_1 = 3$

$y$

X

$d_0 = 5$

$P_0$

$z$

$P_1$ = point $(x_1, y_1, z_1)$

$OP_1 = d_1 = 8.6$

O

X

$d_0 = 5$

$z_1 = 7$

**Diagram 1:** To specify a location in three-dimensional space, a point of origin $(O=0,0,0)$ is selected. The directions from O are given by three coordinates $x, y, z$. In a rectangular system the coordinates are at right angles to each other. Here, for example, the three coordinates are

$$x_1 = 3, y_1 = 4 \text{ and } z_1 = 7.$$

**Diagram 2:** The distance $d_1$ of point $P_1$ from the origin O can be found by first going to two-dimensional space and obtaining the distance $d_0$ of point $P_0$ by applying the Pythagorean Theorem as in

$$x_1^2 + y_1^2 = d_0^2.$$

If, as before, $x_1 = 3$, $y_1 = 4$, then

$$3^2 + 4^2 = 5^2$$

so that the distance of $P_0$ from the origin O is $d_0 = 5$.

**Diagram 3:** In going from two-dimensional to three-dimensional space the Euclidean distance is defined as changes from $x_1^2 + y_1^2 = d_0^2$

to $x_1^2 + y_1^2 + z_1^2 = d_1^2$.

In Diagram 2 $x_1^2 + y_1^2 = 5^2$ and since $z_1^2 = 7^2$ it follows that

$$x_1^2 + y_1^2 + z_1^2 = 5^2 + 7^2$$

and $25 + 49 = 74 = d_1^2$.

Therefore, in three-dimensional space the distance $d_1$ from O equals

$$(x_1^2 + y_1^2 + z_1^2)^{0.5} = 74^{0.5} = 8.6.$$

## Figure 14.4: Distances in Two- and Three- Dimensions
### (coninued)

)

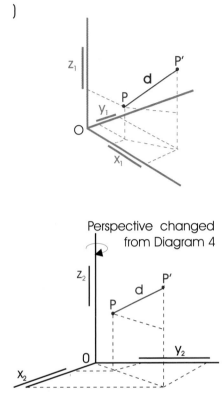

Perspective changed
from Diagram 4

Diagram 4: Here the points PP′ are pictured in a three-dimensional coordinate system. If the system is rotated, the x, y, z description of any one point will change but the distance $d_i$ between two points, say $P_1P_2$ , remains constant so that, in simplified notation, it can be described as

$$d_1^2 = x_1^2 + y_1^2 + z_1^2$$

Diagram 5: Here, for example, the same distance is pictured in another three-dimensional coordinate system. Although the x, y, and z coordinates differ from those in Diagram 4 above, the distance d is of the same length so that $d_1^2$ is also defined by

$$d_2^2 = x_2^2 + y_2^2 + z_2^2$$

Diagram 6: In Diagrams 4 and 5 the $x_1, y_1, z_1$ and $x_2, y_2, z_2$ coordinates differ. When the two systems are superimposed on each other the distance between the two points PP′ remains unchanged so that

$$d_1^2 = x_1^2 + y_1^2 + z_1^2$$
$$= x_2^2 + y_2^2 + z_2^2 = d_2^2$$

This translation of distance from one coordinate system to another is an example of a "symmetry operation." In physics a thing is defined as symmetrical if it looks the same as before, after something has been done to it. This is a Galilean Transformation.

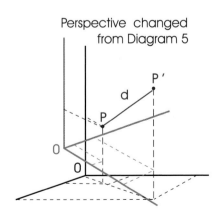

Perspective changed
from Diagram 5

## Figure 14.5: Relativistic Space-Time Coordinates

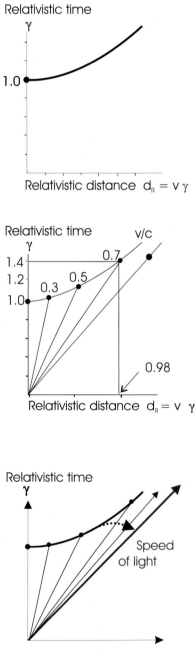

Relativistic time $\gamma$

1.0

Relativistic distance $d_R = v\,\gamma$

Diagram 1: Relativistic time is denoted by the factor gamma $\gamma$ and relativistic distance by $d_R = v\gamma$. The time-dilation factor $\gamma$ is plotted on the vertical axis and the distance $d_R$ on the horizontal axis. When the object's speed is $v = 0.0$, the distance $d_R = v\gamma = 0.0$ and the gamma factor $\gamma = 1.0$. (See Table 14.2 and Appendix Equation 14A.8)

Relativistic time $\gamma$    v/c

1.4   0.7
1.2   0.5
  0.3
1.0

0.98

Relativistic distance $d_R = v\,\gamma$

Diagram 2: This graphically illustrates a few numerical values selected from Table 14.2. As in Diagram 1 above, the vertical axis represents the gamma factor and the horizontal axis the distance. For example, at 98 % of the speed of light ( i.e., $v/c = 0.98$ ), time is dilated 40 % ( i.e., $\gamma = 1.155$), and the distance shrinks to $d_R = 0.5775$ c.

Relativistic time $\gamma$

Speed of light

Relativistic distance $d_R = v\,\gamma$

Diagram 3: At ever greater velocities $v$, the ratio $v/c$ ( i.e., the ratio of velocity to that of light) approaches $v/c = 1.0$. As a result the denominator of the gamma factor comes close to zero and that makes $\gamma$ go toward infinity. It implies that nothing can cross the red-lined barrier in this diagram because no object can exceed the speed of light (e.g., see Appendix Equations A14..1 and A14.7).

## Figure 14.5: Space-Time Coordinates (continued)

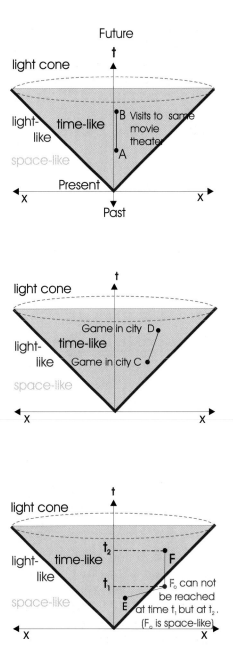

Diagram 4: In this space-time coordinate system the space axis $x$ is in the horizontal plane and the time axis runs vertically. All time-like events within the reach of a light signal fall within the light cone. Events that occur at different times but at the same location are located on a line parallel to the time axis, here at $A$ and $B$. Visits to a movie at the same location are pictured parallel to the time axis as time-like events.

Diagram 5: Visits to ball games in two different cities, $C$ and $D$, are separated by time and distance and can be reached by car or other means of transportation. These two events are also time-like events.

Diagram 6: In contrast, space-like events can not be reached. If in the far future, for example, a meeting would be scheduled on planet $F_o$ of a distant galaxy such that even at the speed of light the meeting could not be reached from planet $E$, it would rate as a space-like event. The meeting would have to be postponed to allow for sufficient time $t_2$, say at $F_1$, to reach it at a speed no greater than light.

# Figure 14.6: Newton's and Einstein's Kinetic Energy

Based on Harald Fritzsch, pp. 167-171.

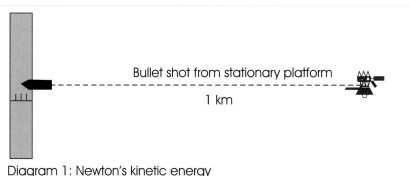

Diagram 1: Newton's kinetic energy

A bullet is fired from a stationary platform at a wooden target one kilometer distant. The velocity of the bullet is 1 km/sec so that the target is reached after one second. Its impact on the target is measured by the penetration of the bullet in the wood. It is determined by the mass and the velocity of the bullet.

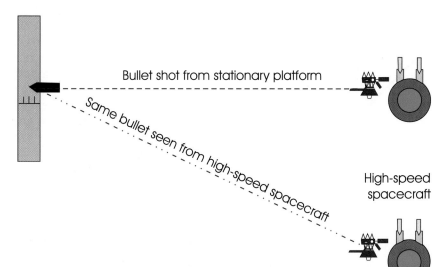

Diagram 2: Einstein's kinetic energy

A high-speed spacecraft passes over the stationary platform, flying parallel to the target and at a distance of 1 km from it, just a fraction of a second after the bullet has been fired. In a one-second interval the high-speed spacecraft travels 298,000 kilometers. Time is dilated by the gamma factor of 10. That means an observer on the craft sees the bullet reach its target in 10 seconds. Since the bullet leaves the same impression as before, its mass must have increased tenfold. If the kinetic momentum is described as $P = mv$, it now becomes $P = (10m)(v/10)$.

# Figure 14.7: Principle of Nuclear Fission

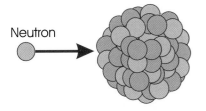

Diagram 1: A neutron strikes a uranium nucleus which contains 92 protons and usually 146 neutrons. The incoming neutron transfers its energy to the nucleus and thereby excites the resulting system.

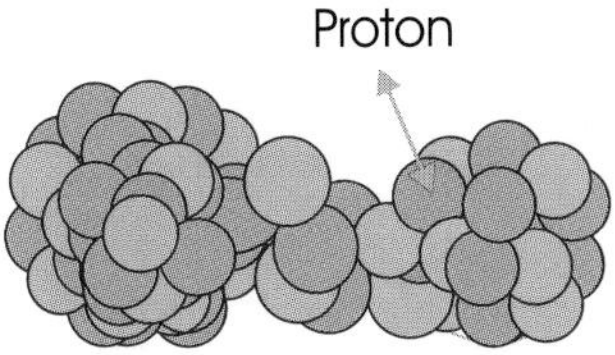

Diagram 2: The nucleus is transformed. The deformation is so drastic that it cannot recover. It pulsates like a soap bubble. The bigger the bubble, the greater is the tendency to break into smaller bubbles or to blow up altogether.

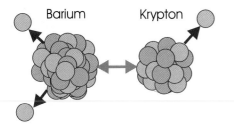

Diagram 3: The nucleus breaks apart or "fissions" and releases two or three neutrons. The fission fragments lose their kinetic energy, come to rest, emitting a number of gamma rays.

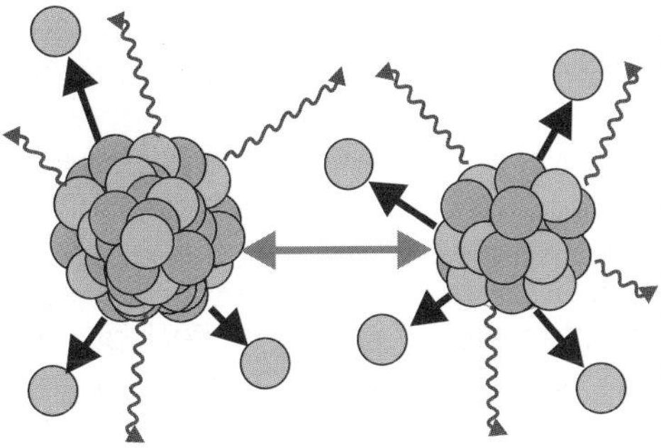

Diagram 4: During fission the nucleus breaks into two smaller nuclei, a barium nucleus with 56 protons and a krypton nucleus with 36 protons, and a number of neutrons. The fission products lose their excess energy, emitting beta particles and gamma rays. About 0.1 percent of the uranium mass is converted into energy during the explosion.

## Figure 14.8: Key Elements of the Special Theory of Relativity

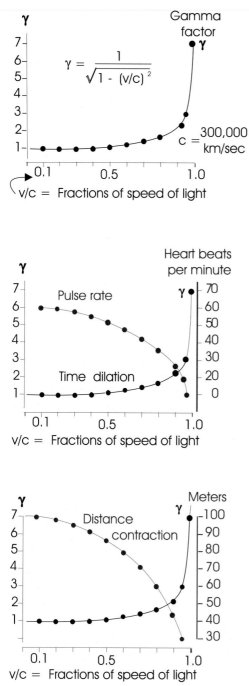

Diagram 1: The gamma factor was introduced in this chapter. It is the keystone of the Special Theory of Relativity. Time dilation, space contraction, relativistic energy, and the speed-of-light barrier are conditioned by it. First shown in Figure 14.2, it was explored in Table 14.2 and in Equations A14.1 to A14.7, B14.4 and B14.5 of the Appendix of this Chapter.

Diagram 2: The black line pictures the relativistic time dilation and the red line the pulse rate per minute. If an astronaut were monitored by an observer on Earth at 90 % of the speed of light, for example, the gamma factor would be 2.29. An observer on Earth would register the astronaut's pulse rate at 60 / 2.29 = 26 heartbeats per minute because time was dilated.

Diagram 3: On a high-speed spacecraft distance shortens at different rates, the higher the speed the more the distance decreases. At 99 % of the speed of light the length of distance $L$ is reduced by the gamma factor, as in $L/\gamma = d_R$. At that speed an observer on the spacecraft would see a distance of 1000 km reduced to $d_R = 1000/2.29 = 437\,km$.

# Figure 14.8: Key Elements of the Special Theory (continued)

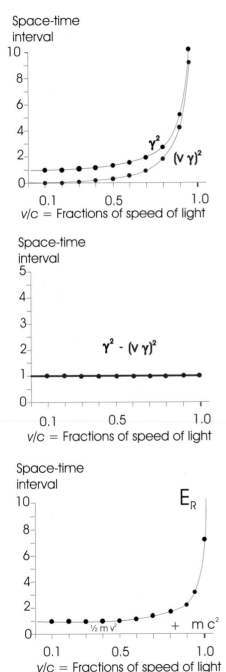

Diagram 4: Figure 14.4 illustrated how the distance between points in two- and three-dimen-sional space is described in a rec-tangular coordinate system. This Diagram depicts the distance between two points in a space-time coordinate system. It is the constant distance between the square of time and the square of distance (i.e., $\gamma^2 - (v\,\gamma)^2 = 1^2$).

Diagram 5: This chart shows that the distance between the black and the red line of Diagram 4 is constant. The essential point is that in a relativistic world where time and distance vary with speed, the difference between the squares of relativistic time and space remains constant whatever the speed. The same idea is conveyed in Table 14.2 .It is a characteristic of symmetry, or of "Galilean Transformation."

Diagram 6: As shown in Appen-dix 14B, Einstein transformed Newton's equation for kinetic energy into the relativistic version $E_R$. The latter consists of two parts, Newton's kinetic energy and Einstein's energy that comes into play at speeds close to light :
$$E_R = \tfrac{1}{2}mv^2 + mc^2$$
Details of the derivation are given in Equation B14.4 of this Chapter.

## Figure 15.1: Einstein's Principle of Equivalence

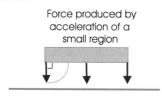

Force produced by acceleration of a small region

Diagram 1: The Principle of Equivalence states that the effects produced by acceleration are equivalent to those of gravity. As long as the effects are created in a small region, they cannot be distinguished from gravitational force.

Force produced by gravity affecting a very large region

Diagram 2: The effects of gravitational force and acceleration differ over a large region such as a continent, because the angle of the gravitational force is directed toward the center. In contrast, an accelerative force acting on the same large object would cause the lines of force to be parallel. Therefore, Einstein limited the Equivalence Principle to any small region where the effects produced by acceleration are the same as those produced by gravitation (see *The Principle of Equivalence* in Chapter 15).

## Figure 15.2: Triangles on Curved Surfaces

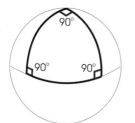

Diagram1: The angles of a triangle drawn on the surface of a sphere will always add up to more than 180°. If, for example, a triangle covers one quarter of a globe, its three angles equal *3 x 90° = 270°*. The surface of a sphere is said to have a positive curvature.

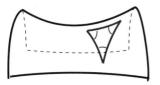

Diagram 2: When drawn on a saddle-shaped surface the angles of a triangle have less than 180.° In this case, the surface is said to have to have a negative curvature.

## Figure 15.3: Circles on Flat and Curved Surfaces

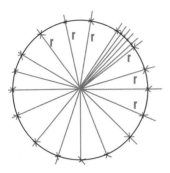

Diagram 1: The circumference of a circle can be approximated by drawing straight lines from a single point, marking them off equidistant all around, and then connecting them. If we compare the length of the circumference with that of the straight line, the circumference will always be approximately 6.3 times as long as the radial lines. The more straight the lines, the closer the value will come to $2\pi = 6.28\ldots.$

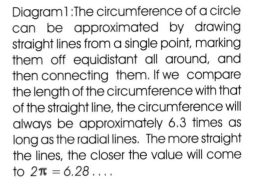

Diagram 2: Instead of drawing straight lines from a single point onto a flat surface, a rope is stretched over the surface of sphere. Marking off the end-points of the rope all around, a circle is formed on the sphere. Assuming the rope is of the same length as the straight radial lines in Diagram 1 above, the circumference of the circle on the flat surface is greater than that of the circle on the curved surface of the sphere. The difference between the two is illustrated in Diagram 3 below.

Two-dimensional
surface radius $R_2$

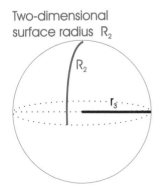

Three-dimensional radius $r_3$

Diagram 3: If we let the three-dimensional radius $r_3 = 1$, measured from the central axis of the sphere to the surface, the distance from pole to equator is one quarter of the equator and equals $2\pi r_3 / 4 = 6.28 / 4 = 1.57$. This is the length of the two-dimensional radius $R_2$ measured on the curved surface from center point to equator. The ratio of the two radii, one in two dimensions and the other in three, is $R_2 / r_3 = 1.57 / 1 = 1.57$. The ratio of their corresponding areas is $A_2 / A_3 = \pi R_2^2 / \pi r_3^2 = R_2^2 / r_3^2 = 1.57^2$.

# Figure 15.4: Flat Space and Curved Space

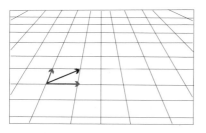

FLAT SPACE

Diagram 1: Einstein applied tensor analysis, an extension of vector analysis. The concept of vectors is readily understood. They are line segments with magnitude and direction. They can be added. Here, for example, the blue vectors are "added" to yield the red vector **V**.

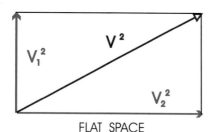

FLAT SPACE

Diagram 2: In search for a relativistic law of gravitation Einstein went from linear vectors to curvature tensors. In case of rectilinear coordinates the vector $V$ is linked to its components by the Pythagorean Theorem as in:
$$V_1^2 + V_2^2 = V^2.$$
The linkage of tensor components is more complex.

In the diagram: $V_1^2$, $V^2$, $V_2^2$

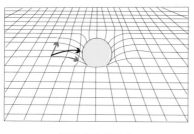

CURVED SPACE

Diagram 3: Einstein believed that gravitational forces warped space and that the coordinate system needed to be adjusted to allow for the curvature of space. Using tensor analysis, he wanted to integrate the relativistic elements of four-dimensional space-time with gravitational forces.

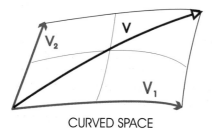

CURVED SPACE

In the diagram: $V_2$, $V$, $V_1$

Diagram 4: At this point it is speculative whether the Pythagorean Theorem could be expanded to accommodate the change from vectors in a rectilinear coordinate system to tensors in a curvilinear system.

# Figure 15. 5: Two-Dimensional Gaussian Coordinates

Based on Max Born, pp. 321-326 and on Albert Einstein (1952), pp. 87-90.

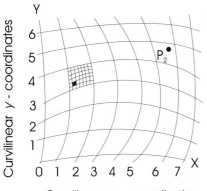

Curvilinear y - coordinates

Curvilinear x - coordinates

Diagram 1: Points in space can be defined by a set of Gaussian coordinates $x_1, x_2, x_3, \ldots, x_n$ and $y_1, y_2, y_3, \ldots, y_m$. The coordinates can be further subdivided and renumbered to form a non-rigid system of reference points. Laid on top of an uneven surface, this coordinate net can be formed so that it makes surface contact. The finer the coordinate net, the greater the number of surface contact points.

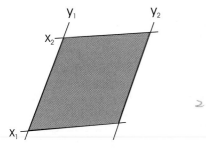

Diagram 2: The coordinates $x_1$, $x_2$ and $y_1$, $y_2$ correspond to the border lines of the tiny area selected in Diagram 1. A point $P_1$ is marked inside the area. The ultimate objective is to find the shortest distance between this point and a second point that is located somewhere else on the curved surface, for example, point $P_2$ in Diagram 1 above.

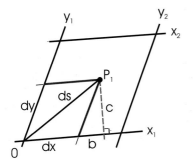

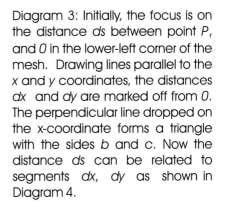

Diagram 3: Initially, the focus is on the distance $ds$ between point $P_1$ and $0$ in the lower-left corner of the mesh. Drawing lines parallel to the x and y coordinates, the distances $dx$ and $dy$ are marked off from $0$. The perpendicular line dropped on the x-coordinate forms a triangle with the sides $b$ and $c$. Now the distance $ds$ can be related to segments $dx$, $dy$ as shown in Diagram 4.

# Figure 15. 5 : Two-Dimensional Gaussian Coordinates
(continued).

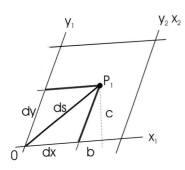

Diagram 4: From the Pythagorean Theorem, (described in Chapter 2, Figure 2.3) it follows that:

$$ds^2 = (dx + b)^2 + c^2$$
$$= (dx^2 + 2\, dx\, b + b^2) + c^2$$

Noting that $b^2 + c^2 = dy^2$ and substituting it into the above, yields

$$ds^2 = dx^2 + 2\, dx\, b + dy^2$$

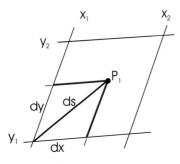

Diagram 5: In a somewhat similar fashion Gauss deduced the Generalized Pythagorean Theorem which reads

$$ds^2 = g_{11}\, dx^2 + 2\, g_{12}\, dx\, dy + g_{22}\, dy^2$$

In this expression the terms $ds$, $dx$ and $dy$ are very small numbers (i.e., differentials) and the coefficients $g_{11}$, $g_{12}$, $g_{22}$ are magnitudes that vary with the point in space under consideration and are called the metric

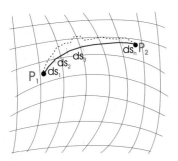

Diagram 6: Lines are not straight on a curved surface. Yet, there are certain lines between two points, say $P_1$ and $P_2$, that make for the shortest connection. Mathematically, they are formed as the smallest sum of the line segments $ds_i$. Linked together they form a so-called geodesic line

$$ds_1 + ds_2 + ds_3 + ... + d_n s_n$$

between two points on the Gaussian surface.

# Figure 15.6: Geodesics on Curved Surfaces

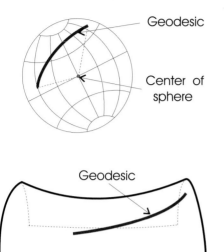

Diagram1: On a spherical surface a curved geodesic is the shortest line connecting two points. On this type of a surface the geodesic is always formed by a plane that passes through the center of the sphere.

Diagram 2: On a saddle-shaped surface the geodesic can be mathematically determined by the Generalized Pythagorean Theorem. It requires a complete set of metric coefficients.

# Figure 15.7: Planetary Orbit Pictured in Space-Time Dimension
### Adapted from George Gamow (1961), Fig. VI-16, p. 206.

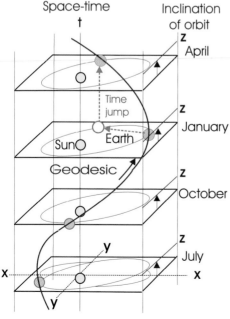

Diagram 1: In this illustration, the red geodesic line traces out the space-time distance in a four-dimensional coordinate system of three space-dimensions $x$, $y$, $z$ and one time dimension $t$.

If we were to picture the Earth's orbit as an ellipse on an inclined plane it might convey the idea that the red geodesic line is not the shortest. As suggested by the broken blue line, a straight line between two orbital positions would obviously be shorter. But this ignores the fact that time elapses between the two positions. Going directly from one season to the next would require a time jump into the future.

## Figure 15.8: Time Slows Down in Field of Acceleration

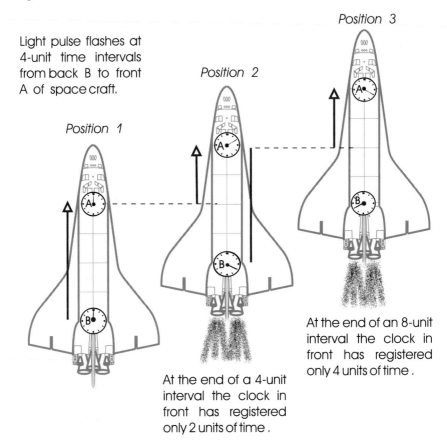

Light pulse flashes at 4-unit time intervals from back B to front A of space craft.

*Position 1*

*Position 2*

*Position 3*

At the end of a 4-unit interval the clock in front has registered only 2 units of time.

At the end of an 8-unit interval the clock in front has registered only 4 units of time.

## Figure 15.9: The Doppler Effect and Einstein's Prediction

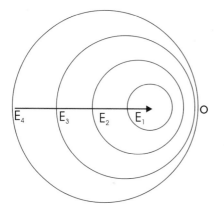

Diagram 1: An object emits sound waves that can be represented by a sphere centered on the emitter. In this diagram the emitter E is moving from left to right. When the emitter of the sound is approaching the observer at point o, the successive spheres grow to $E_2$, $E_3$, $E_4$ and come closer together. Thus the frequency of waves increases and the pitch of sound gets higher.

## Figure 15.9:The Doppler Effect and Einstein's Prediction (cont'd.)

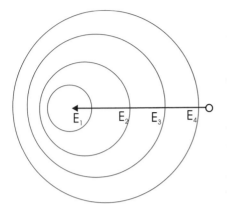

Diagram 2: Depending on the direction of the wave fronts, either coming toward the observer or moving away from the observer, the frequency of the waves changes. When the emitter approaches, the frequency increases, when it recedes it diminishes. In the case of sound, a higher frequency makes for a higher tone and a lower frequency for a lower one. With light waves, the effect is similar.

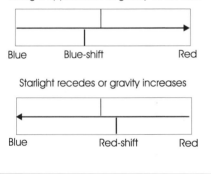

Starlight approaches or gravity decreases

Blue    Blue-shift    Red

Starlight recedes or gravity increases

Blue    Red-shift    Red

Diagram 3: The Doppler effect is reflected in a shift of the spectrum. With light waves from approaching stars, the spectrum is blue-shifted and with light waves from receding stars, it is red-shifted. Doppler discovered that the stars were moving relative to each other. Einstein's analysis showed that a strong gravitational pull made for a red-shift in the spectrum of light waves coming from stars.

## Figure 15.10: Unexplained Advance of the Perihelion of Mercury

The major axis of Mercury's elliptical orbit changes very slowly in the direction of its orbital motion. Prior to Einstein the "unexplained advance" of Mercury's perihelion amounted to 43 of 5600 seconds per century, i.e., 43 secs ahead of Newton's gravitational value. Einstein's Theory of General Relativity reduced the error from 43 seconds to less than 1 per century.

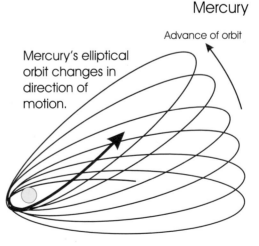

Advance of orbit

Mercury's elliptical orbit changes in direction of motion.

# Figure 15.11: Light Deflected by Gravitational Field

Adapted from George Gamow, p. 196, Delo Mook
and Thomas Vargish, pp. 169, 170.

FLOATING IN SPACE

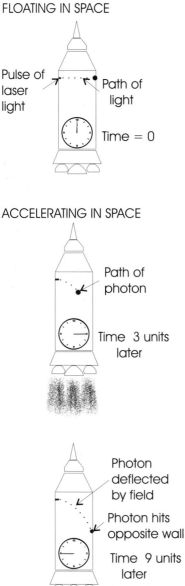

**Diagram 1:** In 1914 Einstein wrote an article in which he asserted that light, like any other material body, will be affected by acceleration. He imagined a chamber floating in interstellar space. While drifting along, a light pulse is sent straight across the chamber to the opposite wall.

ACCELERATING IN SPACE

**Diagram 2:** If the laboratory chamber were accelerated, the path of light would change. The individual photons of light would be pulled toward the floor of the chamber in the direction opposite to the accelerating thrust of the rocket engines. If captured on the film of a precision camera, their path would appear curved.

**Diagram 3:** Assuming the space-craft's engines continue to run, the chamber will accelerate and the photons will continue on their curved path. Similarly to the trajectory of a rock thrown horizontally on Earth, the photons in the chamber would trace out a parabola. It follows that light rays would be bent in a gravitational field as well.

# Figure 15.12: Starlight Deflected by the Gravitational Force of the Sun

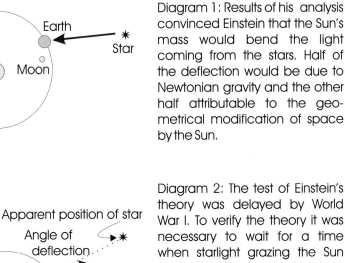

Diagram 1: Results of his analysis convinced Einstein that the Sun's mass would bend the light coming from the stars. Half of the deflection would be due to Newtonian gravity and the other half attributable to the geometrical modification of space by the Sun.

Diagram 2: The test of Einstein's theory was delayed by World War I. To verify the theory it was necessary to wait for a time when starlight grazing the Sun was not blocked out by the glare. In 1918 an eclipse of the Sun offered the needed opportunity. Two British expeditions were mounted, one to Principe in West Africa and the other to Sobral in Northern Brazil, to record the extent to which the Sun deflected light from the stars.

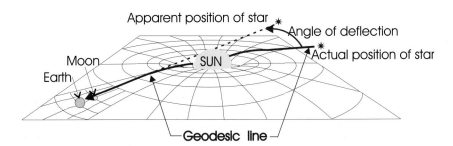

Diagram 3: The two British expeditions were the first to confirm the results of Einstein's General Theory of Relativity. Their observations were later confirmed by other expeditions. The curvature of space-time around the Sun did indeed bend the starlight along the geodesic line of space.

# Figure 16.1: Black-body Radiation and Quantum Theory
Adapted from Serway (1990), p.1148 and Halliday, Resnick, Walker, p.1140.

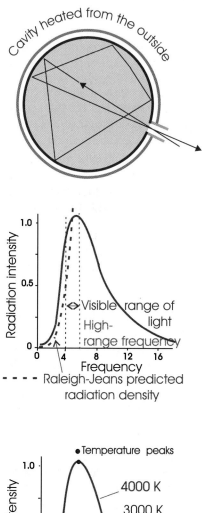

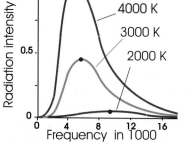

Temperature in Kelvin degrees K

Diagram 1: The radiation emitted by a red hot poker or a bonfire depends on many variables. In the 1890s Wien found that a spherical body was perfect for the study of radiation. Kept at a constant temperature, the body's inner walls reflected rays so many times that only a tiny portion made its way out again. The spectrum of the rays emitted through this opening was very distinct and only affected by the cavity's temperature inside.

Diagram 2: At the turn of the 20th century the Raleigh-Jeans Law predicted that radiation density increased without limit as the frequency increased. At the low end of the frequency range the Law agreed fairly well with the experimental data but not so at the high end. Beyond the highest range of visible light the theory predicted an infinite intensity.

Diagram 3: In 1900, Max Planck published a formula that perfectly agreed with the experimental evidence over the full range of temperatures. His theory was based on the bold idea that radiation is emitted in discrete energy packets which he called quanta. According to Planck the difference in energy between two adjacent quantum states is

$$E = hf$$

where $h$ is Planck's constant and $f$ is the frequency.

# Figure 16.2: Models of the Atom

Adapted from Serway (1990), p.821 and (1994), pp. 846,847.

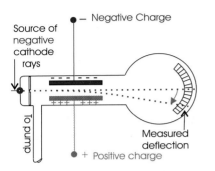

Thomson's apparatus for
measuring the mass of electrons

Diagram 1: In 1897 the English physicist J. J. Thomson showed that cathode rays were deflected when passed between two electrically charged aluminum plates. When the top plate was charged negatively, the cathode rays moved to the positive plate. This proved that the cathode rays consisted of negatively charged particles. From the degree of deflection he deduced that the electrons were 1000 times lighter

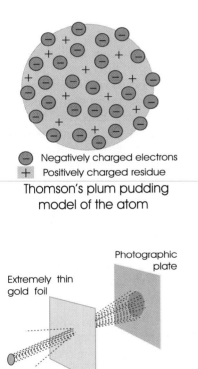

Thomson's plum pudding
model of the atom

Diagram 2: The philosophers of Greek antiquity assumed that matter consisted of extremely small units. They called them atomos (ἄτομος) for indivisible. J. J. Thomson discovered that tiny negatively charged particles, which he called electrons, could be extracted from atoms. They left behind a positively charged residue (nucleus). He concluded that electrons were embedded in the atoms just like

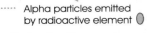

Rutherford's experiment

Diagram 3: In 1911 Rutherford overturned Thomson's model of the atom with his gold-leaf experiment. He had his graduate students beam alpha particles through a thin gold foil. About 1 in 20,000 particles was deflected and of those some came right back through the foil. "It was almost as incredible as if you fired a 15-inch shell at a piece of tissue paper, and it came back to hit you," Rutherford said later. It altered the picture of

# Figure 16.2: Models of the Atom (continued)

*Encyclopaedia Britannica*, "The Bohr Atom"

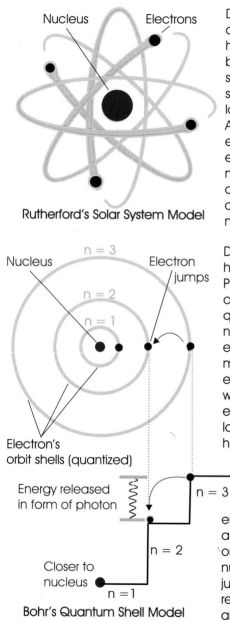

Rutherford's Solar System Model

Bohr's Quantum Shell Model

Diagram 4: In 1911, Rutherford deduced an atomic model from his gold-leaf experiments that can be pictured as a miniature solar system. Roughly, like the Sun in the solar system, the atomic nucleus is located at the center of the atom. All the rest of the atom is nearly empty space. Similar to the planets, the electrons circle around the nucleus. They are negatively charged and extremely tiny compared with the atomic nucleus.

Diagram 5: Niels Bohr published his theory of the atom in 1913. As Planck had shown, radiant energy can only exist in multiple packets or quanta. Bohr believed that the nucleus was surrounded by electron shells and that electrons moved in orbits of fixed size and energy. The energy of electrons would correspond to quantized energy levels, smaller orbits having lower energy levels. Electron orbits have quantized sizes. Energy is emitted from the atom when an electron jumps from one orbit to another closer to the nucleus. For example, when it jumps from orbit $n=3$ to $n=2$, it releases a photon of red light with an energy of 1.89 electron volt.

# Figure 16.3: Other Quantum Characteristics

Diagrams 1 and 3 based on Serway (1990), pp. 1156 and 854.

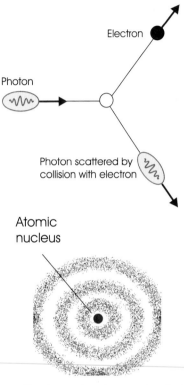

Atomic nucleus

Electron clouds representing probabilities of orbital location

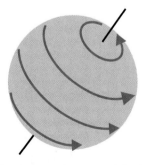

Electrons spin around their axis

Diagram 1: In 1922 Arthur Holly Compton showed by experiment that X-rays behave like particles. Compton demonstrated how a photon could be scattered by an electron. This scattering could be explained by treating photons as point-like particles with energy

$$E = hf$$

where $h$ is Planck's constant and $f$ is an electromagnetic frequency. This photoelectric effect could be explained by quantum theory but not by wave theory.

Diagram 2: Schroedinger believed his wave equations implied that fractions of electrons were spread out in orbits around the atomic nucleus. Max Born claimed that the cloud-like appearance of electrons re-presented the probability of finding an electron at a specific point of its orbit. Today, Born's interpretation is generally accepted as correct.

Diagram 3: Dirac studied the motions of atomic particles. In his efforts to relate quantum theory to relativity theory he discovered that the electron rotates on its axis. Based on considerations of sym-metry, he also postulated that short-lived positive particles should exist. Although at the time their existence appeared doubtful, eventually they were proven to occur.

# Figure 16.4: Particle Accelerator and Cloud Chamber
Based on *Encyclopaedia Britannica*: Synchrotons

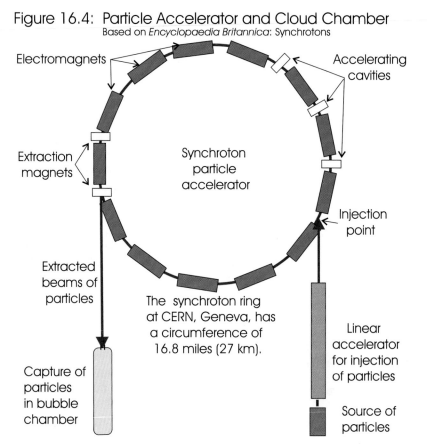

Electromagnets

Accelerating cavities

Extraction magnets

Synchroton particle accelerator

Injection point

Extracted beams of particles

The synchroton ring at CERN, Geneva, has a circumference of 16.8 miles (27 km).

Linear accelerator for injection of particles

Capture of particles in bubble chamber

Source of particles

Diagram 1: The effectiveness of accelerators is characterized by the kinetic energy particles attain. Over the years, the energies have been increased from around 1 to 1,000,000 mega-electron volts.

Diagram 2: Beams of accelerated nuclear particles are passed into cloud or bubble chambers of particle detectors. Charles T. R. Wilson perfected the first cloud chamber in 1912. He used moist supersaturated clean air to make particles visible as they left behind tiny droplets of water on the tracks. His cloud chamber evolved into today's bubble chambers.

# Figure 16.5: The Life Cycle of a Star (simplified)
### Based on Pasachoff and Kutner (1978), pp. 260, 261

Diagram 1: Stars form out of interstellar gas atoms and dust particles in regions of space that have a slightly higher density than their surroundings. It is only when such gas and dust clouds have sufficient mass that the gravitational force comes into play. Eventually, a point is reached where gravity causes the cloud to compress. Gas and dust are heated and form a so-called protostar (from the Greek word *protos,* to be the first).

Diagram 2: For an average-size star like the Sun, the protostar period lasts for about 50 million years. More massive stars of, say, 10 times the mass of our Sun, may pass through the protostar period in as little as 200,000 years. During this time the protostar continues to contract and the temperature rises and acts with outward pressure. Astronomers have discovered objects that are very bright in the infrared range. They believe that these strange objects are dust shells around protostars.

→ Gravitational force
← Counterbalancing
force of nuclear fusion

Diagram 3: The heat energy in stars that are still contracting comes from grav-itational contraction itself. If this were the only source of heat, stars would shine for only 30 million years. But the proto-stars will continue heating up until they become hot enough for nuclear fusion. During that process the element hydrogen is converted into helium. Nuclear fusion creates enough energy to save the star from further gravitational collapse and allow it to shine for billions of years. The star's mass is converted into energy according to Einstein's Equation:

$$E = mc^2.$$

## Figure 16.5: The Life Cycle of a Star (continued)

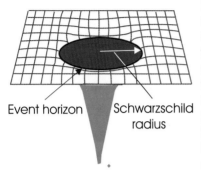

Event horizon     Schwarzschild radius

Diagram 4: In 1916 Karl Schwarzschild found an exact solution to Einstein's tensor equations. It showed that if a massive star collapsed into a small enough region, the space-time warp would be so extreme that nothing, not even light, could escape beyond a certain event horizon. In the case of our Sun, this horizon would have a radius of 1.9 miles (3 km) or, if applied to Earth, of 9mm.

Blue supergiant star

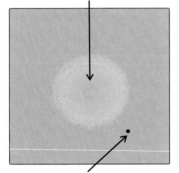

Black hole Cygnus X-1

Diagram 5: By now some 300 pulsars have been identified and 100,000 more are thought to be in our galaxy. The search for black holes has not been nearly as successful. Optically, they are invisible. Astronomers have searched for binary (double) star systems, hoping that one member of the binary could be identified as a black hole. Four binaries were suspected, but their masses were too small. That left only one convincing case that was named Cygnus X-1.

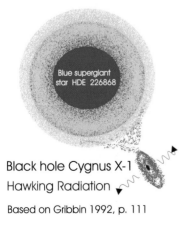

Blue supergiant star HDE 226868

Black hole Cygnus X-1
Hawking Radiation

Based on Gribbin 1992, p. 111

Diagram 6: Cygnus X-1 is an X-ray source that shows up on a negative print similar to the sketch of Diagram 5. Astronomers could identify radiation as coming from the same binary because of matching patterns of X-ray and radio waves. One of the two is the blue supergiant star HDE 226868 and the other a black hole of a mass eight times that of our Sun. Theory predicts that the black hole pulls matter off the blue supergiant companion.

# Figure 16.6:  Theories of More Than Five Dimensions
### Based on: Michio Kaku (1994),  pp.143, 146 and 147.

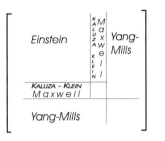

Diagram 1: The Yang-Mills theory was a first attempt to combine Einstein's four-dimensional theory of gravity and space-time with the five-dimensional theory of the Kaluza-Klein model of Maxwell's theory of the electromagnetic force in the Yang-Mills field of the strong and weak nuclear forces.

Diagram 2: In 1976 the quanta with a spin are integrated in a pattern of super-symmetry in which the graviton of gravity has two units of spin and the photon of light has one unit of spin. This matrix came to be called "super-gravity" model because it was based on super-symmetry.

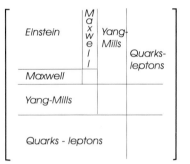

Diagram 3:Corresponding to Diagram 2, the subscripted letters denote coefficients that are needed for a solution of the equations. To solve a 10-dimensional linear-equation system would require 100 coefficients. If the matrix is symmetric, the terms "off" the diagonal will match, and the coefficient require-ment is reduced to $45 + 10 = 55$ values. Even though not all coefficient values have been found, this model comes closest yet to Einstein's vision of a "unified field theory."

$$\begin{bmatrix} g_{11} & g_{12} & g_{13} & g_{14} & l_{15} & n_{16} & n_{17} & m_{18} & m_{19} & m_{110} \\ g_{21} & g_{22} & g_{23} & g_{24} & l_{25} & n_{26} & n_{27} & m_{28} & m_{29} & m_{210} \\ g_{31} & g_{32} & g_{33} & g_{34} & l_{35} & n_{36} & n_{37} & m_{38} & m_{39} & m_{310} \\ g_{41} & g_{42} & g_{43} & g_{44} & l_{45} & n_{46} & n_{47} & m_{48} & m_{49} & m_{410} \\ l_{51} & l_{52} & l_{53} & l_{54} & l_{55} & n_{56} & n_{57} & m_{58} & m_{59} & m_{510} \\ n_{61} & n_{62} & n_{63} & n_{64} & n_{65} & n_{66} & n_{67} & m_{68} & m_{69} & m_{610} \\ n_{71} & n_{72} & n_{73} & n_{74} & n_{75} & n_{76} & n_{77} & m_{78} & m_{79} & m_{710} \\ m_{81} & m_{82} & m_{83} & m_{84} & m_{85} & m_{86} & m_{87} & m_{88} & m_{89} & m_{810} \\ m_{91} & m_{92} & m_{93} & m_{94} & m_{95} & m_{96} & m_{97} & m_{98} & m_{99} & m_{910} \\ m_{101} & m_{102} & m_{103} & m_{104} & m_{105} & m_{106} & m_{107} & m_{108} & m_{109} & m_{1010} \end{bmatrix}$$

*Metric coefficients:*
  g   for gravity
  l   for light
  n   for nuclear force
  m   for matter

# Figure 16.7 : The Grand Unified Theory, or the GUT Model

Based on Brian Greene (1999), pp. 178,179.

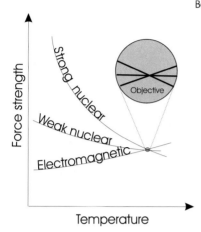

First proposed during the early 1970s, the aim of particle physicists was to develop a "Grand Unified Theory" (GUT). The theory was to combine the three non-gravitational forces of nature: the strong nuclear, the weak nuclear, and the electromagnetic force. Physicists expected the three to merge into one grand force at immense temperatures. Later it was shown that without super-symmetry this would almost, but not quite, happen.

# Figure 16.8 : Symmetry of Subatomic Particles, an Example

*Encyclopaedia Britannica*, "Subatomic Particles: Symmetry."

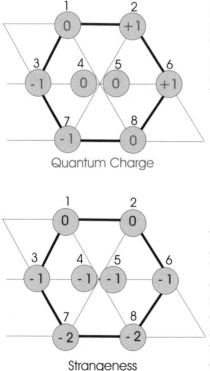

Subatomic particles have various properties and are affected by forces that exhibit symmetry. The pattern is called the "Eightfold Way." For example, one group consists of the (oddly-named) particles:

1. Neutron
2. Proton
3. Lambda
4. Sigma$^+$
5. Sigma$^0$
6. Sigma$^-$
7. Xi$^0$
8. Xi$^-$

The diagrams illustrate how the quantum numbers of "Charge" and "Strangeness" are symmetrically distributed in the Eightfold Way. The names of the particles and their quantum properties may sound a bit strange, but the symmetry-based theory has correctly predicted the existence of certain particles.

# Figure 16.9: More Dimensions and Vibrating Strings

Based on Brian Greene (1999), pp. 144,189,199, 208.

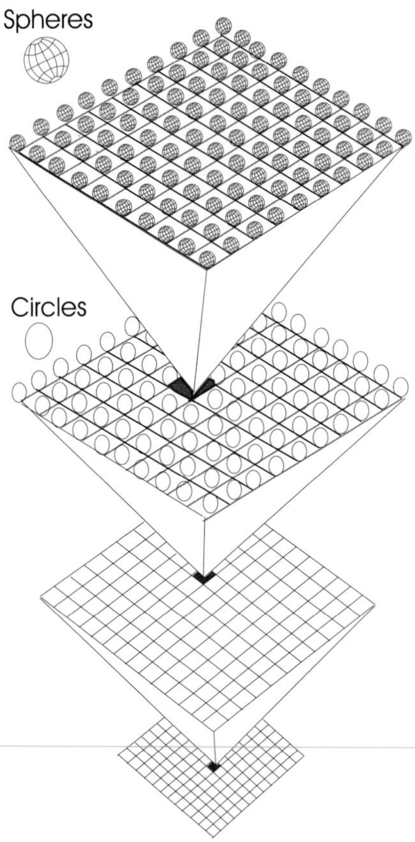

Spheres

Circles

Vibrating strings

Diagram 1: Not long after Einstein surprised the world with his General Theory of four dimensions, Kaluza and Klein added a fifth dimension. Figure 15.7 of Chapter 15 illustrated how four dimensions could be pictured. Adding to it a fifth dimension could be seen as the addition of a tiny circle at each intersection of the x,y,z,t coordinate system.

Diagram 2: To add a sixth dimension the circles in Diagram 1 could be replaced by globes with two dimensions, one for latitudes and the other for longitudes. Extra dimensions could be added by creating more complex structures. The reader is reminded that each higher level represents a substantial enlargement over the previous level. The uppermost level is the most magnified. Yet, It is not visible and purely imaginary.

Diagram 3: In the Superstring Theory a nuclear particle's mass is associated with its vibrational pattern. Stronger vibrations reflect greater energy and mass. In string theory loops are thought to vibrate in resonance like the strings of a violin. Again, this is mathematical imagery. The strings, if they exist, are ultra-microscopic .

## Figure 17.1: Finding a Unifying Theory of Physics

Based on Steven Weinberg, in *Scientific American* (Dec. 1999), pp. 71, 73

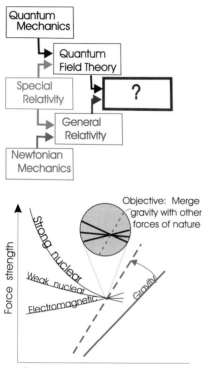

Diagram 1: For many years, from the 1920s to the end of his life in 1955, Einstein tried to combine his Theory of Relativity of the macro-cosm with a theory of the microcosm. He searched for a theory that would unify the forces of nature in one grand model. He pursued his goal relentlessly but did not succeed.

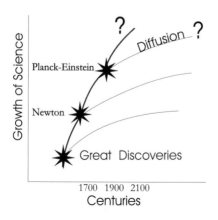

Energy in giga-electron volts

Diagram 2: For years physicists, convinced of the validity of Quantum Theory, were critical of Einstein's approach to unification. When they found, however, that they might be able to unify the three forces of the microcosm, they began to search for a Quantum Theory of the macrocosm to unify all four forces of nature.

## Figure 17.2: Discoveries, Diffusion, and Growth of Science

Adapted from Holton, *Thematic Origins of Scientific Thought*, p. 444

There are indications that such a unified model could be constructed. It would combine the three nuclear forces with the gravitational force. Perhaps further developments of the M-Theory or the discovery of an even more fundamental theory will revolutionize the concept of the four forces of nature. If proven correct it could rank as one of the great discoveries of the new century.

# Figure 17.3: Quantum Foam in Space
Based on Wheeler with Ford (1998), p. 248 and on Greene (1999), p. 128.

## Quantum Foam

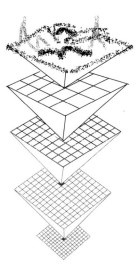

Einstein's Theory of Relativity is based on a smooth geometry of space. Quantum Theory implies violent space-time fluctuations at the Planck scale. This scale has a unit length so small that if it were set equal to the diameter of a sphere, it would take the immense number of $10^{20}$ such spheres to span the width of one proton. And that is really small since it would take 100,000 protons all lined up in a row to reach the size of one atom. Relative to the Planck length, an elementary particle assumes the size of a Skyscraper. Since nobody has ever seen anything at quantum length, quantum foam is a figurative image of abstract quantum mathematics.

# Figure 17.4: Unifying Superstring Theories in the M-Theory
Based on B. Greene, pp. 286, 287

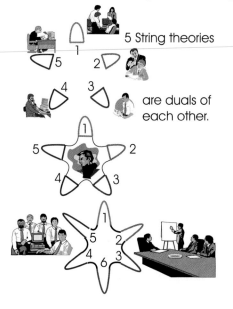

5 String theories

are duals of
each other.

The underlying principle of Special Relativity is symmetry between all constant velocity points; that of General Relativity is equivalence regardless of changes in motion, and that of Quantum Theory is symmetry at the level of subatomic particles. In 1995 Edward Witten showed that five superstring theories are complementary dualities yielding important physical insights. The challenge for the first century of the new millennium is to integrate the string theories with the relativity theory of gravitation in a unified M-Theory.

# Figure 17.5: From Universe to Multiverse

Physicists have settled on a $10 \times 10$ matrix to completely describe the universe. It does not give one solution for the universe but many solutions for a "multiverse" because not all the coefficients are known. In principle this can be illustrated by an equation with two and three variables.

The following equations have two unknowns, $x_1$ and $x_2$:

Equation 1
$$2 x_1 - 4 x_2 = 1$$
$$4 x_1 + 7 x_2 = 17$$

Solution to 1
$$x_1 = 2.5$$
$$x_2 = 1.0$$

Equation 2
$$a_{11} x_1 + a_{12} x_2 = b_1$$
$$a_{21} x_1 + a_{22} x_2 = b_2$$

or in matrix notation as:

Equation 3

$$\begin{bmatrix} a_{11} & a_{12} \\ a_{21} & a_{22} \end{bmatrix} \begin{bmatrix} x_1 \\ x_2 \end{bmatrix} = \begin{bmatrix} b_1 \\ b_2 \end{bmatrix}$$

Where the $a_{ij}$ matrix is called the "coefficient matrix."

Equation 4

$$a_{11} x_1 + a_{12} x_2 + a_{13} x_3 = b_1$$

$$a_{21} x_1 + a_{22} x_2 + a_{23} x_3 = b_2$$

$$a_{31} x_1 + a_{32} x_2 + a_{33} x_3 = b_3$$

$$\begin{bmatrix} a_{11} & a_{12} & a_{13} \\ a_{21} & a_{22} & a_{13} \\ a_{31} & a_{32} & a_{33} \end{bmatrix} \begin{bmatrix} x_1 \\ x_2 \\ x_3 \end{bmatrix} = \begin{bmatrix} b_1 \\ b_2 \\ b_3 \end{bmatrix}$$

Diagram 1: Let $x_1$ be the diameter of the Earth and $x_2$ the diameter of the planet Mercury. The first line implies that two of Earth's diameters minus four of Mercury's equal one unit. The second line suggests that 4 of the Earth's diameters plus 7 of Mercury's equal 17 units. To obtain an estimate of the size of the units, the two equations are solved so that: $x_1 = 2.5$ and $x_2 = 1.0$. It implies that the Earth's diameter is 2.5 times the size of Mercury's. Actually the ratio is:
$$x_1 / x_2 = 2.557 / 1.0.$$

Diagram 2: Equation 1 can be restated in more general terms as in Equation 2. The $a_{ij}$ coefficients and the $b_i$ coefficients are known and the $x_i$ coefficients are the unknowns. For example, in Equation 1 above the solution is:
$$x_1 = 2.5 \text{ and } x_2 = 1.0.$$

Diagram 3: Now, a giant step: assume the whole universe can be correctly described by three equations as suggested in Equation 4. The objective is to find the solution for the three unknowns $x_1$, $x_2$, and $x_3$. Not all coefficients are known, and some examples will illustrate what happens to the solution.

# Figure 17. 5: From Universe to Multiverse (continued)

$$a_{11} x_1 + a_{12} x_2 + 0 \ x_3 = b_1$$

$$a_{21} x_1 + a_{22} x_2 + 0 \ x_3 = b_2$$

$$0 \ x_1 + 0 \ x_2 + 0 \ x_3 = 0$$

$$\begin{bmatrix} a_{11} & a_{12} & 0 \\ a_{21} & a_{22} & 0 \\ 0 & 0 & 0 \end{bmatrix} \begin{bmatrix} x_3 \\ x_3 \\ x_3 \end{bmatrix} = \begin{bmatrix} b_1 \\ b_2 \\ 0 \end{bmatrix}$$

$$\begin{bmatrix} 5 & -2 & 0 \\ -2 & 1 & 0 \\ 0 & 0 & 0 \end{bmatrix} \begin{bmatrix} x_{,1} \\ x_2 \\ x_3 \end{bmatrix} = \begin{bmatrix} 1 \\ -1 \\ 0 \end{bmatrix}$$

Solution: $x_1 = -1, \ x_2 = -3$ .

Diagram 4: No solution can be found for the three unknown. It is possible, however, to find a solution for two of the three equations. This is done by assuming that the universe can be properly described by the two equations . In this case the other coefficients are taken to be zero.

It is to be noted that the coefficient matrix is symmetric. This means that the matrix is square and the $a_{i\,j}$ coefficients are equal to the $a_{j\,i}$ coefficients.

$$\begin{bmatrix} 5 & -2 & 4 \\ -2 & 1 & 0 \\ 4 & 0 & 0 \end{bmatrix} \begin{bmatrix} x_1 \\ x_2 \\ x_3 \end{bmatrix} = \begin{bmatrix} 1 \\ -1 \\ 1 \end{bmatrix}$$

Solution: $x_1 = \dfrac{1}{4}, x_2 = \dfrac{-1}{2}, x_3 = \dfrac{5}{16}$ .

$$\begin{bmatrix} 5 & -2 & 4 \\ -2 & 1 & 2 \\ 4 & 2 & 0 \end{bmatrix} \begin{bmatrix} x_1 \\ x_2 \\ x_3 \end{bmatrix} = \begin{bmatrix} 1 \\ -1 \\ 0 \end{bmatrix}$$

Solution: $x_1 = \dfrac{3}{17}, x_2 = \dfrac{-6}{17}, x_3 = \dfrac{5}{34}$

$$\begin{bmatrix} 5 & 2 & 4 \\ -2 & 1 & 1 \\ 4 & 1 & 0 \end{bmatrix} \begin{bmatrix} x_1 \\ x_2 \\ x_3 \end{bmatrix} = \begin{bmatrix} 1 \\ -1 \\ 0 \end{bmatrix}$$

Solution: $x_1 = 1, \ x_2 = -4, \ x_3 = -3$ .

Diagram 5: The next three matrices have three variables and three unknowns. In each the extra coefficients over the previous equation are shown in red. In the first equation the coefficients 4 and 1 are added. In the second equation 2 and 0 are further modifications, and in the third the coefficient 1 replaces coefficient 2. Each of the equations has different solution shown in blue.

These are equations with three unknowns. Although each has a solution, it will not be a correct for a description of the universe. Indeed, if the matrix were of size 10 × 10, the number of potential coefficients would be very large. It is this number that would make up the multiverse.

## Figure 17.6: Some Features of Black Holes

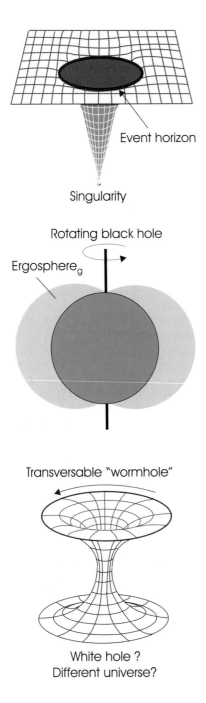

Event horizon

Singularity

Rotating black hole

Ergosphere$_g$

Transversable "wormhole"

White hole ?
Different universe?

Diagram 1: In 1916 Karl Schwarzschild found an exact solution to Einstein's tensor equation. It showed that if a massive star collapsed into a small enough region, the space-time warp would be so extreme that nothing, not even light, could escape beyond a certain event horizon. In the case of our Sun the event horizon would have a radius of 1.9 miles or 3 km.

Diagram 2: In 1963 Roy Kerr solved Einstein's equation by postulating a rotating black hole. Unlike any matter entering a non-rotating black hole as in Diagram 1, matter falling within the range of a rotating black hole would not be barred by a singularity but could pass through. If the rotation was fast enough, Kerr's solution implied no event horizon and, therefore, no visible black hole. Instead a high-energy ergosphere$_g$ would surround the rotating hole.

Diagram 3: The conundrum of mathematical singularities in Einstein's General Theory of Relativity, and the related ideas of black holes and rotating black holes, raised the question of what could be on the other side of the black hole. If symmetry ruled, it could be a white hole. According to Steven Hawking and others it could lead to, or form, a different universe. Conceivably a trans-versable worm hole could be created to open up a passage way.

Chapter 14

# EINSTEIN (1879–1955),
# THE SPECIAL THEORY OF RELATIVITY

*The world of our sense experiences is comprehensible. The fact that it is comprehensible is a miracle.*

Albert Einstein [1]

During the first 15 years of the twentieth century Albert Einstein proposed entirely new ways of thinking about space, time, and gravitation. His theories were a profound advance over Isaac Newton's (1632–1727) physics. Newton deduced from three axioms of motion the universal law of gravitation and, in this way, accounted for the motion of planets, satellites, and comets in the smallest detail. Einstein went beyond Newton and derived a more general account of the dynamics of motion from only two axioms: relative motion and the constant speed of light. These two axioms allowed for deeper insights and yielded a wider range of applications.

Before Einstein, during the 1880s and 1890s, Hendrik Lorentz (1853–1928) and George Fitzgerald (1851–1901) had tried to find an explanation for the constant speed of light. The speed of light did not vary whether light moved with or against the motion of the Earth. Puzzled by this experimental evidence, they suggested that objects shortened when moving at high speed. In 1904, at the International Congress of the Arts and Sciences in St.Louis, the great French mathematician J. Henri Poincaré (1854-1912) gave a key lecture, "On the Present State and the Future of Mathematical Physics." He predicted that "an entirely new mechanics would arise, characterized mainly by the fact that no velocity can exceed the velocity of light, just as no temperature can drop below absolute zero."[2] The search made for a strange framework of physics —strange because it was a patchwork of rules and exceptions. With his Theory of Relativity, Einstein created an attractive and coherent interpretation of the laws of nature.[3]

Einstein published his Special Theory of Relativity in 1905 and the General Theory of Relativity in 1916. He limited the Special Theory to the study of objects moving in a straight line at constant velocities, curving neither left nor right, moving neither up nor down.[4] In the General Theory he dealt with objects that advance, relative to each other, at varying velocities: speeding up and slowing down, traveling on or veering off the straight-line course. In this sense, the Special Theory can be thought of as a "special case" of the General Theory.

With his theories Einstein revolutionized physics and astronomy. For the first time in the history of physics he showed that space and time were not absolute but depended on the observer's speed of motion, that mass was a form of energy interchangeable with other forms of energy, that the gravitational force was indistinguishable from acceleration, and that gravitation was caused by the curvature of space. Moreover, he believed that an understanding of gravity, electromagnetism, and the nuclear forces could be brought together in a single unified field theory. It was an ideal Einstein pursued until the end of his life.[5]

By now several hundred books have been written about Einstein's life and work.[6] This chapter attempts to give highlights and an intuitive understanding of Einstein's Special Theory of Relativity. Aspects of the General Theory are discussed in the next chapter.

### Einstein's Childhood and Early Years

Like Newton, Albert Einstein did not enter this world in perfect physical shape. His grandmother thought he was much too fat. Worried about his weight and his swollen and misshapen head, his parents took him to a doctor for a general examination. He assured them that little Albert was a healthy boy and that, in time, all would be normal. At age three, his parents consulted a doctor again, this time because Albert was late in talking.[7]

*Birthplace*

Einstein was born on March 14, 1879 in Ulm. The city of Ulm is located in southern Germany on the left bank of the Danube between Stuttgart and Munich, at the foot of the Swabian Alps. Ulm happens to be about 60 miles (97 km) southeast of Weil-der-Stadt, where the astronomer Kepler was born some 300 years earlier.

The Einsteins had lived in the Swabian part of Bavaria since the 1750s. They had come from Buchau, a small town about 30 miles (48 km) southeast of Ulm. Albert's father Hermann was a quiet, gentle, and contemplative man with a talent for mathematics. Lack of money prevented him from pursuing a higher education. To better himself he left town and went to Ulm at the age of 19. Some years later, in 1876, he married Paulina Koch in Cannstadt, a small town not far from Ulm. Hermann was 28 and Paulina 17. In spite of the age difference and financial difficulties in later years, their marriage was a very happy one.[8]

With the help of his in-laws Hermann set up an electrical-engineering firm. By 1880, Hermann's younger brother Jakob, who had studied engineering, suggested they set up a business together. Hermann would secure the extra financial support from his in-laws, the wealthy Kochs, and they would set up an electrical-engineering and plumbing business in Munich, a city about 100 miles (161 km) east of Ulm. By then, Munich was the cultural and political center of southern Germany and it was here that young Albert spent his childhood years.[9]

*Preschool*

Albert, the future physicist, was slow in learning to talk. When he finally did, he spoke not just words but formed whole sentences. He would silently recite a sentence to himself, his lips moving, before uttering a word. Nothing suggested that this seemingly slow thinking boy would become one of the greatest thinkers of the century.[10]

In 1881 his sister Maja was born. She was Albert's closest friend during their childhood years and they remained dear friends throughout their adult lives.

When Albert was five years old, his parents engaged a tutor to prepare him for the rigors of schooling. Every so often when something was not to his liking, Albert would throw a temper tantrum. Even his little sister was not quite safe from such outbursts. "Once, he threw a nine-pin-bowling ball at [her] head, and yet another time he used a child's pickax to strike a hole in [her] head." On another occasion when he did not like a lesson, "he grabbed a chair and with it struck the woman tutor, who was so terrified that she ran away in fear and was never seen again."[11] Albert's family believed this trait came from his grandfather Julius Koch. Fortunately, the terrible tantrums disappeared during Albert's first years in school.

All was not smooth sailing for Albert's parents. At first the brothers' business flourished. Then Jacob invented an electric dynamo, which he believed had an enormous market potential. The brothers expanded their plant, installed new machinery and equipment, hired more labor, and ultimately overextended themselves. There was tough competition from big companies and Hermann did not run a very tight ship. They skirted the edge of financial ruin, occasionally turning to the Koch's for more financial support. It was a precarious existence for the Einsteins.[12]

Hermann Einstein may not have been an astute business man but he was an optimist. Failure in business did not impair his positive outlook on life. After work he liked to go on outings with his family, to the lakes and mountains of Munich's beautiful countryside. He also enjoyed dropping in for a hearty meal and a mug of tasty beer at one of the Bavarian taverns. Intellectually, he cherished the poetry of Schiller and Heine. Politically the Einsteins, like most Bavarians, were weary of the Prussian dominance to the north. In short, their way of life differed very little from that of the average citizen.[13]

*Elementary School*
Although they were Jewish, Albert's parents enrolled him in a nearby

Catholic school because the Jewish school was too far from their home. The Einsteins were not orthodox Jews and they believed that, at an elementary school level, academic standards were more important than religious instruction. Also "the teaching staff in the elementary school were liberal and made no difference between denominations."[14]

The elementary school was not very demanding, but young Einstein did not enjoy it. Although resistence to discipline may have played a part in his dislike, it was more so likely because his way of thinking differed from that of other children. In solving a problem Einstein would not always follow his teacher's method but do it his own way. Not being a child prodigy, he displayed no particular aptitude for mathematics. What he lacked in speed, however, he made up for in perseverance and accuracy. As his mother wrote to Albert's grandmother, at the age of seven he passed the grade with a splendid report card.[15]

At age nine he lacked the more fluent speech of other young-sters his age. Again it was, in part at least, because he would express himself only after he had given it some careful thought. Under no circumstances would he want to say something hasty and find out that it was wrong. No, he was not going to tell a lie. His classmates thought of him as an "Honest John" and called him a " Biedermeier," a caricature of the German middle class.[16] Seeing Albert daydreaming, his mother wondered whether Albert would one day become an absent-minded, eccentric professor. [17]

At home Albert was happy with his family, surrounded by friends and relatives. He enjoyed playing with building blocks, constructing houses out of cards up to 14 stories high, or solving puzzles. Then something happened that may have set Albert on the lifelong course of scientific enquiry. He was ill in bed when his father, to cheer him up, gave Albert a pocket compass. As Einstein wrote later, it left a lasting impression on him.

> That this needle behaved in such a determined way did not at all fit into the kind of occurrences that could find a place in the unconscious world of concepts. I can still remember—or at least I believe I can remember—that this experience made a deep and lasting impression upon me. Something deeply hidden had to be behind things.[18]

Why this should have made such a lasting impression on him, Einstein himself could not explain. He wrote:

> A person has little insight into what goes on inside him. Seeing a compass for the first time may not produce a similar effect on a young dog, nor indeed many a child. What then is it that determines a particular reaction from an individual? More or less plausible theories may be constructed about it, but one does not arrive at a deeper insight. [19]

Unable to generalize one can only conclude that it depends on who sees the needle and who perceives it as a miracle. In this instance, it was young Albert Einstein.

Uncle Jakob recognized Albert's interest in such things. When uncle Jakob gave Albert a little book on algebra it stimulated the youngster's imagination. As Albert went on studying it, it amazed Jakob how Albert went about solving problems. Albert even found a new proof of the Pythagorean Theorem. To Jakob it was clear that Albert was able to find the answer even to the most difficult problems.

Albert's mother was artistically inclined. Living under uncertain financial conditions, she found enjoyment and solace in music. She cherished classical music, especially Beethoven's sonatas. When the firm's engineers came over for an evening visit they would sometimes accompany her on the piano. She considered music to be part of general education. Following her wish, Albert took music lessons starting at age six. Although at times it meant tiresome practice and learning by rote, at age 13 he began to appreciate the light-hearted music of Mozart and enjoyed playing it. He kept it up as a hobby for the rest of his life. It enabled him to relax from the strain of his work. In America, the violin nearly became one of his trademarks.

As was customary in Germany (and still is), at age 10 children could, at the request of their parents and depending on their achievements in elementary school, either continue in elementary school (trades focus), go on to middle school, or advance to high school (academic focus). Since graduation from high school was a prerequisite for admission to university, high school was more demanding than the other two. In high school, the study of at least two foreign languages was obligatory. Most other subjects, such as mathematics, physics, and chemistry, were also obligatory. In one stream of study modern languages and science were stressed, in the other stream Latin and Greek were taught before going on to modern languages and less emphasis was given to mathematics and the natural sciences.

### Highschool

When young Einstein left elementary school, his parents enrolled him in the Luitpold Highschool where the study of Latin and Greek was obligatory. As with all languages, learning a new vocabulary was essential. For Einstein the language lessons were tedious and irksome. He hated to memorize new words and grammatical rules, especially in Greek. Not surprisingly, his teacher of Greek believed nothing would ever become of young Einstein.[20]

In Germany, families of the Jewish middle class often gave a helping hand to needy students of their community. Every Thursday Max Talmud, a Russian Jewish student who was enrolled in medicine at the University of Munich, joined the Einsteins for supper. Knowing of Albert's interests he brought along science books, among them Aaron Bernstein's series on popular science (*Naturwissenschaftliche Volksbücher*). They dealt with plant and animal life, their interdependence, volcanoes, earthquakes, evolution, the solar system, meteors and stars. Max lent Albert Büchner's book on Force and Matter (*Kraft und Stoff*) and Alexander von Humboldt's book on the Cosmos (*Kosmos*). He also passed on Spieker's textbook on Plane Geometry (*Lehrbuch der Ebenen Geometrie*).[21]

Albert had just turned 12 and was at a very impressionable age. The science books spurred him on to teach himself what he wanted to know but did not get from science classes at school. He progressed very rapidly, especially in geometry. To him geometry was a revelation. The clarity of exposition, the orderliness of thought, the proof of every proposition, and the connection between diagrams and proofs left an indelible impression on him. Later in life he referred to Spieker's text as the "holy geometry book."[22]

Max also lent him Kant's *Critique of Pure Reason (Kritik der Reinen Vernunft)*. It was a difficult book but gave Einstein some first insights into philosophy. At just about the same time (at age 12) Albert received private instruction in Judaism. Although his parents considered kosher diet and other customs associated with Semitism as outdated superstitions, Albert insisted on following the orthodox line. He even composed songs dedicated to his faith and often sang them to himself while on his way to school.

At age 13 he realized that much of what was being taught in religion could not be reconciled with science. He also saw how students were compelled to attend services in Jewish synagogues whether they liked to or not. To him this kind of coercion did not differ much from the teaching of Greek grammar or from soldiers being drilled on parade grounds. Within a short time his high regard for religious rituals turned into an aversion against orthodox Jewish practices. Rebelling against organized religious teachings and fascinated by science, he began to distrust all handed-down knowledge and tried to "objectively" discover the truth for himself. As he described it later: "Perception of this world, by thought, leaving out everything subjective, became partly consciously, partly unconsciously, my supreme aim."[23] He decided that after graduation from high school he would abandon the Jewish religious community and not join any other religious group.[24]

Unfortunately, in 1894 the family business again ran into financial difficulties. His lighthearted father decided it was time to move on to a better place, to Milan in sunny Italy. He sold the manufacturing plant and their home, and moved across the border to Italy.[25]

This move affected Albert's course of education. Albert was now 15 and still had to take more courses to finish high school. His parents decided to send him to a boarding house in Munich. Although far ahead of others in mathematics and physics, he was behind in Latin and Greek. He did not like to learn simply for the purpose of passing the final examination.

**Italy**

His disenchantment with school intensified after his parents left. One of his teachers told him that it might be better for him to leave school because his disrespectful presence was disruptive and detrimental to the class spirit. This was too much for young Einstein. It did not take him very long to obtain a medical certificate that a nervous breakdown made it necessary for him to leave school so that he could stay with his parents for six months.

On his arrival in Milan he decided to renounce his German citizenship. It freed him from the obligatory military service in later years.[26] To his father, who had not renounced his German citizenship, this was a rather unusual step. Not only because of that but also because at the same time Albert "renounced his legal adherence to the Jewish religious community."[27] This, too, appeared strange to his parents.

Albert was now stateless and not associated with any religious community. He felt free. Hiking through the central Apennine mountains of Italy to Genoa, he looked at the works of art in galleries and churches, listened to music, enjoyed the melodic sounds of the Italian language, and admired the natural friendliness of the Italian people. To him, all this was in stark contrast to Germany. Yet, the idyllic atmosphere was only temporary. His father had encountered new financial difficulties. He urged Albert to find a profession for gainful employment since he could no longer support him.[28]

## Switzerland

Following the wish of his parents, Albert tried his luck at the Swiss Federal Polytechnic (Eidgenössische Polytechnische Schule) at Zurich. Outside of Germany it was the best-known technical school in central Europe. It would not pose a language problem since it was in the German-speaking region of Switzerland, and it would prepare him for a practical profession.

He arrived in Zurich in the fall of 1895. Two years younger than the average candidate and without a certificate of high school graduation, he had been permitted, with the aid of an influential family friend, to take the entrance examination. It consisted of two parts: one, on general knowledge such as literature, history, fluency in German, descriptive natural sciences and the other, on mathematics, physics, chemistry, and technical drawing and freehand drawing. Einstein passed the entrance exams in mathematics and natural sciences with flying colors, but failed because of unsatisfactory results in linguistic and historic subjects.[29]

Einstein was not admitted. As he commented himself: "Even though the examiners were patient and considerate, the examination made the gaps in my education painfully clear. I found it fully justified that I did not pass."[30] In view of his uneven knowledge and being only 16 years old the president of the Polytechnic advised the parents to have their son attend the final grade of a Swiss middle school at Aargau.[31]

### Cantonal School at Aargau

The prospect of going back to gain a diploma at a middle school did not appeal to Einstein even though the lessons and final examination would not be quite as demanding as they were at the Luitpold High School. He would still have to take French but no more Greek and Latin courses. The middle school would not give him sufficient credits to go on to a university, but would entitle him to go to the Polytechnic at Zurich. Einstein feared that going back to school meant the same kind of regimentation as in Munich. His fears were unwarranted. When he arrived at Aargau (20 miles west of Zurich) he was very pleasantly surprised. The Swiss school system was very liberally oriented, teachers encouraged students to think for themselves, and they were always available to them for discussion and counsel. Einstein did well under this system.[32]

### Living with the Wintelers

While attending school in Aarau, Einstein lived with the Winteler family who took in boarders. Einstein felt very comfortable there. He loved the exceptional warmth and liberal openness of the Wintelers. It was a different atmosphere from home. Herr Winteler was a professor, teaching Greek at a Gymnasium, and Frau Winteler enjoyed having some students in her household. She had seven children of her own and welcomed Albert as one more.

For Einstein it was also his first excursion into romance. He was enamored of Marie, the prettiest of the Winteler's three daughters. Like him, she loved music but unlike him she did not share his intellectual curiosity and ardor. After he left Aargau, their relationship gradually faded away. It appears that the parents on both sides would have liked to see their romance evolve into marriage but it was not to be. When invited back for a visit he politely declined claiming that the strict "angels of science" demanded his full devotion.[33]

*First Scientific Paper*

As early as 1895, at age 16, Einstein wrote his first scientific paper. In his paper he referred to the wonderful experiments on electromagnetism, the propagation of light and heat, and the deformation of ether by electrodynamic forces. He wondered whether a deformation of the ether would affect the propagation of waves and whether the effect would differ at right angles to the lines of force. He concluded with the suggestion that experimentation ought to show whether the variation in the density of the lines of force, and the associated deformation, altered resistence to an electrical current. Some people have interpreted this first essay as a fore-runner of the great discoveries to come, while others thought that such claims "overinterpreted" his effort.[34]

Einstein's school record at Aargau reflected his special talents and personal preferences. He gained his highest grades in mathematics (arithmetic, algebra, and geometry), in physics, singing and violin, and his lowest grades in French and German. Einstein's father expressed his concern when he urged Professor Winteler to encourage Albert to make a special effort in modern languages and possibly have him take private lessons.[35] It paid off. After his final exams and successful graduation in September 1896, Albert was allowed to enter the Swiss Federal Poly-technic without passing a further entrance examination.

*Swiss Federal Polytechnic*

By the time he graduated from the cantonal school at Aargau Einstein had made up his mind. His interest was not in pure mathematics, as he once believed in Munich, but in physics. He did not find the teaching of physics at the Polytechnic inspiring because it mainly addressed the principles of technical applications and not the underlying laws of nature.[36] Historically, the science of physics was at a crucial turning point; the excitement of it was not evident at Polytechnic lectures.

Einstein exasperated some of the professors whom he regarded as not up-to-date or even ignorant. As one of his classmates pictured him:

"Unconfined by conventional restrictions, he confronted the world spirit as a laughing philosopher, and his witty sarcasm mercilessly castigated all vanity and artificiality."[37]

At times he showed his disdain quite openly. For instance, he raised the dander of his physics instructor when he threw away the instruction sheet on how to conduct an experiment, without even giving it a glance. His instructor confronted him, told him that he was hopeless and that, for his own good, he ought to switch to law or literature. When Einstein tried to do the experiment his own way, he caused an explosion that injured his right hand, requiring several stitches at the city clinic. After the incident, Einstein proposed a safer but more difficult experiment for measuring the effect of the Earth's motion against the ether wind, but his physics professor turned him down.[38]

*Studying on His Own*

Instead of conscientiously attending the lectures at the Polytechnic, Einstein cut classes and turned to the writings of the pioneers of the new physics. He studied Maxwell (1831–1879) who had shown that electromagnetic waves moved through space at the same velocity as light. He read Helmholtz (1821–1894), who wanted to purge all physics of speculation, rejecting any theory that could not be verified by experiment or demonstration. He went over the writings of Hertz (1857–1894), who had confirmed Maxwell's theory while producing electromagnetic waves. He perused Kirchhoff's (1824–1887) work on electricity, thermodynamics, and spectroscopy. Heeding the recommendation of his friend Besso, he studied Ernst Mach's *Science of Mechanics*. Mach (1838–1916) did not believe in absolute space and suggested that Newton's laws ought to be re-examined.[39]

Einstein was not impressed with the Polytechnic's lectures in physics and mathematics, even though the school enjoyed a good international reputation. Its strength was not in the department of physics but in mathematics. At the time, mathematics was taught by Professor Minkowski (1864–1909). A Russian by birth and still young, he had already established a reputation as a very original thinker. Unfortunately, he was not a very captivating lecturer. Since Einstein had already decided against pure mathematics in favor of physics, he was not very interested in Minkowski's lectures. Yet, it was Minkowski who put forth ideas that would later have a direct bearing on Einstein's theory of relativity.[40]

*Friends*

Einstein considered himself a day dreamer, aloof, and disaffected. Frequently at odds with his professors, he did not lack friends. His classmate Marcel Grossmann deemed him to be in the same league as Professor Mach. Jacob Ehrat, another classmate, admired Einstein's honesty and unwillingness to compromise. Friedrich Adler thought of him as a brilliant misfit who got into trouble because he did not ingratiate himself with the professors. In turn, Einstein thought of Adler as the most idealistic spirit he had ever known. Adler was so convinced of his own righteousness that later in life he assassinated Austria's prime minister in the belief that it would help the cause of peace. Judged insane, his death sentence was commuted.

At a time when Einstein's parents were in grave financial difficulties and could barely support him, Albert found comfort and kindness in the family home of a history professor. Like his other friends, the family enjoyed Einstein's company because of his wit, spontaneity, passion for Mozart and his mockery of the pretentious. Their generous kindness cheered him up.[41]

Einstein's friends were somewhat puzzled when they saw him together with Mileva Marić (pronounced Maritsch). She was a student at the Polytechnic, came from southern Hungary but was of Serbian extraction. Some described her as pretty and smartly dressed, others as taciturn and unassuming. When someone embarrassingly referred to Mileva's obvious limp—the after effect of tuberculosis during childhood—Einstein countered that her voice more than compensated for it. Like so many students from Eastern Europe, she took her studies very seriously. Finding common ground with Einstein in studying the works of the great physicists, the relationship gradually developed into a close friendship.[42]

Mileva lived within a few minutes of Einstein's lodgings, he often visited her. In his final year at the Polytechnic their friendship had evolved into a romance. When, during the summer break of 1900, Einstein's mother asked him what would happen to Mileva after graduation, he casually replied that she would become his wife. Shocked, his mother "threw herself onto the bed, buried her head in the pillow, and wept like a child."[43] While his mother was horrified, his father was concerned, but their son was confident it would all work out in time.

*Final Exams at the Polytechnic*

Despite his disdain for some of his teachers, on the whole, Einstein had some excellent teachers at the Polytechnic. He was undecided which areas of mathematics he ought to select as he did not wish to concentrate on this field. Minkowski was quoted as having once said of Einstein that he was "a lazy dog who never bothered about mathematics at all."[44] Einstein did not respect Professor Weber, the head of the physics department. At the outset Weber was impressed by Einstein's knowledge of physics but soon he became disenchanted with him. Their change in feelings was mutual. Weber once told the 18-year-old: "You are a smart boy, Einstein, a very smart boy. But you have one great fault: you never let yourself be told anything."[45]

In the summer of 1900, three days before the final exam, Weber made Einstein rewrite a term paper because he had submitted it on non-regulation paper. This act of pettiness, rooted in the antagonism that had built up between the two over time, made Einstein lose valuable study time.

Five students took the final exam at the Polytechnic. Einstein came in fourth. Mileva Marić had the lowest score and failed the exam.[46] Einstein scored highest in Weber's electro-technical laboratory and physics courses. He also did well in mathematics courses on determinants and differential equations. Not surprisingly, after the explosion in the laboratory, he received the lowest grade in applied physics for beginners.[47]

## After Graduation from the Polytechnic

Passing this all-important final exam practically assured a position as a teaching assistant at the Polytechnic. Although Einstein had passed the final exam successfully and received two prospective offers, they were withdrawn at the last moment. As he explained later in life: "[The professors] did not like me because of my independence, [they] bypassed me when they needed an assistant."[48]

### Unemployed

As long as he was a student, Einstein received one hundred Swiss francs a year from his wealthy aunt, Julie Koch. After graduation this source of funds dried up.

He and Mileva believed they could make ends meet by giving occasional private lessons. Together they dreamed of unlocking nature's great secrets and of earning enough money to live together and even make bicycle trips to the Swiss countryside. Already some of it had come true. Einstein's paper on capillary action of liquids was accepted for publication by the prestigious *Annalen der Physik (Annals of Physics)*. To top it off, Professor Kleiner of the University of Zurich had accepted Einstein's proposal for a Ph.D. thesis on the kinetic theory of gases.[49]

Now 21, Einstein could have married without his father's consent. Yet, it was not possible without the clearance of the Swiss Department of Naturalization. Concerned that Einstein might become a welfare burden to the Swiss state, an immigration committee interviewed him. They liked his response to their questions. In early 1901 he was granted Swiss citizenship. Three weeks later he underwent a medical examination for the compulsory military service of Swiss citizens. Einstein was excused from service in the Swiss army ostensibly because of varicose veins and flat feet, a medical diagnosis not confirmed in later years.[50]

Having graduated from the Polytechnic, having gained Swiss citizenship, and been freed from military service, Einstein returned home to his parents. From there he mailed letters to many eminent scientists in Europe inquiring if they needed an assistant. He received no replies. However, in the spring of 1901 Einstein was offered a two-month teaching position at a technical school in Winterthur not far from Zurich. He took the job. He liked teaching but his term was not extended. Through one of his college friends he then gained a tutoring position at a private school in Schaffhausen on the Swiss-German border. It was not a very demanding position, had a reasonable salary, and left him enough spare time to work on his Ph.D. thesis.[51]

*Mileva Marić*

He had hardly settled down in Schaffhausen when Mileva wrote that she was pregnant. From what little evidence survived, Einstein appears to have taken the dramatic news rather calmly. In a letter of July 1901 he promised to immediately look for another job and then marry her.[52]

Einstein's mother still was bitterly opposed to the union. Convinced that Mileva was below their family's status, she feared it would destroy her son's future. His father told him that without employment and no means of support, he was in no position to marry anyone.

By December of 1901, when Mileva was in her eighth month of pregnancy and living with her parents, Einstein wrote a long letter asking her to be of good cheer. He believed the sole remaining problem was to decide how they could best accommodate the baby. He felt they needed some good counsel, and recommended that Mileva ask her father for advice. Without pursuing the issue any further, he went on to discuss his latest ideas about molecular forces that come into play as neutral liquids are being mixed.[53]

Mileva gave birth to a baby girl at the end of January 1902. They decided to call her Lieserl (short for Elisabeth). Mileva still lived with her parents. It was not until the end of the year that Mileva joined Einstein in Switzerland, but she arrived without Lieserl.[54]

Since Mileva was raised in a very compassionate family, it is likely that Lieserl grew up with Mileva's family in southern Hungary. However, later attempts by historians to find out more about her fate failed.

Whether Einstein's parents were ever told of the birth of their granddaughter is not clear. It is known, however, that Albert traveled from Bern to Milan to visit his dying father. On his deathbed in October 1902 his father finally consented to his son's marriage to Mileva.

*Working for the Swiss Patent Office*

It took Einstein a long time to gain an adequate income, partly because his former professors cautioned potential employers against him and also because they preferred a "genuine Swiss" before hiring a naturalized "paper Swiss." That Einstein came from Jewish ancestry added to the difficulties.[55] Although 1901 was a year of turmoil for Einstein, it did have a good side.

His former classmate and friend Marcel Grossmann knew about Einstein's employment problems and could not understand how someone so talented could be in such a tough spot. Grossman's father knew Friedrich Haller, the director of the Swiss patent office, and put in a good word for him. When a newly created position opened at the patent office, Haller wrote Einstein to apply for it immediately. Einstein did, was invited for an interview and accepted for future employment. In June of 1902 he started work at the office in Bern.[56]

His job required him to transform written patent applications into clear and concise language. It meant studying many new ideas and picking out of vaguely composed texts the unique and essential features of an invention. Einstein's work at the patent office was neither well paid nor very demanding. It had one great advantage, however, the job left him some spare time for scientific investigations.

Roughly one year after their daughter was born, Einstein married Mileva on January 6, 1903 in Bern, Switzerland. None of their relatives attended the wedding. Only his closest friends witnessed the ceremony. From there the small party went to a photographer, celebrated a little, and went home. Einstein recalled later that he had married from "a sense of duty." What became of their daughter, Lieserl, did not become known.[57] About two years later their first son, Hans Albert, was born. Einstein's mother, Paulina, was still fiercely opposed to her son's marriage. With the security and freedom provided by his office job, Einstein devoted himself with great enthusiasm to his Ph.D. research.[58]

To supplement his income Einstein advertised his services as a tutor. Soon a young Romanian by the name of Maurice Solovin arrived at their small apartment. While studying philosophy at the University of Bern, he wanted to deepen his knowledge of physics. Shortly after, Conrad Habicht joined them. He was a friend from their days together in Zurich. Initially, Einstein charged them both two francs per lesson, but as their friendship grew, he dropped the fee. Together they roamed about the Bern countryside discussing physics and philosophy. Frequently they were joined by Besso, Einstein's closest friend from the Polytechnic, by Chavan, an electrical engineer, and others of similar interests. They called themselves the Olympia Academy. Often they would meet in the evening, have a frugal meal of sausage, some cheese, fruit, honey and tea. For Einstein this period became a time of intense creativity.

In the spring of 1905, probably toward the end of May, Einstein wrote a letter—according to one historian it could well be the most remarkable letter in the history of science—to his friend Habicht in Bern, telling him that he would mail him four papers:

> The first of which I could send off soon, as I am to receive my free copies shortly. It deals with radiation and the energetic properties of light and is very revolutionary. The second paper is a determination of the true size of atoms by way of diffusion [in] liquid solutions of neutral substances. The third proves that particles of the order of magnitude of 1/1000 of a millimeter must perform a disorderly movement, caused by thermal motion, called "Brownian molecular motion." The fourth paper is at the draft stage and is on electrodynamics of motion, applying a modification of the theory of space and time. This is certain to interest you.[59]

Einstein completed these four papers in the short time of March 17 to June 30, 1905. In early May of 1905, he submitted the first of the four to the prestigious *Annalen der Physik*. These four papers have made Volume XVII of the *Annalen* a highly prized collector's item.[60] Their content revolutionized the physics of the twentieth century and beyond.

In the first paper Einstein gave an explanation of the photoelectric effect.[61] Max Planck (1858–1947), a contemporary physicist, had put a dent in the theory of light waves when he claimed that materials emitted and absorbed light in quanta. Einstein went further when he re-asserted Newton's corpuscular theory that light traveled in separate particles. Once a critical threshold level is reached the kinetic energy of the light particle causes electrons to be emitted. The rates of emission increase with Planck's constant and the light's frequency.[62]

In the same year Einstein completed his Ph.D. thesis, *A New Determination of Molecular Dimensions (Eine neue Bestimmung der Molekül-dimensionen)*. When first submitted, Professor Kleiner of Zurich University rejected it for being too short. Later Einstein added one sentence, resubmitted it, and it was accepted. He then reworked it and had it published as his second paper in the *Annalen*.[63]

During one of their get-togethers, Besso had told Einstein of the "Brownian motion." It refers to the irregular motion of microscopic colloidal particles first observed by the Scottish botanist, Robert Brown, in 1827. Brown had noticed that plant spores floating in water were never at rest but flitted to and fro as if they were being kicked around by tiny, invisible wizards. Neither Brown nor other scientists of his day could explain the strange phenomenon. Young Einstein was the first to develop a mathematical model that could account for the jittery behavior of the floating particles—it was the subject of his third paper.

In his fourth paper for the *Annalen*, Einstein discussed key aspects of the Special Theory of Relativity. The theory also emerged after a discussion with his friend Besso.

> For years Einstein had been puzzling about the problem of electric and magnetic fields and the effect of motion on them. Suddenly in mid-May, the breakthrough came. For weeks he had been discussing the problem with Besso at the office. One night while walking home with him, Einstein confided that he was ready to abandon the problem; the difficulties, he said, were insurmountable. Then that night, perhaps because of the strain of weeks, even months of hard thinking had suddenly ceased, everything came together. He awoke in the morning with the answer. Rushing to the office he told Besso of his discovery.
>
> The key, he decided, was time. Newton's concept of absolute time had been accepted for about 200 years. Einstein, however, was convinced that time was not absolute. Different observers in different states of motion would not necessarily see time pass in the same way. Furthermore, not even space was absolute; the only absolute nature, as far as he was concerned, was the speed of light.[64]

Einstein's fourth paper was published under the title "On the Electrodynamics of Moving Bodies (Zur Elektrodynamic bewegter Körper)" and the other, a follow-up to it, under "Does the Inertia of a Body Depend on Its Energy Content? (Ist die Trägheit eines Körpers von seinem Energieinhalt abhängig?)." Together the two papers formed the base of the *Special Theory of Relativity*. They culminated in Einstein's well-known equation $E = mc^2$, which states that the energy contained in a material body equals its mass multiplied by the (square of the) speed of light.

## Einstein's Special Theory of Relativity

Einstein's Special Theory of Relativity is based on two fundamental postulates, simply stated as: 1. all motion is relative, and 2. the speed of light is constant.[65]

### All Motion Is Relative

The concept of relative motion is easy enough if we think of our everyday experience. Suppose we are cruising in a car along a straight highway at a steady speed of 60 miles per hour (at roughly 100 km/h). We take it for granted that our car's speedometer shows the speed of the car on the road. Yet, this measure of speed is not absolute. We travel on Earth, while the Earth is revolving around its axis. To complete one revolution takes the Earth 24 hours. At a circumference of, say, 24,000 miles (38,600 km), a point on the equator moves eastward at a velocity of 1000 miles per hour (or at 1609 km/h). If we were to travel in a car along the equator, from west to east, at a steady speed of 60 miles per hour (approx. 100 km/h), after one hour it would arrive at a point some 60 miles (approx. 100 km) east on land plus 1000 miles farther from the equatorial point of departure. If, in addition, we were to combine this speed with that of the orbital motion of the Earth around the Sun, we could add another 70,000 miles (or some 112,000 km/h) to it. Knowing that the Earth is orbiting the Sun, the Sun is orbiting the center of our galaxy, and our galaxy is moving away from other galaxies, it is clear that all motion on Earth or in the universe is relative. How then could it be possible to determine the velocity of any object in space if all motion is relative? Something must be constant!

### The Speed of Light Is Constant

Einstein recognized the speed of light as an absolute constant of the universe. Michelson (1852–1931) and others had shown by careful experimentation that light traveled at 186,000 miles per second (300,000 km/s).[66] Einstein added a new wrinkle to it by stating that the speed of light is constant "relative to the observer." As harmless as this may sound, it was a revolutionary step in the history of physics. Einstein's choice contradicted the basic axiom of classical mechanics that speeds are additive. This yielded some wondrous and far-reaching results.

Before going deeper into Einstein's theory, however, another look at the conventional perception of motion is in order. Going back to the earlier example of travel by car, assume again that we are driving on a highway at a steady speed of 60 miles per hour (about 100 km/h). If a second car were to approach us from the opposite direction at a speed of 75 miles per hour (about 120 km/h) the distance between the two cars would shorten at the rate of *60 + 75 = 135* miles per hour (about 220 km/h). This is what we would expect when we take it for granted that the speeds of objects in motion are additive.

Yet, this is where Einstein's second postulate of the constant velocity of light contradicts our everyday experience. Suppose a distant galaxy is receding from the Earth at a speed of 16,000 miles per second (26,000 km/s).[67] According to Einstein, the light from the galaxy will be emitted at 186,000 miles per second (300,000 km/s) and travel toward Earth at that speed. It will not travel at 170,000 miles per second (274,000 km/s) as we would expect from everyday experience (*186,000-16,000 = 170,000*). Or, if a galaxy is moving toward the Earth at 16,000 miles per second (26,000 km/s), its light will not approach Earth at 202, 000 miles per second (*186,000 + 16,000 = 202,000*) (326,000 km/s) . The observed speed of light will always be 186,000 miles per second (300,000 km/s), no matter what the speed and direction of the source of light.

**Time Dilation**

Einstein's proposition of the absolute speed of light has some extraordinary consequences. The first is that time does not flow as evenly as we are inclined to believe. The passage of time varies with the speed of travel. At very high speeds, "time is dilated." This means that at very high speed the time interval between two events lengthens and the clock slows down. The idea may seem strange simply because we have not experienced it and it runs counter to common sense.

When we arrange to meet someone at a certain time, it can happen that we miss each other. Perhaps our watch ran fast and we arrived too soon, or the traffic was slow and we were too late. It would never occur to us, however, to claim that we were driving so fast that we "dilated time" and, therefore, arrived too late. Nor would Einstein contend that this could happen unless we were to travel in interstellar space at close to the speed of light.

Newton's perception of time was much closer to ours. Intuitively, we believe (as Newton did) that time is absolute. Some three hundred years ago, Newton wrote: "All motions may be accelerated or retarded, but the flowing of absolute time is not liable to any change."[68] He went on to say that the duration of time is the same whether the motions are swift or slow, or none at all. As he saw it, absolute time could be measured by a pendulum clock or by the duration of the eclipses of the moons of Jupiter. He conceded that there might well be some errors in measuring the passage of time but declared that time itself will flow evenly as the passage of time is immutable. Common sense told him so then, just as it tells us today.

### Simultaneity of Events

Einstein started out with the simple proposition that in everyday use time specifies the simultaneity of events. For example, if a schedule states that a plane will arrive at 9:00 p.m. we would expect that on arrival our watch shows 9:00 p.m. (assuming the plane's time of arrival can be measured with utmost precision and our watch is accurate to the second). Simultaneity implies that upon arrival of the plane the hour hand of our watch points at 9 on the dial, the minute hand at 12, and the second hand at 60. Thus, time refers to the simultaneity of two events, the plane's arrival and the precise position of the three hands on our watch.[69]

One hour before the arrival at the airport, our watch will show 8:00 p.m. Provided the plane lands precisely on schedule and the watch keeps time accurately, it does not matter whether the wristwatch is on a passenger of the incoming plane or on a visitor waiting for the plane at the airport. Time differences could arise because the plane was not cleared for landing or the two watches were not synchronized properly. But aside from such "natural events" we would not expect that the passenger's watch would have slowed because the plane was in motion and, therefore, showed 8:55 p.m. instead of 9:00 p.m. No, we would anticipate that on landing the passenger's watch, just like the visitor's watch, points at 9:00 p.m.

*Time Intervals*

Einstein stressed that two events observed in a stationary reference frame (e.g., at an airport terminal), where they are separated by a specific time interval, would not be separated by the same time interval when observed from a high-speed reference frame (e.g., on a spacecraft in extremely fast motion). Observers moving at different velocities would experience different time intervals between the same pair of events.

To illustrate this point consider an experiment.[70] Put the speed of light at 186,000 miles per second or 300,000 kilometers per second (km/s) and continue with kilometers for ease of computation.[71] Ignoring any technical or economic difficulties, assume that a satellite is in stationary orbit at exactly 150,000 km above a selected geographic point on Earth. A "laser light-pulse" bounces back and forth between the satellite straight overhead and a reflector stationed at Earth. The straight-line round trip of each light pulse, from satellite to Earth station and back, will take precisely one second for the round trip, i.e., *2 x 150,000 km = 300,000* km in one second. Since the satellite is positioned in a stationary orbit, the "laser clock" ticks at one-second intervals.

Now assume that a spacecraft travels past on a straight-line course at close to the speed of light. An observer on the craft will see the same light signals follow a zigzag path (assume single photons$_g$ can be seen). This may seem strange but a simple analogy may help clarify the situation.

Imagine a bus stops at red light. While waiting for the light to change, a youngster opens a window (fourth window from the front door in Figure 14.1) and bounces a red ball off the road, catching it every time it comes back up (Figure 14.1, Diagram 1). But now assume we are parked in a car right beside the bus and are also waiting at the stop light. Something strange happens: while the youngster continues to bounce the ball off the road, the bus appears to be slowly rolling backward (Figure 14.1, Diagram 2). Before we realize that it is actually our car inching forward, the trajectory of the ball appears to be moving backward alongside the bus.

The ball bounces back up as the bus appears to move further back. Unable to account for the backward motion unless we look at a fixed point of reference, for example, the stationary stop sign, the bouncing ball appears to follow a V-shaped trajectory. If our car were to keep on rolling forward, the ball would appear to trace out a zigzag pattern going backward alongside the bus (Figure 14.1, Diagram 2).

This image roughly corresponds to the visual impression a passenger on the high-speed spacecraft would have. Although the ball dropped from the window of the bus travels at a much, much slower speed than light, its V-shaped trajectory corresponds to the light signal flashing back and forth. Seen from the stationary satellite the light signals flash straight down and up (assume individual light photons$_g$ are visible) but when observed from the high-speed craft they follow a zigzag course. Not being aware of the craft's motion, a passenger on the craft would see the light pulse travel from the space station toward the Earth up front, observe it reflected from Earth while passing by, and coming back up from behind.

*Illustration of Time Dilation*

As seen from the stationary satellite the round trip of the light pulse is exactly 300,000 km in precisely one second. Since the zigzag path as seen from the spacecraft is longer than the straight up-and-down distance from the stationary satellite, it takes the light impulse longer to reach the space-craft. If, for example, the spacecraft passes the Earth at two-thirds of the speed of light or at 200,000 km/s with respect to Earth, it would take the laser light pulse 1.2 seconds to reach the moving craft. This compares with the 1.0 second time interval on the stationary satellite (Figure 14.2). Evidently, the time interval between the two events (i.e., between two successive light impulses) is longer on the fast spacecraft than on the stationary satellite or on Earth. If we agree that time is determined by the interval between successive events and not by a watch stationed on Earth, time on the spacecraft slows down. Possibly, this idea is the most difficult concept of the Special Theory of Relativity. Time itself becomes variable as time stretches out at speeds approaching that of light.

This thought experiment—Einstein would call it a "Gedanken Experiment"—implies that the principle of simultaneity of two events no longer holds because one second is longer for the observer on the high-speed spacecraft than for the person on the stationary satellite or on Earth. How much longer depends on the speed of the spacecraft. The faster it moves, the more the zigzag trace of the light signal will be lengthened, and the more stretched out will be the time on the spacecraft.

If this is what is meant by "time dilation," could it not be interpreted as a mere illusion? Certainly the earlier example of the backward motion of the bus was an illusion. When it comes to the laser light signal, it is not. Before the light signal can reach the retina of the passenger's eye on the fast-moving craft, it must have crossed the intervening space. Thus, during the one-second time interval on Earth the light signal had to travel a greater distance to reach the high-speed spacecraft. Once we accept that the speed of light is the ultimate "constant" of nature at 300,000 km/s, the light can only cover the longer distance if the one-second interval on the spacecraft is correspondingly longer.

### Gamma: the Time Dilation Factor

Flying at nearly the speed of light past the stationary or Earth-bound light signals, time is dilated on the fast-moving spacecraft. The time dilation is the ratio of the distance the light impulse travels as seen from the high-speed spacecraft to the distance between the reflector on Earth and the stationary satellite.[72] In our example this ratio is $C/A = 187,278/150,000 = 1.2$. It implies that the time interval on the fast-moving spacecraft is 1.2 times longer than on the stationary satellite (Figure 14.2, Diagram 2).

This time dilation factor plays a key role in the Special Theory of Relativity. It first appeared in the Lorentz transformation equations[73] (named after the physicist H.A. Lorentz, 1853–1928, see Chapter 13) and is a crucial element of Einstein's Special Theory of Relativity because the gamma factor is needed to compute the time dilation that would be experienced at speeds close to that of light. To recapitulate, the time dilation factor is described once more in Equation 1.

At low speeds the ratio $C/A$ will be so close to $A/A$ that the time dilation factor will be 1.0. At speeds close to that of light the distance $C$ will become much larger than A and the gamma factor (time dilation factor) will become correspondingly greater. Consequently, the numerical

Equation 14.1: Time Dilation at a Speed of 200,000 km/second

> *As illustrated in Figure 14.2, Diagram 2, the time dilation factor is given by*
>
> $$\gamma = \frac{C}{A}$$
>
> *At a speed of 200,000 km per second*
>
> $$\gamma = \frac{C + C'}{2\,A} = \frac{2\,C}{2\,A} = \frac{2\,(180\,278)}{2\,(150\,000)} = 1.2$$
>
> *where*
>
> $A$ = *distance between the satellite and the reflector as seen from the stationary satellite,*
>
> $C$ = *distance between the satellite and the reflector as seen from a high – speed spacecraft.*
>
> *The ratio 1.2 implies that the time interval on the fast – moving spacecraft is 20% longer than on Earth.*

value will become much larger than A and the gamma factor (time dilation factor) will become correspondingly greater. Consequently, the numerical value of the time dilation factor $C$ an vary widely with the speed of the craft. A more rigorous definition of the time dilation or gamma factor is given in Appendix A of this chapter (Equations A14.1 and A14.2).

It was Einstein's great intuitive insight that led to the discovery of time dilation. At low speeds the time dilation is so small that for all practical purposes it is negligible. For example, a car traveling at a highway speed of *67* miles per hour (*108* km/h) moves at *33* yards per second (*30* m/s). By contrast, light travels at a speed of about 186,000 miles per second (300,000 km/s). This makes the ratio of the car's speed to that of light extremely small, and it makes the dilation far too small to detect. We would have to move much faster to experience a significant time dilation.

Suppose we traveled at a much greater speed of 1860 miles per second (3000 km/s) which is equivalent to *3600 x 1860 = 6.7 million miles per hour (3600 x 3000 = 10.8 million km/h).* Even then, the time dilation or gamma factor $\gamma$ would be less than *1/1000*. To produce any significant effects of time dilation, a craft would have to reach a speed of, for instance, *25,000* miles per second (about *40,000* km/s). That is *90* million miles per hour (about *144* million km/h). Then the time dilation factor or gamma factor $\gamma$ would be *1.009*, a time dilation of nearly 1%. It implies that one hour is lengthened by roughly half a minute. As yet, we are unable to reach such speeds (see Table 14.1). Even at such an enormous speed the time dilation would be barely noticeable.(For computational detail see Appendix A, Equation 14A.4.)

It is clear that speeds close to that of light are not an everyday life experience. Einstein's theory predicted that variations in measured time intervals occurred at extreme velocities. This needed to be verified by experiment. But how could it be shown when no one had ever traveled at such enormous speeds?

It was not the first time that such difficulties cropped up in physics. Some 300 years earlier Galileo had claimed that an object would continue to move if not impeded by friction or any other force. Newton went even further and asserted that motion in outer space would forever follow a straight-line course if no force acted on it. At a time of horse and buggy neither Galileo's nor Newton's assertions could readily tested by experiment, yet the laws of physics they derived were shown to be correct.

To early twentieth century physicists, Einstein's theory appeared to be no more than speculation unless it could be supported by convincing empirical evidence. The proof of time dilation was not discovered until many years later. It did not come from a spacecraft or any other large object moving at extreme speed, but from small subatomic particles. Some of these particles, the muons$_g$, tend to disintegrate after a very short lifespan. It is not exactly known why they behave like this, but they do obey the time-dilation principle of Einstein's theory of relativity.[74]

Muons are the most abundant subatomic particles in cosmic rays that are streaming toward Earth from outer space at extremely high speeds.[75] Muons were first detected in 1940 in an experiment (by Bruno Rossi *et al.* near Denver, Colorado) designed to study cosmic rays. On entering the upper atmosphere mesons$_g$ collide with atomic nuclei and produce tiny explosions that produce the muons.They are similar to electrons but have 200 times their mass. The muons fly away from the point of explosion at almost the speed of light. Their life span is a mere two microseconds (a microsecond is one millionth of a second).[76] Since their life time is so very short, they were not expected to travel farther than some *3300* feet (about *1000* m). Yet, most of the muons travelled much farther than expected and many actually reached the surface of the Earth. In fact, the Earth's crust is constantly bombarded by muons even though the Earth's atmosphere is about *19* miles thick (about *30* km).

The Italian physicist Enrico Fermi (1901–1954), a 1938 Nobel laureate of physics who had fled fascist Italy to work in the United States, suggested that Rossi's results could be attributed to the high-speed instability of the mesons. If the muons broke up sooner or later than expected it was the result of variations in relativistic time dilation.[77] Following Fermi's lead, other scientists accepted his conjecture that time was dilated for some muons more than for others. Those that traveled faster, at speeds closer to light, aged more slowly and therefore made it farther down (Figure 14.3, Diagram 1).[78]

This proposition was not proven until many years after Einstein's death when, in 1976, an Experiment at CERN, the European Center for Particle Physics, confirmed the time dilation of muons. Physicists created muons by particle collisions, inserted them immediately into a ring-shaped vacuum tube, "stored" them at a constant speed of *99.94%* of light, and detected their decay times by monitoring the emission of electrons. They found that the lifetime of muons lasted *44* microseconds at a speed of *0.9994* times that of light, yielding a gamma factor of *28.9* (Table 14.1). That is to say, their life span was nearly 30 times as long as that of a muon at rest.[79]

### Contraction of Length

If time is not constant and can run slower or faster, can space be as variable as time? Every day experience tells that distance traveled equals time interval times speed. But what happens at extreme velocities when time stretches out? To make this plausible, assume two physicists watch a muon entering the atmosphere; one stationed on Earth and the other moving alongside the muon. The physicist on Earth would measure the muon's life span at 20 microseconds while the other would measure it at only one

Table 14.1: Time Dilation at Different Speeds

| Object | Speed per Second $v$ (km/s) | Speed as Percent of light $v/c$ | Gamma Factor $\gamma$ | Time Dilation in % |
|---|---|---|---|---|
| Car | 0.03 | 0 | 1 | 0 |
| Airplane | 0.5 | 0.0002 | 1 | 0 |
| Rifle bullet | 1 | 0.0003 | 1 | 0 |
| Space probe | 40000 | 13.33 | 1.009 | 0.9 |
| Spacecraft Fig.14.2 | 200000 | 66.67 | 1.34 | 34 |
| Future craft? | 270000 | 90 | 2.29 | 129 |
| Muons | 299625 | 99.875 | 28.9 | 2790 |

Source: Based on Harald Fritzsch, pp. 116, 133 and this Chapter, Appendix A, Equations A14.1 to A14.5.

microsecond. That is because time slows down for the high-speed physicist. Traveling at the muon's speed, the physicist would pass the full height of a mountain such as Mount Everest in one microsecond, so that its height from top to bottom (but not its width) would shorten at the same rate as time lengthens, from its 29,029 feet (8848 m) to 1450 feet (442 m), or to 1/20th of its actual height[80] (Diagram 2, Figure 14.3). It means that the high-speed observer would see Mount Everest vertically shrink by the gamma factor (see this Chapter's Appendix, Equation A14.6).

Thus the theory of relativity implies not only a dilation of time but a corresponding contraction of space. This contraction shortens the distance as the high-speed observer perceives it (at rest in the muon's reference frame) and in this example by the factor 8848/20 or more generally, by the distance divided by gamma (a more detailed example is given in this Chapter's Appendix A, Equations A14.5 and A15.6).

Physicists have estimated that it takes about 2.5 billion (2.5 x 10⁹) atoms, side by side, to make up a length of 10 inches. If a 20 inch ruler were moving in a straight line at the speed of a muon, the 5 billion atoms would shrink to *20/20 = 1* inch. The individual atoms would then no longer be spherical but would look like horizontally compressed disks. Experiments at CERN (Conseil Européen pour la Recherche Nucléaire) have shown that protons accelerated to the speed of muons behave, when colliding with a nucleus or another proton, as if their mass were not distributed in tiny globe-shaped spheres but in slim disk-shaped spheroids (Figure 14.3, Diagrams 3 and 4).[81]

All this leads to the conclusion that the gamma factor plays a dual role: it lengthens time and shortens length (for more detail see this Chapter's Appendix A, Equation A14.7).

*Distance in Three-Dimensional Space*

Accustomed to living in three-dimensional space, experience has taught that it is not possible to walk through the thickness of a wall without a door, that climbing the height of a ladder entails the risk of falling down, and that it is not safe to walk into water without knowing its depth.

When looking at a three-dimensional object, its width, height, and depth are easily recognized. Yet what is seen are not the real dimensions but only their appearances.[82] Each of the three dimensions vary in appearance with the angle of view. On walking around an object or on turning it over, the brain immediately adjusts to retain the image of width, height, and depth. Thus the appearance of an object's dimensions translates into different aspects of the same thing in space.

The three dimensions of an object can also be pictured in an abstract manner by a coordinate system. To specify an object's location in space, it suffices to decide on a point of origin, $O$, and to give the directions or coordinates that measure the distances from this point. One coordinate measures the distance from the origin of a point on a line. Two coordinates measure the distance of a point in a plane, and three the distance of a point in space (Figure 14.4, Diagram 1 to 3).[83]

A convenient coordinate system is rectangular, that is to say, the coordinates are pointed at right angles to each other. If turned or rotated, the description of any one point in such rectangular coordinate systems may change, but the distance between two points remains unchanged. In physics this is an example of symmetry (Figure 14.4, Diagrams 4 to 6).

## Space–Time

Never having traveled at speeds close to light, time is not customarily included as a fourth dimension in the perception of space. If cars were to visibly shorten on the highway and mountains were to visibly flatten when seen from a landing craft, not allowing for the effects of the fourth dimension could spell disaster. In the world of super-fast motion, time and space are interrelated.

*The Space-Time Interval*

Buried in Einstein's relativistic relations of space and time is the phenomenon of "space time."

As shown earlier, distance between two points is described in two- or three-dimensional coordinate systems$_g$. They are known as "Galilean transformations," named after Galileo because he was the first who correctly described the laws of straight-linear motion (Figure 14.4). In a four-dimensional coordinate system of space-time the squared interval between two points remains unchanged before and after transformation.[84] Assume, for example, a particle is moving at a fraction of the speed of light. In squaring the relativistic time dilation and length contraction factor, and subtracting one from the other, the result is 1.00. This numerical value of the space-time interval is constant for all velocities between zero and the speed of light (Table 14.2, and this Chapter's Appendix A, Equation A14.8).

This is numerically shown in Table 14.2 by the time dilation factor gamma $\gamma$ which increases from 1.0000 to 7.0887 as the ratio of an object's velocity to that of light $v/c$ goes from 0.0 to 0.99. Over the same range of speeds, the difference between the squares of the time dilation factor $\gamma$ and the distance factor $d$ is constant at 1. This constant refers to the distance light travels in a one-second interval. Whereas Newton believed that the duration of time was absolute whether motions were swift or slow, or none at all, Einstein asserted that time varied with speed. According to him only the "space-time interval" remained absolute and constant.

Table 14.2: Constant Space-Time Intervals at Various Speeds

| Ratio of speed $v$ to light $c$ $v/c$ | Time Dilation factor $t = \gamma$ | Distance observed from rest $d = v\gamma$ | Square of time (time)$^2$ $\gamma^2$ | Square of distance (distance)$^2$ $(v\gamma)^2$ | Constant Space-Time Interval* $\gamma^2 - (v\gamma)^2$ |
|---|---|---|---|---|---|
| 0 | 1 | 0 | 1 | 0 | 1 |
| 0.1 | 1.005 | 0.1005 | 1.0101 | 0.0101 | 1 |
| 0.2 | 1.0206 | 0.2041 | 1.0416 | 0.0416 | 1 |
| 0.3 | 1.0483 | 0.3145 | 1.0989 | 0.0989 | 1 |
| 0.4 | 1.0911 | 0.4364 | 1.1905 | 0.1904 | 1 |
| 0.5 | 1.155 | 0.5775 | 1.334 | 0.3335 | 1 |
| 0.6 | 1.25 | 0.75 | 1.5625 | 0.5625 | 1 |
| 0.7 | 1.4003 | 0.9802 | 1.9608 | 0.9608 | 1 |
| 0.8 | 1.6667 | 1.3334 | 2.7778 | 1.7779 | 1 |
| 0.9 | 2.2942 | 2.0648 | 5.2634 | 4.2634 | 1 |
| 0.95 | 3.2026 | 3.0425 | 10.257 | 9.2568 | 1 |
| 0.99 | 7.0887 | 7.0178 | 50.25 | 49.2495 | 1 |

\* A general description of the constant space-time interval is given in this Chapter's Appendix A, Equation A14.8.

To graphically illustrate the relation between time dilation and distance, their values are plotted for different speeds in Diagrams 1 and 2 of Figure 14.5.[85]

Beginning at the point of rest when the particle does not move at all, the object's or particle's time dilation factor is $\gamma = 1.0$ and the distance traveled is zero. At 70% of the speed of light (i.e., when $v/c = 0.70$) time slows by 40% as the time dilation factor $\gamma$ reaches 1.4003 and the one-second distance $d$ amounts to $d = 0.9802c = 0.9802 \times 300\,000$ km (Figure 14.5, Diagrams 1 and 2, based on columns 1, 2 and 3 of Table 14.2 and

Equation A14.7 of Appendix A). The curves illustrate diagrammatically the functional relation between speed of travel relative to light $v/c$, the distance $v\gamma$, and the time dilation $\gamma$ in a space-time coordinate system. They also suggest that the speed of light sets an ultimate limit to the speed of motion (Figure 14.5, Diagram 3).

An important point of the numerical values of Table 14.2 is that the square of the time coordinate minus the square of the space coordinate (last column of Table 14.2) is the same for all observers, whatever their speed of travel. This is not a relative but an absolute number. It reconciles the strange phenomenon of time dilation and space contraction. The switch from one reference system at rest to another in rapid motion is equivalent to the conversion to space-time where the difference between the squares of time and space remains constant. This again is characteristic of symmetry, or of a "Galileo Transformation." It was encountered earlier in two- and three-dimensional space (Figure 14.4) and is evident here in four-dimensional space (Table 14.2 and this Chapter's Appendix Equations A14.8 and A14.9).[86]

*Time-Like and Space-Like Events*

Three years after Einstein's paper on Special Relativity was published, the Russian-German mathematician Hermann Minkowski—Einstein's former mathematics Professor at Zurich—suggested one should no longer talk of space and time separately but only of "space-time." He wrote: "Henceforth space by itself, and time by itself, are doomed to fade away into mere shadows, and only a kind of union of the two will preserve an independent reality."[87]From there he went on to describe a space-time coordinate system that allows to differentiate between time-like, light-like, and space-like events.

"Time-like" events are within reach of the light signal, whether the light comes from distant stars in the past or reaches Earth in future. In either case, such time-like events fall within a so-called light cone that can be described by space time coordinates. The remaining events fall outside the light cone and are classified as "space-like." They are beyond the reach of light, such as stars disappearing in black holes or galaxies vanishing beyond the edge of the universe.

Different types of events can be pictured in a simple space-time diagram. In Figure 14.5 distance is marked off on the horizontal x-axis in units of 186,000 miles (300,000 km) and time is marked off on the vertical axis in light seconds. Events that occur at the same location but at different times are located on a line parallel to the vertical axis, others that occur at the same time but at different locations are on a line perpendicular to the vertical axis.[88] Depending on distance and speed of travel, they could either be "time-like" or "space-like" events.

For example, if one movie is shown on Monday and another on Tuesday, both in the same theater, they could be represented as time-like events by points *A* and *B* in Figure 14.5, Diagram 4. Or if one football game were held on Saturday and another on Sunday, but in two different cities, they could be represented as events *C* and *D* in Figure 14.5, Diagram 5. Although the two games are held at different locations they are nevertheless time-like events because they are within easy reach of bicycle, car, train, or plane. Both sets of events are time-like because they either happen concurrently or are scheduled at different places but are reachable by today's modes of travel (at speeds of less than 186,000 miles per second or 300,000 km/s).

If, however, two events occur in different places that are so far apart that they are beyond reach even if we could travel at the speed of light, they are space-like events. Say, for example, future astronauts were to attend some intergalactic meeting at the space-coordinates $F_o$. If the meeting were scheduled at this location and at a date so near that the astronauts would have to travel at speed greater than that of light to get there in time, it would be a space-like event. Time-like and space-like events are separated by a red line (in Figure 14.5, Diagrams 4–6), which denotes the speed of light. They could, of course, try to have the meeting postponed and rescheduled to coordinates *F* so that they could make it there, traveling at less than the speed of light. It would then no longer be a space-like but a time-like event. As suggested in Figure 14.5, Diagram 6, the rescheduling could be represented by moving the time of the meeting from point $F_o$ across the red light-like line to point *F*.

Picturing space-time in only two dimensions, *x* and *t*, is an over-simplification of four dimensions. True, the two are linked and their functions are in a one-to-one relation. Yet, the make-up of the four dimensions is not quite as symmetrical as a two-to-two relation. As described by Einstein, space-time does not consist of four coordinate axes but only of three plus one. As of today it is not known why space has three coordinate axes and time has only one. Nevertheless, all four properties are interconnected by the universal speed of light.[89]

During 1907–1908, Minkowski organized some seminars jointly with the German mathematician David Hilbert (1862–1943) on the new developments in electrodynamics. Minkowski elaborated on the underlying mathematical structure of Einstein's Theory of Relativity and drew attention to the harmony between pure mathematics and physics. To this Einstein is reported to have said: "Since mathematicians pounced on the relativity theory I no longer understand it myself."[90]

## Force and Energy

Einstein proposed not only a new way of thinking about space and time, but he also established a radically new concept of energy. Until then Newton's premise had prevailed: The mass of a body remains constant no matter how its constituent parts are rearranged. If a material body is split up, the sum of its parts still equal the original mass. With Einstein, mass lost its absolutness. Just as distance and time lost their former uniqeness, mass lost its absoluteness. More revolutionary, Einstein anticipated mass as a new source of enormous energy.

Yet, Newton's definition of Force and energy had differed from the earlier classical definition too. Aristotle believed that it takes a continuous application of force to move an object at a steady speed.[91] Newton defined force as the acceleration caused by an instantaneous application of force, be it the force of pull by a horse on a wagon or the force of gravity by the Sun on a planet (Newton's mechanics were described in Chapter 12).

*Newton's Force: $F = m\,a$*

In his second law of motion Newton stated: "The change in motion is proportional to the motive force impressed."[92] He went on to say that if a force generates a change in motion, double the force will double the change in motion, and triple the force will triple it (the force being impressed in the same direction). The same idea can be conveyed by saying that the impact of a force $f_1$ or $f_2$ on an object of a given weight or mass $m$, accelerates an object proportionate to the size of the force applied (Equation 14.2).

Equation 14.2: Newton's Second Law

*The acceleration of an object is directly proportional to the force applied, or in short*

$$\frac{f_1}{f_2} = \frac{a_1}{a_2}$$

*where*

$\quad f_1 \quad = \quad force\ 1,$

$\quad a_1 \quad = \quad acceleration\ from\ force\ 1,$

$\quad f_2 \quad = \quad force\ 2,\ and$

$\quad a_2 \quad = \quad acceleration\ from\ force\ 2\ .$

*If , for example , $f_2$ is twice the force of $f_1$ ,*

$$f_2 \;=\; 2\ f_1 \quad then \quad \frac{f_1}{2\ f_1} = \frac{a_1}{2\ a_1}\ ;$$

*or if* $\quad f_2 \;=\; 3\ f_1 \quad then \quad \dfrac{f_1}{3\ f_1} = \dfrac{a_1}{3\ a_1}\ .$

For objects of different weight but of the same material, different rates of acceleration are to be expected. For example, suppose a force is applied to two metal bars, both of the same purity but one twice the size of the other. If the same force $f_1$ is applied to both, the acceleration of the bigger metal bar would be only half as large as that of the smaller metal bar. For any object of a given weight, the ratio of force to acceleration $f_1/a_1$ is constant. For example, doubling the force from $f_1$ to $2f_1$ will yield twice the acceleration $2a_1$, triple the force $f_1$ to $3f_1$ will yield triple the acceleration $3a_1$. The same idea of force being proportionate to acceleration is conveyed in this Chapter's Appendix B, Equations B14.1 and B14.2.[93]

Work can be described as the force needed to move an object across a distance: the greater the required force and the longer the distance, the heavier the work. The ideas of force $F$, distance $d$, and acceleration $a$, can be combined to arrive at a more formal definition of kinetic energy $K$ (see this Chapter's Appendix B, Equation B14.3).[94]

Kinetic energy (from the Greek word *kinein* (κινεῖν), to move) is only part of a large pool of energy sources.[95] Others are intrinsic to solid, liquid, or gaseous substances. Solid coal is excavated to provide heat and to drive engines. Liquid oil is distilled into kerosene, diesel oil, and gasoline, to propel cars, trucks, and planes. Natural gas is transmitted by pipelines to heat homes. Hydroelectric power derives from the kinetic of falling water and provides electricity for homes and industry.

The many different kinds of energy can be combined under such headings as $H$ for heat, $C$ for chemical, $M$ for electromagnetic, $S$ for solar, and others. Some of this energy is in use today, a large remainder is potential energy that is available for use in the future. In short, the total energy $T$ available to us today can be equated to kinetic energy K and potential unused energy $U$ so that $T = K + U$. To make it additive requires that all energy be quantified in comparable units.

Embedded in the concept of total energy is the "law of the conservation of energy." Although the idea of energy goes as far back as Galileo in the seventeenth century, the law was not recognized until the nineteenth century. It was only in the 1840s that the physicists James Prescott Joule of England (1818–1889) and Hermann von Helmholtz of Germany (1821–1894) recognized heat as a form of energy. They developed the theoretical models that linked heat and kinetic energy.

*Einstein's Law of Energy: $E = m\,c^2$*

In the twentieth century the conversion of nuclear energy by fission and fusion processes revolutionized the concept of total energy. It is utterly amazing that Einstein formulated the theory of this new form of energy near the turn of the last century, long before nuclear energy was first exploited. It was his equation, $E = mc^2$, that changed the world.[96] Einstein wrote:

The most important result of a general character to which the special theory of relativity has led is concerned with the conception of mass. Before the advent of relativity, physics recognized two conservation laws of fundamental importance, namely, the law of the conservation of energy and the law of the conservation of mass; these two fundamental laws appeared to be quite independent of each other. By means of the theory of relativity they have been united into one law. [97]

Newton's concept of mass can be translated into the theory of relativity as illustrated by the following thought experiment. Imagine two spacecraft, one parked one mile distant from and parallel to a wooden board and the other passing by the board at a gamma factor of 10, again one mile distant and parallel to the wooden board. A bullet is shot from the spacecraft at rest at the board at a right angle from the spacecraft at rest.[98] The bullet travels at a speed of 1 mile per second, hitting the board at the distance of 1 mile from the gun. The depth of penetration $P$ depends on the bullet's momentum, which is in direct proportion to the bullet's mass $m$ and its speed (velocity $v$), as in $P = m\, v$.

Space contraction does not affect the spacecraft at rest and has no impact on the bullet's path. To the observer on the second spacecraft, passing by at nearly the speed of light, say, at 185,000 miles per second (298 000 km/s) neither the stationary space ship nor the wooden board is at rest. They zoom by at 185,000 miles per second (298,000 km/s). Because of the time dilation factor $\gamma = 10$, the observer on board of the high-speed spacecraft sees the bullet flying by on a "V-shaped" trajectory. It does not take one second but 10 seconds on the high-speed craft before the bullet is seen to hit the target.

How deeply the bullet shot from the stationary first craft penetrates the board is totally independent of the high speed of the second craft. The force of impact is not affected, no matter what the speed of the second craft. The damage done to the board depends solely on the momentum of the bullet. Its impact is directly proportionate to the force created by the bullet's momentum.[99] The impact can be observed objectively. Whether a heavier bullet is fired at lower speed or a lighter bullet at higher speed, both will penetrate the board to the same degree if the momentum is the same. The depth of the bullet's penetration is solely determined by its momentum. Momentum is defined as the product of mass times speed or as $P = m v$. The conclusion is that the high-speed time dilation and the corresponding reduction of speed must somehow fit into the formula $P = m v$ where $P$ remains unchanged. Since the speed $v$ has been reduced by the gamma factor $\gamma = 10$ to $v/10$, the mass $m$ must have increased to $10\,m$, so that $P = (10\,m)(v/10)$ remains at $P$, the same as before (Figure 14.6).

Newton defined the kinetic energy of a material object as a function of the object's mass and speed. Kinetic energy is created when the material body is in motion. It does not exist when the material body is at rest. In abbreviated form the same idea is conveyed by $K = \frac{1}{2}\,mv^2$, a formula derived in this Chapter's Appendix B, Equation B.3. It describes the kinetic energy $K$ as a function of the object's mass $m$, velocity $v$, and the constant $\frac{1}{2}$.

Einstein modified Nwton'sconcept of energy. It is best known in its symbolic form as $E = m\,c^2$. He derived this equation from the more comprehensive version[100] that includes not only mass and speed of light but also the ever-present gamma factor. Newton's concept of kinetic energy is shown together with Einstein's version in Equation 14.3.

Einstein's relativistic energy equals the sum of Newton's equation for zero energy at rest, Einstein's equation allows for enormous energy. Stated as $E = m c^2$, the relativistic energy $E$ refers to an object at rest. At rest an object's speed $v = 0$, the ratio $v/c = 0$, the denominator of the gamma factor becomes 1.0 and the energy content $E = m c^2$. Where Einstein's relativistic energy equals the sum of Newton's equation for zero energy at rest, Einstein's equation allows for enormous energy.

The immensity of this energy potential was not realized until 40 years after Einstein's discovery of the formula $E = m c^2$. With his formula, Einstein equated energy to the product of mass times the (squared) speed of light, an incredibly large number. This intrinsic nuclear energy amounts to some 25 million kilowatts for every gram of matter.[101]

## Equation 14.3: From Newton's Energy to Einstein's Equation

*Einstein transformed Newton's formula for kinetic energy into his formula for relativistic energy.*

*Letting*

$E$ = *energy,*
$m$ = *mass,*
$v$ = *speed of craft,*
$c$ = *speed of light,*
$\gamma$ = *gamma,*                    *then*

*Newton's Kinetic Energy is defined as*

$$K = \tfrac{1}{2} m v^2 \qquad \text{and}$$

*Einstein's Relativistic Energy is defined as*

$$E = m [\, gamma \; c^2 \,]$$

$$= m \, \gamma \; c^2 m \, [ \frac{1}{\sqrt{1 - (\frac{v}{c})^2}} \; c^2 \,]$$

*It can be shown that this is equivalent to*

$$E = \tfrac{1}{2} m v^2 + m c^2$$

*Thus Einstein's relativistic energy contains Newton's kinetic energy. The derivation of this sum is shown in Appendix B, Equation B14.4 and B14.5 of this Chapter.*

### Confirmation of Einstein's Equation

Proof of its empirical validity jarred the world when on August 6, 1945 the first atomic bomb destroyed the city of Hiroshima, Japan. In later years the development of the much more powerful hydrogen bomb created a specter that has haunted humankind ever since. Yet, not all is lost if the knowledge of nuclear physics is put to more productive uses. Already nuclear reactors provide some of the world's energy. Still plagued by radiation problems of waste disposal, nuclear fusion may be the answer to future energy shortages. Eventually, it may even deliver the power for interstellar space travel.

Einstein wrote in his 1905 paper: "It is not to be excluded that this theory can be tested, using highly variable energy content—such as radium salt for example." This means that the energy mass conversion could be tested by a close study of the energy radiated by the element radium. It took several decades before this was done.[102]

Otto Hahn (1879–1968), Lise Meitner (1878–1968), and Fritz Strassmann (1902–1980), German pysicists, were the first to study nuclear decay. In the 1930s they investigated the products of neutron bombardment. In 1938, Lise Meitner, who was Jewish, left Nazi Germany. By the end of 1938 Hahn obtained conclusive evidence, contrary to earlier expectation, that one of the products from uranium was a radioactive form of a much lighter element, barium. It indicated that the uranium atom had split into two lighter elements. He sent an account of his work to Meitner who, with her nephew Otto Frisch (1904–1979), clarified the physical characteristics of this division and in 1939 proposed the term "fission" for the process (Figure 14.7). Hahn was awarded the Noble Prize for Chemistry in 1944 and shared the Enrico Fermi Award with Lise Meitner and Strassmann in 1966.[103]

Their finding, and the work of some 2000 researchers at the Manhattan Project in the United States, many of them Nobel prize winners, eventually led to the A-Bomb and later to the H-Bomb. The A-Bomb is based on nuclear fission and 0.1 % of its mass is converted to energy. The more powerful H-Bomb, based on nuclear fusion, changes 1% of its mass into energy.

The law of relativistic kinetic energy has another, very critical implication. In accelerating the speed of electrons or other nuclear particles, the increase in mass requires greater energy. As the mass approaches infinity so does the energy requirement. This—according to Einstein's Special Theory of Relativity—sets the ultimate limit to attainable speed: no matter how much energy is applied, a particle will never exceed the speed of light.

In more recent years protons have been accelerated in the CERN accelerator at Geneva, reaching speeds of 0.9999973 times that of light. At such speed their mass increased to 400 times the mass at rest.

## Summary

Einstein's theory started with two postulates: all motion is relative and the velocity of light is constant. The first postulate had long been recognized and was described by Galileo and Newton. The second was a break from the traditional view. It meant that the velocity of light was not affected by the motion of the source of light and its measured velocity was the same irrespective of speed or direction of the observer.

From the two propositions it follows that time stretches out at very high speeds. The degree of time dilation is determined by the gamma factor (Figure 14.8, Diagram 1). At conventional speeds the ratio $v/c$ will be so close to zero that the gamma factor is near 1.0. At 90% of the speed of light, 1 hour stretches out to 2.3 hours, at 99% it stretches out to 7.1 hours (Figure 14.8, Diagram 2). Some empirical evidence comes from the lengthening of the decay times of muons. While time stretches, distance shortens. For an observer moving at a speed close to light, length shortens in the direction of motion. It shortens by the ratio of length over gamma (Figure 14.8, Diagram 3). Although time and distance vary with speed, the difference of their squares remains constant (Figure 14.8, Diagrams 4 and 5). Near the speed of light the mass increases sharply, the energy requirements increase dramatically and it becomes impossible to accelerate any object beyond the speed of light (Figure 14.8, Diagram 6).

These results came from Einstein's Special Theory of Relativity. Selected features of Einstein's General Theory of Relativity will be described in the next chapter.

## APPENDIXES

### Appendix A: The Gamma Factor

Using the same symbols as in Figure 14.2, Diagram 2, Equation A14.1 gives the derivation of the gamma factor. It illustrates how time is dilated on a spacecraft traveling at high speed. At low speeds the side B in Diagram 2 approaches zero, so that the ratio $B^2 / C^2$ in the last line of Equation A14.1 comes close $0 / C^2 \approx 0$ and the gamma factor takes on the value *1.0*. At very high speeds close to that of light, side *B* approaches the length of *C*, so that the ratio $B^2 / C^2$ approaches *1.0*, the expression *(1 - $B^2 / C^2$)* approaches *(1 - 1) = 0*, the gamma factor becomes very large and, at the limit, reaches infinity. That is because multiplying time by a gamma factor of *1.0* does not lengthen time. By contrast, at speeds close to that of

Equation A14.1: The Gamma Factor in Figure 14.2

*The triangle ABC in this figure is rectangular. From the Pythagorean Theorem described in Chapter 2, it follows that*:

$$A^2 \ + \ B^2 \ = \ C^2 \quad and, therefore,$$

$$\frac{A^2}{C^2} + \frac{B^2}{C^2} = 1 \quad and \quad \frac{A^2}{C^2} = 1 - \frac{B}{C^2}$$

*so that*
$$\frac{A}{C} = \sqrt{1 - \frac{B^2}{C^2}}$$

*The gamma factor in Figure 14.2, Diagram 2, is given as*

$$\gamma = \frac{C}{A} \quad which \ is \ the \ inverse \ of \ \frac{A}{C} \quad so \ that \ \gamma \ becomes:$$

$$\gamma = \frac{1}{\frac{A}{C}} \qquad \gamma = \frac{1}{\sqrt{1 - \frac{B^2}{C^2}}} \qquad where$$

$$\gamma = \quad gamma \ factor, \ and \ A, B, \ and \ C = the \ sides \ of \ the$$
*triangle in Figure 14.2 .*

light, the gamma factor becomes large and, at the limit, infinitely large. At such high speeds, time is multiplied by the gamma factor and dilated until it barely moves if at all.

Embedded in the same Diagram 2 of Figure 14.2 are also the velocities of the spacecraft and of light. As shown in Equation A14.2, the gamma factor can be expressed in terms of the two velocities. In Diagram 2 the length of side *B* represents the distance the craft travels in ½ second and side *C* the distance light covers in ½ second. The ratio of the two sides, therefore, is equivalent to their velocities as in Equation A14.2.

Equation A14.2: The Gamma Factor Defined

$$\frac{B \,/\, 1/2 \ \text{sec}}{C \,/\, 1/2 \ \text{sec}} = \frac{2 \ B \,/\, \text{sec}}{2 \ C \,/\, \text{sec}} = \frac{B}{C} = \frac{velocity \ of \ craft}{velocity \ of \ light}$$

*After substituting v for B and c for C in the last term of Equation 14.A.1*

$$\gamma = \frac{1}{\sqrt{1 - \dfrac{B^2}{C^2}}} \quad becomes \quad \gamma = \frac{1}{\sqrt{1 - \dfrac{v^2}{c^2}}}$$

*where*

$\gamma$ = *the time dilation factor,*
$v$ = *speed of the spacecraft, and*
$c$ = *speed of light*

## Examples of Relativistic Time Dilation and Space Contraction

*Time Dilation at Highway Speed*
Relative to the velocity of light, the speed of a car is extremely small. The time dilation experienced in the car is, by today's technology, immeasurably small as shown in Equation A14.3.

Equation A14.3:  Time Dilation of a Car at Highway Speed

*If a car travels at 67 miles per hour it is equivalent to*
*roughly 108 km / 3600 sec = 0.03 km / sec (33 yards).*
*Following Equation 14 A.2  the time dilation factor*
*gamma is computed as:*

$$\gamma = \frac{1}{\sqrt{1 - \dfrac{v^2}{c^2}}} = \frac{1}{\sqrt{1 - \dfrac{(0.03)^2}{(300,000)^2}}} = \frac{1}{\sqrt{1 - \dfrac{3^2 \; 10^{-4}}{3^2 \; 10^{10}}}}$$

$$= \frac{1}{\sqrt{1 - 10^{-14}}} \approx \frac{1}{\sqrt{1 - 0}} = 1.000$$

*The term* $(1 - 10^{-14})$ *differs from 1.0 by 1/100 trillion.*
*It follows that the gamma factor is very close to 1.0 and*
*that the relativistic time dilation at today's highway speed*
*is too small to be detectable.*

Equation A14.4: Time Dilation of a Spacecraft Moving at 40,000 km/s

*At 40,000 km / second a craft would cover a distance*
*of 40,000 km × 3600 seconds = 144 million km per hour.*
*In that case the time dilation factor gamma would be:*

$$\gamma = \frac{1}{\sqrt{1 - \dfrac{v^2}{c^2}}} = \frac{1}{\sqrt{1 - \dfrac{40,000^2}{300,000^2}}} = \frac{1}{\sqrt{1 - \dfrac{4^2 \; 10^8}{3^2 \; 10^{10}}}}$$

$$= \frac{1}{\sqrt{1 - \dfrac{16}{9 \, (100)}}} = \frac{1}{\sqrt{\dfrac{900 - 16}{900}}} = \frac{1}{\sqrt{\dfrac{994}{900}}}$$

$$= \frac{1}{\sqrt{0.9822}} = \frac{1}{0.9911} = 1.009$$

*Dilation on a High-Speed Spacecraft*

Today's spacecraft moves much faster than a car. The first astronauts circled the Earth at a speed of some 20,000 miles per hour. The Earth's circumference is 24,900 miles (or roughly 40,000). At a speed of about 19,000 miles per hour (30,000 km/h) it would take one hour and 20 minutes to cover the distance of 24,900 miles (40,000 km). If a future spacecraft could travel at 89.5 million miles per hour (144 million km/h), it would orbit the Earth in roughly one second. The gamma factor of Equation A14.4 shows how large the time dilation would be at that speed.

The gamma factor 1.009 implies that time is dilated at 9/10 of 1%. Considering that the spacecraft is traveling at well over 60 million miles per hour (100 million km/h), the time dilation is still minute. A craft would have to move much faster before time dilation becomes significant.

In Equation A14.5 one more example of time dilation is given. It illustrates that near the speed of light, time stretches out dramatically. Muons are elementary particles produced when cosmic radiation is absorbed high in the Earth's atmosphere. They are unstable and decay, after a short life span, into something else. Their life span and distance vary with the speed at which they enter the atmosphere. In Equation A14.5 their speed is set at 99.875% of that of light.

*Space Contraction*

Time dilation is not the only aspect of relativistic motion. Figure 14.3, Diagrams 1 to 4, suggest that "time-dilation" and "length contraction" are two sides of the same coin. To an observer riding along side the muon, the distance would appear to be shorter. As shown in Equation A14.6, time-dilation and space contraction are inversely related.

A comparison of Equations A14.5 and A14.6 shows by how much, at a speed close to light, time is dilated and distance shortened. Obviously the two aspects are interrelated. It can be shown that, for any velocity, the arithmetic product of time dilation and length contraction does not vary with changes in velocity because the two are inversely related. The greater is the speed, the more time will be lengthened and distance shortened. Arithmetically, the reduction in distance compensates exactly for the expansion of time as is examplified by Equation A14.7.

Equation A14.5: Time Dilation of a Muon Moving at 99.875% of the Speed of Light

*At 99.875% of the speed of light a muon travels a dis − tance of .99875 × 300,000 = 299,625 km / sec. At this velocity a muon's time dilation factor gamma is*

$$\gamma = \frac{1}{\sqrt{1 - \dfrac{v^2}{c^2}}} = \frac{1}{\sqrt{1 - \dfrac{.99875^2 \; 300,000^2}{300,000^2}}}$$

$$= \frac{1}{\sqrt{1 - .99875^2}} = \frac{1}{\sqrt{1 - .9975015}} = \frac{1}{\sqrt{.0024985}}$$

$$= \frac{1}{.0499849} \approx 20.0$$

*It means that at this speed a muon's life span is twenty times as long as it is for a stationary observer. In this connection also see Figure 14.3, Diagrams 1 and 2.*

Equation A14.6: Relativistic Space Contraction

*The distance a muon travels in the atmosphere can be derived from its speed and the time interval of its lifespan. Letting*

$$\begin{aligned}
\gamma &= \text{time dilation factor,} \\
\gamma_{.99816} &= 20 \text{ from Equation 14 A.5} \\
c &= \text{speed of muon (approx. the same as light),} \\
t_{life} &= \text{muon's life span in seconds, here} \\
&\quad 1.5 \text{ microseconds (i.e., } 1.5 / 10^6 \text{ seconds).}
\end{aligned}$$

*Then*

$$\begin{aligned}
d &= \gamma_{.99816} \times c \times t_{lifespan} \\
&= 20 \times 300,000 \times \frac{1.5}{10^6} \\
&= 2 \times 10 \times 3 \times 100,000 \times \frac{1.5}{10^6} \\
&= 6 \times 1,000,000 \times \frac{1.5}{10^6} = 9 \\
&= 9 \; km.
\end{aligned}$$

# Equation A14.7: The Inverse Relation Between Time Dilation and Space Contraction

*In Table 14.2 the space – time in tervals are given for various velocities. Setting the speed of light at c, the factor gamma is defined as*

$$\gamma = \frac{1}{\sqrt{1 - \left\{\frac{v}{c}\right\}^2}} \qquad where$$

*where the relativistic distance depends on the particle's speed relative to that of light. For example, at a speed of v = 150,000 km / s = 0.5 c, time is dilated by*

$$\gamma = \frac{1}{\sqrt{1 - \left\{\frac{0.5\ c}{c}\right\}^2}} = \frac{1}{\sqrt{1 - 0.25}} = \frac{1}{\sqrt{0.75}} = \frac{1}{0.866}$$

$$= 1.155 \ .$$

*It implies that time is dilated by 15.5 percent. The particle traverses in one second the relativistic distance* $d_R$

$$d_R = [dilated\ time] \times [\ speed\ ]$$

$$= [\ t \times \gamma\ ] \times [\ 0.5 \times c\ ]$$

$$= [\ 1\ sec \times 1.155\ ] \times [\ 0.5 \times c\ ] = 0.5775\ c \qquad so$$

*that the distance d ( for a stationary observer) to* $d_R$ *becomes*

$$\frac{d}{d_R} = \frac{0.5\ c}{0.5775\ c} = \frac{150,000}{173,250} = 0.8658\ ,$$

*It implies that the relativistic distance amounts to to 86.58 percent of the distance for a stationary observer.*

*Noting that*

$$1.155 \times 0.8658 = 1.0\ , \ confirms$$

*that time dilation is the inverse of space contraction.*

In our everyday experience the three dimensions of width, height, and depth unite to make up our perception of space. In Einstein's Special Theory of Relativity the three dimensions of space unite with time and the speed of light to make up the space in which the events of the universe occur. As described relativistic time measures the interval in the text of the is chapter of this chapter, the between events. Although this time varies with the speed of motion of the observer, its inverse relation to length or distance, makes for a constant space-time linked to the constant speed of light. This feature is generalized in Equation A14.8. The estimates of the space-time intervals at various velocities in Table 14.2 are based on this formulation.

Equation A14.8: Distance and Space-Time Interval

*The relativistic space – time interval $d_R$ is defined by the difference between the square of dilated time $c\,\Delta t$ and the sum of squares of the three coordinates x, y, and z.*

$$d_R^2 = (c\,\Delta t)^2 - [(\Delta x)^2 + (\Delta y)^2 + (\Delta z)^2]$$

*This space – time interval is invariant from one system frame to another because the speed of light is constant (as illustrated in Figure 14.4, Diagrams 4 – 6).*

*This constant interval can be described algebraically. From the earlier equations, 14A.2 for time dilation and 14A.6 for space contraction, the relativistic interval $d_R$ can be written as:*

$$d_R^2 = \gamma^2 - [t^2\,\gamma^2](\frac{v}{c})^2$$

*On inserting the proper term for the gamma ($\gamma$) factor, and on expressing v as a fraction of the speed of light v / c, one obtains*

$$d_R^2 = (\frac{1}{\sqrt{1-(\frac{v}{c})^2}})^2 - [t^2 (\frac{1}{\sqrt{1-(\frac{v}{c})^2}})^2]\,(\frac{v}{c})^2$$

$$d_R = \frac{1}{1-(\frac{v}{c})^2}\,[\,1 - (\frac{v}{c})^2\,] = 1.0$$

Thus, we have gone from the geometric ratio $B$ over $C$ in Diagram 2, Figure 14.2, to one that links the time-dilation factor gamma to the ratio $v/c$ (i.e., the speed of the craft to that of light c). As deduced here in Equation A14.8 and shown in the last column of Table 14.2, the relativistic time interval equals 1.0 irrespective of the object's speed.

## Appendix B: Newton's and Einstein's Laws of Force and Energy.

The idea of force being proportionate to acceleration was suggested in Equation 14.2 of the text. Usually Newton's Law is expressed in the more general form of Equation B14.1.

Equation B14.1: Newton's Law of Force

*Following the notation of Equation 14.2 of the text, let*

$$
\begin{aligned}
f_1 &= \text{force 1} \\
a_1 &= \text{acceleration from force 1} \\
f_2 &= \text{force 2, and} \\
a_2 &= \text{acceleration from force 2}
\end{aligned}
$$

*The first line of 14.2 of the text reads:*

$$\frac{f_1}{f_2} = \frac{a_1}{a_2} \quad \text{which can be rewritten as}$$

$$\frac{a_2}{a_1} \frac{f_1}{a_2} = \frac{a_1}{a_1} \frac{f_2}{a} \quad \text{and after cancelling terms}$$

$$\frac{f_1}{a_1} = \frac{f_2}{a_2}.$$

*If $f_1$ and $f_2$ are applied to one and the same object, it accelerates relative to each force so that the ratio of force to acceleration is constant. The characteristic ratio is defined as the mass $m$ of an object as in*

$$\frac{f_1}{a_1} = \frac{f}{a_2} = m \quad \text{and more generally}$$

$$\frac{f_1}{a_1} = \frac{f_2}{a_2} = \frac{f_3}{a_3} = \ldots = \frac{f_i}{a} = m \quad \text{where} \quad f_i = m_i\, a_i$$

*or, in short*

$$F = m\, a = \text{force equals mass times acceleration.}$$

When a force is applied to an object, the object's mass will be the same for all ratios $f_i/a_i$ . This statement can be shortened to F = ma. To illustrate, we start with the first line of Equation 14.2 of the Chapter text which suggests that the acceleration of a given object is directly proportional to the force applied. The definition of force is also linked to the weight of an object but it is not immediately clear how. Equation B14.2 describes it by given an astronautical example.

Equation B14.2: Example of the Relation Between Weight and Mass

*Letting*
| | | |
|---|---|---|
| *w* | = | *weight of astronaut on the Earth* |
| $w_M$ | = | *weight of astronaut on the Moon* |
| $g_E$ | = | *gravitational force on Earth* |
| $g_M$ | = | *gravitational force on Moon* |
| *m* | = | *mass* |
| *kg* | = | *1 kilogram (kg) is 2.2046 pounds (lbs.)* |

*On the Earth's surface an astronaut may weigh, say,*
*176 pounds (roughly 80 kilograms). The astronaut's*
*weight can be defined in terms of mass and gravitational*
*force (at the equatorial surface) as in*

$$w_E = m \ a = m \ g_E$$
$$= m \ (kg \ / \ sec^2)$$
$$80 \ kg = m \ (9.78 \ kg \ / \ sec^2) \quad and \ if \ sec = 1$$
$$m = 8.18$$

*On the surface of the Moon the same astronaut would*
*weigh in, assuming no weight loss during the trip, at*

$$w_M = m \ a = m \ g_M$$
$$= 8.18 \ (1.62 \ kg \ / \ sec^2) = 13.25 \quad so \ that$$

$$\frac{w_M}{w_E} = \frac{13.25}{80} = \frac{1}{6} \quad or,$$

*at 1 / 6 the astronaut's weight on Earth, at 29 pounds,*
*because the acceleration on the Moon's surface is only*
*one sixth of that on Earth.*

It is customary to quantify weight in kilograms or in pounds and to measure acceleration in meters per second $^2$ or in feet per second $^2$, abbreviated to $m/s^2$ or $ft/s^2$. The underlying idea of mass is to assign a quantity to an object independent of its force. By contrast, the weight of an object is the result of the gravitational force that pulls it toward Earth or toward any other astronomical body. To convey the relation between weight and mass, the description with Equation B14.2 may suffice. The example given shows how weight, mass, and gravitational force are linked together. Weight is described as the combination of mass and gravitational force. Mass is depicted as what remains after account is taken of the gravitational force.

The physicists' concept of work is also based on the elements of force and acceleration but incorporates distance and speed as well. Intuitively, it seems obvious that more energy is needed if an object is to be moved across a distance. Yet Newton, and Galileo before him, concluded that, aside from overcoming friction, no additional energy is needed to keep an object moving. So how can work be related to velocity and distance? To arrive at a definition of work the concepts of force, distance, and acceleration are combined as shown in Equation B14.3. In the last line of Equation B14.3 Work $W$ and Kinetic Energy $K$ are shown to be a function of an object's mass and the force of acceleration needed to achieve its speed $v$.

As shown in the last line of Equation B14.3 the kinetic energy required to move an object varies in direct proportion (or at a linear rate) with the mass of the object and more than proportionately (or at a geometric rate) with the speed of motion. In Equation 14.3 of the text, Newton's concept of kinetic energy was compared with Einstein's relativistic concept. The derivation of Einstein's equation is indicated in Equations B14.4 and B14.5.

Equation B14.3 Work and Kinetic Energy

**Work is defined as being directly proportional to the force
required to move an object. Let**

$$W \ = \ work \qquad\qquad F \ = \ force$$
$$d \ = \ distance \qquad\quad m \ = \ mass$$
$$a \ = \ acceleration \qquad v \ = \ velocity$$
$$t \ = \ time \qquad\qquad K \ = \ kinetic\ energy.$$

**The work is $W = F \times d = m \times a \times d$. So defined, the
amount of work varies with mass m, acceleration a, and
distance d. In Chapters 11 and 12 it was shown how far
an object moves when a force is applied. That distance is**

$$d \ = \ \tfrac{1}{2}\, a\ t^2 \qquad\qquad Replacing\ d\ in$$

$$W \ = \ m\ a\ [d] \quad by\ [\tfrac{1}{2}\, a\ t^2] \qquad yields$$

$$= \ m\ a\ [\tfrac{1}{2}\, a\ t^2]$$

$$= \ \tfrac{1}{2}\, m\ a^2\, t^2 \qquad and\ from\ Chapter\ 11,$$

$$v \ = \ a\ t \qquad so\ that \qquad v^2 \ = \ a^2\ t^2\ .$$

**Substituting $a^2\ t^2$ for $v^2$, work $W$ can be equated to
kinetic energy $K$ as in**

$$W \ = \ \tfrac{1}{2}\, m\,v^2 \ = \ K \qquad so\ that$$

**work is defined as half the mass times velocity squared.**

Equation B14.4: From Newton's Kinetic Energy to Einstein's Energy
Equation E = m c²

Let:    *E = Energy*        *m = mass*
        *v = speed of object*    *c = speed of light*

*Einstein transformed Newton's formula for kinetic energy into*

$$E = m\,\gamma\,c^2 = m\ \frac{1}{\sqrt{1 - (\frac{v}{c})^2}}\ c^2 .$$

*When the ratio* $\dfrac{v}{c}$ *is small,* $\gamma$ *can be approximated* * *by*

$$\gamma = \frac{1}{\sqrt{1 - (\frac{v}{c})^2}} \approx [1 + \tfrac{1}{2}\,(\tfrac{v}{c})^2]$$

*so that*

$$E = m\,\gamma\,c^2 = m\,[1 + \tfrac{1}{2}\,(\tfrac{v}{c})^2]\,c^2$$

$$= m\,c^2 + \tfrac{1}{2}\,m\,v^2 .$$

*It follows that at low speeds the total relativistic energy is the sum of*

*Einstein's*    $E = m\,c^2$
    +
*Newton's*    $K = \tfrac{1}{2}\,m\,v^2 .$

* *The approximation is shown in the next Equation B14.5.*

Equation B14.5: Binomial Expansion of the Gamma Factor

*The Binomial Theorem deals with expressions of the type* $(a + b)^n$ *. For example, if*

$$n = 2 \quad (a + b)^2 = a^2 + 2ab + b^2$$
$$n = 3 \quad (a + b)^3 = a^3 + 3a^2b + 3ab^2 + b^3$$
$$\text{but if } a = 1 \quad (1 + b)^3 = 1 + 3b + 3b^2 + b^3$$

*Newton generalized the expression so that it reads*

$$(1 + b)^{\frac{m}{n}} = 1 + \frac{m}{n}b + \frac{1}{2}\frac{m}{n}(\frac{m}{n} - 1)b^2 + \ldots$$

*Einstein's Equation B14.4 of relativistic energy is*

$$E = m\gamma \ c^2 = m \ \frac{1}{\sqrt{1 - (\frac{v}{c})^2}} \ c^2$$

$$= mc^2 \ [(1 - (\frac{v}{c})^2]^{-\frac{1}{2}} .$$

*Applying Newton's binomial expansion yields*

$$E = m \ c^2 \ [ \ \{1 - (-\frac{1}{2}) \ (\frac{v}{c})^2\}] \quad \text{and,}$$

*therefore, Einstein's relativistic energy equates to:*

$$E = m \ c^2 + \frac{1}{2} \ m \ v^2 \qquad \text{and this}$$

*expression corresponds to that of Equation 14.3 of the text.*

Chapter 15

# EINSTEIN'S GENERAL THEORY OF RELATIVITY

*Nobel Prize winner Max Born considered Einstein's Theory of Relativity "a great work of art" and "the greatest feat of human thinking about nature, the most amazing combination of philosophical penetration, physical intuition, and mathematical skill."*

Denis Brian[1]

The previous chapter described Einstein's early years and his Special Theory of Relativity. This chapter continues to follow Einstein's life and introduces his General Theory of Relativity.

In the Special Theory Einstein postulated that all motion must be considered relative to the speed of light. He restricted his theory to the special case of objects moving at constant velocity, in straight-line motion. He deduced that at speeds close to light, time is dilated, space is contracted, and objects are shortened. However, at lower speeds—like that of cars, airplanes, or even bullets—these effects cannot be detected by conventional measuring devices. Most important, he deduced from the theory his famous equation $E = m\,c^2$, stating that energy equals mass times the square of the speed of light, a value enormously greater than Newton's (1642–1727) theory predicted. When Einstein published the Special Theory in 1905, his conclusions appeared to be speculative. It was not until after publication of the General Theory that his theories were shown to be valid.

In February 1916, Einstein published a 50-page treatise on the "Foundations of the General Theory of Relativity." It was published in the *Annalen der Physik* and postulated that the laws of nature have the same space-time relations for any observer, whether moving at constant velocity or at accelerated motion. He deduced that the passage of time is altered by gravity. Namely, time passes more slowly in a stronger gravitational field than in a weaker field. According to Einstein the presence of mass creates a curved space-time. This curvature dictates the path a freely moving object must follow. His concept of curved space-time provided a logical explanation for Newton's theory of gravity and yielded some revolutionary insights. Newton's theory became a special case of Einstein's General Theory.[2]

This chapter elaborates on certain aspects of Einstein's General Theory of Relativity and describes how Einstein's theory was confirmed by empirical tests in later years.

Professor Kleiner, mentioned in the previous chapter, was convinced that Einstein was among the foremost theoretical physicists of the times. Eventually, Kleiner did succeed in having Einstein appointed associate professor at the University of Zurich. At the outset he had only two or three students in his class, but his teaching improved and by 1909 he had a class of 24 students.[3] Soon after, Einstein negotiated for a full professorship with the German University of Prague. Yet, by 1911 he was back in Zurich, this time at the Polytechnic where his friend Marcel Grossmann had become the Dean of Physics.[4]

**The Search for a General Theory of Relativity**

Einstein had confined the Special Theory of Relativity to the study of objects moving in a straight line at constant velocities. As illustrated in Chapter 14, at speeds close to light, time is dilated (Figure 14.2) and space is contracted (Figure 14.3). Every motion is relative to the speed of light. The measured velocity of light is an absolute constant. As a result, time and space merge in "absolute space-time."[5] Also, at extreme speeds an object's relativistic mass increases, raising an insurmountable barrier as it approaches the speed of light (Figure 14.5). Thus, no object can go faster than light. As described in Chapter 14, these findings can be deduced by Euclidean plane geometry.

Einstein felt that the idea of space-time needed to be generalized and reconciled with Newton's classical theory of gravity. In Newton's theory and also in Einstein's Special Theory of Relativity, the law of inertia held for all objects. Whether an object was initially at rest or in motion, its state remained unchanged unless affected by an external force: either the object remained at rest or it continued to move in linear direction at the same speed.[6] In either state the laws of nature were the same.

Yet, what would happen under acceleration? It seemed that the same laws of nature would no longer hold. Einstein wondered why the behaviour of accelerating objects should differ from those at rest or under constant speed. Why should one state of motion be given preference over another?

Also a related problem, the puzzle of a "rotating disk," bothered him. A rotating disk might barely move at the center while its circumference, if sufficiently large, could revolve at great speed. The Special Theory would dictate that a disk rotating at extreme speed would have to shrink along the circumference as space contracts. Yet, the radius being at a right angle to the direction of rotation, would not change its length. This implied that near the speed of light the circumference would shrink while the radius remained unchanged.[7] Einstein thought that no person with a logical mind could be satisfied with this state of affairs. It made him search for a general principle of relativity that would resolve this strange contradiction.[8]

*The Principle of Equivalence*

In 1907, while working at the Swiss patent office (see Chapter 14), it suddenly occurred to Einstein that a man falling freely in space would not feel his own weight. The simple thought that a falling body would not feel its own weight, and that other objects would fall at the same rate, as if in the same state of rest, gave him a sudden insight. Later he called this sudden insight "the happiest thought of my life."[9] The idea impressed him so deeply it impelled him to develop a new theory of gravitation. The scientific thinking of the day was that gravitational force was an absolute that could be determined by measuring the acceleration of a falling object. Suppose, Einstein said, someone was confined in an enclosed space—a box or an elevator—and moving in free fall. Neither this person, nor any other person in the same space, would experience the acceleration. Unless they could look outside and lock onto a point of reference, they would not detect their acceleration. This "happiest thought" triggered in Einstein the idea that just as the sense of gravity could be lost in a free fall, it could also be created. If a person or objects were raised upward at a constant rate of acceleration, the experience would be equivalent to that of gravity.

This idea evolved into Einstein's Principle of Equivalence: "The effects produced by gravitation, in any small region, are the same as those produced by acceleration."[10] In 1934 Einstein wrote in an article:

> The equality of inertial and gravitational mass was now brought home to me in all its significance. I was in the highest degree amazed at its existence and guessed that in it must lie the key to a deeper understanding of inertia and gravitation. I had no serious doubts about its strict validity even without knowing the results of the admirable experiment of Eötvös, which—if my memory is right—I only came to know later.[11]

Nowadays, this idea does not appear strange to us at all. It is well known that astronauts experience additional G-forces on takeoff and landing; for them the G-force is the same no matter where it originates, whether it comes from acceleration on take off, or deceleration on landing, or simply from the Earth's force of gravity.[12] The room in a spaceship today is so small that the principle of equivalence condition for effects ( produced by acceleration are the same as those produced by gravitation) created "in any small region" readily applies (Figure 15.1, Diagram 1).

If a spacecraft were enormously large, as large as a continent, a careful observer could distinguish between acceleration and gravitation. Just as the angles of the lines of gravitational force on Earth differ between two distant geographic locations, they would differ in space if a large object was attracted by the gravitational force of a planet or another massive celestial body (Figure 15.1, Diagram 2). The closer the object to the center of gravitational force, the closer the lines of force will come together. In contrast, an accelerative force acting on the same object would cause its lines of force to be parallel to each other. Therefore, the stated necessity for creating the effects "in any small region."[13]

*Gravitational and Magnetic Fields*

In contemplating gravitation Einstein compared it with a magnetic field. If a magnet attracted a piece of iron it was because the magnet formed a field that linked the iron to the magnet through an intermediary medium. The magnetic field worked on the iron and made it move toward the magnet. To Einstein, the similarities between electromagnetism and gravitation were striking. Just as an electromagnetic field could attract electrically charged objects, a gravitational field could attract objects. Unlike a magnetic field, however, a gravitational field would not vary with the material of the object. While magnetic force attracts iron but not wood, gravitational force attracts wood as much as iron. Although no evidence of gravitational waves or gravitational fields existed or could be generated, Einstein was convinced that they did exist and that they could be generated.

Einstein went further and believed that any acceleration created a gravitational field. He believed that the Earth radiated a gravitational field. He speculated that on an elevator, a person experiences the force of a field, sensing a gain of weight on going up or of losing weight on going down. Similarly, a passenger would notice the force of a field when a car is pulling away from a stop or slowing down to a halt. Or when a baseball is hit, it would create its own gravitational field. Even the acceleration of walking, placing one foot in front of the other, would create a field.

In each case a change in the field is caused by a shift away from the normal state of rest or constant motion. Yet, such fields had never been detected. If they really existed and had never been detected, it was simply that such gravitational fields were so much more difficult to detect than electromagnetic fields. In a bold, intuitive move, Einstein decided that acceleration produced a field. As well, he was convinced that inertial and gravitational mass were both the same.[14]

*Riemannian Geometry*

After his return to Zurich, Einstein devoted his energies to generalizing the theory of relativity. He found it very difficult going and reportedly said to his friend Grossmann, "Help me . . . or I 'll go crazy."[15] Grossman had done his thesis on non-Euclidean geometry and introduced him to Riemann's geometry. Georg Friedrich Bernhard Riemann (1826–1866) had been a German mathematician who had obtained his doctorate at Göttingen under the renowned Carl Friedrich Gauss (1777–1855) and who, in 1859, succeeded him as director of the Göttingen observatory. In one of the most acclaimed lectures in the history of mathematics, Riemann independently formulated a non-Euclidean geometry, unaware of the work of Lobachevsky (1829) and Bolyai (1832). It was an alternative to their models of non-Euclidean geometry as well as to that of Gauss (1816). He correctly foresaw that his work could benefit the physics of space. Fifty years later Einstein drew on Riemann's pioneering mathematics to create the General Theory of Relativity.[16]

In Euclidean geometry straight lines are the shortest connection between two points. In Riemannian geometry the same idea is generalized into geodesic$_g$ lines, or simply geodesics. They are the shortest connections between two points on a curved surface.[17] The equations for these geodesics contain certain components that form the basis for the geodesic curvature.

Although experts in the field believed that Riemann's abstract tensor calculus$_g$ could yield nothing new, Riemann considered it possible to link it to certain characteristics of space. Deemed to be too theoretical and too speculative, his allusions to space were ignored. Only William Kingdon Clifford (1845–1879), a British philosopher and mathematician who translated Riemann's work into English, believed that Riemann's tensor calculus could be fused with the physics of space. Clifford even ventured that matter and motion formed the structure and curvature of space.[18]

In 1876 Clifford published a paper called "On the Space-Theory of Matter," in it he wrote:

I hold in fact
(1) That small portions of space are in fact of a nature analogous

339

to little hills on a surface which is on the average flat; namely that the ordinary laws of geometry are not valid in them.

(2) That this property of being curved or distorted is continually being passed on from one portion of space to another after the manner of a wave.

(3) That this variation of the curvature of space is what really happens in that phenomenon which we call motion of matter, whether ponderable or ethereal.[19]

In Clifford's time this notion of space was regarded as utterly fantastic. It aroused strong opposition among those who believed in the Kantian doctrine. To them, Euclidean geometry was based on *a priori* judgements that existed beyond reason and experience. A questionable argument, which may or may not be reconcilable with the perception of space, time, and Kantian ideas.

Einstein needed tensor calculus for formalizing his idea of space. Riemann's tensor calculus had been further developed by later mathematicians.[20] Working with Grossmann, Einstein wrote a paper on tensor analysis. Invited by the physicists Max Planck (1858–1947) and Walter Nernst (1864–1941) to join them at the University of Berlin, Einstein accepted the offer. It was at a higher salary and gave Einstein the freedom to pursue his research with no other obligations. He found the tensor analysis much more difficult than he had expected. He wrote: "Every step is devilishly difficult. I have never been so tormented. Compared with this problem the original relativity was child's play."[21] What guided him was that the solutions had to be invariant to different coordinate systems (Chapter 14, Figure 14.4) and that in weak gravitational fields the solutions had to be the same as Newton's.

**Berlin and War**

Einstein formally accepted the appointment to Berlin in December 1913 and moved with his family early in March of 1914. His wife Mileva was very apprehensive about this move. She hated Germany and Berlin, and refused to stay there. In July she left with their two sons to go back to Switzerland. Their marriage was not a success. For years she had suffered from an ongoing feud with Einstein's mother who had been opposed to their marriage from the outset. And, for some time, Einstein had been involved with Elsa Löwenthal, a cousin of his in Berlin.[22] While Einstein attempted to reconcile with Mileva, the outbreak of World War I in August of 1914 made travel to Switzerland difficult and reconciliation became impossible. By December of 1914 he had sent Mileva what furniture he could spare and promised to provide quarterly financial support. He did as promised but it was not enough. Mileva had to give lessons in mathematics and music to make ends meet.[23]

The outbreak of war in 1914 surprised many. Yet, the political sores had been festering in Europe for some time. Alliances and counter-alliances had been formed. King Wilhelm II had dismissed Bismarck and his successors lacked the wisdom and diplomatic skills of the former chancellor. All over Europe arms dealers accumulated riches by marketing new and more deadly war technologies. While the military interests in Europe kept growing, Germany made long range plans for mobilization, aggravating tensions between former alliances. Einstein regarded war advocates as lunatics. Rather than advocating international class solidarity against war, Socialists encouraged and intensified the nationalist fervour. No one foresaw the incredible deprivations World War I would bring.[24]

By the fall of 1915 Einstein was totally absorbed in his work. Skipping meals and working far into the night, he finally found, after ten years of hard work, the solutions he had been searching for. He concluded that gravity was not a physical force acting through space, but a characteristic of the geometry of space. The Princeton mathematician John Archibald Wheeler (1911– ) later summarized the underlying concept this way: "Space-time tells matter how to move; matter tells space–time how to curve."[25]

Einstein had completed his masterpiece, the *General Theory of Relativity*. He was euphoric.[26] Although the theory can be elegantly summarized by tensor calculus, the mathematics behind it is awesome. Banesh Hoffman, Einstein's colleague and biographer, explained the gravitational field equations, describing the space curvature as follows:

> If written out in full instead of in compact tensor notation, [the equations] would fill a huge book with intricate symbols (in one form, millions of them). And yet there is something about them

that is intensely beautiful and almost miraculous. Their power and utter naturalness in both form and content give them an indescribable beauty.[27]

In the present context it is impossible to convey a full appreciation of Einstein's achievement. Only some of the underlying principles will be sketched here. Since Einstein's space-time is a four-dimensional concept, some simple relations of dimensions of lower order are considered first.

## Looking at Another Dimension

Surveyors often deal with the problem of uneven surfaces when they map the surface of hilly land. To estimate such land areas they measure out, in straight lines, small triangles or quadrangles and link them together. By combining them, they approximate the size of the larger area. For more precise estimates of uneven areas, however, a network of curved lines that smoothly and continuously cover the areas would be more appropriate.[28] Doing so would require stepping from the two dimensions of a plane up to a three–dimensional space, and that alters the results.

### Triangles on Curved Surfaces

In traditional plane geometry the three angles of any triangle add to 180°. In a triangle drawn on a sphere, however, the three angles exceed 180°. In Diagram 1 of Figure 15.2, the three angles of the triangle on the surface of the globe add up to 270°. The globe is said to have a positive curvature since additional degrees (over 180°) are gained. In Diagram 2 of Figure 15.2 the triangle is on a saddle-shaped surface. Its three angles add to less than 180°, and it has a negative curvature since some degrees (from 180°) are lost. From this it can be concluded that a divergence from a tri-angle's 180° implies the triangle is not located on a perfectly even surface.

To explore the possibility that space is curved it is tempting to measure the angles of an appropriate triangle. In fact, in 1900, the German astronomer Karl Schwarzschild (1873–1916) tried to do just that. He measured the angles of a triangle formed between a star, some 1600 light years from Earth, and two positions along the Earth's orbit. If the sum of the three angles had differed from 180°, he would have had proof that space was curved. But it had not. From this result he concluded that if space were curved, it would only be noticeable beyond 1600 light years from Earth.

*Circles on Even and Curved Surfaces*

A look at how a circle on a two-dimensional surface differs from one on a three-dimensional surface is considered next. According to Euclidean geometry the circumference of a circle is $2\pi$ or 6.28 times its radius. Conceivably, this numerical value could be found by drawing, on a perfectly even surface, straight lines in all directions from a single point. Mark off each line at the same distance from this point and connect the marks by a line. Then compare the length of the circumference with that of the straight lines radiating from the central point (Figure 15.3, Diagram 1). The comparison between circumference to straight line will always yield the same ratio $2\pi = 6.28$, irrespective of the size of the circle. (This ratio was trigonometrically derived in Chapter 6, Table 6.1 and Figure 6.4.)

What would happen if the same method is applied on the curved surface of a sphere? Without knowledge of the three dimensions of the globe, the distances would have to be marked off on the curved surface as if it was an even plane. Instead of a stiff straight-line ruler, a flexible ruler or a string could be used to mark the equidistant endpoints in all directions. On connecting the endpoints, the circumference of this circle will not be 6.28 times as long as the radial distance, but shorter. That is because in a two-dimensional world the lines radiate from the central point (the pole) down the curved sides of the sphere (Figure 15.3, Diagram 2).

To illustrate the difference in measuring radius and circumference in two- and three-dimensional space, assume that the globe or sphere has a radius $r_3 = 1$ ($r_3$ stands for the smaller radius in three dimensions) so that the circumference at the equator of the sphere measures $2\pi r_3 = 6.28$. If rational creatures living in two-dimensional space and unaware of a third dimension were to slide down the globe and measure the radius $R_2$ in two-dimensional space they could do so by stretching a rope over the surface from the pole down. They would find that the two-dimensional radius is $R_2 = 1.57$ or 1.57 times as large as the three-dimensional radius $r_3$. That is to say the excess of $R_2$ over $r_3$ is 0.57. It shows that circles measured in two- or three-dimensional spaces differ in radius and size of area (Figure 15.3, Diagram 3).[29]

From this illustration several conclusions can be drawn. On two-dimensional curved surfaces the geometry is not the same as on a three-dimensional surface. On curved surfaces, the three angles of a triangle will not add up to 180°. And the area of a circle formed by the equator of a sphere will not match the larger two-dimensional surface on the sphere. This illustrates how measures of a three-dimensional curvature are reflected in a two-dimensional world.

## Step into the Fourth Dimension

Einstein's theory of relativity is four-dimensional—the three dimensions of space (i.e., width, height, and depth) plus the one dimension for time. Following the same line of thought it is conceivable to gain an impression of a four-dimensional world from a three-dimensional perspective. Even though it is not obvious what a four-dimensional world would look like, it follows from the preceding discussion that the radius of a four-dimensional curvature is likely to differ from that of a three-dimensional one.[30]

As explained in Appendix A of this chapter, the formula for it specifies the algebraic ratio of a three- to a four-dimensional radius $R_3/r_4$. From the previous example, it would follow that the numerical value of this ratio can be expected to be greater than 1.0. Einstein's formula of the excess of $R_3$ over $r_4$ is shown in Equation 15.1. It implies that the radius excess depends on Newton's gravitational constant, sharply reduced by the term $3c^2$, and enlarged by the mass $M$. Applying this formula, Feynman estimated the excess radius for the Earth at 1.5 millimeters or approximately 1/17 of an inch. Because of the Earth's (relatively) small mass and radius, the excess is too small to detect. And even then it gives only information about the average curvature and not about local variations of the mass. Accommodating such local variations, however, is a key factor of the General Theory of Relativity.

For the time being the problem of excess curvature is set aside and the variations in curved surfaces are more closely examined.

Equation 15.1: Einstein's Equation of Radius Excess of Three over Four Dimensions[31]

$$\text{Radius Excess} \;=\; R_3 - r_4 \;=\; \frac{G}{3c^2} \times M$$

where     $G$ = *Newton's gravitational constant*

           $c$ = *velocity of light*

         $M$ = *mass of matter inside a sphere*

$$M \;=\; \frac{4\pi\rho\, r^3}{3} \quad \text{and where}$$

$\rho$ = *density of matter inside the sphere.*

*Vectors*

Chapter 12 showed how Newton explained the shape of planetary orbits. Kepler had described the orbit of Mars and other planets as elliptical, a drastic break away from the circular orbits of antiquity and even those of Copernicus and Galileo. Newton uncovered how gravity forced the planets to trace out this elliptical course. He showed how the Sun's gravitational force redirected the planet's motion, from straight (recti-linear) to orbital (curvilinear) motion. According to Newton the shape of planetary orbits was dictated by the size and direction of the force resulting, at each instant, from the combined inertial and gravitational forces (Chapter 12, Figure 12.1).

Technically, the size of the resultant force or vector came from the addition of two components. In Newton's explanation the inertial and gravitational forces were the component vectors, and the resultant force directed a planet toward the Sun. Graphically, vector components can be added by what is known as the parallelogram rule of addition.[32] As illustrated in Figure 15.4, Diagrams 1 and 2, the diagonal vector $V$ represents the resultant force of two component vectors $V_1$ and $V_2$.

*Tensors*

Einstein wanted to find a precise geometric expression for his idea of gravitational fields in space. As long as all motion was rectilinear at constant speeds, the Special Theory of Relativity applied. But now he wanted to deal with motion and gravity in a curvilinear field. This he did by tensor analysis. A tensor is an abstract mathematical concept used for transforming one set of curved coordinates into another. It is a generalization of the vector concept. There are many different types of tensors. The number of tensor components varies with the number of dimensions and the metric properties of higher dimensional structures. In Einstein's General Theory of Relativity the metric tensor had 10 components to describe the differences in space-time intervals. His curvature tensor has 20 components to account for the deviation of space-time from flatness.[33]

The central problem of the General Theory of Relativity was that neither the differences in the spatial coordinates could be measured directly by a standard measuring rod nor the differences in the time coordinates by a standard clock. Einstein wanted to describe the laws of nature in such a way that he obtained the same result in all coordinate systems. He wrote: "The general laws of nature are to be expressed by equations which hold good for all systems of coordinates, that is, are covariant with respect to any substitution whatever."[34] Einstein called it the "requirement of general co-variance." It is reminiscent of the earlier illustration (Figure 14.4) of distances in two- and three-dimensional coordinate systems of the Special Theory of Relativity. To meet this requirement in the General Theory of Relativity Einstein resorted to tensor analysis (Figure 15.4). He worked on it for nearly 10 years. Only a greatly simplified account of some of the underlying ideas is presented here.

*Gaussian Coordinates*

In a popular exposition of his theory, Einstein refers the reader to Gaussian co-ordinates.[35] Named after Carl Friedrich Gauss, the co-ordinates form a non-rigid system of reference points that could rest on top of an uneven surface like a tightly woven net. Each knot of the net represents the intersection of two Gaussian coordinates (Figure

15.5, Diagrams 1 and 2). The net can be deformed and bent to make contact with an uneven surface, but it cannot be torn and the links from one mesh to the next cannot be changed in length within a particular system. For example, if two lines intersect they retain this property and the length of any segment remains the same no matter how the net is deformed. Hence the distance between two adjacent points, measured along the surface, does not change.[36] Unlike the rectilinear coordinate system with reference lines at right angles to each other, the Gaussian coordinates measure neither length nor angle. Any point in such a system must be related to the intersections of the coordinate system. The points are ordered by consecutive numbers.[37]

To illustrate, a system of x- and y-coordinates is shown in Figure 15.5.[38] From the geometric constructs (Figure 15.5, Diagrams 3 to 6), Gauss derived the Generalized Pythagorean Theorem, which defines the distance on a curved surface as shown in Equation 2.

Equation 15.2 : The Generalized Pythagorean Theorem

*As illustrated in Diagram 5 of Figure 15.5, this theorem can be written as*

$$ds^2 = g_{11}\, dx^2 + 2\, g_{12}\; dx\; dy + g_{22}\, dy_2$$

*where the terms ds, dx, and dy are very small line segments called differentials. The terms and $g_{11}$, $g_{12}$, and $g_{22}$ are the metric coefficients.*

If the metric coefficients are known for every mesh of the net covering the uneven surface, the true distance from a point $P_1$ to any arbitrary point $P_2$ on the surface can be calculated provided the Gaussian coordinates are given. Although the coordinates can be chosen arbitrarily so that one network is characterized by the metric coefficients $g_{11}$, $g_{12}$, and $g_{22}$ and another by $g^*_{11}$, $g^*_{12}$, and $g^*_{22}$, they can be transformed so that both sets of coefficients yield exactly the same distance $P_1 P_2$ (Figure 15.5, Diagram 6). Gauss proved that the curvature can be defined by metric coefficients so that the distance between any two distant points is invariant to a change in the coordinates. Some restrictions do apply. Among them, the coordinate net must cover the whole surface without gaps and no point on the surface is covered more than once.

The metric coefficients could be either constants or functions. Although there are no straight lines on a curved surface, the lines that connect the points on the coordinate net are the "straightest."[39] They measure the "shortest" distance between any two points as the sum of small measurable segments $s_1$, $s_2$, $s_3$, ... $s_n$ that are joined end to end. The size of these segments can be computed from the Generalized Pythagorean theorem if the coefficients $g_{11}$, $g_{12}$, and $g_{22}$ are known. The segments' size will vary with the weave of the coordinate net. However, irrespective of such variations, the distance between two points on the net, as computed by tensor analysis, will be shorter than any other arbitrary line drawn across the same surface (Figure 15.5, Diagram 6).

This shortest distance is called a *geodesic* or *geodetic*. It is the minimum length between two points in mathematically defined space.[40] For example, on a spherical surface the geodesic lines are formed by the surface edge of the plane that passes through the center of the sphere (Figure 15.6, Diagram 1). On other surfaces they may be defined by more complex expressions. Comparable to a straight line in Euclidean geometry, the geodesics are the shortest possible path between two points on a curved surface (Figure 15.6, Diagram 2).

*Riemannian Coordinates*

To formulate the laws of general relativity Einstein needed to work with a four-dimensional geometry: three dimensions for space and one for time. The four-dimensions might be pictured graphically as in Figure 15.7,[41] but their logic is algebraically described with greater precision.

Gauss had formulated the basic idea for two-dimensional surfaces. Riemann, his successor at the University of Göttingen, generalized it to three and more dimensions. In later years, Tullio Levi-Cevita developed the technique further. When applied to two dimensions the tensor analysis depends on four $g_{ij}$ coefficients, when applied to four dimensions on sixteen $g_{ij}$ coefficients. When the coefficients are arranged in rows and columns (as shown in this chapter's Appendix, Equation A15.2), there is some duplication, since the coefficients above the diagonal values $g_{11}, g_{22}$ , ..., $g_{ii}$ mirror those below the diagonal row of coefficients. For example, in the case of two dimensions $g_{12} = g_{21}$ so that the summation consists of only three different coefficients $g_{11}$, $g_{12}$, and $g_{22}$. In three dimensions it consists of six different coefficients, and in four dimensions it consists of 10 such coefficients. Under appropriate conditions the value of each of the coefficients can be computed.[42]

With the goal of incorporating gravity in the model, Einstein derived the Tensor Equation of General Relativity. It represents the different configurations of space-time, mass, and energy. The formula[43] for it is represented by Equation 15.3.[44] It appears to be simple but is derived by tensor calculus, an esoteric and difficult subject, well beyond Einstein's Special Theory and well beyond the scope of this book.

Equation 15.3:  Einstein's Tensor Field  Equation of General Relativity

$R_{ij}$ = *tensor describing a specific dimension*

$_i$ = *subscript for dimensions 1, 2, 3, or 4* [45]

$_j$ = *subscript for dimensions 1, 2, 3, or 4*

$\kappa$ = *proportionality factor which varies with the choice of the measurement standard (e.g., centimeters, grams, and seconds)*

$T_{ij}$ = *energy momentum tensor*

$g_{ij}$ = *tensor describing differential coefficients of metric components*

$T$ = *scalar* $T_\mu^{\ \mu}$ *for mass and energy components at a given space* <sub>time</sub>

$$R_{ij} = \kappa \ (Tij - \tfrac{1}{2} g_{ij} T)$$

*The left-hand side of the equation refers to the curvature at a given point in space time. On the  right-hand side, the factor* $\kappa$, *is a constant that allows for the specific units of  measurement  chosen for the remaining terms.* $T_{ij}$ *is  the  energy component of matter and the gravitational field and the half* $g_{ij}$ *represents the metric reflecting the variations in curvature of space-time*

The Einstein Tensor $R_{ij}$ of Equation 15.3 is related at every point of space–time to the mass–energy tensor. It stands for the distribution of energy and matter and involves the metric coefficients encountered  in Equation 15.2.

## Curved Space-Time

By applying the method of tensor calculus, perforce only sketchily explained here, Einstein arrived at the unique results of the General Theory of Relativity. First to the key question: is space really curved? Earlier attempts to measure any astronomic curvature had failed. From his calculations, Einstein concluded that space must be curved and that the massive stars and other celestial objects are the underlying cause of the curvature.

Physicist Richard Feynman (1918–1988) showed that the difference between the three-and four-dimensional curvature is directly proportional to the mass of matter inside the sphere (as suggested in this chapter's Appendix, Equation A15.4).[46] Applied to Earth, its radius measured in conventional three-dimensional space would shrink by about 1.5 millimeters due to its curvature in four-dimensional space. As pointed out earlier, this kind of estimate refers to the average curvature. The local curvature would vary with the altitude from the Earth's surface. At any rate, the 1.5 millimeter difference is so minute that it defies empirical verification.

### *The Twin Paradox*

Even before Einstein completed his General Theory some questions were being raised. One of them was the so-called "twin paradox." What would happen if an astronaut were to travel at speeds close to light. Would the astronaut age more slowly? According to Einstein's theory, aging would slow. If an astronaut were to return from a five-year high-speed trip in outer space, on his return the astronaut's twin on Earth would be older than the space traveler.

Instead of one twin leaving the other behind, wouldn't the result have been the same if both had moved at equal speeds away from each other? But if not, should not both twins have aged at the same rate? Very likely their difference in age would not have been the result of speed alone. According to Einstein's General Theory, the acceleration of the craft would have made a difference too.

Assume for the moment that a spacecraft sits on the launchpad in position 1 (Figure 15.8).[47] At regular time intervals a laser light flashes from the back to the front of the cargo bay. At rest, it takes the light exactly four units of time (say, four one-millionths of a second) to traverse the distance from clock B in the back to clock A in front. As the spacecraft takes off, it accelerates very rapidly. At the end of the first time interval the craft arrives at position 2. The clock at the back has ticked off four units. Yet the clock in front ticked off only two units—because of the high acceleration of the craft the light flash went only half the way. The same happens when the craft accelerates further and reaches position 3. And it will happen again after each successive time interval. As the craft continues to accelerate, the extra distance will be added each time, and clock A in front will fall further behind clock B in the back. It follows that clock A runs slower than clock B.[48]

Since the astronaut aboard the spacecraft was exposed to accelerative forces and high-speed motion, the time on the spacecraft slowed. For the twin on Earth it did not. The astronaut on board the craft will age, therefore, more slowly than his twin on Earth.

Admittedly, this is merely a thought experiment and not proof that it must be so. Yet, Einstein insisted that these events followed directly from time dilation and the principle of equivalence of gravitation and acceleration. He unerringly pursued his goal. Not all in the scientific community agreed with him. Some argued that the rate of heartbeat, cell growth, and other life processes are controlled by the body's own clock and will continue to do so at the same rate under moderate acceleration. High acceleration would distort these rates and cause bodily harm. Indeed, if the life processes adjusted to very high speeds, the crunch would come later, when on return to Earth the force of deceleration would make the rates accelerate to the normal rate and cause more bodily harm.[49] It seems that this issue can only be resolved by future experimentation just as some other aspects of Einstein's theory were tested in later years.

*Einstein's Three Tests*

The General Theory of Relativity has been confirmed many times. When Einstein completed it in 1915, he suggested three tests for empirical verification:

1. The gravitational red-shift,

2.  The precession of the perihelion$_g$ of Mercury, and
3.  The solar deflection of starlight.

*1. Gravitational red-shift*

Stars are distant suns. Some of them are much greater in mass than our own. Einstein postulated that the effect of a stronger gravitational field could be shown in a visible shift of the star's spectrum. This shift has something to do with a change in the frequency of light waves. It is a phenomenon similar to the changing pitch of sound waves we hear when, for example, a train whistles by.

That the frequency of sound waves depends on the motion of the source of sound was first discovered by Christian Doppler (1803–1853), an Austrian physicist and professor of experimental physics at the University of Vienna. Long before him, it was known that the pitch of sound varied with frequency. At the time of Galileo (1564–1642), the calibrating of musical instruments with tuning forks suggested that the higher the pitch, the more rapid the vibrations of the fork and the greater the frequency of the sound waves. Doppler discovered that the frequency of sound waves is greater when the source of the sound is moving toward the point of the observer, and smaller when moving away from it.

Although his earlier writings were on mathematics, in 1842 Doppler published a paper titled "On the Colored Light of Double Stars." [50] He theorized that light coming from a star should vary with the star's velocity relative to the Earth. If a star or a galaxy moved at high speed away from Earth, their characteristic blue light emitted by helium should turn yellow and, at still greater speeds, turn red or even infrared (Figure 15.9). [51]

It has already been shown how acceleration can slow down time. A higher rate of acceleration would make for a greater slow-down. Einstein's Principle of Equivalence implied that the gravitational force in the neighborhood of a celestial body slows down time, and the more massive the body and the greater the gravitational force, the greater the slowdown of time. In line with this, Einstein correctly predicted that spectral lines emitted by atoms near a large mass would have lower frequencies, causing them to shift away from the high-frequency blue end of the spectrum toward the lower frequencies of yellow and red. Both of these aspects were special cases of the more general proposition that all processes near a large mass slow down (Figure 15.9, Diagram 3).[52]

Just like Newton's law of gravitational force, the change in spectral frequency is inversely proportional to the distance from the center of a large mass. The greater the distance from it, the smaller the gravitational red–shift from the blue end of the spectrum. Conversely, the smaller the distance and greater the mass of the object, the greater is the gravitational force and the greater is the gravitational red-shift. An example of tensor analysis of the shift in spectral frequency is given in Appendix B, Equation B15.1 of this chapter.

## 2. Precession of Mercury's perihelion

The perihelion refers to the point of an elliptical orbit closest to the Sun's center. Some 50 years before Einstein's General Theory of Relativity, astronomers had become aware that the perihelion of the elliptical orbit of the planet Mercury was slowly advancing in the direction of its orbit around the Sun (Figure 15.10). In the nineteenth century astronomers had shown that the planet's precession, amounted to about 5600 seconds or to about 1.56° of arc per century.[53] The most careful computations of Newton's law of gravitation, combined with the effects of perturbations caused by other planets, accounted for 5557 of the 5600 seconds per century. This left 43 seconds or about 1% of 1° per century unexplained. A discrepancy of this size may seem minute but it is at least 100 times as large as the admissible error of today's astronomical observations.

In 1916, Einstein derived the theoretical value of the advance of the perihelion of the planet Mercury. He used tensor analysis to tackle this discrepancy. The results of Einstein's analysis are shown in Appendix B of this chapter. For him, the discovery of the unprecedented match between theory and observation was the ultimate confirmation of his theory. Emotionally it was a great moment. As his colleague and biographer Abraham Pais described it:

> Nature had spoken to him. He had to be right. "For a few days, I was beside myself with joyous excitement." Later he told Fokker

his discovery had given him palpitations of the heart. What he
told de Haas is even more profoundly significant: When he saw that
his calculation agreed with the unexplained astronomical
observation, he had the feeling that something actually snapped in
him.[54]

Although for Einstein this confirmation of the General Theory may have
been the greatest triumph, his popular fame came from the third test of
verification, the solar deflection of starlight.

### 3. *The solar deflection of starlight*

Newton's corpuscular theory of light was still in vogue long after his
death.[55] In 1801 the German mathematician and surveyor Johann Georg
von Soldner (1776–1833) postulated that starlight could be deflected by
the force of gravitation. In estimating the degree of deflection he treated
the movement of a ray of light like that of a comet approaching the Sun at
the speed of light. Like the orbit of a planet, the hyperbolic orbit of a comet
does not depend on its mass. Following the same approach, the estimate
of the deflection of the light is independent of the photons' mass.[56] Based
on Newton's corpuscular theory of light Soldner estimated that the gravity
of the Sun would deflect the light from a star by .87 arc seconds$_g$. His
estimate was strictly based on Newton's theory of gravity. Einstein decided
to estimate the degree of deflection based on his own General Theory of
Relativity.

In switching over to Einstein's analysis, a thought experiment may
be helpful. Suppose a laser is mounted on one side of a rocket-powered
space laboratory. It is set to flash its light against the opposite wall. When
the rocket engines are shut off, the laboratory floats in space and the light
flashes straight across to the opposite wall.[57] When the engines are turned
on, the space-laboratory accelerates, and the light photons$_g$ no longer
strike the opposite wall at the same spot but follow a curved path
(Figure 15.11).[58] Convinced that the Principle of Equivalence applied,
Einstein believed the gravitational field of a massive body such as the
Sun would bend the light toward the source of the gravitational force.

When Einstein included the effects of the curvature of space-time in
his computations, the deflection of starlight by the Sun increased from

Soldner's estimate of .87 to 1.75 arc seconds. To verify it by empirical observation posed a problem. It meant comparing the position of a star with and without the intervening mass of the Sun (Figure 15.12). The effects of the light's deflection were difficult to observe because the Sun overwhelms the light of the stars. Astronomers had to wait for the next opportune moment when the Sun was blocked out by a lunar eclipse. A most favorable eclipse occurred on May 29, 1919. Two British expeditions were ready for the astronomical observations. One team went to Sobral in Northern Brazil and the other team went to the West African Isle of Principe in the Gulf of Guinea. The Brazilian team found that the visual telescopic image of the stars had moved by an average of 1.98 arc seconds and the African team estimated that they had moved by 1.6 seconds of arc, the two groups averaging 1.79 seconds of arc. Their estimates came closer to Einstein's prediction of 1.86 arc seconds than to Soldner's of 0.87 arc seconds. Astronomers were prepared to accept it as proof in favor of Einstein's General Theory of Relativity.

In later years, observations were scattered around the results of those of the first two expeditions (Table 15.1). The best among them had an error of ±0.10 arc seconds. Others were not nearly as precise. Astronomers had hoped that, eventually, superior optical techniques would yield better

Table 15.1: Empirical Evidence of the Deflection of Starlight by the Gravitational Force of the Sun

| Location | Date | Results ± Error |
|----------|------|-----------------|
| Australia | Sept. 21, 1922 | 1.77 ± 0.40 |
| Sumatra | May 9, 1929 | 2.24 ± 0.10 |
| U.S.S.R. | June 19, 1936 | 2.73 ± 0.31 |
| Brazil | May 20, 1947 | 2.01 ± 0.27 |
| Sudan | Febr. 25, 1952 | 1.70 ± 0.10 |

Sources: Jeramy Bernstein (1996), *A Theory for Everything,* p. 40 and *Encyclopedia Britannica.*

estimates, but they never did. Instead, radio astronomy$_g$ delivered estimates of far greater precision. In 1975 astronomers observed the deflection of radio sources over a period of a whole month and obtained an estimate of 1.763 ± 0.016. All these estimates of the deflection of starlight by the Sun were roughly twice the size of those derived from Newton's theory of gravity. Astronomers accepted these empirical findings as convincing confirmation of the validity of Einstein's theory.[59]

**International Fame**

During the first half of World War I Einstein had lived like a bachelor. Like Newton he had paid little attention to meals or sleep. By 1917 he was mentally and physically exhausted. He had taken the first steps toward a divorce but his wife, Mileva, resisted. Einstein became very depressed and sick. Many years of overwork, the stress of a senseless and cruel war, the breakdown of his marriage, and his unhealthy lifestyle had taken their toll. Within a short period of time, he lost 56 pounds. Diagnosed with an ulcer and jaundice, he spent much of his time in bed. That changed when Elsa Löwenthal entered his life. Her motherly care brought him back to health. In November of 1918 the war ended. His divorce from Mileva was formalized. He had agreed to give her and their two sons the proceeds from the Nobel Prize, if and when he won it. For several years scientists had nominated him for the award and he was assured to receive it sooner or later.[60]

*Lecture Tours*

In the spring of 1919, Einstein married Elsa. He lived quietly with her and her two daughters in Berlin.[61] Now 40, he had revolutionized physicists' view of the universe. The *Times* in London wrote of "Revolution in science, a New Theory of the Universe, and the Overthrow of Newtonian Ideas." After years of reporting on the tragic events of war, the tabloids snatched up the ideas of warped space, light traveling in curves, and Newton's gravity being replaced by Einstein's curved space. Suddenly, the journalistic focus had shifted from the senselessness of politics to the rationale of science. The president of the Royal Society in England had acclaimed Einstein's theory "as perhaps the most momentous product of human thought."[62] Yet, scientists and journalists ran into trouble explaining it.The legend of Einstein, the incomprehensible genius was born. Revolutionary as it was, Einstein's theory was an extension of Newton's that became critical under extreme conditions: at speeds close to light, at the release of atomic power,and under the impact of the ultimate forces in the universe.

Einstein made easy copy for the press. Wherever he traveled, he was interviewed. Invited to lecture on relativity he spoke in Leiden (The Netherlands) and lectured on his theories of relativity in Prague (Czechoslovakia) and Vienna (Austria).[63] He was asked to tour the United States. Enthusiastically welcomed on his arrival, Einstein spoke at Columbia University and visited Harvard University. At Princeton University he was lauded as the new Columbus of Science and given an honorary degree.[64] For the next three years he continued on the lecture circuit, journeying through Europe, South America, the Middle East and Far East.

*Nobel Prize*

While in Shanghai (China) a cable reached him that he had been awarded the 1921 Nobel Prize for his theoretical work on the photoelectric effect.[65] Relativity was not mentioned. From the outset, very few had claimed to understand it. Even the president of the British Royal Society, Joseph Thomson (1856–1940), a Nobel Prize winner (1906) and Master of Trinity College, admitted confusion when he stated that "Perhaps Einstein has made the greatest achievement in human thought, but no one has yet succeeded in stating in clear language what the theory of Einstein really is." [66] Sir Oliver Lodge (1851–1940) of Birmingham University considered it repugnant to common sense.[67] Among American critics Nicola Tesla (1856–1943), a pioneer in the applications of electricity, called atomic energy an illusion. Yet, in spite of all the critics, or perhaps because of them, by 1919 Einstein had attained world fame.[68]

In Germany, opinions of Einstein's work varied just as widely, but there an additional element entered the debate. A caption in the *Berliner Illustrierte Zeitung* described him as, "A new figure in world history whose investigations signify a complete revision of nature, and are on par with insights of Copernicus, Kepler, and Newton."[69] Others countered with criticisms. Einstein, along with Jewish and non-Jewish supporters, had begun to help Jews who had fled from the anti-Semitism of Poland, Hungary and Rumania, to Germany. Amid the economic turmoil in post-war Germany, calls were heard to stem the influx of Jews by deporting them. Einstein objected to this on humanitarian grounds. Also he had publicly urged an investigation of German war crimes. Anti-Semitism raised its ugly head.

Among the anti-Semitists was the physicist and 1905 Nobel Prize winner Philipp Lenard.[70] He and others spouted anti-Semitic insults. Looking for a scapegoat for Germany's defeat in war, the rampant monetary inflation and economic malaise of the post-war years, they were the forerunners of the Nazis. With the zeal of demagogues they denounced Einstein's theory as a publicity stunt and accused him of plagiarism. Rumours circulated that Einstein, because of these ugly attacks, wished to leave Germany. But Einstein stated that Berlin was the place to which he felt most closely bound and expressed his sincere gratitude for the support he had received from his colleagues and many admirers in Germany. He did not wish to follow a call to a foreign country unless changing conditions would compel him to do so.[71]

During the 1920s, Einstein searched for the laws governing the relationship between electromagnetism$_g$ and gravitation. Since the atomic model was in some respects similar to the planetary system, he hoped to find a mathematical expression for the physics of everything in the universe, from the cohesion of subatomic particles to the gravitational fields of the universe. This was Einstein's search for a unified field theory.

In the meantime, Max Planck's (German physicist, 1858–1947) Quantum Theory$_g$ had evolved under Neils Henrik Bohr's (Danish atomic physicist, 1885–1962) leadership to include Heisenberg's Uncertainty Principle (Chapter 16 will describe Quantum Theory in more detal). According to this principle, speed and position of subatomic particles could not be determined simultaneously and that, in turn, lowered predictability at the subatomic level. Quantum mechanics relied on statistical methods of probability and complex matrix algebra. While these techniques delivered results, Einstein rejected the probability approach because he believed in the classical precision of absolute laws. His feelings were conveyed in the phrase "God does not play dice." To this, the quantum theorist Stephen Hawking (1942– ) replied, "But all evidence indicates that God is an inveterate gambler and He throws the dice on every possible occasion."[72]

## Last Years in Germany

As early as 1929, the year of Einstein's 50th birthday, the Prussian Academy published his first version of a unified field theory. Again it caused a sensation in the press but because of shortcomings it could only be called a preliminary version.

Other disappointments followed. In Palestine the Arabs fought the newly arrived Jewish settlers. In Germany the collapse of the economy was worse than in the rest of Europe. Oppressive war reparations and trade restrictions imposed by the Treaty of Versailles aggravated Germany's economic situation. Rampant monetary inflation wiped out the savings of the middle class. Germany's government was faltering. Looking for alternatives, German voters swelled the ranks of the communists and nationalists. Promising law and order, Adolf Hitler subdued street violence with his storm troopers. Gaining fertile ground through anti-Versailles and anti-communist rhetoric, he reinforced his position by raising the specter of Marxian communism. He blamed its spread on international Semitism. The 1929 stock market crash in the United States foreshadowed the worldwide economic crisis. With the onset of the Great Depression, unemployment grew to unprecedented high levels. Germany's economy deteriorated further. Hitler and his Nazis were on their way to power.[73]

For Einstein sorrow struck on a personal level. In Mileva's household, Einstein's second son Eduard, born in 1910, was the center of attention. In 1929 he went to study medicine at the University of Zurich. A great admirer of Freud, he intended to become a psychiatrist. At university he became severely depressed, possibly because of an unhappy love affair. In letters to his father he wrote hysterically that he hated him. It appeared that Eduard's intense feelings toward his father were a mixture of worship and rejection. He blamed him for ruining his life. Mileva tried to care for Eduard at home but in late 1932 he was admitted to the Burghölzli Mental Institution and treated for schizophrenia. His sickness could not be cured. Einstein was deeply affected by his son's illness. He had hoped to see Eduard once more but it did not happen.[74]

In Germany, Hitler's party gained power in January 1933. Although Einstein's pacifism may have been an utopian illusion, he had realistically anticipated the trend toward a political dictatorship of Germany. He had visited the United States during the winter of 1930–1931 and returned again the next two winters. After some negotiations he accepted an appointment at Princeton University beginning in October 1933.[75] Einstein passed his last weeks in Europe at Le Cocque sur Mer, a beautiful ocean resort in Belgium. Located close to the German border, Einstein's life was endangered. Within days of gaining power, the Nazis had assumed absolute control over the press. Systematically and brutally, they crushed any opposition by whatever means necessary. With a bounty on Einstein's head, Nazi fanatics could easily have slipped across the border to kill him. The Belgian government assigned two bodyguards to protect him day and night.[76] In October of 1933 Einstein, his wife Elsa and his secretary Helen Dukas were taken by private yacht from Belgium to England. From there, they embarked on the ship that took them to the United States.

**In America**

When Einstein arrived in Princeton he had aged. As a friend wrote, "It was as if something had deadened him. He sat in a chair in our place, twisting his white hair in his fingers and talking dreamily about everything under the Sun. He was not laughing anymore."[77] Toward the end of November he gave his first impressions of Princeton in a letter to Queen Elizabeth of Belgium:

> Princeton is a wonderful little spot, a quaint and ceremonious village of puny demigods on stilts. Yet, by ignoring certain social conventions, I have been able to create for myself an atmosphere conducive to study and free from distraction. Here, the people who compose what is called "society" enjoy even less freedom than their counterparts in Europe. Yet, they seem unaware of this

restriction since their way of life tends to inhibit personality development from childhood.[78]

It is strange that he spoke of societal restrictions after coming from a regimented society.

At Princeton, Einstein missed the intimate and regular association with the great European scientists. In Berlin he had attended weekly seminars and colloquia, and had·relished the sessions with other physicists. At Princeton, his fellow professors were mostly mathematicians and only one had worked on relativity. The absence of colleagues working in his field, problems with working in another language, and the growing differences with the proponents of quantum theory scientifically isolated him.[79]

Nonetheless, a routine evolved in his daily work. His assistants dropped by his residence in the morning, walked with him to the institute, and on the way discussed the state of world affairs. At the office they planned the work for the day. Mostly they focused on issues related to the search for a unified field theory that would combine the celestial macroforces with the subatomic forces at the microlevel. Einstein was often drawn away from it, be it to attend speaking functions, give an interview for a school paper, talk to a religious group, or participate in a fund-raising event for Jewish refugees. He auctioned off some of his books and manuscripts to add to the funds.[80]

In 1935 Einstein applied for American citizenship. His son Hans Albert came to the United States in 1937. When Hitler intensified the persecution of Jews in Germany and Mussolini adopted the same policy in Italy, Einstein tried to have U.S. immigration restrictions eased. But it was to no avail. The American policy was so restrictive that more than 400,000 places under the immigration quota for Nazi-dominated countries remained unfilled.[81]

## Atomic Energy

In 1938, Niels Bohr came to Princeton with the news that the physicists Otto Hahn (1879–1968) and Lise Meitner (1878–1968) had split the atom in Germany and that nuclear fission was possible. Leo Szilard (1898–1964), a Jewish immigrant from Hungary, had predicted the possibility of a nuclear chain reaction nearly five years earlier. With Germany already restricting the exports of uranium ore from Czechoslovakia, scientists believed that the construction of an atomic bomb was possible. Einstein, Szilard, and Teller composed a letter to U.S. President Rosevelt warning of the potential danger of a superbomb. After some delays, a federal committee finally recommended that the U.S. government go ahead with atomic research. President Roosevelt signed the bill for funding the research (Manhattan Project). It was November 1940. In July 1945, the Americans detonated the first atomic bomb in the New Mexico desert.[82]

## Unified Field Theory

Although Einstein's 1905 equation $E = m\,c^2$ formed the theoretical basis of the bomb, he himself did not actively participate in the U.S. atomic bomb project. Robert Oppenheimer was appointed the scientific director of it. He guided the development of the research to its completion. During and after the war, Einstein continued with his own research on the unified field theory. Like many other scientists of the younger generation, Robert Oppenheimer had little patience with Einstein's critical approach to the discoveries in quantum theory. He had once called Einstein "completely cuckoo."

Leading physicists of the older generation, among them Einstein and Planck, remained skeptical, reluctant to accept the tenets of quantum theory.[83] Not so Einstein's friend Max Born. They agreed to disagree. In a discussion with Born Einstein put it this way:

> You believe in God who plays dice, and I in complete law and order in a world which objectively exists, and which I, in a wildly speculative way, am trying to capture. I hope that someone will discover a more realistic way, or rather a more tangible basis than it has been my lot to find. Even the great initial success of the quantum theory does not make me believe in the fundamental dice-game, although I am well aware that our younger colleagues interpret this as a consequence of senility.[84]

After more than 20 years of research on a unified field theory, Einstein was discouraged.[85] At the time of his death in 1955 quantum theory reigned, yet the renaissance of relativity was coming. In 1965 astrophysicists discovered the microwave radiation that pervades the universe. In 1967 the first pulsars were discovered and shown to be neutron stars.[86] These discoveries started the search for black holes which had been considered bizarre objects predicted by Einstein's General Theory of Relativity. With the aid of his theory, physicists worked out the big-bang history of the universe in 1983. In 1995, in Boulder Colorado, researchers produced a new form of matter by cooling atoms to near absolute zero. Some 70 years earlier, this possibility had been predicted in the Bose-Einstein Condensation Theory. And today a leading physicist, Stephen Hawking, believes that a unifying principle of gravity and electromagnetism may well exist. The Princeton physicist John Wheeler is of the opinion that the superstring theory (see final chapter) could lead to a Grand Unified Theory or even the kind of "superquantum theory" that Einstein was searching for.[87]

As for one of the world's greatest minds, Einstein quietly passed away in his sleep in the early morning hours of April 18, 1955. As Niels Bohr put it: "He gave us a world picture with a unity and harmony surpassing the boldest dreams of the past." [88] In his later years Einstein had searched relentlessly for a unified theory that would describe all forces of nature in a unified framework. Driven by a passionate vision that such a theory would reveal the ultimate wonder of the universe, he never saw his vision realized.

## APPENDIXES

### Appendix A: Selected Characteristics of Curved Space

Since stepping from one dimension into a higher dimension is not an everyday experience, Einstein's idea of four dimensions appears to be a bit of a mystery. In a world of three dimensions objects are commonly described by their width, height, and depth. In a flat, two-dimensional world objects would have only width and depth but no height. It is conceivable, however, that in a two-dimensional world some three-dimensional objects could be recognized by their unique geometric properties. For example, according to Euclidean plane geometry a circle with a radius *R=1* has a circumference of $2\pi = 6.283$ (Figure 15.3, Diagram 1). A circle drawn on a three-dimensional sphere with the same-size radius measured from the sphere's pole down its sides, has a smaller circumference (Figure 15.3, Diagram 2). Thus, a change from one dimension to another can be described by geometry. In switching from two- to three-dimensional space the numerical relation between radius and circumference is altered (Figure 15.3, Diagram 3).

Based on this result, it would be reasonable to find that a switch from the conventional three dimensions to a world of four dimensions would also be reflected in geometry. An analogous ratio between a measured and actual circle is outlined in Appendix Equation A15.1. In Einstein's four-dimensional relativity theory, however, the derivation is more complex. As shown in earlier in Equation 15.1 of the text, the numerical value of the "excess" radius is conditioned by Newton's constant of gravity and the speed of light.

Equation A15.1: From Two to Three Dimensions, and From Three to Four Dimensions

*In Diagram 3 of Figure 15.3 the size of a two-imensional radius of a sphere was compared with its three-dimensional counterpart. To recapitulate, let*

$R_2$ = *radius of a circle in two-dimensional space*

$C_2 = 2\pi R_2$ = *circumference of a circle with radius* $R_2$

$r_3$ = *radius in three-dimensional space*

$C_3 = 2\pi r_3$ = *circumference of circle with radius* $r_3$

*Setting* $r_3 = 1$

$$\frac{C_2}{c_3} = \frac{2\pi R_2}{2\pi r_3} = \frac{R_2}{r_3} = \frac{1.57}{1} = 1.57$$

*This shows that the circumference in two-dimensional space is 1.57 times the size of its counterpart in three-dimensional space.*

*Following an analogous procedure, it is tempting to compare a three-dimensional sphere with a four-dimensional one. Recall that the surface area* *of a three-dimensional sphere of radius $R_3$ is*

$$A_3 = 4\pi R_3^2 = \text{surface area of three-dimensional sphere}$$

*then:* $\quad R_3^2 = \dfrac{A_3}{4\pi} \quad$ *or, equivalently,* $\quad R_3 = \sqrt{\dfrac{A_3}{4\pi}}.$

*The ratio of the radius of the three-dimensional sphere over the four-dimensional sphere, therefore, is*

$$\frac{R_3}{r_4} = \frac{1}{r_4}\sqrt{\frac{A_3}{4\pi}} = \frac{\sqrt{A_3}}{2\,r_4\,\sqrt{\pi}}$$

*This gives the algebraic expression for the ratio, but it does not reveal how large the four-dimensional radius would be. According to Einstein the excess radius is*

$$R_3 - r_4 = \sqrt{\frac{A_3}{4\pi}} - r_4 = \frac{G}{3c^2} \times M \quad \text{where} \quad M = \frac{4\pi\rho r^3}{3} \quad \text{and}$$

*where* $\quad G = \text{gravitational constant of Newton's theory}$
$\qquad\qquad c = \text{speed of light, and}$
$\qquad\qquad \rho = \text{the mass inside the sphere.}$

*This relation will be used later to describe the effect a relativistic four-dimensional radius will have on that of the Earth (Equation A15.4).*

## Curved Space-Time

Curvature in space can be accurately described by tensor calculus. In his Theory of General Relativity Einstein applied Riemann's tensor analysis. Gauss had developed a theory for the algebraic description of two-dimensional curved surfaces. Having studied under Gauss, Carl Georg Riemann generalized this theory to a tensor analysis of many dimensions.

The following gives an abbreviated and simplified description of the underlying principles.

Equation A15.2: From Two- to Many-Dimensioal Tensors

*As shown earlier in the text (Equation 15.2) and illustrated in Figure 15.5, the Generalized Pythagorean Theorem of two dimensions reads*

$$ds^2 = g_{11} dx^2 + 2g_{12} dx\, dy + g_{22} dy^2$$

*Alternatively, the expression can be written by naming the differentials $dx_1$, $dx_2$ and then replacing the equation by a double summation as in:*

$$ds^2 = g_{11} dx_1^{\,2} + 2g_{12} dx_1\, dx_2 + g_{22} dx_2^{\,2}$$

$$= \sum_{i=1}^{i=2} \sum_{j=1}^{j=2} g_{ij}\, dx_i\, dy_j$$

*where the metric $g_{ij}$ - coefficients can be arranged so*

$$
\begin{array}{cc}
g_{11} & g_{12} \\
g_{12} & g_{22}
\end{array}
$$

*These two-dimensional versions can be expanded to three dimensions as a summation or coefficient matrix as in*

$$ds^2 = \sum_{i=1}^{i=3} \sum_{j=1}^{j=3} g_{ij}\, dx_i\, dy_j$$

$$
\begin{array}{ccc}
g_{11} & g_{12} & g_{13} \\
g_{21} & g_{22} & g_{23} \\
g_{31} & g_{32} & g_{33}
\end{array}
$$

*and where $g_{ij} = g_{ji}$ , or to four dimensions as in*

$$ds^2 = \sum_{i=1}^{i=4} \sum_{j=1}^{j=4} g_{ij}\, dx_i\, dy_j$$

$$
\begin{array}{cccc}
g_{11} & g_{12} & g_{13} & g_{14}
\end{array}
$$

366

$$g_{21} \quad g_{22} \quad g_{23} \quad g_{24}$$
$$g_{31} \quad g_{32} \quad g_{33} \quad g_{34}$$
$$g_{41} \quad g_{42} \quad g_{43} \quad g_{44}$$

*where* $g_{ij} = g_{ji}$.

The set of $g_{gj}$-coefficients make up the metric tensors. Individual $g_{ij}$'s are the components of the metric tensor and their numerical values vary with curvature of the surface and the values of the coordinates. If the coordinates are changed then new coefficients can be deduced from the old ones by following a precise set of mathematical rules.[89]

In the Special Theory of Relativity Einstein described all rectilinear motion in four dimensions. As shown in Equation A14.8 and Table 14.1, Chapter 14, the concept of space-time interval can be defined similarly to Equation A15.3.[90]

Equation A15.3: A Fundamental Invariant: The Space-Time Interval

*From the Special Theory of Relativity it follows that*

$$t^2 - d^2 = t^2 - (x^2 + y^2 + z^2) = 1 = F$$

*where F is the fundamental invariant that can be rewritten as*

$$F = x^2 - c^2 t^2 \qquad or\ as$$

$$s^2 = (x^2 + y^2 + z^2) - c^2 t^2 \ \ and\ the\ interval\ as$$

$$s = \sqrt{(x^2 + y^2 + z^2) - c^2 t^2}.$$

*Whichever way it is written, the expression consists of the four dimensions x, y, z, and t, i.e, three for space and one for time.*

Also as shown in Equation A15.1, stepping from a dimension of lower order to one of higher order is reflected in the ratio of the radius to the circumference.

Feynman computed the impact on the Earth's radius that a step-up from the conventional three dimensions to Einstein's four dimensions would have.

Equation A15.4: Impact on Earth of Switch from Three to Four Dimensions

*If the difference between the radius of the curvature of a three-dimensional sphere and that of a four-dimensional one is denoted by $R_3 - r_4$, then according to Einstein (Equation A15.1), the following relation holds*

$$R_3 - r_4 = \sqrt{\frac{A}{4\pi}} - r_4 = \frac{G(M)}{3c^2} = \frac{G(4/3\,\pi\,r^3\rho)}{3c^2}$$

*where*    $R_3 = \sqrt{\dfrac{A}{4\pi}} =$ *radius of three-dimensional sphere*

$A =$ *corresponding surface area*

$\pi = 3.1415$

$\frac{4}{3}\pi\,r^3 =$ *volume of sphere*

$\rho =$ *density of matter inside the sphere*

$c =$ *speed of light*

$G =$ *Newton's gravitational force*

*Applied to Earth the values are*

$G/3c^2 = 25 \times 10^{-29}$ *per gram*

$M =$ *mass of the Earth at* $6 \times 10^{27}$ *grams*

*and, therefore:*

$$R_3 - r_4 = 6 \cdot 10^{27} \cdot 25 \cdot 10^{-29} = 150/100 = 1.5\ mm$$

This change-over from three to four dimensional space would result in an excess radius of 1.5 millimeters or roughly 1/17 of an inch. This is too small to be verified by observational methods.

## Appendix B: Einstein's Three Verifiable Tests of the Relativity Theory

1. The gravitational red-shift of spectral lines,
2. The precession of the perihelion of Mercury, and
3. The deflection of star light by the Sun's mass.

*1. The red-shift of spectral lines*

According to the General Theory of Relativity a strong gravitational force should lower the rate of vibration and therefore shift the spectrum of light toward the red. Astronomers have confirmed this phenomenon by observation of the companion star of Sirius.

When the gravitational field of a star is described by a coordinate system in which the star is not rotating but at rest, the mean velocity of atoms of the star's outer layer is zero. As a result of this simplifying assumption, the frequency of the spectral line can be expressed as by the tensor Equation B15.1:

Equation B15.1: Gravitational Shift of Spectral Lines

$$v = \sqrt{g_{44}} \; v_0 \approx \left(1 - \frac{\kappa \, m}{R}\right) v_0$$

*where* $v =$ *coordinate frequency*

$v_0 =$ *proper frequency*

$g_{44} =$ *requency observed*

$\kappa =$ *numerical constant*

$m =$ *mass of star*

$R =$ *radius of star, and where*

$$\delta v \approx -\frac{\kappa \, m}{R} v_0 = \text{``gravitational shift'' of lines.}$$

The size of the spectral red-shift, therefore, hinges on the ratio of the star's mass m to its radius R as in $\kappa \, m/R$. The greater the ratio $m/R$, the lower will be the frequency $v$, and the more pronounced will be the red-shift.[91]

For the Sun in our solar system the red-shift computed in this manner is barely observable. For the extremely dense companion star of Sirius, however, the red-shift is about 20 times as large.For Sirius the ratio of mass $m$ to radius R of its companion star is sizeable and the computed frequency $v$ significantly lower. The red-shift has also been observed in the light of some white dwarfs.[92] Einstein's theory agrees with these observations.

*2. Advance of Mercury's perihelion by tensor analysis*
Astronomers discovered that Newton's theory did not fully account for the observed motion of the planet Mercury, at least not with the accuracy of the astronomical instruments around 1900.

Einstein estimated the advance of Mercury's perihelion by tensor analysis. In this case the tensor components took the form of Equation B15.2.[93]

Equation B15.2: Advance of Mercury's Perihelion

*Letting* $\quad$ M $=$ *mass of star*

$r =$ *its radius*

$\kappa =$ *numerical constant*

*the metric tensor takes on the form*

$$g_{11} = - \frac{1}{1 - \dfrac{2\kappa m}{r}}$$

$$g_{22} = -r^2$$

$$g_{33} = -r^2 \cos^2 \theta$$

$$g_{44} = 1 - \frac{2\kappa m}{r}$$

*all other* $g_{rs}$ *tensor components being zero.*

By solving the last set of equations via some complex manipulations, Einstein obtained the solution in terms of radians per revolution as shown in Equation B15.3.

Equation B15.3: Excess Perihelial Movement of Mercury Explained by
Einstein's Theory

*The secular rotation of the elliptical orbit of a planet expressed
relativistically in radians per revolution amounts to*

$$\sigma = \frac{24\ \pi^3\ a^2}{(1-e^2)\ c^2\ T^2}$$

*where*   $\sigma$ =   *radians per revolution*
    $\pi$ =   *3.1415 ...*
    $a$ =   *semimajor axis of planetary orbit*
    $c$ =   *speed of light at $3 \times 10^{10}$ cm/sec*
    $T$ =   *period of planet's revolution in seconds.*

The numerical value of the solution $\sigma$ gives the amount by which the radius
from Sun to planet exceeds one complete revolution of 2 between
successive perihelia. Since the square of the speed of light $c^2$ appears in
the denominator, the value of $\sigma$ (Greek letter sigma) is very small. The
theoretical value of $\sigma$, calculated in this manner, amounted to 43.03
seconds of arc per century and compares with an observed value of
43.11.[94]

*3. Deflection of star light by a gravitational field*

By solving his tensor field equations Einstein could show that the
deflection of starlight by the curvature of space time modified Newton's
gravitational constant $G = 6.67\ (10^{-8})$ by the factor $8\pi/c^2$ as shown in
Equation B15.4.[95]

   The result from this equation is an angle of 1.76 arc seconds. This
is Einstein's approximation by how much the light from a star should have
been deflected by the Sun's mass. Later, more rigorous solutions of the
field equations put the predicted value between 1.70 and 1.75 arcseconds.[96]

Equation B15.4: Deflection of Starlight by the Sun

*The constant $\kappa$ is derived from Einstein's field equations and is linked
to Newton's gravitational constant G as in*

$$\kappa = \frac{8\pi G}{c^2} = \frac{8\pi \cdot 6.67 \cdot 10^8}{9 \cdot 10^{20}} = 1.86 \cdot 10^{-27}$$

*where*

$\kappa$  $\kappa$  = *Einstein's approximation of the deflection of star-Light by the Sun*

$\pi$ = *3.1415 ...*

G = *Newton's gravitational constant*

$c^2$ = *speed of light squared in cm/ sec.*

Chapter 16

## CROSSING NEW FRONTIERS

*The dream of a single, all-encompassing, law of Nature spanning the whole of fundamental physics, showing the dissimilar forces of Nature to be but different manifestations of one underlying influence, has risen many great physicists from their slumber of contentment with the status quo.*

John D. Barrow[1]

Many books have been written on twentieth century physics and astronomy. They cover an enormous range. In no way can one short chapter do justice to all the information available. This chapter introduces attempts by physicists to "unify" Quantum Theory$_g$ with the Theory of Relativity, but does not go into depth on the many underlying concepts of modern-day physics.

In the mid-nineteenth century James Clerk Maxwell (1831–1879) created the first unified theory.[2] Based on Faraday's (1791–1867) experimental evidence, Maxwell mathematically described the relation between magnetism and electrodynamics$_g$. He showed that they were two aspects of the same phenomenon. Until then, magnetism and electricity appeared to be distinctly different. From his set of four "field equations" Maxwell deduced that light was part of the much wider spectrum of electromagnetic radiation$_g$. Decades later his theory was confirmed by the invention of wireless telegraphy, radio, television, microwaves, and other practical applications (Chapter 13, Figure 13.8).

In the early twentieth century Albert Einstein (1879–1955) created a new unified field theory of gravitation, the Theory of Relativity—light became the new constant of nature, mass translated into energy, and space tended to be curved (Chapters 14 and 15). Einstein's theory enhanced Newton's (1642–1727) clockwork model of the universe. It yielded greater precision in the interpretation of cosmological phenomena and eventually, in 1945, the energy-mass equality was dramatically confirmed by the first atomic explosion. Both unifying theories brought a better understanding of the forces of nature and yielded entirely new technologies.

This chapter addresses the drive toward the next unification—the focus on unifying the quantum theory of the microcosm with the relativity theory of the macrocosm. Unlike the theories of electrodynamics and relativity—each almost singlehandedly created by Maxwell and Einstein, respectively—many physicists are engaged in pursuing the goal of a field theory that will unite all fundamental forces of nature.

The universe is made of four stable particles: protons$_g$ , neutrons$_g$, electrons$_g$ , and neutrinos$_g$ . Each interacts with a different mix of the four fundamental forces of nature: gravity, electromagnetism, the strong nuclear force$_g$ and the weak nuclear force$_g$. All four are of magnitudes critical for the existence of the universe. Gravity is the only fundamental force which always attracts. It is incredibly weak. The ultimate goal is to develop a theory that will unite the four fundamental forces of nature. Even if it is true that physics is littered with the corpses of dead unified field theories,[3] physicists feverishly pursue the search for the ultimate unified theory.


## Early Quantum Theory

*Max Planck (1858–1947)*
Before Einstein created the Theory of Relativity, another far-reaching theory had emerged. On December 14, 1900 Max Planck gave a lecture to the German Physical Society on an innocuous subject. He described the way in which hot objects radiate energy. This proved to be the first entry of Quantum Theory, a strange theory that would eventually revolutionize twentieth century physics. Based on statistics, Quantum Theory was a

radical departure from Newton's and Einstein's precise laws of gravitation and motion. Yet eventually, Quantum Theory would turn out to be one of the most accurate theories in physics.

Max Planck was born in Kiel, Germany. He was the sixth child of a family devoted to scholarship, idealism, and conservatism. His father was a law professor, first at the University of Kiel and later at the University of Munich. At highschool in Munich, Max excelled in all subjects. After graduation he chose physics over languages, although he felt at home in both. He was also an excellent pianist and found relaxation at the keyboard, favoring the works of Schubert and Brahms. He liked to hike and climb in the mountains, a pastime throughout his life.

While still a student at high school, Planck decided to become a physicist because, as he recounted later, he had concluded that there was something absolute, independent of humanity, in the existence of the laws of nature. The first law that deeply impressed Planck was that of the conservation of energy: it implies that energy is neither created nor destroyed but merely changes its form.[4] He felt that the search for such laws would be the sublime scientific pursuit in life.[5]

At age 16 Planck entered the University of Munich. He attended the lectures of the physicists Hermann von Helmholtz (1821–1894) and Gustav Kirchhoff (1824–1887). Despite their eminence in science, Planck was not impressed. He often studied on his own. He became acquainted with the second law of thermodynamics$_g$, which is the law of entropy, that states heat will flow, of its own accord, only from a hot object to a cooler object. He was convinced that this second law of thermodynamics was as absolute as the first. He made it the subject of his doctoral dissertation at the University of Munich. At the unusually young age of 21 he obtained his Ph.D., at 22 he became a lecturer, and at 25 he was appointed associate professor at the University of Kiel. By 1892, at age 34, he was a full professor lecturing theoretical physics at the University of Berlin, in the city where he settled.

*Ultraviolet catastrophe*

While lecturing on the theory of thermodynamics Planck ran across a problem that bothered him every time he saw it. Outsiders might have viewed the problem as minor, but some theoretical physicists saw it as a catastrophe.

From earlier research it was known that radiation emitted from any body depended on the temperature of the body itself. The heat emission of many materials, such as iron, copper, and glass varied directly with their luminous glow. It seemed obvious that a white hot metal emitted more light than a red hot or barely glowing metal.[6]

In 1893 Wilhelm Wien (1864–1928), a German physicist, discovered that a spherical oven with a small hole was nearly ideal for producing black-body radiation. "Oven" is perhaps a misnomer; it has also been called an "ideal radiator" since it not only radiated energy but also absorbed any light that entered the body's cavity. The oven or radiator was ideal because the radiation it emitted from its cavity through the tiny opening was determined solely by the temperature of the walls inside. That was because the inner walls reflected many times over any rays entering through the small hole so that only a tiny portion of rays made their way out again (Figure 16.1, Diagram 1).[7] This tiny bit of radiation emitted through the hole closely approximated the oven's interior spectrum of radiation.[8]

According to theory, energy was also linked to the frequency of radiation. The higher the frequency, the shorter the waves and the greater the energy; the lower the frequency, the longer the waves and the smaller the energy. Physicists were interested in black-body radiation because they wanted to measure the "spectral radiancy" that would tell how much power was radiated per unit area of the cavity's aperture. Although a radiating body glows in a dark room, only a small part of the radiated energy lies in a visible range of the spectrum (Figure 13.8, Diagram 7). Most of it falls into the low-frequency infrared (long wavelength) end of the spectrum.

When physicists studied the spectrum of black-body radiation in the laboratory, they expected to find much more radiation energy at the high-frequency ultraviolet (short wavelength) end of the spectrum than at the low-frequency infrared (long wavelength) end of the spectrum. They were surprised when they found as little energy at the high-frequency as at the low-frequency end.

To get around this unexpected phenomenon, sometimes called the "ultraviolet catastrophe," physicists used two formulas for the description of black-body radiation: for the ultraviolet, high-frequency range they adopted Wilhelm Wien's Law and for the red low-frequency range they used that of Rayleigh-Jeans' Law.[9] Named after two English physicists Lord John William Strutt Rayleigh (1842–1919) and Sir James Jeans (1877–1946), the latter formula described the distribution of the red end of the radiation spectrum. Together the two laws gave a pretty good approximation of black-body radiation even though each covered only half the spectrum (Figure 13.8, Diagrams 5-7).

Physicists wondered how Maxwell's field equations could cover the whole range of the electromagnetic radiation when the black-body radiation appeared to be divided into two distinct parts? This conundrum puzzled Planck. Physicists were well aware that the radiation of light varied with the temperature of the object, longer waves at lower temperatures, and shorter waves at higher temperatures. At different temperatures the peaks of radiation could be derived directly from Maxwell's equation. But until Planck came along nobody had managed to derive one formula that fitted the whole spectrum of black-body radiation (Figure 16.1, Diagrams 2 and 3).

*Planck's law*

Planck believed that Wien's and Rayleigh-Jeans' Laws ought to be combined into one. Planck proposed a formula for spectral radiancy that perfectly fit with the experimental data of black-body radiation at all temperatures. Planck's radiation law reads:[10]

Equation 16.1: Planck's Radiation Law

$$S(\lambda, T) \;=\; 2\,\pi\,h \; \frac{c^2}{\lambda^5} \; \frac{1}{e^{hc/\lambda kT} - 1}$$

where  $S(\lambda,T)$  =  *spectral radiancy so that $S(\lambda)d\lambda$ is the power radiated per unit area of a cavity's opening, at temperature T,*
       c  =  *speed of light*
       $\lambda$  =  *Greek letter lambda for wave length,*

$$T \ = \ \textit{temperature in Kelvin degrees,}$$
$$h \ = \ \textit{Planck's constant,}$$
$$\pi, k \ = \ \textit{other constants.}$$

In essence, Planck's law states that the spectral radiation is determined by the speed of light, the wavelength, the temperature of the radiation, and Planck's constant. The whole expression on the right of the equal sign is related to the Gaussian probability formula.

Without going into the difficult aspects of his theory, Planck's law quantifies the black-body radiation by multiplying each probability frequency by a fundamental constant that Plank called $h$. The constant implied that atoms could absorb or emit only integer multiples of the probability frequencies, that is, multiples 1, 2, 3, 4, ... n. To Planck it meant that the atoms could only manage to deal with discrete bundles of energy, which he called "quanta" (plural of quantum for quantity, from the Latin word quantus, for how much). This novel formulation enabled Planck to calculate the precise value of the constant $h$ at $6.6 \times 10^{-34}$. [11] Although his formula was hailed as indisputably correct, to him it was simply a lucky, intuitive guess. It revealed that the radiation energy $E$ must be related to its frequency $f$ as in the well-known formula

$$E = h \times f$$

where $h$ came to be known as Planck's constant. Linked to radiation energy, it has become one of the most important constants in physics. At very high frequencies and short waves, the energy needed to emit one quantum of radiation is very large. At very low frequencies and long waves, little energy is needed to emit one quantum and, therefore, many low-energy quanta are emitted.

Planck himself was not happy with his solution. Having been trained in classical physics he wanted to derive his mathematical formulation from the second law of thermodynamics. But Planck was driven by pure logic to go with this kind of probability-oriented formulation. As one historian put it, Planck became a reluctant revolutionary. He was 42 years old when he derived the quantum formula of energy in 1900. Some physicists of the day believed that Planck's Quantum Theory was no more than mathematical trickery, but in time its significance became recognized. It won him the Nobel Prize for physics in 1918 and brought him many honors later.

Yet, Planck's personal life was to become increasingly difficult. Tragedies struck. After 22 years of happy marriage, his first wife died in 1909. His elder son was killed in action during World War I. Both of his daughters died in childbirth. When the Nazis came to power, Hitler was obsessed with his fanatical idea of ethnic cleansing. As one of Germany's leading scientists, Planck urged him to stop the devastating racial policies. He failed to convince Hitler of the damage it would inflict on German science. Yet, Planck remained in Germany to preserve whatever would be left of German physics. Opposed to the Nazi regime, he lost his position as president of the Kaiser Wilhelm Society in 1937 and his position as secretary of the Prussian Academy of Sciences in 1938. Planck's house was destroyed by allied bombs in 1944. In yet another tragedy, his younger son Erwin was implicated in the assassination attempt against Hitler on July 20, 1944. Erwin died a horrible death at the hands of Hitler's secret police, the Gestapo. This cruel act finally destroyed Planck's will to live.

At war's end, in 1945, an American officer gave Planck and his wife free passage from Berlin to Göttingen, West Germany. Planck died in 1947. Today his name is honored by the Max Planck Institute, centers of research created after the war to promote science in Germany.

## Photoelectric effect

Planck's new statistical view of science was not readily accepted by the scientific world that relied on precise (deterministic) formulations. It was Einstein, while still an unknown clerk at the patent office in Switzerland, who gave a radical but plausible explanation of Planck's quanta. He suggested that a beam of light consisted of particles, later called photons. Einstein asserted that whenever a photon hit an atom, an electron was ejected.

The scientific community received Einstein's idea with no more enthusiasm than Planck's formulation of energy radiation. After all, scientists had debated the nature of light for several centuries. During the 1600s Newton had suggested that light was transmitted by tiny particles or corpuscles, while Huygens (1629–1695) believed that light traveled in waves. Newton's theory prevailed until Thomas Young (1773–1829) showed by experiment that light had certain wave-like characteristics (Chapter 13, Figures 13.2, 13.3 and 13.6).

By the turn of the nineteenth century the wave theory of light was well established. So well, that Einstein's brash idea irked the U.S. physicist Robert Andrews Millikan (1868-1953). For the next ten years Millikan tried to prove Einstein wrong. His own experiments and precise measurements, however, only confirmed what Planck and Einstein had stated earlier: light energy was transmitted in packets or quanta. It could be said that Millikan contributed to their Nobel Prizes, Planck's in 1918 and Einstein's in 1921. In recognition of his own experimental work on the size and charge of the electron, Millikan received the Nobel Prize in physics in 1923.[12]

## Models of the Atom

*Thomson's Plum-Pudding Model*

During the early 1900s, while Planck worked on Quantum Theory and Einstein on the Theory of Relativity, Thomson's model of the atom ruled. Sir Joseph John Thomson (1856–1940), an English physicist and Nobel laureate, pictured the atom as an ultramicroscopic compact object. According to him each atom consisted of a number of negatively charged electrons (plums) embedded in positively charged gel (pudding). The negative charge of the electrons exactly balanced the positive charge, so that the atom was electrically neutral.

He based his model of the atom on a carefully conducted experiment. When electricity was passed through thin gas in a sealed tube luminous effects were produced similar to the familiar flourescent tubes later used for illumination and advertisement. Physicists debated whether the luminous effects were the result of waves or particles. Thomson showed by his experiments what other physicists had failed to show—that the luminous (negative) cathode rays were indeed particles. Using better pumps to come closer to a near vacuum, Thomson showed that the cathode beams were deflected by a positively charged plate. On comparing the degree of deflection with that of hydrogen atoms he deduced that electrons were about 1000 times smaller than hydrogen ions (Figure 16.2, Diagrams 1 and 2).[13]

*Rutherford's Solar-System Model*

In 1911, Ernest Rutherford (1871-1937) conceived a new model of the atom. Five years earlier he had noticed that alpha particles—positively charged particles emitted by radioactive elements such as uranium—left a sharp-edged picture when beamed through a hole onto a photographic plate. Yet, when beamed through a thin sheet of mica (5000th of an inch thick or about a 200th of a millimeter thick), the alpha particles would leave a picture with blurry edges. Remembering those results he had Hans Geiger (1882–1945), a post-doctoral fellow from Germany at Cambridge and later of Geiger-counter fame, refine the experiment. Geiger, together with an undergraduate student, aimed a stream of alpha particles at a very thin gold foil (one millionth of an inch thick, roughly 40,000th of a millimeter thick). Again, they found that the particles left a blurred picture on the photographic plate but noticed, too, that a few, about one in 10,000 particles were deflected. Among them, a very small number bounced straight, back emerging on the same side of the foil on which they had entered it (Figure 16.2, Diagram 3).

Rutherford concluded that almost all the mass of the atom was concentrated in a small nucleus some 10,000 times smaller in diameter than that of the entire atom. He further concluded that each atom must have a minute but massive center carrying a positive charge surrounded by swirling negative charged electrons. As the electrons revolved around the center at high speed, the centrifugal force kept them from uniting with the atomic nucleus at the center. At the same time most of the particles emitted by the radioactive material could pass through unimpeded as long as they did not hit the nucleus. Functioning like a microcosm of the Sun's planetary system, Rutherford's atom became known as the "solar-system model" (Figure 16.2, Diagram 4).[14]

*Bohr's Quantum-Shell Model*

As early as 1913 Niels Bohr (1885–1962) of Denmark, one of the foremost scientists of the twentieth century, embedded the atom in quantum theory.[15] His father, Christian Bohr, was professor of physiology at the University of Copenhagen and his mother, Ellen Adler Bohr, came from a wealthy Jewish family prominent in banking and politics. Growing up in warm family surroundings, Niels' early interest in science was encouraged. While his younger brother Harald took to mathematics, Niels opted for physics.

At the University of Copenhagen, young Bohr won a gold medal from the Danish Academy of Sciences and Letters for his experiments on the vibration and surface tension of water jets. In 1911 he completed his Ph.D. thesis on the electron theory of metals. Having critiqued the classical theory of matter at the atomic level, he went to Manchester England to join Ernest Rutherford's group and to continue his work on the structure of the atom. Bohr was impressed with Rutherford's research and his interpretation of the results. Rutherford, in turn, once said to a friend: "This young Dane is the most intelligent chap I have ever met."[16] Bohr applied the ideas of Planck, Einstein, and others to the atom, postulating discrete states of energy levels for different types of atoms. After his return to Copenhagen in 1912 he was appointed to a professorship and married.

In 1921 the new Institute of Theoretical Physics opened its doors. Bohr served as its director. He and his coworkers developed a consistent quantum theory of the properties of the atom. Consistency required that the complex patterns of the spectra emitted by the atoms could be linked to the regularities of the periodic table of the chemical elements. Einstein admired Bohr's early work and referred to it as "the highest form of musicality in the sphere of thought." Yet, Einstein did not endorse Bohr's later work and disagreed with Bohr's claim that quantum mechanics$_g$ was a "rational generalization of classical physics." Bohr's research in the field of nuclear physics played a key role in the understanding of nuclear processes and the energy release in splitting the atomic nucleus.

Until the outbreak of World War II Bohr's Institute of Nuclear Physics continued to be the center of annual conferences on nuclear physics and of formal and informal visits of quantum physicists. Among his graduate students Bohr was known for his slowness in thinking and understanding. It could happen that a visitor gave a brilliant talk on some intricate problem of Quantum Theory and everyone in the audience, except Bohr, would follow the line of reasoning. Then one and all would try to explain to him the point he had missed. Finally when the ensuing turmoil died down and Bohr began to understand, it would become clear that Bohr's interpretation of the problem differed from the lecturer's, but that Bohr's was right and the visitor's wrong.[17]

Although much pioneering work was done at the Institute—often by young researchers from other countries, some of whom became Nobel laureates in later years—it was not all work. At times, when he was tired, Bohr felt like doing something else. Inevitably this meant going to the movies, preferably cowboy movies. Bohr was not always quick in following the plot because he could not help but apply his scientific mind to analyze the events. But he was a keen observer and an astute judge in the interpretation of the screen actions. As George Gamow told it:

> Bohr's addiction to Western movies resulted in a theory which is unknown to all but his movie companions of the period. Everybody knows that in all Western movies (Hollywood-style at least) the scoundrel always draws first, but the hero is faster and always shoots down the scoundrel. Niels Bohr ascribed that phenomenon to the difference between willful and conditioned reaction. The scoundrel has to decide when to grab for the gun, which slows his actions, while the hero is faster because he acts without thinking when he sees the scoundrel reach for the gun. We all disagreed with that theory, and the next morning the author [Gamow] went to a toyshop to buy a pair of cowboy guns. We shot it out with Bohr, he playing the hero, and he killed us all.[18]

In Bohr's quantum shell model of the atom, the electrons revolved around the atomic nucleus in circular orbits, a pattern similar to Rutherford's solar-system model. The difference was that they moved in different orbital sizes and energy levels. Their orbits were somehow related to the hierarchy the Russian chemist Dmitri Ivanovich Mendeleyev (1834–1907) had devised in his periodic table of the chemical elements in 1868. With his table Mendeleyev systematized the properties of the known chemical elements and even predicted characteristics of elements such as gallium and germanium that had not yet been discovered.

Bohr also proposed that energy was emitted from the atom when an electron jumped from an outer orbit to one closer to the nucleus. He showed that the light energy emitted during the jump was related to Planck's formula $E = h{\times}f$ (Figure 16.2, Diagram 5).[19] For his work on atomic theory Bohr received the Nobel Prize in physics in 1922. Bohr's theory did have some drawbacks. For example, it did not explain the properties of atoms of the heavier elements containing many electrons. This was not understood until the development of quantum mechanics in later years—a topic touched on in the next section.[20]

*Acceptance of the Quantum Theory*

In scientific circles the opposition to a Quantum Theory, couched in probabilities, persisted for some time. But in 1922 the American physicist Arthur Holly Compton (1892–1962) found the first convincing evidence that electromagnetic radiation consisted of particles. While investigating the scattering of X-rays he observed that they lost energy with the scattering angle: the greater the angle, the greater the chance of a high-speed collision with an electron at rest. Based on the relativistic formulas for the energy and momentum, Compton showed that the Planck energy ( $E = hf$ ) of a photon, made visible in a cloud chamber by the recoiling electron, was equal to Einstein's relativistic energy $E = mc^2$ of the electron. It proved once and for all that the photon existed and interacted with an electron just like two billiard balls bounce off upon striking each other (Figure 16.3, Diagram 1).[21]

## Quantum Mechanics

From the beginning quantum theory dealt with light, radiation, matter at the subatomic scale, and the interactions of atomic particles. Physicists attempted to describe and account for the behavior of matter and radiation on that scale. This was difficult since the patterns that emerged often seemed peculiar because they conflicted with common sense. But a new generation of quantum physicists grew up. They were more receptive to the unusual aspects of quantum theory. Their efforts culminated in quantum mechanics, a theory behind the theory.

The study of "Quantum Mechanics" illustrates a method of physics that has been extremely successful. It has yielded correct results in almost every situation. In the early years Planck's theory of black-body radiation was shown to be precise, but the theory behind it and its implications for physics were not clearly understood. Then Niels Bohr widened the range of its applicability. He applied Quantum Theory successfully to the atomic structure. Quantum mechanics, a new branch of Quantum Theory, appeared later. By 1926 it reached fruition in three approaches: matrix theory, wave mechanics, and transformation theory. Together the three formed a consistent body of physical law.

*Matrix Theory of Quantum Mechanics*

In atomic physics Werner Heisenberg (1901–1976), a German physicist, philosopher and public figure, was much influenced by Einstein and Bohr.[22] He helped establish the modern science of quantum mechanics. Inclined toward abstract mathematics, he represented the quantum conditions by arrays of numbers that obeyed the rules of matrix algebra. In this algebra as a rule the multiplicative product $A \times B$ differs from $B \times A$ and, according to Heisenberg, this formalism carried over into nuclear physics.[23] Letting A stand for the momentum of an electron and B for its position, he proved that the statistical (standard) errors of measurement will always be greater than Planck's constant $h$.

From this Heisenberg concluded that it was possible to measure either the electron's momentum or its position with great precision, but that it was impossible to measure both at the same time. Yet, in spite of this uncertainty which sets limits to precise measurement, it has been shown time after time that the quantum theory is enormously successful in predicting experimental outcomes.

Heisenberg collaborated with Max Born (1882–1970), his former professor of theoretical physics at the University of Göttingen.[24] Born produced a most satisfactory mathematical statement of the first law of thermodynamics. He also came up with a very useful technique for solving problems related to the scattering of atomic particles and he showed that solutions of wave equations of particle radiation have a statistical meaning of physical significance.

Both, Heisenberg and Born received Nobel Prizes for their work in physics.

*Wave Mechanics*

Just about at the time when Heisenberg applied abstract matrix algebra to quantum conditions, the Austrian theoretical physicist Erwin Schroedinger (1887–1961) set out to find a wave equation for matter. It would give a particle-like propagation when the wave length becomes very short. Schroedinger deduced from the equation he derived that the electron was spread out in space and that its density could be computed by solving the wave equation for any specific point at x,y,z.

Max Born gave a different interpretation to Schrödinger's result. He proposed—an interpretation physicists generally accept today—that the density is the probability of finding the electron at point x,y,z. Where Schrödinger would say that at this point a fraction of an electron would be detected, Born would say most of the time nothing would be found at that point, but when something was observed it would be the whole electron. Thus the concept of a point particle moving around the atomic nucleus in a well defined path in Quantum Theory is replaced in wave mechanics of Quantum Theory by clouds whose density at any point describe the probabilities of electrons being at that location (Figure 16.3, Diagram 2).[25]

When Schrödinger's paper on wave mechanics appeared in the *Annalen der Physik (Annals of Physics)*, a paper by Heisenberg in the *Physikalische Zeitschrift (Physics Magazine)* was dedicated to the same topic. Although the two authors started from entirely different assumptions and using different mathematics—Schrödinger basing his result on a partial differential equation and Heisenberg his on matrix algebra—they both arrived at the same conclusion: the same spectral lines of energy radiation. In a subsequent paper Schrödinger managed to prove—to the surprise of theoretical physicists of his day—that one could always derive one from the other. Thus, depending on the physicist's preference, wave and matrix mechanics can be used interchangeably to calculate radiation intensities at the atomic level.[26]

Schroedinger shared the Nobel Prize in physics for his work on wave mechanics with the British physicist Paul Dirac in 1933.

*Transformation from Relativity to Quantum*

Paul Adrien Maurice Dirac (1902–1984) was born in Bristol, England. His father was born in Switzerland and insisted that his son only converse with him in French. Paul's mother, sister, and brother had to eat in the kitchen because their conversational French was not up to par. Perhaps as a result of this upbringing, Paul Dirac chose his words with great care and seldom spoke. His impressive ability in mathematics showed at an early age. To put it to good use he opted for a practical career and studied engineering at the University of Bristol. Ironically, after graduation he did not find employment. Aided by a grant he switched over to study theoretical physics and obtained his Ph.D. at St. John's College, Cambridge. There his faculty supervisor acquainted him with the current state of atomic physics.[27]

Intent on studying the laws of motion of atomic particles, Dirac applied Einstein's Special Theory of Relativity to quantum mechanics. The problem was that Relativity Theory and Quantum Theory did not fit well together and there were always some discrepancies marring the solutions.[28] But it was possible to add some adjustments that made for a better fit. In elegant mathematical language Dirac captured the electron's motion in four simultaneous differential equations. From the adjustments and the solution to his equations, he deduced that the electron rotates on its axis and that there must also exist negative states of energy. He suggested that such energy deficiency could result from a short-lived positive particle (Figure 16, Diagram 3).[29]

Although at the time the notion of an energy deficiency appeared doubtful, eventually photographs showed that such a positively charged particle, the "positron," did indeed exist. In 1932 Dirac was appointed Lucasian Professor of Mathematics, the chair once held by Sir Isaac Newton, and in 1933 he was awarded the Nobel Prize in physics.

Dirac was totally focused on his research. Towering above contemporaries in the field he did not waste much time on other activities. When interviewed in 1929 by a reporter for the *Wisconsin State Journal,* for example, his answers were short and to the point. Part of the dialogue went like this:

REPORTER: Now, doctor, will you give me in a few words the low-down on all your investigations?

DIRAC: No.

REPORTER: Will it be all right if I put it this way: "Professor Dirac solves all the problems of mathematical physics, but is unable to find a better way of figuring out Babe Ruth's batting average."

DIRAC: Yes.

REPORTER: What do you like best in America?

DIRAC: Potatoes.[30]

Although taciturn, Dirac had some good friends. Neils Bohr said of him that of all the physicists, "Dirac has the purest soul."[31] Dirac looked at research as an aesthetic experience. To him it was art, symmetry, and beauty combined.

By the 1930s Quantum Theory had moved to center stage. Although Einstein had been the first in interpreting the experimental evidence of light quanta correctly, he did not like the theoretical foundation of quantum mechanics. It contradicted his intuitive sense of a smooth geometric interpretation of nuclear forces. In quantum mechanics the nuclear energy is not a continuous force, it comes in packets of tiny particles, the quanta. Different quanta give rise to different forces.[32]

Ever more powerful accelerators were spewing out a perplexing mixture of particles. Rutherford's experiments, based on radiation of radioactive materials, created rare particle collisions that changed the model of the atomic structure. Accelerators were designed to produce a fast-moving beam of electrically charged atomic particles that interact on collision with atoms and other nuclear particles. In the U.S. the first high-voltage accelerator was installed at Princeton University in 1931; ever more powerful cyclotron accelerators have been built since. Hundreds of particles were found in the photographic debris of accelerators. As 1938 Nobel Prize winner Enrico Fermi (1901–1954) put it: "If I could remember the names of all these particles, I would have become a botanist."[33]

Modern accelerators produce all sorts of nuclear particles with energies of millions or even billions of electron volts. It took years before a more comprehensive theory emerged. Today the largest accelerators used in particle research operate as colliding beam storage rings (Figure 16.4, Diagram 1). At CERN (Conseil Européèn pour la Recherche Nuclèaire) in Geneva, Switzerland, the European accelerator, a large synchroton collider—a ring structure of 16.8 miles (27 km)—accelerates electrons to 50 giga-electron volts.

In the early experiments it was difficult to determine how the different particles behaved. Eventually, cloud chambers solved the problem. Charles Thomson Rees Wilson (1869–1959), a Scottish physicist and eventual Nobel laureate (1927) discovered that in clean moist (supersaturated) air, clouds did not form until charged particles (e.g., alpha particles) passed through. By experiment he found that radiation left a trail of condensed water droplets in a cloud chamber. Perfected in 1912, his chamber proved indispensable to the study of nuclear physics. In the early 1950s it led to the development of the bubble chamber. Such radiation detectors were linked to accelerators. They used a superheated liquid that boils into tiny bubbles along the tracks of subatomic particles. Pictures of the tracks enabled physicists to interpret the unique characteristics of different particles (Figure 16.4, Diagram 2).[34] Still, the challenge of finding an all-unifying mathematical model of quantum and relativity theories had not been met.

## The Renaissance of the Relativity Theory

Just as the Theory of Relativity temporarily ran out of steam in the early 1930s, Quantum Theory ran into difficulties in the 1960s. For decades the gulf between Quantum Theory on one side and Relativity Theory on the other, appeared to be unbridgeable. The problem of how to cross the chasm between the two bedeviled Einstein and other physicists.[35]

Long ago, the validity of Einstein's Theory of Relativity had been confirmed by the gravitational red-shift of a star's spectrum, the precession of Mercury's perihelion, and by deflection of starlight skimming the Sun (see Chapter 15). But some deep mysteries of the universe remained hidden.[36] In 1952 these mysteries induced physicist John Archibald Wheeler (1911– ) to teach a course on relativity, the first course on relativity to be put on the Princeton University curriculum.

Robert J. Oppenheimer (1904–1967), known as the man who built the atomic-bomb, and his colleagues had shown that the collapse of a star to a singularity, a geometric point of infinite density, was the consequence of relativity theory and not just a mathematical trick. John Archibald Wheeler picked up on this idea and studied the properties of "black holes." In fact he was the scientist who had coined the term "black hole." As he put it, he "was looking for a way out." Aristotle of Greek antiquity had said that nature abhors a vacuum and Wheeler was convinced that nature loathed a singularity. He believed that some structure should exist even at the center of a black hole. From quantum theory he knew that the point-like protons of the atomic nucleus have inside an electrical field which is very strong but not infinite in density and force. He asked whether quantum mechanics would enter the picture and change the prediction of relativity, preventing total collapse. Wheeler said: "What I learned in teaching the course [at Princeton University] was that the riches of Einstein's theory had been far from fully mined. Hidden beneath the equations . . . was a lode waiting to be brought to the surface and exploited."[37] Without going deeper into theoretical aspects, this chapter offers a brief look at some of the "relativity nuggets" discovered since the 1950s.

### Life Cycle of a Star

The life cycle of a star begins with an enormous cloud of gas. Like all material matter it consists of atoms with electrons orbiting the particles of the atomic nucleus.[38] The Great Nebula in Orion is a photogenic example of an enormous hydrogen gas cloud. A star forms when, after millions of years, the atoms of the gas cloud, mostly hydrogen, come close enough together to pull on each other and thereby bring them even tighter together. It is the beginning of gravitational attraction. The gravitational force accelerates the particles and they convert the extra energy into higher temperatures.

Working against the gravitational force, individual atomic nuclei repel each other. Once the gravitational force overcomes the nuclear repellant force, the atomic nuclei fuse, form helium, and create nuclear energy. The more massive the star, the hotter the core must be to create enough pressure to counteract the gravitational force. Eventually, the star's gravitational force and the pressure from the nuclear fusion balance each other (Figure 16.5, Diagrams 1 to 3). [39]

*White Dwarf Stars*

Even though more massive stars have more nuclear energy to burn, they use it up at a much faster rate and go through it more quickly than average stars. Toward the end of a star's life cycle the forces of gravitation and fusion become unbalanced. What happens next depends on the size of the star. According to Wheeler's analysis, a star of the size of the Sun will eventually shrink and become a white dwarf. As a middling star, it will become small, but not extremely small and it will become dense, but not extremely dense. Atoms in the dwarf's center will remain atoms and relativity theory will play no special role in the dwarf's core. Our Sun is such a dwarf star. It formed about 4.6 billion years ago. Younger than the average star in our galaxy, it is expected to shine for another five billion years before its energy will be exhausted.

*Neutron Stars*

According to relativity theory stars much more massive than our Sun collapse and explode. They suddenly become visible as supernovas. The remnant they leave behind after the explosion is an object far smaller and denser than a white dwarf. Extreme gravity forces electrons and protons so tightly together that their atoms are crushed and form what physicists call neutrons. Such "neutron stars" last indefinitely. They do not release energy and cannot shrink any further. A neutron star equivalent to two our Sun's solar masses, for example, will shrink to a diameter of about 15 miles (24 km) and have a density a million billion times that of our Sun.

When Wheeler reported the results of his computations in 1958 no one had ever detected a neutron star. It took another decade before Susan Jocelyn Bell Burnell (1943– ), a graduate student working with astronomer Antony Hewish (1924– ) at Cambridge University of England, discovered a pulsar in 1967. It was identified as a neutron star. Located at the center of the Crab Nebula, where the supernova lit up the sky in 1054 A.D., it blinks 30 times per second as it spins around its own axis. The immediate thought was that it was a beacon sent out by extraterrestrials. Bell Burnell and Anthony Hewish gave the radio source of these pulses the temporary name LGM, for "Little Green Men." Soon after, Bell Burnell located another three pulsars. Since then, dozens of others have been discovered, with revolving periods ranging from hundredths of a second to four seconds.[40]

### Black Holes

The third possibility to end the life cycle of a star is a the collapse to a "black hole." The idea of a black hole went against Wheeler's grain. However, in the early 1960s he realized that mathematically nothing could prevent the ultimate collapse of matter to a dimension smaller than the "Schwarzschild radius" (see Figure 16.5, Diagram 4) of a black hole. Outwardly, a black hole has its own characteristic mass, electric charge (if any), and spin around its axis (if any), but inwardly light and everything else is trapped.

Wheeler did not subscribe to the idea that no structure existed inside a black hole. He believed then (and still did in 1998) that a new theory of physics, operating at the Planck scale, would prove that structure existed within a black hole.[41] The subject fascinated him. He wrote:

> None is a more important constituent of this universe we call home. The black hole epitomizes the revolution wrought by general relativity. It pushes to an extreme—and therefore to the limit—the features of general relativity. Space-time curvature, geometry, [and] gravitational radiation. All of these things become, with black holes, not tiny corrections to older physics, but the essence of newer physics.[42]

While the outside of a black hole is rather simple the inside of it remains a mystery. The question of entropy$_g$ has come up. The law of entropy fascinated Max Planck in his student days. It is a measure of complexity. Anything large and complex has great entropy, and when reduced to utmost simplicity its entropy can decrease no further. It is a one way street: once time has leveled something, it cannot level it any further.

In 1970 Stephen Hawking, the well known English physicist,

discovered that the area of a black hole's horizon never decreases. After careful consideration, Jacob Bekenstein, one of Wheeler's students, came up with the idea that the area of the black hole's horizon is the black hole's entropy. He based his proposition on quantum theory and Wheeler urged him to publish it. When Stephen Hawking came across Bekenstein's paper, he was not prepared for it, but was eventually convinced by Bekenstein's compelling logic. In 1974 Hawking published a paper with the startling conclusion that every black hole radiates energy (Figure 16.5, Diagram 6). This radiation is just tiny enough to confirm Bekenstein's postulate of the black hole's entropy.[43]

According to Hawking's relativity theory, stellar black holes could be all over the universe. It is just that they are hard to find because they are invisible. In 1978 the first X-ray telescope, the Einstein Telescope, was put into operation. It was the first telescope that could focus X-rays and pinpoint the sources of emission just like an optical telescope tracks starlight.

Conceivably, black holes could be found among binary stars, one being a shining star and the other a black hole of similar mass. In 1974, 10 years after it was first detected as a strong source of X-rays, Cygnus X-1 was identified as a convincing candidate (0.955 certainty) of a black hole. Its binary companion is the very bright giant blue star HDE 226868 (Figure 16.5, Diagrams 5 and 6). Several other potential candidates are currently under study but it may take superior instrumentation before they can be confirmed as black holes and before their unique characteristics can be explained by theory.[44]

**Bringing Quantum Theory and Relativity Theory Together**

As already discussed, at times, Relativity Theory and Quantum Theory reinforce each other. The ultimate goal of physicists is, now more than ever, to bring together in one unifying theory the forces of nature at the macrocosm where the theory of relativity reigns, with the forces at the microcosm where quantum mechanics rules. In fact, they are pursuing Einstein's dream of long ago.

*Four Forces of Nature*

Between the time of the ancient Greeks and now, philosophers and scientists discovered that all the phenomena of the universe can be attributed to four forces:

1. The gravitational force that keeps us from floating away, that saves the air from being diffused in space, and that keeps the planets in their orbits;

2. The electromagnetic force that makes magnets point North and that feeds our appliances and gives us light;

3. The weak nuclear force that creates the heat of radioactive materials, that can be as deadly as the radiation of the nuclear reactors at Chernobyl (scene of the world's worst nuclear disaster); or that can be used in health care for cancer treatment,

4. The strong nuclear force that holds the atoms together, that fuels the stars, gives us sunshine, and is the force that was first released in nuclear bombs.

Physicists are trying to explain these four forces in a comprehensive unified theory. As of now their theoretical models do have one thing in common: all require additional dimensions over and above Eintein's four-dimensional theory. It appears that the secret of unification may be uncovered by further application of Riemann's metric tensor$_g$ analysis. When first proposed, the new hyper-dimensional (i.e., more than three-dimensional) theories were considered wild speculations. Much research has gone into the mathematical models of unification since. On the theoretical side the findings are still speculative.

Riemann's metric tensor analysis made it possible to mathematically describe space of any dimension by its characteristic curvature. Schematically (but not mathematically) it is quite easy to expand the four-dimensional metric tensor arrangement to five, or any number of dimensions. It is only necessary to augment Einstein's four-dimensional square matrix by additional sets of metric coefficients. Einstein expanded the conventional three-dimensional space into four dimensions. As illustrated earlier (Chapter 15, Appendix Equation A15.2) this required more coefficients (e.g., 16 coefficients instead of 9) before he could find the mathematical solution for his tensor equations. The same applies here:

if more dimensions were added to Riemann's space, additional coefficients are required for the mathematical solution.

*Kaluza-Klein Model*

A few years after Einstein published his paper on General Relativity, Theodor Kaluza proposed a fifth dimension. He was an unknown mathematician of the University of Königsberg in Germany. In April 1919 Kaluza mailed a letter to Einstein in Berlin. On reading it, Einstein was perplexed. In a short and precise paper Kaluza had integrated Einstein's theory of gravity with Maxwell's theory of electromagnetic radiation (Chapter 13, Figure 13.8) by adding a fifth dimension to Einstein's four. What astounded Einstein was that Kaluza's fifth dimension was based on Maxwell's set of equations.

Like Riemann before him, Kaluza believed that light was a vibration in a higher dimension. Einstein found Kaluza's mathematical reasoning irreproachable, even elegant in its simplicity and, after two years of careful consideration, he approved of its publication under the title *On the Unity Problem of Physics*.[45] He did not realize that this route would eventually lead to an even greater number of dimensions and further into hyperspace$_g$, space well beyond the conventional three dimensions.[46]

Schematically, Einstein's coefficient array of four dimensions can be readily expanded to Kaluza's five (see Equation 16. 2).[47] However, adding a fifth dimension immediately raises a new question. Everybody is aware of the three dimensions of width, height, depth and perhaps has heard of a fourth dimension. But had anyone ever experienced a fourth or even a fifth dimension? If not, where could it be? To this Kaluza had a very simple answer: the fifth dimension is too small to be seen! It is all curled up in circles so small that even an atom would be too big to fit into it. But if it were possible to step into this fifth dimension, a person could travel from one end to the other, and arrive at the start again. A curious theory.

In 1926 the mathematician Oscar Klein improved on Kaluza's theory.[48] He believed that quantum theory could explain why the fifth dimension was so tightly curled up. He calculated the size of the fifth dimension at one quantum length or at $10^{-33}$ centimeters (cm). For comparison, the size of the smallest dust particles is about $10^{-2}$ cm, the diameter of a hydrogen atom is $10^{-8}$ cm, an atomic nucleus is $10^{-12}$ cm, and a proton is $10^{-13}$ cm. It put the size of the fifth dimension at much less than one trillionth of a proton, far too small to be measured by any instrument. Immeasurably small in its dimension, the Kaluza-Klein Theory could not be verified. Neither proven right nor wrong, it was pure speculation and by the 1930s it had gone out of fashion. For years the Kaluza-Klein Theory remained dormant.

Equation16.2: The Generalized Pythagorean Theorem for Four and Five Dimensions

*As shown in Chapter 15 (Equation 15A.2) the Generalized Pythagorean Theorem for the distance between two nearby points on a four-dimensional surface is given by:*

$$d s^2 = \sum_{i}^{4} \sum_{j}^{4} g_{ij} \, dx_i \, dx_j \quad where \quad G_4 = \begin{bmatrix} g_{11} & g_{12} & g_{13} & g_{14} \\ g_{21} & g_{22} & g_{23} & g_{24} \\ g_{31} & g_{32} & g_{33} & g_{34} \\ g_{41} & g_{42} & g_{43} & g_{44} \end{bmatrix}$$

*This square array or matrix of 16 coefficients depicts the metric tensor of four-dimensional space $G_4$. Kaluza expanded Einstein's metric tensor from $G_4$ to $G_5$ by adding 9 elements for Maxwell's Equations as suggested by:*

$$d s_5^2 = \sum_{i}^{5} \sum_{j}^{5} g_{ij} \, dx_i \, dx_j \quad where \quad G_5 = \begin{bmatrix} g_{11} & g_{12} & g_{13} & g_{14} & l_{15} \\ g_{21} & g_{22} & g_{23} & g_{24} & l_{25} \\ g_{31} & g_{32} & g_{33} & g_{34} & l_{35} \\ g_{41} & g_{42} & g_{43} & g_{44} & l_{45} \\ l_{51} & l_{52} & l_{53} & l_{54} & l_{55} \end{bmatrix}$$

*where*    $g_{ij}$ =    *tensor elements of Einstein's metric and*
           $l_{ij}$ =    *tensor element of Maxwell's metric.*

*Yang-Mills Fields*

After many failures, including Einstein's attempts to integrate the subatomic forces into the framework of relativity, a new set of field equations for the forces at the subatomic level finally emerged in the 1970s. They are now called the Yang-Mills Fields (field equations are sets of equations, such as Maxwell's and Einstein's equations described in Chapters 13 and 15).

In 1954 Chen Ning Yang and his student Robert L. Mills published a paper on *"Gauge Invariance and Isotopic Spin"* in the *Physical Review*. It was the foundation on which modern quantum field theory is built. Their model was based on an analogy with photons. If photons resulted from an exchange of quantum energy in the collision of electrons, then could the weak particles not result from an exchange of quantum energy in the collision of electrons and neutrinos? And could gluon particles, carrying the strong force, not result from strong interactions?

The idea had first occurred to Yang in 1948 while a graduate student at the University of Chicago. Born in China in 1922, he had left war-torn China to study under Enrico Fermi. Yang's field theory was largely created at Brookhaven National Laboratory in 1954. At first the theory was viewed with scepticism and even derided as purely mathematical without any physical significance. But then it was found powerful enough to account for several forces and many particles in existence. In 1957 Chen Ning Yang shared the Nobel Prize in physics with Tsung Dao Lee for contributions to the laws of fundamental nuclear particles.[49]

The great advantage of the Yang-Mill Fields was that by creating a hyperspace of more than five dimensions, it looked as if Einstein's field equations could be fit together with the quantum equations of nuclear force and matter (Figure 16.6, Diagram 1). An even greater advantage was that physicists could now calculate the energy requirements that might enable them to warp space. As it turned out, a warp-space would require energies equivalent to the gravitational force of the Sun or other stars. According to solutions of their field equations the needed energies would go far beyond anything available on Earth today.

Physicists believe the only time such vast energies could ever have been produced was at the time of creation of our universe (i.e., at the moment of the so-called "Big Bang"). Astrophysicists—physicists specializing in the study of the physical nature of the universe, the objects in it, and the composition of space between them—believe that at the time of the Big Bang the sudden release of enormous energy caused an explosion so powerful that our universe is still expanding today. If humanity should ever be able to produce such an incredible force it could harness the power of hyperspace and perhaps make time travel a reality.[50]

Compelling as the Yang-Mills theory was to those who worked in high-energy physics, it seemed to have a fatal flaw. When physicists tried to solve the equations for the interactions among the particles they found them to be far more complex than Maxwell's equations. More disturbing, when they made certain standard quantum corrections they ran into a wall. The expected minor adjustments turned out to be similar to divisions by zero, an operation not permissible because any number divided by another that is infinitely large yields a number that is indistinguishable from zero. Try as they might, physicists could not avoid them and, hence, could not obtain meaningful results for even simple interactions.[51]

*Renormalization*

Eventually, in 1971, a Dutch graduate student Gerard 't Hooft, while still in his twenties, found a solution to the Yang-Mills puzzle. Applying a technique first conceived by his thesis advisor, Martinus Veltman, they managed to overcome the problem of the perplexing infinities. They did so by replacing the ratios of infinities with known values and by rearranging the afflicted terms in the field equations until they canceled each other. This enabled them to develop the mathematical foundation for an electroweak theory, a theory revealing the underlying unity between everyday electromagnetism and the weak force governing some nuclear reactions. Their novel idea spread like wild fire.

It helped explain the behavior of subatomic particles. In 1999 't Hooft and Veltman shared the Nobel Prize in physics.[52] They had developed a technique which enabled physicists to formulate new variation of the equations after some of the disturbing infinities had been eliminated. In this context "avoiding infinities" goes by the technical term "renormalization." Since it was not possible to mathematically eliminate the annoying infinities, they did it by inserting known data coefficients into the field equations. For example, the value of the mass of the electron was known from direct experimental measurements. By inserting that value where the theory would only give an electron cloud, they removed an unwanted infinity from the equations. This trick was called "renormalization" and applied to the field equations wherever possible.[53]

Renormalization worked but was not without critics. Paul Dirac, mentioned earlier in this chapter, considered renormalization rules artificial and did not accept them as correct. The irreverent physicist Richard Feynman (1918–1988), who helped renormalize quantum mechanics called the method "dippy" and a "shell game." Asked what he had received the 1965 Nobel Prize for, he said "for sweeping them [the infinities] under the rug."[54]

By the mid 1970s the Yang-Mills theory, combined with renormalization, had been successfully applied to strong nuclear interactions. Thought to be the key to unlocking the secrets of atomic forces, physicists could explain the experimental evidence of subatomic particles up to about a trillion electron volts generated by the most powerful particle accelerators.[55] Because the Yang-Mills theory was so successful, it became the Standard Model used by other physicists and further developed toward a more comprehensive theory of nuclear forces.

## The Standard Model

Based on the Yang-Mills field equations, the Standard Model contained among its field equations Maxwell's equations that dealt with the interactions of electrons and light. As time went on, physicists discovered that protons, neutrons, and other nuclear particles were composed of even smaller constituents. It became apparent that they were held together by the exchange of energy quanta representing the strong nuclear force. In contrast, neutrinos and some other particles only interacted with matter through a weak nuclear force. Too weak to bind together strongly, the latter particles were small in number.[56]

The Standard Model emerged after some fifty years and several hundred million dollars for research into subatomic particles. For decades physicists had worked in high-energy laboratories in a frightful tangle of disorder and confusion and then, all of sudden, the Standard Model appeared on the scene, the work of many actors. It looked as if the final chapter had been written. Physicists hoped that an expanded version of the Standard Model could account for all matter and could accommodate all additional experimental data. But as the model further evolved, it became apparent that it had some serious shortcomings.

When the gravity of relativity theory was inserted in the Standard Model, it did not yield sensible results because again, quantum gravity yielded infinities. They could not be avoided by renormalization. Researchers also disapproved of some other ugly features. The model contained certain fudge factors for masses and constants. They were not determined by theory. Moreover, some of the smaller particles were so much alike that they appeared to be redundant.[57]

By contrast, Einstein's model of General Relativity conveyed a sense of beauty. It substantiated a vast amount of experimental data with a most frugal one-line mathematical expression. Going beyond Newton, physicists derived from it the warping of space, black holes, and the idea of the Big Bang. As Chen Ning Yang explained it:

> Nature seems to take advantage of the simple mathematical representations of the symmetry laws. When one pauses to consider the elegance and the beautiful perfection of the mathematical reasoning involved and contrasts it with the complex and far-reaching physical consequences, a deep sense of respect for the power of the symmetry laws never fails to develop.[58]

Or, as Feynman put it:

> You can recognize truth by its beauty and simplicity. When you get it right it is obvious that it is right—at least if you have any experience—because usually what happens is that more comes out than goes in.[59]

In a lecture given in New Zealand in 1975, Paul Dirac expressed his dissatisfaction with renormalization in the Standard Model: "This is just not sensible mathematics. Sensible mathematics involves neglecting a quantity when it turns out to be small—not neglecting it just because it is infinitely great and you do not want it." He concluded his lecture by stressing the need for a drastic change in the model, to make it mathematically acceptable.[60]

## GUT Models

Since the Standard Model did cover a lot more ground than the Kaluza-Klein Model but seemed improvised rather than elegant, physicists continued to search for something more appealing. One of the earliest attempts came under the name of the Grand Unified Theory or GUT. It quickly became the latest challenge, and even a campus fashion trend. Some graduate students in astrophysics wore T-shirts with the imprint "Cosmology takes GUTs" in front and a diagram of "three converging curves" in the back. The three curves stood for the strong nuclear, weak nuclear, and electromagnetic forces. All three curves converged at a point marked $10^{-29}$ suggesting that at the time of the Big Bang there were not three forces but just one (Figure 16.7).[61]

GUT models were designed to unify the three elementary particle forces—the strong, weak, and electromagnetic—by integrating them into a coherent set of Yang-Mills fields. The set of the three forces ought to converge at the same temperature. Many researchers became involved and different approaches were pursued.[62]

Several versions of GUT models predicted that the proton particle —one of two kinds of particles of the atom's nucleus—was unstable when heretofore it was believed to be a perfectly stable. According to GUT theories it disintegrated into other particles, a decay that could not be avoided. The estimates of decay rates varied among researchers but in all cases the expected lifetime was extremely long. It meant that the whole cosmos would ultimately disintegrate, though perhaps only after trillions of times its present age. Nevertheless, it was of interest to find out if there was any empirical evidence in support of this aspect of the GUT theories.[63]

Several multimillion dollar projects were set up to test for proton decay. The first proton detector was approved for installation in the Kolar gold mine of India in 1978. Weighing around 100 tons it was put more than six thousand feet below ground level. Other proton detectors were positioned in a salt mine near Cleveland, Ohio; in the Mont Blanc tunnel near the French-Italian border; in the Silver King mine near Park City, Utah; in the Kamioka lead and zinc mine near Takayama, Japan, and a second 300-ton detector was placed later at Kamioka, Japan.[64] By the end of the 1980s, six gigantic proton detectors were in operation. All were placed deep underground to keep them isolated from any interference by cosmic background radiation. Yet, by 1994 no convincing evidence of proton decay had been detected. And even if it had been observed, gravity was still not part of the GUT Model. It seemed that the Yang-Mills field was not enough to bring all four forces together. What to do next? The time was ripe for a drastic change.[65]

*In Search of Symmetry*

Symmetry became a key issue in the search for an all-inclusive model of the forces of nature. Atomic physicists had identified some 200 elementary nuclear particles. Could they ever be integrated into a formal model? Without a well-defined structure it was simply a collection of particles without meaningful interrelations. If they were to group them into categories they needed to find the underlying reason for such groupings. If a logical base was found, it could lead to unification of the quantum forces of the microcosm and that, in turn, to the ultimate unification with the relativity forces of the macrocosm.

As mentioned earlier in connection with Bohr's quantum model of the atom, the Russian chemist Dmitri Ivanovich Mendeleyev had arranged the atomic elements in groups. He not only captured the similarities of their group characteristics, but identified the gaps of some missing elements that were discovered later. Similarly, some of the early findings of the atomic physicists, based on mathematical models of nuclear particles, suggested some previously unknown characteristics. From Wolfgang Pauli's (1900–1958) work had emerged the idea of two-valuedness of spin: spin up and spin down. On purely theoretical grounds, Dirac had suggested that every particle had an anti-particle with the mirror image of its properties. Eventually, the anti-proton was discovered.

Heisenberg had asserted that a single particle should always have two values of charge. These ideas gave the first inkling of an underlying logic for groupings.[66]

In the early 1960s Murray Gell-Mann (1929– ) of the U.S. and, independently, Yuval Ne'eman (1925– ) of Israel, were the first to arrange the elementary particles into symmetric patterns.[67] Gell-Mann named his approach the Eight-fold Way.[68] In 1964 he advanced the idea that protons and neutrons each consisted of three particles. Having run across "three quarks for Muster Mark" in *Finnigans Wake*[69] (a novel by James Joyce), he coined the word quark to refer to three different sets of particles that make a proton or a neutron.[70]

In their search for a mathematical expression of patterns of symmetry Gell-Mann and others turned to topology, a branch of mathematics which goes beyond the intuitive perception of space and geometrical relationships.[71] It is a theory of groups in which the group elements represent points in space that satisfy certain operations. For example, group elements can be added, subtracted, multiplied, and divided. Named after Sophus Lie, a Norwegian mathematician, the Lie groups are the most important and most intensely studied among them. They are topological groups whose structure near each point is like that of a three-dimensional surface (or more generally, like that of n-dimensional space). They can be rotated around a central point while preserving their spatial characteristics.[72]

Initially, three kinds of quarks were identified: up, down, and strange. Later, three more were added: charm, bottom, and top. At first reluctantly accepted, they became key features of the nuclear particle field. Eventually all six types of quarks were found and identified. The top quark, for example, was recognized at the Fermilab particle collider in Batavia, Illinois as recently as 1995. Also, it was discovered that the three quarks of protons and neutrons were tied together by gluons. They were the strong nuclear force, called the color force.[73]

It is impossible here to go deeper into this kind of analytical description. To do so would require discussion of subgroups of particle elements that are related to each other by symmetric transformations somewhat like the rotation of a hexagon through a 60° angle. Gell-

Man and others recognized that the interactions of quarks, as a well-behaved exchange of gluon particles, could be pictured in an eight-fold way (Figure 16.8).[74]

Physicists found that the gluons allowed the quarks limited freedom. Just like members of a chain gang, the quarks could move freely as long as they stayed close together. But when an imprisoned quark tried to flee, the full force of the gluons' strength prevented the escape.

## New Models

In 1968 a young physicist, Gabriele Veneziano, a research fellow at CERN in Switzerland, tried to make sense out of experiments performed on the strong nuclear force. He had worked on various aspects of it for several years. One day he found, much to his surprise, that the beta-function, an esoteric formula developed by the renowned Swiss mathematician Leonhard Euler (1707–1783), filled the bill. The beta-function described many of the properties of the strongly interacting particles.

At the time, it stimulated a flurry of research. But neither Veneziano nor anyone else knew what was lurking behind this strange coincidence. All long, physicists had believed that the elementary elements were point-like particles. This followed from the observation that in experiments particles rebounded on collision with other particles as if they were points, or sub-microscopic billiard balls. In mathematics this idea was enshrined in the long-standing quantum field theories. While successful in many ways, the quantum field theories were plagued by infinities. Physicists tried to eliminate them, as indicated earlier, by renormalization. Often this worked but sometimes it did not and that posed a serious obstacle to unification attempts.

### Gamma and Beta Functions

Not all infinities represent numerical values of infinite size. When infinite number sequences occur in calculations, their sums may or may not be infinite. When number sequences are added, the sums of some of them diverge to reach ever greater values while the sums of others converge to a specific value. For example, the sequence of integer numbers $_g$ in Equation 16.3, *(1)* , gets bigger with each term. As the number of terms in the sequence approach infinity, their sum becomes infinitely large. At the limit, the sum of integers becomes infinite and the series is said to diverge.

Equations 16.3: Examples of Diverging Number Series

(I) $\quad 1 + 2 + 3 + 4 + 5 + 6 + 7 + 8 + \cdots = \infty$ *(infinity)*

(II) $\quad \dfrac{1}{1} + \dfrac{1}{2} + \left[\dfrac{1}{3} + \dfrac{1}{4}\right] + \left[\dfrac{1}{5} + \dfrac{1}{6} + \dfrac{1}{7} + \dfrac{1}{8}\right] + \left[\dfrac{1}{9} + \cdots + \dfrac{1}{16}\right] + \cdots = \infty$

$1 + 0.5 + [0.58] + [0.62] + [0.66] + \cdots = \infty$

The second series *(II)* of Equation 16.3 diverges towards infinity even though each successive fraction gets smaller. This divergence is demonstrated by adding batches of successive fractions of *(II)*: one, one, two, four, eight, sixteen, ... etc. In the next three series, however, the successive terms get smaller and, as the number of terms approach infinity, the sums of their terms converge toward a specific value. They are examples of Euler's converging series.

Equations 16.4: Examples of Euler's Converging Series

$$x - \frac{x^3}{3!} + \frac{x^5}{5!} - \frac{x^7}{7!} + \frac{x^9}{9!} - \frac{x^{11}}{11!} + \cdots = \sin x$$

where n! $= 1 \cdot 2 \cdot 3 \cdot 4 \cdot 5 \cdot 6 \cdot 7 \cdot \ldots \text{ n}.$

*The gamma function is*

$$\Gamma\left(\tfrac{1}{2}\right) = n!\, n^{\frac{1}{2}} \; \frac{1}{\tfrac{1}{2}\left(\tfrac{1}{2} + 1\right)\left(\tfrac{1}{2} + 2\right) \cdot \ldots \cdot \left(\tfrac{1}{2} + n\right)} = \pi^{\frac{1}{2}}$$

*where*

$\Gamma$ = *Gamma (Greek capital letter)*

$n!$ = $1 \times 2 \times 3 \times 4 \times 5 \times 6 \times 7 \times ... \ n$

*The expression for the beta-function can be derived from the gamma-function*

$$\beta(p,q) = \frac{\Gamma(p)\ \Gamma(q)}{\Gamma(p+q)}$$

These series converge. Most significant in the context here, they converge to numerical values directly linked to sinusoidal$_g$ wave functions.

Then Yoichiro Nambu of the University of Chicago and others showed that Euler's beta-function applied if the elementary particles were modeled not as points, but as very tiny one-dimensional, vibrating strings as, for example, the photons (Figure 16.3, Diagram 1). If small enough, the strings could act just like particles. Unfortunately, it did not take long until high-energy experiments showed that the string model led to some contradictions with new empirical evidence.[75]

By the early 1980s physicists were so dismayed by their failure to integrate gravity with the other three forces of nature, they returned to the Kaluza-Klein Model of five dimensional space: three for spatial dimensions, one for Einstein's space-time, and one for Maxwell's electromagnetism. Recall that, from the outset of this chapter, it was Einstein's dream to integrate all forces of nature into one model. The beauty of the Kaluza-Klein Model was that the addition of the fifth dimension made for symmetry.[76]

Supergravity

This time around physicists tried to incorporate Einstein's original model in a newly expanded version that contained Maxwell's equations and the Yang-Mills Fields. When they succeeded, they found that their new model had a symmetry just like Einstein's four-dimensional model. Daniel Freedman, Sergio Ferrara, and Peter von Nieuwenhuizen of the State University of New York at Stony Brook were the first physicists to design this kind of model. They believed it would be best to incorporate symmetries in their model wherever they could. In fact, they planned to design a "supersymmetric" model of quantum field theories. With this in mind they coined the term "Supergravity Model" (Figure 16.6, Diagrams 2 and 3).

In its simplest form their Supergravity Model was a metric tensor of 11 dimensions with over 100 point-particle components. As Michio Kaku recounted, finding the mathematical solution to a supergravity problem could be very difficult. So difficult that it took several hundred pages of computations resulting in several thousand terms, which in the end had to sum up to precisely zero. Again, despite such horrendous efforts, the theory of supergravity ran into some baffling infinities devoid of any meaning.[77]

Superstrings

However, physicists persisted and came up with another new model, the "Superstring Theory." Generically, it has been classified as a superunification theory. Its central objective is to unify not just the three forces of nature, but to bring all four forces together—the electromagnetic, the weak and strong nuclear forces, as well as the force of gravity—on a single unifying basis. Although pure theory, this model has the advantage over earlier models in that it actually predicts the number of necessary dimensions: 10. It accommodates all four forces in 10 possible dimensions. This superstring model leans over from the quantum side to draw in relativity. Einstein tried to do unify the forces by bringing all forces in under relativity. Nevertheless, the new theory comes closest to Einstein's 30-year dream of a great unified theory.

The Superstring Theory was first put forth in 1984 by physicists Michael Green of the University of London and John Schwarz of the California Institute of Technology. They proposed that all matter consisted of vibrating superstrings. Edward Witten (1951– ) of the Institute of Advanced Study in Princeton became the acknowledged champion and trailblazer of it. He was born with physics in his blood. His father, Leonard Witten, was a professor of physics at the University of Cincinnati, an expert on Einstein's Theory of General Relativity. His mother Chiara

Nappi was a physicist at the same Institute. After Edward graduated from Princeton, he taught at Harvard and at age 28 became a full professor at Princeton. In 1990 he received the Fields Medal, an award in mathematics that is said to be as prestigious as the Nobel Prize in the sciences.

All the research previously described has been about efforts to unify the forces of Quantum Theory. Once it works mathematically and the theory is empirically verified, it is expected to yield new insights. More significantly, it might well revolutionize today's technology.

The Superstring Theory is being hailed as the ultimate theory that will integrate Einstein's theory of gravity with Quantum Theory. Einstein's General Theory of Relativity deals with enormous astronomical scales of outer space. In the absence of massive objects, that space appears to be flat. However, on the ultra-microscopic scale, everything is subject to quantum vibrations. They are violent random fluctuations, inherent in Heisenberg's Uncertainty Principle, and the fluctuations get relatively larger in smaller regions of space.

Superstring Theory is based on a consistent geometry of 10 dimensions (or 26).[78] The so-called strings of it are incredibly small, roughly 100 billion billion times smaller than a proton. According to this theory, matter consists of tiny strings that vibrate in an infinite number of harmonies (Figure 16.9).[79] Assorted matter is formed from distinct sets of harmonies. When the parameters for space-time were first calculated from the superstrings, physicists were awed because Einstein's equations emerged from the strings. This, after it had been thought for decades that quantum theory was incompatible with Einstein's Theory of Relativity.[80]

So Einstein's original idea of a geometric interpretation of all natural forces was right after all. All theories of the natural forces—Einstein's, Kaluza-Klein's, Yang-Mill's, the Standard Model, and even the Super-gravity Theory—appeared to be contained in the Superstring Theory. Still, the race to prove that this theory is really self-consistent in all aspects, goes on. The underlying principles of some of its strange features are shrouded in mystery. And more critically, among the solutions that have been found for the equations, there are many that could describe universes very different from our own. Whether any of them exist we do not know, at least not yet. Nor is it known why the theory must be of 10 dimensions and not any other number.[81]

# APPENDIX

In Matrix Multiplication [A][B] does not equal [B][A]
In every-day arithmetic it is taken for granted that in multiplication the order of factors does not affect the result. For example, the multiplicative product $3 \times 4 = 12$ and $4 \times 3 = 12$. Similarly in algebra it is axiomatic that $a \times b = b \times a$. Other examples illustrate this commutative property of multiplication. In matrix algebra, however, multiplication is usually not commutative because the product of two matrixes [A]×[B] differs from [B]×[A]. To illustrate we use a very simple example of two-by-two matrixes, in both arithmetic and in algebraic notation. In Equation A16.1 we define the A-Matrix by a set of four numbers and the B-Matrix by a second set of four numbers.

Equation A16.1 : In Matrix Multiplication $A{\times}B \neq B{\times}A$

$$Matrix\ A = \begin{bmatrix} +2 & -1 \\ -1 & +2 \end{bmatrix} \quad and \quad Matrix\ B = \begin{bmatrix} +1 & +3 \\ -1 & +1 \end{bmatrix} \quad then:$$

*by standard matrix multiplication:*

$$A \times B = \begin{bmatrix} (+2)(+1) + (-1)(-1) & (+2)(+3) + (-1)(+1) \\ (-1)(+1) + (+2)(-1) & (-1)(+3) + (+2)(+1) \end{bmatrix} = \begin{bmatrix} +3 & +5 \\ -3 & -1 \end{bmatrix}$$

$$B \times A = \begin{bmatrix} (+1)(+2) + (+3)(-1) & (+1)(-1) + (+3)(+2) \\ (-1)(+2) + (+1)(-1) & (-1)(-1) + (+1)(+2) \end{bmatrix} = \begin{bmatrix} -1 & +5 \\ -3 & +3 \end{bmatrix}$$

*so that*

$$A \times B = \begin{bmatrix} 3 & 5 \\ -3 & -1 \end{bmatrix} \neq \begin{bmatrix} -1 & 5 \\ -3 & 3 \end{bmatrix} = B \times A \ .$$

Chapter 17

# PAST, PRESENT, AND FUTURE

*If an elderly but distinguished scientist says that something is possible*
*he is almost certainly right, but if he says that it is impossible he is very*
*probably wrong.*

Arthur C. Clarke[1]

This chapter concludes the narrative of how the knowledge of space evolved historically. The critical turning points of the past will be briefly reviewed, current ideas a bit further explored, and potential future developments considered.

The objective of this book was to make the story of astronomy more believable by adding some mathematics here and there. Although most of the mathematical concepts did not go beyond high school level, providing mathematical explanations was done in the hopes of generating a greater appreciation of the astronomers' ideas of space and our universe.

From the geometry of Greek antiquity to the superstring theory of today, the desire to comprehend the universe has been driven by the Platonic ideal that the world is a reflection of mathematical form, a structure of perfection and beauty. It is strange that mathematics should play such an important role. Indeed, it remains a mystery why, in spite of its incredible effectiveness in the sciences, it is so difficult to find an *a priori* argument as to why the world should be organized according to mathematics as a universal code for science.[2]

Over the centuries, progress in science and astronomy did not advance evenly. In part, the irregular growth has come from external events—variations in economic growth, wars, religious doctrines, and governmental interference. In part, it was due to the uneven development of science itself. Sometimes, mathematical concepts of astronomy were formed first and later found to represent the real phenomena. At other times new empirical evidence caused a revision of earlier mathematical constructs. The time lags caused by interactions of all these factors have varied unpredictably.

## The Past

### *The Science of Greek Antiquity*

Pythagoras (ca.580 B.C.–500 B.C., Chapter 2), best known perhaps for the theorem named after him, discovered that harmonic tone intervals on a monochord resulted from certain number ratios of the length of strings. This discovery led him to believe that the number ratios formed the shape of the cosmos. He tried to establish that harmony existed in the heavens by relating the distances of the planets to that between the Earth and the stars. Being aware that heavenly bodies moved along circular orbits, he and his disciples considered the circle to be a beautiful geometric construct. Pythagoras defined beauty in terms of harmonious proportions of the parts to the whole. Several hundred years later, the Pythagorean concepts of ideal form, harmony, beauty of proportions, and mathematics found their way into the philosophies of Plato (427–347 B.C.) and Aristotle (384–322 B.C.).[3]

Hipparchus and Ptolemy (ca. 180 B.C.–170 A.D., Chapter 6), the two greatest astronomers of Greek antiquity, combined accurate celestial observations with a formidable theory. They believed that the Earth was stationed at the center of the universe and that the stars and planets moved on circular orbits around it. The precision of their model of planetary motions in relation to the Earth and the stars established a foundation of astronomy that lasted for the next thousand years.

### *A New Socialistic Philosophy*

As if they had anticipated the impending economic decline of Greece, the stoic philosophers believed in simplicity of life and faith in God. They lived serenely in poverty, searched for tranquility, and attempted to bridge the gap between philosophy and religion. As philosophers they had grown wary of the search for the ultimate truth, recognized religion as a basis of morality, and idealized communism (Chapter 7).

Around 200 B.C. Rome was on its way to power and the Romans excelled in large-scale government. Mostly interested in practical things, they made no effort to preserve the literature of Greek philosophers. Julius Caesar sailed across the Mediterranean Sea and invaded Egypt. During the invasion the Alexandrian library caught fire and burnt down. Christian monks destroyed what was left of it. All would have been lost, had not a few Greek scholars saved and summarized the greatest scientific works of their predecessors. Their efforts would have been wasted too if Islamic scholars had not translated the Greek manuscripts into Arabic.

Between 800 A.D. and 1200 A.D. Islamic scholars wrote treatises on algebra and on mathematics in general, dealt with questions related to the Hindu system of decimal numeration, and produced astronomical and trigonometric tables. The Islamic caliph Al-Ma'mūn, during his reign from 813–833 A.D., built a "House of Wisdom" with an extensive library and an astronomical observatory.

Even though the Christian Church opposed the teachings of Islamic culture, Latin translations of their work reached the West via Spain. Eventually, Thomas of Aquinas (1225–1298 A.D.) tried to reconcile the ideals of science with Christian beliefs, linking Aristotelean logic with the doctrine of the Church and interpreting science as a search for truth (Chapter 7).

*The Renaissance*

International merchant trade and banking brought economic wealth to Italy. It swept away some of the rigidities that Christian doctrine had imposed on the land. After the fall of Constantinople (1453) many scholars fled to Italy. They brought with them the latest books in science. With renewed economic growth the arts flourished. Gutenberg's invention of the printing press made knowledge more widely available (ca. 1440).

The discovery of America (1492 A.D.) and the Protestant Reformation expanded intellectual horizons.

Copernicus (1473–1543), a Polish astronomer, delivered the opening shot of a revolution in astronomy. About 1800 years earlier the Greek astronomer Aristarchus (310–230 B.C.) had first proposed a Sun-centered (heliocentric) system in which the Earth moved around the Sun. His idea did not gain any followers, mainly because he did not have sufficient observations to prove his hypothesis. Copernicus based his theory almost exclusively on the observational data collected by the last Greek astronomers, Hipparchus and Ptolemy, who lived centuries after Aristarchus. By detailed trigonometric analysis, Copernicus demonstrated that a heliocentric system could effectively explain the motions of the Earth and the planets (Chapter 8).

Tycho de Brahe (1546–1601), a Danish Aristocrat, was the first astronomer who insisted on precision in celestial observations. He designed his own astronomical equipment, built a great observatory and recorded, with the help of several assistants, his observations on a day-by-day basis, year in, year out, with unprecedented accuracy (Chapter 9). Tycho de Brahe invited Kepler (1571–1630), a German astronomer with impressive mathematical talents, to reexamine the orbit of the planet Mars, since Tycho's recorded observations did not exactly fit a circular orbit. Earlier, Copernicus had adopted the Greek proposition of circular orbits. After many years of painstaking calculations, Kepler proved that Mars and the other planets circled the Sun in elliptical orbits and that the planets' distances from the Sun were related their orbital periods (Chapter 10).

Galileo Galilei (1564–1642), an Italian physicist, searched the nightly sky with his new telescope and discovered that several moons orbited the planet Jupiter. He took these new observations as convincing evidence for the Copernican heliocentric view. The Church of Rome was not pleased and, eventually, the Inquisition of the Catholic Church put him under house arrest (Chapter 11).

*Newton's Theory of the Universe*
Isaac Newton (1642–1727), an English scientist, mathematician, and

astronomer lectured at Cambridge University. From the observations of astronomers he derived the theory of gravitation. He showed how the force of universal gravitation made massive bodies attract each other in space and how this force depended on the mass of objects and distances between them. Although he couched his analytical astronomy in geometric terminology, his invention and understanding of calculus underpinned the theory. Newton's discoveries of the laws of planetary motion and gravitation were published in the *Mathematical Principles of Natural Philosophy* in 1687. His book, considered one of the greatest single contributions in the history of science, contained the first unified system of scientific principles explaining the planetary motions in space (Chapter 12).

Newton's discoveries in astronomy, physics, and mathematics widened and intensified scientific research. In astronomy the next two centuries yielded significant improvements in instruments and further advances in theory. They enabled astronomers to measure the speed of light, to estimate the distances of the planets with greater precision, and to obtain the first realistic estimates of the stars' distances from the solar system. More refined instrumentation yielded new information on the transmission and speed of light.

*Limits of Science?*

However, before the turn of the nineteenth century a feeling of uncertainty and futility flowed through the scientific community. Immanuel Kant (1724–1804), a German philosopher, believed that an unbridgeable chasm existed between what "is" and what human beings are able to perceive. This uncertainty of knowledge was underlined by the subsequent discovery that Euclid's geometry was not the ultimate logically consistent construct. Other non-Euclidean geometries of equal consistency were discovered and so the idea of absolute truth was called into question because what would be false in one system could be true in another.[4]

The French philosopher Auguste Comte (1798–1857) concluded that it was futile to seek the absolute truth in the natural sciences. He advocated that scientists ought to be content with working models and not search for the ultimate causes of the unknowable. In the 1870s, at a public lecture at the University of Chicago, a scientist stated that all the basic laws of physics had been discovered. Future discoveries in physics, he believed, would be relegated to changes in measurements at the sixth decimal place. Max Planck (1854–1947) recalled that in 1875 his eminent teacher advised him to study biology rather than physics because in theoretical physics all that could be known was known and that the limits of science had been reached.

## Twentieth Century Physics

With the discovery of atomic structure, quantum theory, and the theory of relativity, these pessimistic views were proven totally false. Joseph John Thomson (1856–1940) proved experimentally that hydrogen atoms contained electrons. In 1900, Planck discovered and reluctantly accepted the strange results of his Quantum Theory. Then Albert Einstein (1979–1955) almost single-handedly created the Theory of Relativity between 1905 and 1915 (Chapters 14 and 15). These two theories, Quantum and Relativity, dominated physics of the twentieth century (Chapter 16).

## Einstein's Vision

In the public's mind Einstein had become the successor of the great Newton. Yet, Einstein was not satisfied. He searched for a theory that would unify all forces of nature in what he called a "unified field theory." The striking similarity between Ernest Rutherford's (1871–1937) model of the atom and the solar system may have tempted Einstein and his coworkers to search for a unification of the celestial macro-model with the atomic micro-model. They tried to construct a unified field theory in which electromagnetism, the nuclear forces, and gravity would merge as different aspects of a single fundamental field. In this mathematical formulation energy forces at the subatomic level would also be integrated with the forces of gravity in space. Although Einstein and his colleagues worked on this unification for many years, they did not succeed. While Einstein's uneasiness about quantum theory went a long way back, his vision of a unification of all forces of nature was far ahead of the experimental results that were yet to come.

With his decision to unify the nuclear forces under the Theory of Relativity, Einstein chose not to follow the route of Quantum Theory. He did not believe that Quantum Theory could yield the classical precision he longed for. Early in his work, Einstein discovered that adding a fourth dimension dramatically improved on the description of natural laws. It unified the concepts of space, time, energy, and gravity. Also, he worked under a very serious handicap. During the 1930s, 1940s and 1950s the particle theory of the nuclear forces was not as far advanced as it was in later decades. Every so often he and his coworkers published an article in a scientific journal, but their theories were incomplete. At the time of his death some unfinished manuscripts were still on his desk.

Einstein disliked the results of Quantum Theory because Planck's theory was not deterministic but stochastic, that is, based on probabilities. Einstein summed up his feelings in the phrase "God does not play dice." Years later, Stephen Hawking would counter: "But all evidence indicates that God is an inveterate gambler and that he throws the dice on every possible occasion."[5]

## The Present

For the last 30 years of his life, from the 1920s to the 1950s, Einstein tried to unify the natural forces of the macrocosm with those of the microcosm. Initially in doubt, today many scientists pursue Einstein's dream, albeit from a different angle. After half a century of intensive effort they have not yet reached the elusive goal. Going from Yang Mills Fields, the Standard Model, GUT Model, Supergravity, and Superstring theories, all discussed in Chapter 16, physicists now have a glimpse of a new domain beneath Planck's quantum length. At that level neither time nor space are expected to exist independently. Nevertheless, physicists speculate that by combining theories at the micro-level with those at the macro-level, they will somehow bridge the chasm between the three forces of nature and gravity, not today but possibly in the new century (Figure 17.1, Diagram 1).[6]

Superstring theories suggest that at extremely high energy levels of 16 gigaelectron volts, the strong nuclear force, the electromagnetic, and the weak nuclear forces will be of equal strength[7] (Figure 17.1, Diagram

2).[8] To produce particle energies of such enormous size would, by today's technology, require a particle accelerator of several light-years in diameter. Physicists hope that experimental processes at lower energy levels will yield results to extrapolate to much higher levels. Perhaps a radically new theory will overcome the obstacles to progress.

Scientific progress is marked by great discoveries and periods of intermittent diffusion (Figure 17.2).[9] At the turn of the last century Max Planck created Quantum Theory and Albert Einstein revolutionized physics with the four-dimensional Theory of Relativity. Events of the macrocosm have proven Einstein's theory to be infallible. Quantum Theory allows for an accurate description of the microcosm. As long as the two theories are not unified, however, physics is still in an interim period of diffusion. In a recent article Steven Weinberg wrote that a young theorist may solve the problem of unification tomorrow, then again it may remain unsolved until the year 2050 or 2150.[10] The search for the deeper structural relationships of the cosmos continues.

After going out of fashion, the Theory of Relativity was revived because of new discoveries—quasars, pulsars and compact x-ray sources, changes in the pulse of neutron stars, and a black hole in the neighborhood of a blue supergiant star—all indicating the existence of very strong gravitational fields.[11] In the past few years, hope has arisen that physicists might develop a theory of quantum gravity.[12] By now, at the beginning of the twenty first century, Quantum Theory is considered central to the unification of all forces of nature. It appears more reasonable now than in Einstein's time to envision a connection between the macro-cosmos and micro-cosmos as a link between General Relativity Theory and Quantum Theory.

*Quantum Foam*

If our universe is perceived as large objects embedded in a flat space of enormous scale, the focus needs to be shifted from away from this macro-cosmic scale to that of micro-cosmic scale so that the ultra-microscopic properties of space become more clearly recognized. Surely, the vast expanse of an ocean should not preclude the study of waves nearby. By sequentially magnifying a region of space its image can change dramatically from a smooth, flat, and curved space to violent quantum foam (Figure 17.3).[13] It is at this level that the theories of relativity and quantum mechanics run into each other and then, unfortunately, yield pernicious infinities.

In the late 1980s, it looked as if the Superstring Theory could provide the ultimate picture of the universe. Almost, but not quite. One reason was that there were five competing versions of superstring theories that appeared to be quite different even though they had some features in common. All required 10 space-time dimensions, their vibrational patterns determined mass and force charges, and at the ultra-microscopic level they were curled up in similar shapes. The other reason was that the equations of each of the five theories did not have just one unique solution but many solutions—somewhat like the Diophantean equations encountered earlier in Chapter 7. And quite a few of the solutions were related to worlds with characteristics not relevant to our universe.[14]

### The M-Theory

Then came the second super string revolution. In March 1995, physicists attended a "strings conference" at the University of Southern California. Inspired by the work others had done during the previous decade, Edward Witten (1951– ) of Princeton initiated the second revolution by showing that the five competing string theories were really "duals" of each other. In physics, as in other disciplines (e.g., in economics), the dual model describes in mathematical terms a second set of concepts logically connected to the first set, the primal. It is more than a mere mirror image of the first because a dual does yield some significant new insights (Figure 17.4).[15]

If, for example, one model were to yield a solution based on the characteristic properties of water, the dual might provide a new set for ice. Both are dealing with the same general subject but under a different set of temperature conditions. Now the search is on to combine the five superstring models and unify them with supergravity in what came to be called M-Theory. The M of M-theory appears to stand for many things: matrix, membrane, mystery, and even "mother of all theories." The unification, if successful, should reveal that the characteristics of our universe are the inevitable consequence of its underlying mathematics.[16]

*Multiverse*

Careful calculations have shown that an incredibly large number of three-dimensional universes—a multiverse instead of one solitary universe—can be derived from the ten-dimensional superstring theory. This sounds a bit strange but it is due to the fact that physicists have not determined all the relevant coefficients of their 10×10 matrix. In general terms such a coefficient matrix was pictured in Chapter 16 (Figure 16.6, Diagram 3). Unless the numerical values of all the coefficients have been determined beforehand, no unique solution can be found. The situation can be illustrated with a simple example of three equations with three variables. It consists of three equations and three unknowns x, y, and z. As shown in Figure 17.5 the numerical values of the solution depend on the coefficient matrix. If not all of the coefficients are known, many possible solutions exist. But if they all are known, the solution can be precise and unique. If, however, one of the coefficients is missing and several numerical values could be inserted for the blank, then it is possible that a new solution can be found for each inserted value.

Attempts to complete and solve the equations of a ten-dimensional universe, illustrated in Figure 16.6, Diagram 3, have been made. Some of the theoretical universes came very close to the Standard Model, others were radically different, and a few even had undesirable properties such as being devoid of material bodies. Among the most fascinating challenges facing superstring theorists today is to find out by what mechanism our own four-dimensional world was selected and which, if any, of the great number of other alternative universes actually do exist. At present there is no definitive proof—aside from mathematical conjecture—if or why they should exist.[17]

The Superstring Theory has never been experimentally tested. To confirm it by experiment would take the power of $10^{19}$ billion electron volts at the Planck energy level, a requirement that is beyond today's technology. It would take about 10 million times more energy than the proposed U.S. "superconducting supercollider" would have been able to produce, and even this project was canceled (by the U.S. House of Representatives in 1993) because of the extreme cost.[18]

*Loop Quantum Gravity*

To complicate things even more there is an additional theory. The story began in the late 1950s with a different subject—the physics of superconductors. Below a critical level electrons are liberated from the atom and can travel freely with no resistance. Cosmologists who work in this area consider String Theory an important step towards a quantum theory of gravity but believe it is not be a complete theory. Abhay Ashtekar (1986) fashioned a new simpler formulation of Einstein's Theory. His equations gave an exact description of physics at the Planck scale where space was constructed from relationships among discrete elementary objects. It occurred to Smolin, another researcher subscribing to Loop Quantum Theory, that area and volume of space consist of discrete particles and, if true, space would have an atomic structure. One of the results of this Loop Quantum Theory is that loop states could be arranged in very attractive geometric constructs.[19]

Is this theory right? No one knows yet. The Loop Quantum Theory is consistent with String Theory. In the end, experiment will have to decide but that is only possible at the Planck Scale which is 20 orders smaller than a proton. String theorists and loop quantum researchers are working in opposing camps. It looks as if each is dealing with parts but not a complete theory of the system. It is reminiscent of Kepler and Galileo, neither one was much interested the other's discoveries but each contributed essential elements to Newton's system of the universe. Both String Theory and Loop Quantum theory have been used to study black holes with spectacular results coming from both. But is either one working on a complete system? At this time it is as if they were looking at the world through two different windows, each seeing only part of it.[20]

*Planetary Travel*

Human beings are like fish in a glass bowl. They can look out but most of what they see is beyond their reach. It is true astronauts can leave the Earth and travel to the Moon or send space probes farther out into space, but beyond our own planetary system lies an infinite universe. If other universes really exist, it might eventually have implications for inter-stellar space travel. But at present, such travel is beyond our grasp and is likely to remain so for the next few centuries.

Over the past several decades the drive behind the space program has been political. Inflamed by the passions of the Cold War, the landings on the Moon were the direct result of the USSR/U.S. confrontation. Isaac Asimov satirized it by saying "We scored a touchdown. We won the game, now we go home."

The Russian space station MIR orbited the Earth for about 15 years. Because of gradual failure of its systems, it was abandoned. In 2001, it reentered the Earth's atmosphere and was destroyed on its way down to the Pacific Ocean. In an international effort, another space station is now being built. When completed it will weigh about 450 tons. Its solar panels will be about the size of a football field. Six astronauts will work out of its seven laboratories. Its total price tag will include about 60 shuttle missions at $1 billion per shot. The space shuttle has been an albatross for NASA (the U.S.'s National Aeronautics and Space Administration) research. Because of only eight launches per year—more launches per year would lower the cost—it has been called the "most effective device known to man for destroying dollar bills."

It is expected that this dismal cost picture for exploring space is going to change. In 1996 U.S. President Clinton awarded $1 billion to Lockheed Martin to develop a radically new rocket design that could substantially lower the cost of space travel. With about triple the number of launches per year, it could be the beginning of a new era in space travel. Other launch vehicles are currently being planned. The objective is to reduce the cost of launching and maintaining low orbit satellites by 95% by 2010.[21]

But, in the meantime, much will be done to expand our knowledge of space. In April 2001 Hubble (telescope) researchers studied a supernova that occurred some 10 billion years ago and found to their surprise that the expansion of the universe was not even but slowed down and then speeded up again as if the repulsive dark energy won out over gravitational pull.

*Modern Cosmologies*

Theorists have introduced this force by adding a lambda factor in their equation, for a constant anti-gravitational force that propels the universe outward at just the right rate to give it a small net rate acceleration outward. Some astronomers say that it smacks of a cosmic fudge factor. In 1992 Lee Smolin proposed that the universe behaved like this because when stars collapse to form black holes they spawn baby universes each inheriting the physical laws that existed in their "parent" universe. The baby universes, in turn expand and push the surrounding universes for continuous expansion. Only those that give rise to new universes form black holes. It would be a cosmic Darwinian selection that allows for this sort of development. As of now no method has been devised to put this theory to a test.[22]

In her book on *How the Universe Got Its Spots*, cosmologist Janna Levin of Cambridge University, describes how she came to believe in an edgeless, finite cosmos by relying on topology. It is a branch of mathematics that deals with smooth deformations of connectedness and volume, that is to say without surface tearing or hole punching. For example, in topology a coffee mug with one handle and a doughnut are the same, punch a hole in the bottom of the cup and it is topologically the same as a cup with handles on both sides or the frame of a pair glasses. Now if the universe did actually have "holes" and "handles" the all pervading microwave pattern would tell us something about the topology of the universe, would it have handles and holes? If so, scientists could test the current theories of a unified theory of the very big (Relativity Theory) and the very small (Quantum Theory), it would be the first observational evidence of quantum gravity.[23]

*Discovery of New Planets*

Since the ninth planet Pluto was discovered in 1930, Astronomers discovered a planet beyond Pluto, it is 1300 km in diameter, going around the Sun once every 288 years at a distance of 6.4 billion kilometers. Although only half the size of Pluto it is larger than Pluto's moon Charon. Discoverd by Michael Brown and postdoctoral scholar Chadwick Trujillo in images taken on June 4, 2003 using the Palomar Observatory near San Diego.

They provisionally named it Quaoar after an Indian mythology in southern California. [24]

Astronomers have discovered a new extra-solar planet in the constellation Sagttarius. At 5000 light years (30,000 trillion miles) from Earth, it is the farthest planet found yet. It has a diameter of 115,000 miles and has been named OGLE-TR-56b. It is so close to its star that researchers have estimated its surface temperature to be about 3000 degrees Fahrenheit. About 1.3 times as big as Jupiter, it orbits the star in only 29 hours, and is washed by rains of liquid iron, it is not hospitable.[25]

In April 2001 the Mars orbiter Odyssey was launched. At the end of the millennium, astronomers had discovered about a dozen extra-solar planets. All of them are Jupiter like, in such familiar constellations as the Big Dipper, Virgo, and Pegasus. Just as the planet Jupiter exerts a pull on our Sun, so do these planets tug on the their neighboring stars, creating for astronomers on Earth, a "wobble" of these stars. The nearest star with such evidence of a planet is only 8.1 light years away. Until it was discovered, all the planets that had been detected were as big or bigger than Jupiter. But with the 1996 discovery of the wobble in the star system of Lalande 21185, there was evidence that two smaller planets are orbiting it. Now there are 85 known planets orbiting other stars. NASA's Kepler Spacecraft, to be launched in 2007, will look for the dips in starlight caused by planets passing in front of their stars. All this is a lead up to the Terrestrial Planet Finder, planned for the year 2015, to detect planets within 50 light years from Earth.[26]

And, in another decade, a new generation of instruments may find dozens of Earth-like planets. It is now possible to combine the light coming from one star, captured by two telescopes separated by a large distance. By having the light rom the same star precisely merge, the light beams will form an interference pattern (Figure 13.6, Diagram 2). By careful analysis astronomers can obtain an image that corresponds to a telescope equal in size to he distance that separates the two telescopes. NASA is also planning on launching a new satellite telescope so sensitive it could see an astronaut on the Moon passing a flashlight from one hand to the other. With this kind of telescope astronomers hope to detect up to 2400 extra-solar planets, of which 100 could be Earthlike.[27]

*Space Travel*

In the meantime, spacecraft and telescopes will expand our knowledge of space. For example, in April 2001 the Mars orbiter "Odyssey" was launched. A major goal of this mission is to find evidence of life on Mars. Odyssey will help scientists to narrow the list of potential landing sites for two "rover vehicles" to be launched in 2003 and land on Mars in 2004. This will be followed up by the launch of a smart rover, capable of traveling seven or more miles across the Martian surface and of collecting soil samples from six feet or more underground.[28]

While missions to the planets of Mars, Jupiter, and Saturn and their moons will be the most publicly visible unmanned space projects, NASA, the ESP (European Space Agency), and Japan's Institute of Space and Astronautical Science have kicked off the twenty first century with an unprecedented survey of comets, asteroids, and solar winds. Plans call for the launch of a nuclear powered spacecraft in 2008, that will determine whether a liquid ocean exists on Europa, one of Jupiter's moons. Another spacecraft will be launched in 2009 to bring more soil samples back from Mars.[29]

These are space missions with concrete goals, others are aimed at more puzzling questions. In 2001, Hubble researchers studied a super-nova that occurred about 10 billion years ago, and found that the expansion of the universe slowed down and then speeded up again. Scientists want to know why. In 2002 ESP launched the Inter-national Gamma Ray Astrophysics Laboratory to help resolve the mystery of gamma-ray bursts first discovered by a space craft in 1991. That same spacecraft discovered 10 rare gamma-ray pulsars, and more than 2500 gamma-ray bursts, among them the most gigantic explosions since the Big Bang. NASA also plans to launch a Swift Gamma Explorer to help resolve this mystery of gamma-ray bursts.[30]

In 2007 ESP plans on launching a spacecraft, named in honor of Planck, that will map the background radiation of the universe. In 2009 NASA will put a new space telescope into orbit that will peer even deeper than the Hubble telescope. It will have a segmented mirror of 20 feet in diameter with nearly 6.5 times the power of light collecting of the Hubble telescope. Finding extra-solar planets has become one of the hottest new fields of astronomy. A database maintained by a Paris observatory listed (by June 2001) 58 confirmed extra-solar planets orbiting stars and two pulsartype planetary systems. It is expected that within 10 years we should know if any Earthlike planets exist and within 20 years if any of those support life.[31]

## Future

More ambitious projects are planned for later decades. For example, by 2015 one of the large telescopes or superscopes, working with interferometers, will be operational. By the end of 2020 such space-based telescopes will be working in concert to test for gravitational waves left over from the Big Bang. Inevitably, our knowledge of space will grow in leaps and bounds, old theories will fall and new ones emerge.[32]

By the year 2020 radically new types of rocket engines will perform long-haul interplanetary missions. Quite possibly they will be equipped with solare electric ion engines. Their solar fuel cells can generate electricity indefinitely although chemical rockets will still be needed to get them into orbit before the solar-electric ion engines kick in. Such "a diversified system of solar-electric spacecraft will make the entire solar system about as accessible for commerce or for explorations as the surface of the Earth was in the age of steamships."[33]

*Catastrophe*

In 1991, NASA estimated that there are 1000 to 4000 asteroids that are more than half a mile across. If one of those should collide with the Earth it could inflict enormous destruction. In June 1996 it came to a close call. At that time the asteroid 1996JA1, about one third of a mile across, came within 280,000 miles (450,600 km) of the Earth. It would have hit the Earth with the force of 10,000 megatons of explosive power, more than the combined power of the U.S. and Russian atomic arsenal.

The most recent impact occurred in 1908 in Russia near the Tunguska River where a meteor or comet of about 50 yards across exploded in midair and flattened some 1200 square miles (3000 square km) of forest. About 20,000 years ago a meteor the size of a 10-story building hit Arizona, creating the Barringer Crater, which is almost three quarters of a mile across (1.2 km). And about 65 million years ago a comet or meteor gouged out an enormous crater of 180 miles (290 km) near Yucatán in Mexico—this comet or meteor may have killed off the dinosaurs. Within the next 300 years another Tunguska-sized impact could wipe out an entire city, within the next 1000 years a Barringer-sized impact could wipe out a whole region, and within millions of years a Yukatán-sized impact could wipe out most of humanity.[34]

In 2002 an asteroid the size of a football field came within 75,000 miles (120,000 km) of the Earth, an event that astronomers consider to be a close shave. The space rock passed well within the orbit of the Moon at a speed of approximately 23,000 miles (36,800 km). Had this asteroid, called 2002MN, hit the Earth the damage would have been similar to that caused by an atomic bomb of about 10 megatons. It would have been similar to that of Tunguska, Siberia, in 1908. And an asteroid a kilometer wide is headed for a catastrophic collision with Earth but it won't happen before March 16, 2880. When it comes to that size scientists start thinking about a global catastrophe.[35]

We must prepare for such a catastrophe by setting foot on other planets. This will be a two-step affair. The first is to get to another planet. The most likely candidate is Mars. After the initial landing and robotic recovery of rocks there might be an attempt to extract oxygen as fuel propellent. Mars is a frozen desert, with sub-freezing temperatures, a thin carbon dioxide atmosphere, and tremendous planetary storms. If it is possible to extract nitrogen in addition to oxygen, the creation of an atmosphere may become feasible. Conceivably, mining operations for other elements could be initiated. Eventually a self-sustaining colony from Earth could be formed. This would be the beginning of a new civilization. But it may not be the end. If a supernova suddenly occurs in our neighborhood, it could immerse the solar system in an X-Ray bath from which few, if any, may emerge. To avoid this interstellar calamity, a move to an Earthlike planet in another solar system would be needed. Such a step calls for different mode of propulsion.

*Interstellar Travel*
To escape the gravitational pull of the Earth a space vehicle must reach an

escape velocity of at least 25,000 miles (40,000 km) per hour. The nearest star to our Sun is Alpha Centauri, at a distance of 4.3 light years. Since light travels roughly at 5.9 billion billion miles ($9.5 \times 10^{18}$km) per year it would take, traveling at 40,000 kilometers per hour, roughly 117,000 years to reach the nearest star.[36] Even if traveling close to the speed of light it would still take a decade for the round trip. Since our galaxy is around 100,000 light years across it would be impossible for astronauts to travel from one side of the galaxy to the other. Intergalactic travel would certainly be ruled out if they wanted to come back to meet people they knew when they left. But other modes of travel are conceivable. Before looking at this possibility it is useful, however, to take a step back.

*Black Holes*

Einstein's four-dimensional theory predicted that the force of gravity warps the gravitational field in space. The greater the mass of a celestial object, the stronger the force of gravity and the greater the distortion of space. If it were feasible to exploit the force of gravity, might it not be possible to shorten the distances of space?

In 1916, shortly after Einstein found the approximate solutions to his tensor equations, Karl Schwarzschild (1873–1916), director of the Astrophysical Observatory at Potsdam, Berlin, discovered an exact solution. It enabled him to calculate the radius of what was first called a dark or frozen star and what later became known as a "black hole"—so named by the mathematical physicist John Archibald Wheeler (1911– ) (Chapter 16, Figure 16.5, Diagram 4).[37] Falling into a black hole could have some dire consequences. Once in it, the gravitational force would become infinitely large, material objects would disintegrate, their molecules smashed, and the electrons stripped of atoms. To escape from it, an object would have to go faster than light and that, according to Einstein, is impossible. Flowing with the gravitational force, the object could possibly end up in another universe but that is pure speculation.

*Einstein-Rosen Bridge*

The mathematical connection between two universes became known as the Einstein–Rosen Bridge, named after Albert Einstein and Nathan

Rosen. According to the equations of Einstein's General Theory of Relativity, matter may not only disappear into the mysterious inner region of a black hole, but could do the opposite and emerge elsewhere, from a "white hole," in another universe.[38] The idea of another universe—a mirror universe at the end of the tunnel did not appeal to Einstein. He took some comfort, however, from the fact that the tunnel appeared to be impassable because it would take a speed greater than light to reach the other side, which is impossible according to Einstein's own Theory of Relativity. Although the same result (a mirror universe) turned up in other solutions of gravitational equations, it was thought to be a mathematical quirk. Ignored and almost forgotten, it came back in the early 1960 (Figure 17.6, Diagram 1).[39]

In 1963 the New Zealand mathematician, Roy Kerr (1934– ), found a second, exact solution to Einstein's tensor equations. He added a new wrinkle to Schwarzschild's stationary solution by assuming that a collapsing star would be rotating, and on further collapse would rotate even faster. Spinning at ever greater speed it would flatten and eventually form a ring, an ergosphere (Figure 17.6, Diagram 2).[40] In the center of this ring would be a zone where the force of gravity would not be infinite. A space probe entering at the center of the ring would not be crushed, but could possibly pass unscathed through this gateway to a universe on the other side.

Yet, it could also happen that future space travelers, while passing through the connecting tunnel, would be stretched into thin, spaghetti-like shapes.[41] Would it then be any consolation to know that some random assortment of the voyager's body particles might make it to the other side? Or if a black hole were created artificially, would the energy matter to create such a gateway be so large that certain quantum corrections would close it? Or worse, would the radiation emitted by the entrance to the black hole be so intense that it would kill anybody trying to enter? And even if on entering, death could be prevented, the time inside the black hole could pass so slowly that it would take billions of years before astronauts would return to Earth.[42]

In our own galaxy a black hole is waiting for us to experience such a trip. Reinhard Genzel and Rainer Schodel and colleagues of the Max

Planck Institute for Extraterrestrial Physics in Garching, Germany, report after a decade of high-resolution imaging a black hole in the neighborhood of Sagittarius A (SgrA). Located at the center of the galaxy it is large, with a mass of 2.6 million times that of the Sun, and certainly big enough to allow ample room for a spaceship. What would happen after the spaceship enters this black hole, however, is open to question.[43]

*Wormholes*[44]

Clearly, to advance the space frontier, a better strategy would be needed. When, in 1985, Carl Sagan completed the manuscript of his novel *Contact,* he sent a copy of it to Kip Thorne, a respected cosmologist at the California Institute of Technology. Sagan asked him whether it was at all possible to overcome the speed of light barrier. Recall that Einstein's Special Theory of Relativity stated that nothing can travel faster than light (Chapter 14).

Thorne and his colleagues were intrigued and took up the challenge. They assumed a future civilization not bound by the limits of today's technology. Their solution was not a black hole, but what they called a "transversable wormhole"[45] (Figure 17.6, Diagram 3).[46] Surprisingly, they found that, for a space traveler, the trip through the wormhole could be as comfortable as a plane ride, never exceeding the gravitational force experienced on Earth. To create such a convenient mode for intergalactic travel would require creating an electric field so powerful that it would puncture the structure of spacetime. Just like a puncture in a tire connects the inner tube with the outside, the wormhole would connect the two regions of spacetime, one on Earth and the other at an intergalactic location of choice. But, what is needed is enough energy to produce such a wormhole.

*Hawking's Quantum Cosmology*

Not all agree that "wormholing" of this kind could solve the problem of intergalactic travel, even if future civilizations were capable of generating the enormous energies needed for such ventures. Stephen Hawking, the Lucasian professor of physics at Cambridge

University, a chair formerly held by Paul Dirac and Isaac Newton, has expressed some reservations about Kip Thorn's theory. He believes that the feedback from radiation at the entrance of the "hyperenergy" hole would distort it and possibly lock it forever. Instead, he proposed another mode that appears to be even more outlandish.[47]

Born in 1942, Stephen Hawking is struggling against the devastating effects of a motor neuron disease that attacks his muscular and nervous functions.[48] While unable to walk and talk, confined to a wheel chair, the genius of Stephen Hawking tackles the mathematics of quantum cosmology.

Starting with Einstein's classical universe, he and his colleague James Hartle "quantized" it. Hawking treated the universe as if it was one gigantic quantum particle. Taking his theory to its conclusion allows for an infinite number of universes, a "wave function" spreading over all of them. Some of the universes could be like ours, others so different that our laws of physics would not apply. The wave function of our universe, for example, could be very large and that of other universes incredibly small, 100 billion billion times smaller than a proton. In this model, wormholes could exist forming links among them. Unlike Thorne's four-dimensional model, however, Hawking's model consists of ten dimensions. Conceptually, they would be linked together by wormhole, but travel from one to the other may or may not be feasible, certainly not by today's technology.[49]

*In the Long Run*

Science may advance in unexpected ways, but some long term trends are conceivable. The Russian astronomer Nikolai Kardashev, for example, saw future civilizations advance to three distinct levels of technology.[50] At Level I, a civilization will have explored all and colonized some of the planets of its solar system; it will control the weather, avert earthquakes, and mine deep into the planet's crust. At Level II, a civilization will use the full power of the Sun and colonize the planets of the nearest stars. And at Level III, a civilization will harness the power of its galaxy and manage spacetime to its full advantage.

By this grouping our civilization is still at level zero, where energy is derived from fossil fuels, fusion power is released only by hydrogen bombs, and a significant colonization of the Moon and Mars is several decades away. Advancing to Star Trek technology of Level II may take several thousand years. And to exploit the energy of our galactic center at Level III may take several million years. In the meantime, a nuclear war, a catastrophic encounter with a comet or an asteroid, or the deadly radiation of a nearby supernova could make these projections irrelevant.

Even if humanity should be saved from such catastrophes, all intelligent life may be doomed by the ultimate fate of the universe. According to Einstein's tensor equations, the universe will expand forever until all of it freezes at absolute zero on the Kelvin scale (i.e., at -273.2° Celsius). Alternatively, it could collapse into a fiery inferno of infinitely high temperature. Which way the universe will end depends on the average density of matter in the universe. If it is less than 10 milligrams of matter over a space volume equal to the Earth, it will expand forever or, if more, it will collapse. As of now, the invisible dark matter in the universe confounds the estimates of the critical average density. In either case, intelligent life on Earth is eventually doomed unless much more advanced technologies can save it.

### The End of it All?

If, ultimately, the universe were to collapse, its temperature would have to rise progressively higher. After the collapse, the universe would be reissued again, by what is commonly referred to as the Big Bang. However, assuming intelligent life had reached the technology of Level III and was able to put up gigantic high energy shields to avert a fiery death, it could escape the ultimate crunch when the four and six dimensions converge. At that point it could transfer into another dimension, possibly into another parallel universe similar to ours before the final collapse.

Or, if the universe were to expand forever, the creation of enormous energies could prevent the ultimate paralysis that would be caused by the deepest deepfreeze. What may now appear to us as science fiction could become reality long before the impending end of the universe, in billions of years from now. By then, large parts of the universe could be colonized by Level III civilizations. However, all this is speculation.

*Other Future Scenarios*

At least three theories imply that the Big Bang of the universe never happened.[51] One is the "tired-light" hypothesis. In our cosmos, starlight travels vast distances, often spanning billions of years. If starlight were to lose energy on its way, it could create a red shift that has nothing to do with the expansion of the universe. At present, no experimental proof exists that either supports or rejects this hypothesis. It would contradict, however, Einstein's General Theory of Relativity, which implies a continuing expansion or contraction of the universe.

A second theory favors a "steady-state universe." It maintains that matter is created constantly and drives the expansion of the universe. It does not explain the source of the cosmic background radiation that is usually attributed to the Big Bang.

A third theory relates to the "plasma model" of the universe. Plasma cosmologists, among them the 1970 Swedish Nobel Prize winner, Hannes Alfvén (1908–1995), maintain that no empirical evidence exists to support a ten-dimensional universe, that dark matter between the galaxies may or may not exist, and that the universe is full of super-clusters of galaxies that are linked together by enormous plasma filaments. Followers of Alfvén believe that this empirical evidence runs counter to a smooth universe that should have evolved had the big cosmic bang ever happened. And if the Big Bang never did occur, we would have to change our concept of time as well. The dominant theory today asserts that our universe is finite in time, existing over a period of billions of years, stretching from a fiery start to a fiery finish, or eventually reaching a dark freezing end. If the universe were not finite in time it would last forever. Infinite in duration, it would continue to evolve.[52]

*Heisenberg's Uncertainty*

Even if the Big Bang did occur and Hawking's interpretation of it is correct, it raises another issue. Hawking treated the whole universe as if it was a single quantum particle. In ten-dimensional space some universes would be like ours, others so different that our laws of physics would not apply. To reach a desirable degree of symmetry the universes ought to abide by the laws of quantum mechanics. If the laws of the macro-cosmos were the same as the laws of the micro-cosmos, the same principles ought to apply to both. Would Heisenberg's Principle of Uncertainty carry over from one to the other? In nuclear physics a particle's momentum and position are indeterminate. Would measurements of the momentum and position of distant galaxies be free of error, even if they reached billions of years back in time? Or would they be equally uncertain?

Hartle, of the Hawking-Hartle quantum cosmology mentioned earlier, GellMann (1929– ) and another cosmologist Andrei Linde (1948– ) interpret it somewhat differently. They do not see our universe evolve from a single past. They think of it as one of many potential universes, some extremely small, others as large our own, some at the early moments of evolution and others at the end of it. Some could be expansionist and others static. To some of them our laws of physics would apply, to others not.

*Bubble Universes*

The steady-state theory of the universe comes in different versions. Aside from Einstein's universe, another theory postulates that the Big Bang is only one of many cosmic explosions.[53] Referred to as a "Bubble Universe," it was developed in the early 1980s by Richard Gott. According to him our universe is expanding continuously with no singularity at its origin. This is compatible with quantum theory, which never allows for a perfect vacuum. In this universe old bubbles would be pulled apart making room for new arrivals to expand.

Another version of it is Linde's (and Arthur Mezhlumian's) stationary universe. It would start off from an imperfect vacuum, sprinkled with small cosmic seeds or fluctuations. Some of them would grow rapidly, others not. Eventually, black holes would form among them and from these, in turn, would come new fluctuations, new cosmic seeds, and more inflationary universes.

*Black-Hole Cosmic Evolution*

Lee Smolin, a professor of physics at the Center for Gravitational Physics and Geometry at Pennsylvania State University, proposed in 1997 yet another speculative scenario. According to him, the critical constants of nature could have evolved through many generations of universes. They regenerate and multiply through the collapse and creation of black holes. As he readily admits, his views are neither strongly supported by evidence nor widely embraced by his colleagues.[54]

Smolin asserts that if the gravitational force was stronger by a factor of one hundred (i.e., $10^{36}$ instead of $10^{38}$), the average lifetime of a star would shrink from 10 billion years to only 10 thousand years. If the strong nuclear force was only half as strong as it is, the electrical repulsion could no longer be overcome and most atomic nuclei would fall apart. Similarly, the characteristics of the electromagnetic and weak nuclear forces are of critical size.[55]

Since the particles and their interactions with the four forces are so mysteriously balanced, Smolin questions whether all this could be mere coincidence? From Earth, astronomers can see by telescope some $10^{22}$ stars. The probability of all the stars having been formed accidentally is incredibly small, roughly one chance in $10^{229}$. In fact, this probability is so small that it could explain all or nothing. There ought to be a better interpretation for the origin of the universe. Smolin offers three alternatives, one alternative is faith in a God who created the world. He calls it a mysticism that lies outside the domain of physics. Another is that the existence of the universe derives from a mathematical model that makes it the inevitable consequence of deeply rooted rational principles, which would make its formulation so unique that even God would have had no other choice to create it. A third alternative is that the universe's parameters are not immutable but can change over time. Under this paradigm occurrences of the past would have set the parameters of our universe today and new events would change them in future. Somewhat analogous to the Darwinian theory of biological evolution, our cosmos would be alive and continue to evolve.[56]

Black holes are the essential feature of Smolin's proposal for a cosmological evolution. In our universe, a conservative estimate puts the number of black holes at one in every 10,000 stars. That translates into 100 million black holes per galaxy. What exactly happens inside the black holes is not known. If a collapsing star exploded in a black hole after the event horizon has formed, it could not be observed from the outside. At the time of collapse the parameters inside the hole could have changed. Conceivably, what lies beyond the black hole is as large or even larger than our own universe. Thus, the invisible regions could well exceed the size of our own visible universe.

If a new universe with a new set of parameters were to emerge from each hole, each could produce more stars and more black holes. Some might not produce any black holes while others could give birth to many. Those with a greater progeny, would multiply faster. At each transition their characteristic parameters could slightly differ from the preceding generation. Eventually, the universe would only consist of those black holes whose progeny outnumbers all others. Our own universe could well be a typical member of this clan. On the basis of these arguments Smolin concludes that the laws of nature in our universe are not eternal and continue to evolve through self-organization, in a sort of "Darwinian Cosmology."[57]

## *Alternative Physics?*

Cosmological theories of this sort are based on mathematics or some interesting hypotheses and not on empirical observation. Einstein was very skeptical of theories that can only be judged by clever mathematics and not be confirmed by empirical evidence. Niels Bohr (1885–1962) believed that physics is what we can say about nature and not about the essence of things. If that requires quantum theory, so be it. Or as Richard Feynman (1918–1988) put it in a seminar: "The theory of quantum electrodynamics describes nature as absurd from the point of view of common sense. And it agrees fully with experiment. So I hope you can accept nature as she is—absurd."[58]

Quantum cosmology, like quantum theory, can be quite confusing. Bohr used to joke about quantum theory when he told the story:

> A young rabbinical student went to hear three lectures by a famous rabbi. Afterwards he told his friends: 'The first talk was brilliant, clear and simple. I understood every word. The second was even better, deep and subtle. I didn't understand much but the rabbi understood all of it. The third was by far the finest, a great and unforgettable experience. I understood nothing and the rabbi didn't understand much either.[59]

Nevertheless, the search for the deeper principles in physics continues. Today's quantum theory could eventually become part of a more comprehensive theory. It might well be that deeper insights can only be gained if a new theory of mathematics or physics, or of both, emerges in time.

*Religion*

Neither today's Quantum Theory nor the Theory of Relativity have explained how God fits into the picture. It is highly unlikely that a unified field theory would throw any light on this question. Aristotle made God the great mover who kept the stars in circular orbits. Kepler emphasized the beauty of it. He even went so far as to let the planets describe harmonic ratios. Einstein believed that God did not play dice and Bohr countered that he should not tell God what to do. But in all these situations God was never very far from science. Yet, what does science tell us about God? The answer to this question: very little.

There are at least three arguments for the existence of God. The argument from design, the cosmological proof, and the ontological proof.[60]

In the argument from design, according to Sir Fred Hoyle (1915– ) carbon is the fourth most abundant cosmic element without which life would be impossible. To make one carbon atom takes three helium nuclei. Were the carbon resonance level only 4% lower, carbons would not form in the first place. Were the oxygen resonance level only .5% higher, virtually all the carbon would have combined with helium to form oxygen. No carbon, no us; so this fine-tuning depends on the two resonances. However, this design argument suffers from at least two defects.

First, the design assumes man is the final aim of the universe. And the second defect is the assumption that there exist many universes with many different sets of laws, and that only in some universes may life arise. The fact that in some universes the conditions are favorable for life, and on others they are not, is a mystery. But this mystery should not be equated with the existence of God.

The cosmological argument relates to motion. It goes back to Aristotle and claims that the ultimate source of motion is "God the Mover." Why this requires God is not clear. Either God has a free will to create a universe haphazardly, and then there is no need for him, or, if God has made the universe in the most reasonable way, then he had no free will. In either case there is no need for God.

The ontological argument states that God is perfect because we can not imagine anything more perfect. If someone were to believe that there is something more perfect, it is inconceivable because there would be something still more perfect. In *The Critique of Pure Reason*, Kant demolished the ontological proofs. Having postulated that thing exist, it puts the tag of existence on things, and then goes on to require the existence of an ultimate being. This is circular reasoning.

There is one more argument. That is the creation of something out of nothing. Previously it was said that the universe could collapse, or expand forever. In either case it must have been created. Or, alternatively it existed forever. It is not only a question of how this was done. The more puzzling question is: "Why?"

# ENDNOTES

## Introduction

1. Joel Davis (1985), *Journey to the Center of Our Galaxy: a voyage space and time*, Contemporary Books, Illinois, pp. 26, 27.

2. Harald Fritzsch (1994), *An Equation that Changed the World: Newton, Einsteinand the Theory of Relativity*, The Chicago University Press, p. xi.

## Chapter 1

1. Sir Thomas L. Heath (1981), *A History of Greek Mathematics*, pp. 128, 137.

2. Will Durant (1966), *The Life of Greece,* pp. 134, 135.

3. *Encyclopaedia Britannica*, "Wise Men," and "Solon." It is likely that the earliest list of wise men was drawn up by the Greeks before the 5th century B.C. The list of the "Seven Wise Men" contained the names of intellectually and politically prominent people. Among them were Pittacus of Myteline (650–570 B.C.) who distinguished himself as statesman and commander in war; Anacharsis (early 6th century B.C.), a prince who exemplified basic virtues; Solon (630–560 B.C.), an Athenian statesman who substituted capitalistic for aristocratic control; and Thales (624–547 B.C.), the philosopher. The list of seven was still accepted by the Greek philosopher Plato (427–347 B.C.) but was later expanded to 10 and even more to accommodate other outstanding persons.

4. Heath (1981), p. viii-xx.

5. Ibid.

6. Aubrey de Sélincourt, *Herodotus, the Histories,* p. 70.

7. Some historians doubt that Thales predicted the eclipse of the Sun at the time of the battle. John North, *Astronomy and Cosmology*, p. 61, for example, attributes it to "myth-making at the time of Aristotle." However, it was Herodotus who reported the event and he was born some hundred years before Aristotle.

8. J. L. E. Dreyer, *A History of Astronomy from Thales to Kepler.*

9. Dinsmore Alter, Clarence H. Cleminshaw, and John G. Phillips, (1983), 5th ed. *Pictorial Astronomy*, p. 106. The Babylonians discovered that the eclipse of the Sun occurred every 6585⅓ days which corresponds to 223 synodic (from new moon to new moon) months. Although this period is often referred to as the Saros cycle, John North (*Astronomy and Cosmology*, pp. 35, 36) relates it to a much longer periodicity of 3600 years. Note that neither the Babylonians nor the Greeks had a decimal system. Instead they used fractions, i.e. not 6585.33 but 6585⅓.

10. Anton Pannekoek, *A History of Astronomy*, pp. 67–73.

11. Lancelot Hogben, *Mathematics for the Million,* p. 44.

12. Dirk J. Struik, *A Concise History of Mathematics*, p. 38.

13. *Encyclopaedia Britannica*, "The History of Mathematics, Geometry." Egyptian geometers also managed to approximate the area of a circle by reducing the diameter by 1/9 of its width and then squaring it. If, for example, the diameter was 9 units they arrived at $(9-1)^2 = 64$. The result is within 0.6 percent of the more accurate estimate of $\pi r^2 = 3.14159 \ (4.5)^2 = 63.6$. They also knew how to estimate the volume of a truncated pyramid.

14. Leon Terry, *The Mathmen*, pp.18–21; and *Encyclopaedia Britannica,*"Thales of Miletus."

15. Jerry P. King,, *The Art of Mathematics*, p. 52: "One of the things mathematicians know and the rest of us do not is that all of mathematics follows inevitably from a small collection of fundamental rules. These rules are called axioms and there are several sets of axioms from which you can begin the development....And the knowledge that the subject can be developed in this way gives the mathematician an overall view of mathematics that none of the rest of us has seen." King then quotes Bertrand Russell, who said of this view:

"The discovery that all of mathematics follows inevitably from a small collection of fundamental views is one which immeasurably enhances that intellectual beauty of the whole; to those who have been oppressed by the fragmentary and incomplete nature of most chains of deduction this discovery comes with all the overwhelming force of a revelation; like a palace emerging from the autumn mist as the traveller ascends an Italian hillside, the stately storeys of the mathematical edifice appear in due order and proportion, with a new perfection in every part."

16. Suffice it to say that two triangles are congruent if, when superimposed, they coincide at all points. The definitions of geometric "congruence" vary somewhat among different sources. *The World Book Encyclopedia* (1975), vol. 8, p. 105, states that "mathematicians do not make a formal definition of the term congruence" but "we may say that if you can put one figure on top of another so that they match throughout, the figures are congruent." *Compton's Interactive Encyclopedia* (1996) defines congruence as "the property of a plane or solid figure that makes it coincide with another plane or solid figure after a rigid transformation." The *Encyclopaedia Britannica* (1997) describes it under the axioms of congruence in Hilbert's terms as "two sets of points [X], [Y] will be called congruent if they can be put into one-to-one correspondence in such a way that if A, B in [X] correspond to A', B' in [Y], then (A, B) is congruent to (A', B')." From there the text goes on to give four elementary constructions and theorems that can be proved."

17. The letters Q.E.D. are often listed at the end of a mathematical proof and stand for the Latin "Quod erat demonstrandum." The phrase translates into "which was to be proven." It has become customary to add Q.E.D. at the end of a mathematical proof to indicate that the original objective has been met.

18. Hogben, p. 130.

19. The proportionality of similar triangles is described in Chapter 4.

20. Terry, pp.14–16.

21. Struik, p. 38.

22. Some might say the at the expanse is finite but unbounded. The author is indebted to Dr. Neil Swan for this comment.

## Chapter 2

1. Proclus on Euclid, Volume 1, p. 65, 15–21, as in Sir Thomas Heath, Vol. I, p. 141.

2. Thomas Taylor (1986), *Iamblichus, Life of Pythagoras*, p. 3.

3. Sir Thomas L. Heath (1991), *Greek Astronomy*, p. xxv lists the year as 572

B.C.; according to J.L.E. Dreyer (1953), p. 35 and Will Durant (1966) Pythagoras was born ca. 680 B.C.

4. Taylor (1986), pp. 7–9.

5. Durant (1966), p. 142.

6. Porphyry's account as translated and quoted by J.A. Philip, "Pythagoras and Early Pythagoreans," pp. 139,140.

7. Durant (1966), p. 162.

8. Ibid., pp. 163–164.

9. Definitions based on *The World Book Encyclopedia* ( 1975), Vol. G, p. 105.

10. Terry, pp. 61–66.

11. Isaac Asimov (1992), *The Secret of the Universe*, p. 133.

12. Eli Maor, є *The Story of a Number*, p. 51.

13. Michael S. Schneider, *A Beginner's Guide to Constructing the Universe; The Mathematical Archetypes of Nature, Art, and Science, A voyage from 1 to 10*, pp. 236, 237, 245.

14. Heath (1991), pp. xxv, xxvi.

15. In his book E.T. Bell (1986), *Men of Mathematics, the Lives and Achievements of the Great Mathematicians from Zeno to Poincaré*, p. 21, refers to Pythagoras having declared that "God is number." Durant (1966), pp. 176– 177 states that the Greeks believed in many gods, divided them into a number of groups: sky-gods, earth-gods, fertility gods and others. In this context it is quite possible, therefore, that Pythagoras spoke of one of many deities and not of one universal God.

16. Taylor, p. 19.

17. For example, Polyhistor, Laertius, Iamblichus and Porphyry, were biographers of Pythagoras who lived some 600 to 800 years after him. According to Thomas L. Peter Gorman, *Pythagoras, a Life*, Polyhistor (first century B.C.) was the most reliable of the three.

18. Durant (1966), p. 163.

19. The Euclidean proof of the Pythagorean Theorem is described in much greater detail in William Dunham, pp. 27–60.

20. C. M. Bowra, and the editors of Time-Life Books (1965), p. 59.

21. In his book *Journey Through Genius, The Great Theorems of Mathematics,* William Dunham refers readers who are interested in alternative proofs of the Pythagorean Theorem to a book by E.S. Loomis, *The Pythagorean Proposition*, "for a bewildering if not mind-numbing, collection of hundreds upon hundreds of proofs of this remarkable theorem."

22. Dunham, *Journey Through Genius, The Great Theorems of Mathematics*, p. 48.

23. Max Born, *Einstein's Theory of Relativity*, p. 323.

24. King (1993), p. 67.

25. Ibid., p. 51.

26. Ratios of integer numbers can always be converted to integer numbers. For example, the ratios 3/11, 4/11, and 5/11 make up a Pythagorean triplet as the corresponding squares 9/121, 16/121, 25/121 are multiples of 3, 4, and 5 as in 1/121 $(3^2 + 4^2 + 5^2)$.

27. According to King, p. 67, it was Professor Morris Kline who called the

drowning of Hippasus "an early example of publish *and* perish". Philip, pp. 191,192, cites a number of other versions of Pythagoras' death.

28. Gorman, Rutledge & Kegan Ltd. , London and Boston, Mass., p. 175.

29. Ibid., p. 175.

30. According to an ancient Greek legend Milo of Croton, a celebrated weight lifter, is said "to have lifted a newborn calf and then continued to lift it each day as it grew until he was lifting a full-grown bull." (Isaac Asimov (1995), *A Memoir*, p. 157).

31. Gorman believed that the personal vengeance of Kylon played a key role in the uprising against the Pythagoreans, that Pythagoras knew what was coming, and "hoping that his absence would curb the wrath of Kylon" departed for Metapontum.

## Chapter 3

1. Aristotle (384 B.C.–322 B.C.), *Metaphysics*, bk. 1, ch. 1, as quoted Robert Andrews, *The Columbia Dictionary of Quotations*.

2. Pannekoek, p. 10.

3. Heath (1981), pp. 3, 4.

4. Russell (1959), *Wisdom of the West*, p. 18.

5. Heath (1981), pp. 3-8.

6. Heath, ibid, pp. xxiv.

7. Morris Kline, *Mathematics, The Loss of Certainty*, p. 11.

8. Albert E. Avery, *Handbook of the History of Philosophy*, p. 16.

9. Russel (1959), p. 36.

10. Heath, (1981), p. xxxiii.

11. Heath, ibid, p. xxxiv.

12. Avery, p. 16.

13. Heath (1981), pp. xxxvi, xxxvii.

14. C. M. Bowra, et al. *Classical Greece; in Great Ages of Man, a History of the World's Cultures*, pp. 69-78; Durant (1966), pp. 241, 242.

15. *The World Book Encyclopedia*, "Sophist Philosophy," Vol. 16, pp. 484, 485.

16. A. H. Armstrong, *An Introduction to Ancient Pilosophy*, p. 23.

17. Avery, pp. 17–18.

18. Ibid., p. 21.

19. Armstrong, p. 26.

20. Armstrong, pp. 25–26.

21. The *Encyclopaedia Britannica* (1997) puts his year of birth at ca. 460 B.C., Durant and Dunham put it at ca. 440 B.C. In either case, he lived at about the same time as Hippocrates, the Greek physician.

22. Based on Dunham, p. 11; and on Heath (1981), p. 183.

23. In Figure 3.1, Diagram 2; the sides of the triangles match the diameter of the semicircle. If we let the diameter of the semi-circle equal 2r, its area will be $\frac{1}{2}\pi r^2$. The corresponding area of the square will be $4r^2$ and the ratio of the semi-circle to square will be $\frac{1}{2}\pi r^2 / 4r^2$ or $\pi/8$. In connection with this Heath (1981), p. 202, wrote: 'But the most remarkable fact of all is that, according to Eudemus, Hippocrates actually proved the theorem of Euclid XII.2 , that circles are one to another as the squares on their diameter, afterwards using this proposition to prove

that similar segments are one to another as the squares on their bases. Euclid of course proves the theorem by the method of exhaustion, the invention of which is attributed to Eudoxus." A detailed description of the Lunes of Hippocrates is given in Heath (1981), pp. 183-202.

24. Dunham, p. 23. More than 2000 years passed before the German mathematician Ferdinand Lindeman (1855-1639) proved that the squaring of the circle is impossible.

25. The description of this geometric method follows Dunham, p. 23.

26. A. H. Armstrong, pp. 33-35.

27. Dreyer , p. 62.

28. Schneider, pp. xxix and 80.

29. Isaac Asimov (1972), *Asimovs Guide to Science*, p. 226.

30. Hermann Menge, Karl-Heinz Schäfer and Bernhard Zimmermann, *Langenscheidts Taschenwörterbuch der Griechischen und Deutschen Sprache*, The strangely sounding names tetrahedra, octahedra, dodeca-hedra, and icasohedra are composites of the Greek numbers four (τετρα-), eight (οκτα-), twelve (δωδεκα-), and twenty (εἴκοσα-) and of faces as in poly-hedra (many faced)  The Diagrams and text of Figure 3.3 are adapted from Dunham (1990), p. 79.

31. Schneider, p. 81.

32. Translation from Phaedo as given in Heath (1991), pp. 43, 44.

33. Attributed to Plutarch's Marcellus by Durant (1966), p. 500.

34. Dreyer, p. 86.

35. Durant (1966), p. 501; and Dreyer, p. 88.

36. Cyzicus was located on the southern coast of the Marmara Sea.

37. Costello B.F.C. and J.H. Muirhead, *Aristotle and the Earlier Peripatetics*, pp. 499, 500.

38. The definition of the "zodiac" in the glossary as given by Chet Raymo, *365 Starry Nights, An Introduction to Astronomy for Every Night of the Year*, p. 225.

39. Durant, (1966), p. 502

40. Pannekoek, p. 110.

41. Ibid., p. 111.

42. Dreyer (1953), p. 89: Heath described the system of Eudoxus in volume I., on pages 330 ff., but refers the reader to fuller details he gave in *Aristaarchus of Samos, the Ancient Copernicus*, pp. 193–224.

43. In Greek mythology Phaeton was a son of the Sun god  Helios. When Phaeton asked to drive the chariot of the Sun for one day, his father granted him the wish. Phaeton, however, could not control the fiery horses. To prevent disaster Zeus hurled a thunderbolt at Phaeton causing him to fall from the chariot to his death (Source: *The World Book Encyclopedia*, vol. 15, p. 315).

44. Heath (1981), p. 323.

45. Will Durant (1966), p. 501M.

46. Costelloand Muirhead, pp. 1-17.

47. Durant (1966), p. 525.

48. Ibid.., p. 526.

49. Dreyer, pp. 108–110.

50. Ibid., p. 113.

51. Pannekoek (1989), p. 116.

52. Terry, p. 105.

53. What is given here in the text is a basic representation of Aristotles' complex ideas. Definitive material on Aristotles' Mathematics is found in Heath, vol. I, pp. 335–348. A summary of his astronomy is given in Pannekoek, mainly on pp. 223–233.

54. Durant (1966), p. 525.

55. David Park, *The How and Why, An Essay on the Origins and Development of Physical Theory*, pp. 53, 54.

56. Russell (1959), pp. 80, 81.

# Chapter 4

1. Heath (1981), vol. 1, p. 354.

2. John A. Garraty and Peter Gay, eds., *The Columbia History of the World*, p. 180.

3. *The World Book Encyclopedia*, vol. 1, p. 326.

4. Ibid.

5. Schneider, p. 55.

6. Will Durant (1966), pp. 550, 551.

7. Garraty and Gay, p. 182.

8. Anton Pannekoek (1989), p. 122.

9. *Encyclopaedia Britannica*, 1997: "History of Education, Ancient Greeks, Origins" and "Hellenistic Age." The era of the *Hellenic* civilization followed the Greek Dark Age from the eleventh to the eighth century B.C. and lasted from the eighth century to Alexander's death in 323 B.C., or from Pythagoras to Aristotle. The Hellenistic civilization dated from 323 to 30 B.C., or from Alexander's death to the conquest of Egypt by Rome.

10. Durant (1966), p. 634.

11. Edward Teller, Wendy Teller, and Wilson Talley (1991), *Conversations on the Dark Secrets of Physics*, p. 38.

12. Diels, Doxigraphi Graeci, Berlin, 1879, p. 378; as quoted by Pannekoek, pp. 117, 503; Aëtius, Placita, III, 13,3. Referring to Herclides' views on the universe, Aëtius is reported have said, "Heraclides of Pontus and Ecphantus the Pythagorean make the Earth move, surely not in the way of progressing but in the way of turning, in the manner of a wheel, from west to east about its own centre." Simplicius, *Commentary to De Coelo*, II, Cap. 8. and II, 13 as quoted by A. Pannekoek, ibid., pp. 116, 503. And Simplicius, in discussing one of Aristotle's arguments, wrote: "Because there have been some like Heraclides of Pontus and Aristarchus, who suppose that the phenomena can be saved when the Heaven and the stars are at rest, while the Earth moves about the poles of the equator from the west, completing one revolution each day, approximately;" and, "Heraclides of Pontus, by supposing that the Earth is at the centre and moves in a circle and the Heaven is at rest, thought to save the phenomena.

13. Colin Wilson (1980), *Starseekers*, p. 68, 69.

14. Pannekoek (1961), p. 117.

15. Hippocrates of Chios; Books IV, VI, XI, XII are concerned with

the ideas of the Pythagoreans and Athenians. Books VII-X deal with higher mathematics.

16. Dunham (1990), pp. 31, 33, 34, 36.

17. Heath (1956), pp. 115, 241.

18. Ibid., pp. 325-326.

19. Hogben,(1993), pp. 124, 125.

20. Durant (1966), pp. 501, 628.

21. Durant (1966), p. 628; and Isaac Asimov (1977), *Asimov on Numbers*, p. 75.

22. Royston M. Roberts (1989), *Serendipity, Accidental Discoveries in Science.*

23. Will Durant (1966), pp. 629, 630. Ten of Archimedes' works survive: 1. *The Method*, 2. *A Collection of Lemmas*, 3. *The Measurement of a Circle*, 4. *The Quadratur of Parabola*, 5. *On Spirals*, 6. *The Sphere and the Cylinder*, 7. *On Conoids and Spheroids*, 8. *The Sand-Reckoner*, 9. *On Plane Equilibrium* , 10. *On Floating Bodies.*

24. Dunham (1990), p. 99.

25. The fraction 8/9 corresponds to 0.888889 (rounded up) in the decimal system which was introduced about 500 to 1000 years later.

26. Maor, pp. 41, 42. For example, if a circle of diameter 2.0 is inscribed in a square, the area of the circle should be according to the Rhind formula, 8/9 times the size of the square. In this case the size of the square is $(2.0)(2.0) = 4.0$ and that of the circle would be $[8/9 \, (2.0)]^2 = [0.888 \, (2.0)]^2 = [1.777]^2 = 3.1577$. Compared with a modern day value 3.1415, the old Egyptian formula yields 3.1577 and that is within less than 0.6 percent of the modern-day value.

27. Maor, ibid, pp. 41–42.

28. The technique of estimating complex geometric areas and volumes to any desired degree of accuracy by minimizing the deviation from their true values was first introduced by Eudoxus (390–337 B.C.). Kline, pp. 22, 23.

29. According to Stuart Hollingdale, *Makers of Mathematics*, pp. 30, 31 the method of exhaustion is contained in Euclid, Proposition X,1 of the *Elements.*

30. This algorithm is based on two of Archimedes' recurrence formulas. A generalized version is given in Heinrich Dörrie (1965), *One Hundred Great Problems of Elementary Mathematics, Their History and Solution*, pp. 184–188. The original version is described by Heath (1981), pp. 50-56. In either case, the derivations of the perimeter estimates of $\pi$ are rather laborious.

31. Will Durant (1966), p. 632.

33. Ibid., p. 633.

34. Terry, p. 184.

35. Dörri, p. 32.

36. Kline, p. 52.

37. Maor, p. 53, and Banesh Hoffman, *Relativity and Its Roots*, p. 16.

38. Hollingdale, pp. 59–61.

39. Terry, p. 172.

40. Hollingdale, p. 61.

41. Durant (1966) , p. 628.

# Chapter 5

1. Bertrand Russell (1959), p. 105.

2. Laurence Urdang and Stuart Berg Flexner, *The Random House Dictionary of the English Language*, p. 878; Menge, Schäfer and Zimmermann, p. 297. Museion comes from the Greek word *museion* (          ), which originally denoted the holy shrine of the Muses, the nine daughters of Zeus (including Urania the Muse for astronomy) who presided over the arts. Typically, the shrine was located at the center of a school or a research institute. Later it became identified with the Museion of Alexandria.

3. Timothy Ferris (1989), *The Coming of Age in the Milky Way*, p. 35.

4. *Encyclopaedia Britannica*, "Aristarchus of Samos."

5. Heath (1981), p. 2.

6. Ibid., p. 3.

7. Ibid., p. 4.

8. Raymo, p. 5. The full circle of the sky, of the Zodiac, all around the Earth, is 360°. The angular size of the Moon is about ½ ° or about one-half the width of the little finger when held at arms' length. Aristarchus' estimated the width of the Moon at 2° or about four times its actual size.

9. The estimation procedure illustrated in Figure 5.3 is a simplified version of that given in Heath (1981), p. 4-6.

10. *The World Book Encyclopedia* (1975), "Moon," Vol. 13, p. 646a. According to modern-day estimates the shortest Moon-to-Earth distance is 221,462 miles (356,399 km), the longest is 252,718 miles (406,699 km), and the mean distance 238,863 miles (384,403 km). The Moon's diameter is about 2160 miles (3476 km). This translates into three estimates of moon-diameters for the moon-Earth distance, i.e., $356399/3476 = 102.53$ for the shortest, $406699/3476 = 117.00$ for the longest, and $384403/3476 = 110.59$. Kilometers are converted into miles at a rate of 1.6093 km/mi.

11. Heath (1981), pp. 8–10.

12. George O. Abell, *Exploration of the Universe*, pp. 19, 20.

13. Jay M. Pasachoff and Marc L. Kutner, *University Astronomy*, p. 178. According to modern-day estimates the average distance of the Earth from the Sun is about 93,000,000 miles (150,000,000 km) Dividing the average Moon-Earth distance of 238,863 miles (384,403 km) into it, yields approximately 390 instead of 19.

14. Heath, (1981), pp. 4, 11–15. In applying the geometric method of Aristarchus, the size of the Sun depends on the relative size of the Moon to Earth. If the Moon were one-half the size of the Earth, as Aristarchus assumed, the shadow of the Earth would be the breadth of two Moons. As shown in Figure 5.4, this leads to a Sun-to-Earth ratio of 10:1. In his geometric analysis Aristarchus uses the 2:1 Earth/Moon ratio as well as some additional ratios of 88:45, 108:43, 60:19 as relative diameters of Earth to Moon. Correspondingly, there are variations in the ratios of Sun to Earth ranging from $225/22$ to $43/6$, i.e., 10.23 to 7.17.

15. *The World Book Encyclopedia*, vol. 18, p. 781.

16. At the time of quadrature of the Moon when the terminator plane, separating the light from the dark side, is exactly in line with the observer, the true

value of the Moon-Earth-Sun angle in Figure 5.3, is not 87° as given by Aristarchus but 89°50′, a difference of 2°50′. This adjustment in the Earth-Sun-Moon angle, has the effect of lowering the sine value and raising the Earth-Moon distance. It enlarges the estimate of the Sun's diameter from roughly 10 to 81 times the diameter of the Earth. That still falls short of the actual size of the Sun, but it does come closer to today's estimate of 109 times the diameter.

17. Asimov (1992), p. 133.

18. Durant (1966), p. 585.

19. Durant, (1966), pp. 636, 637.

20. Terry, pp. 186–189.

21. Heath (1981), p. 242.

22. Terry, pp. 185, 186.

23. Terry, p. 186.

24. John Wilford, "Revolutions in Mapping," *National Geographic Magazine*, pp. 8, 9. Located near Aswan, Egypt, the ancient well still exists today. Several stories deep, its bright illumination still marks the day of the summer solstice. Combining knowledge of geometry with a measure of distance, Eratosthenes had arrived at an excellent estimate of the Earth's circumference. Later estimates were so far short of the mark that some 1700 years later Christopher Columbus mistakenly believed that India was only half as far away going west across the Atlantic Ocean than going east across land.

25 . Lawrence S. Leff, *Geometry the Easy Way*, p. 53.

26. Abell, pp. 21, 22. The accuracy of the estimate of the Earth's circumference depends on a conversion factor of 10.218 stadia per mile. The ancient Greeks used various stadia. If Eratosthenes had used the Olympic stadium as a measuring scale, his estimate would have been off by some 20 per cent. At the scale commonly used and given in the text, his estimate was nearly perfect.

27. Heath (1981), pp. 106, 346; and Hogben , p. 206, 207.

# Chapter 6

1. *Encyclopaedia Britannica* (CD 1997), "Almagest."

2. Struik, p. 55.

3. Terry, pp. 197, 198.

4. Although other authors suggest that fragments of Hipparchus' have been found, Durant (1966), p. 635, stated that only a written commentary on the *Phainomina* of Eudoxus survived.

5. Ibid.

6. Heath (1981), p. 255.

7. Christopher Walker, *Astronomy Before the Telescope*, pp. 76–82.

8. Pannekoek (1989), pp. 65–72.

9. Walker, ed. (1996), pp. 42, 55–58.

10. Abell, pp. 97, 98. Actually the celestial pole does move. While today the extension of the Earth's axis is closely aligned with the North Star, Polaris, the position of the celestial pole will gradually change along a circular orbit. In the course of 26,000 years the celestial north pole will move along a circle of about 23.5° so that by the year 14,000 the star Vega will be closest to the celestial north pole.

11. Raymo, p. 80.

12. Struik notes that "antiquity never was able to muster a scientific organization sufficient to do any large-scale mapping," p. 55.

13. *Encyclopaedias Britannica*, "Hipparchus."

14. It is not certain whether or not Hipparchus actually witnessed the appearance of a nova. Pannekoek, pp. 129, 130; refers to a statement by the Roman Pliny (ca. A.D. 70) who claimed that Hipparchus undertook his work after he discovered two new stars, possibly supernovas. It might also be that his work simply resulted from an increasing interest in the stars and constellations at that time.

15. *Encyclopaedia Britannica*, "Hipparchus," under the section "Stellar Observations" it is stated that Hipparchus' interest in a star catalogue had been stimulated when he observed the appearance of a new star in 134 B.C.

16. Pannekoek, p. 130.

17. The same system is still in use today, the parts being 360°, each degree being 60 minutes and each minute being 60 seconds. On the Earth's surface, one minute is equivalent to one nautical mile (i.e. $1/(360 \times 60) = 1/21600$th of the circumference of roughly 40 000 km, or 6076 feet (1.852 km), i.e., one nautical mile.

18. Walker, ed., pp. 49,50. The final system of the twelve zodiac signs at 30° each, became the classical reference system for the positions of the planets and stars. For more detail see Glossary: Zodiac.

19. Heath (1981), vol. II, pp. 257, 258.

20. Abell (1982), p. 22.

21. *Encycopaedia Britannica*, "Equinoxes, precession of the."

22. Ian Ridpath , *A Dictionary of Astronomy*, pp. 373, 374. This wobble of the Earth's axis is caused by a recurrent combination of gravitational forces of the Sun, Moon, and the planets.

23. An excellent description of this geometric approach is given in Hogben, pp. 144–148.

24. The details of this geometric approach are given in Hogben, pp. 118–167.

25. The more appropriate, but also more elaborate, approximation of a circle's circumference by inscribing and circumscribing polygons is given in Hogben, pp. 150–155.

26. A more accurate value of $\pi$, the numerical ratio of the circumference to the diameter of a circle, is 3.141592.

27. Hogben, p. 228. Hipparchus may have combined the "sine rule" with the "cosine rule" to estimate the Moon-to-Earth distance d (e.g.: OM = (r sin $\triangle$1) / sin ($\triangle$4 - $\triangle$1) and $d^2 = r^2 + OM^2 + 2 r (OM) \cos \triangle4$). Both rules will be seen again and discussed in greater detail in the chapter on Kepler.

28. The *World Book Encyclopedia* (1975), vol. 13, p. 646a.

29. John North, *The Fontana History of Astronomy and Cosmology*, p. 100. Hipparchus estimated the eccentricity to be 1/24 of the radius, when it ought to have been close to 1/160. Also a reminder that the Greek astromers used fractions rather than the decimal notation. Decimals were introduced later. See Figure and text adapted from Michael J. Crowe, *Theories of the World from Antiquity to the Copernican Revolution*, p. 41; details of the terms used in Figure and text are given in the glossary.

30. North, pp. 101
31. Heath (1981), vol. II, p. 257. Even if Hipparchus did not invent trigonometry, he was the first to use it systematically.
32. Durant (1966), p. 635.
33. Michael J. Crowe, *Theories of the World from Antiquity to the Copernican Revolution*, p. 45.
34. Heath, vol. II (1981), pp. 273, 274. More accurately the Greek title for the 'Great Collection' was *Megala Syntaxis* (          ). The Greek for the superlative "Greatest" was magistos (          ). The Arabs combined the Greek word with the article Al and made Al-majisti out of it, which eventually became Almagest.
35. Colin Wilson, *Starseekers*, p. 79.
36. Michael J. Crowe, pp. 42, 50.
37. Based on Pasachoff and. Kutner, pp. 344, 345; and Abell, p. 23.
38 Hogben, pp. 145–149.
39. Ibid., p. 228.

# Chapter 7

1. Pannekoek, p. 173.
2. Durant (1966), pp. 642, 643.
3. The Greek word for pillar hallway or portico is stoa (στοά) from which the word "stoic" was derived. (Garraty and Gay, p.184, and *The World Book Encyclopedia* (1975), Volume 21, p. 495).
4. Durant (1966), pp. 650–656.
5. Ibid., pp. 657, 658.
6. Ibid., p. 659.
7. Ibid., pp. 663–665.
8. Russell (1959), p. 115; and Pannekoek, p. 161.
9. Lloyd Motz and Jefferson Hane Weaver (1993), *The Story of Mathematics*, p. 58.
10. Hollingdale, p. 86
11. Russell (1959), p. 115.
12. *Encyclopaedia Britannica*, "Pappus of Alexandria," and Hollingdale, pp. 88–91.
13. *Encyclopaedia Britannica*, "The History of Mathematics, Survival and Influence of Greek Mathematic."
14. Hogben, pp. 234, 235.
15. *Encyclopaedia Britannica*, "Hypatia."
16. Sir Isaac Newton, *Principia, Volume I: The Motion of Bodies*, pp. 53, 54.
17. A rigorous treatment of Apollonius' *Conics* is given in Heath, (1981), vol. II, pp. 126–196. The essential features of the proof of this particular theorem are described on pages 137–147.
18. *Encyclopaedia Britannica*, "Projective Geometry, Perspective Projection." Perspectives vary by type. Under a linear perspective an object varies in size with distance, the object getting smaller with greater distance. Under perspective projection the object is pictured from an external viewpoint so that the properties are

not altered by their mapping from one plane onto another. In the case at hand the objects are thought to be mapped from the circle onto the plane of the ellipse so that their properties are not altered by this method of projective mapping.

19.    The major and minor axes divide the ellipse into four congruent segments. A line drawn from the centre of the ellipse to a point on its circumference can be copied to all four segments, so that all four lines will be of equal length forming two conjugate diameters arranged at congruent angles around the two axes.

20.    Russell (1959), p. 138.

21.    Park, p. 39.

22.    Edward Rosen, *Copernicus and the Scientific Revolution,* pp. 38– 39.

23.    Ibid., pp. 41, 42.

24.    Park, pp. 79, 80.

25.    Struik, p. 60.

26.    Ibid., p. 65.

27.    Colin Ronan, "Astronomy in China, Korea and Japan," in Walker, *Astronomy before the Telescope,* pp. 245–268.

28.    Pingree (1996), "Astronomy in India," in Walker, pp. 123–142.

29.    *Encyclopaedia Britannica,* "Iran."

30.    Struik, pp. 66, 67, 68. For a description of the advantages of the decimal system see Struik, p. 61.

31.    Ibid., p. 65.

32.    Edward Rosen, *Copernicus and the Scientific Revolution,* p. 43.

33.    Struik, p. 65.

34.    Ibid., pp. 68, 69.

35.    Struik, p. 73.

36.    Ibid., p. 70.

37.    Edward Rosen, p. 43.

38.    Russell, p. 151.

39.    Stewart, pp. 142, 143.

40.    Russell, p. 151.

41.    Edward Rosen, pp. 43–47.

42.    *Encyclopaedia Britannica,* "Muhammad and the Religion of Islam" and Desmond Stewart, and the Editors of Time-Life Books, *Great Ages of Man, A History of the World's Great Cultures: Early Islam,* p. 105.

43.    Ibid., pp. 43–47.

44.    Russell, p. 125.

45.    *The World Book Encyclopedia* (1975), vol.1, p. 543.

46.    Edward Rosen, p. 52.

47.    Anne Fremantle and the eds. of Time-Life Books (1965), *Great Ages of Man, a History of the World's Cultures: Age of Faith,* p. 98.

48.    Russell, pp. 156, 157.

# Chapter 8

1.    *Encylopaedia Britannica,* "The History of Science, The Scientific Revolution: Copernicus."

2.    Based on "Nicene Councils," vol. 14, and on "Renaissance," vol. 16, in the

*World Book Encyclopedia,* and in the *Ecyclopaedia Britannica* under Nicene Councils.

3. Urdang and Flexner ed., *The Random House Dictionary of the English Language,* "Renaissance Man," p. 1117.

4. Fred Hoyle, *Nicolaus Copernicus, An Essay on His Life and Work,* p. 18.

5. Ermland formed part of East Prussia until the end of World War II, when East Prussia was taken over by Russia and Poland.

6. Hoyle, pp. 20, 21 and Edward Rosen, *Copernicus and the Scientific Revolution* p. 57.

7. Jerzy Neyman, ed., "The Heritage of Copernicus: Theories Pleasing to the Mind," in *The Copernican Volume of the National Academy of Sciences,* p. 2.

8. Ibid., p. 2.

9. Edward Rosen (1984), p. 57.

10. Hoyle, pp. 20–22. Professor Adalbert Brudzewski had himself studied under Johann Müller also known as Regiomontanus, 1436–76, at the University of Vienna. Professor Müller, in turn, was a devotee of Georg Peurbach (1423–1461), who had written the Epitome in Ptolemaei Almagestum, a book describing the treatise of Ptolemy. In 1472 Peurbach wrote another book on the New Theory of the Planets in which he attributed the variations in the appearance of the planets to their eccentric revolutions around the Earth.

11. North, p. 280.

12. Edward Rosen, p. 58.

13. Nicolaus Copernicus, *On the Revolutions of Heavenly Spheres,* p. vii.

14. Hoyle, p. 24.

15. Ibid., pp. 24–27.

16. Frauenburg was a small town that, until the end of World War II, was located in Eastern Prussia adjacent to the Frisches Haff (now Zalew Wiślany), a bay that borders on the Gulf of Danzig (now Gdansk).

17. Hoyle, p. 31.

18. Ibid., pp. 30–34.

19. Ibid., pp. 34–36.

20. Menge, *Langenscheidt's Taschenwörterbuch: Latein. Commentariolus* is the Latin word for design, sketch, model, plan. North, p. 280: In his design Copernicus adhered to the principle of circular motion, avoided the use of the equants, and had all planets share a common center, not quite at the Sun but at the center of the Earth's orbit.

21. Hoyle, pp. 36–39.

22. Copernicus, pp. 4, 5 (pp. ii[b], iii[a] in the original).

23. Urdang and Flexner, Lateral Council refers to a council of the Church of St. John Lateran, the cathedral of the Pope as Bishop of Rome, p. 757.

24. David Eliot Brody and Arnold R. Brody (1997), *The Science Class You Wish You Had.The Seven Greatest Scientific Discoveries in History and the People Who Made Them,* p. 8.

25. Copernicus, pp. 5 and 7.

26. Ibid., p. 9.

27. Ibid., pp. 9, 10, 11.

28. Ibid., pp. 11, 12.

29. Ibid., p. 12.

30. Ibid., pp. 19, 24.

31. Kline, p. 36.

32.   Copernicus had access to the observations of Hipparchus, Ptolemy, and others. According to Arthur Koestler (1960), *The Watershed, a Biography of Johannes Kepler*, p. 88, Copernicus himself recorded only twenty-seven observations of his own in the whole *De Revolutionibus Orbium Coelestium*.

33. Copernicus (1994) , p. 12.

34. Ibid., p. 13.

35. Ibid., pp. 11–13.

36. Ibid., pp. 15, 16.

37. Ibid., p. 14.

38. Ibid., pp. 14, 17, 18.

39. Ibid., p. 15.

40. Ibid., p. 19.

41. Copernicus, p. 25, and  Pasachoff and Kutner,  p. 345.

42. Ridpath, *A Dictionary of Astronomy,* p. 135. More precisely the orbital period of the Earth is 365.256 days.

43. Ridpath, pp. 333, 334. The angle between the Earth's equator and the orbital plane is technically referred to as the *obliquity of the ecliptic.* It is of the same size as the angle of the Earth's axial tilt from the vertical.It is currently estimated at some-what over 23° 26' and is gradually decreasing at the rate of 47" per 100 years.

44. Copernicus, p. 57 (p. 29a in the original). To determine the inclination of the Earth's axis to its orbital plane, Copernicus estimated the equivalent of the angular distance between the northern and southern tropics and by that arrived at a measure of the ecliptic.

45. Copernicus, p. 57. Some 1300 years earlier Ptolemy estimated it at 23°51'20."

46.   Simon Mitton, *The Cambridge Encyclopaedia of Astronomy*, p. 159.

47.   Copernicus, pp. 86, 87.

48.   Ibid., p. 87.

49.   Ibid., p. 144.

50.   Ibid., p. 87.

51.   Ibid., p. 87.

52.   Raymo, p. 161.

53.   Copernicus, p. 230 (p. 134[a] in the original).

54.   Schäfer and Zimmermann, p. 332.

55.   In the Ptolemaic system the planets move along  the circumference of the epicycles while the center of the epicycle advances along the larger orbit of the deferent concurrently. In Figure 8.6 this motion is pictured by a planet progressing from positions 1 to 7. The Figure is simplified by putting several planetary positions on the same epicycle. More accurately, the motion should have been represented by seven epicycles that allowe the planet to advance from one to the next as the epicycle continued to track along the deferent.

56. Mitton, p. 163.

57. Copernicus, p. 230.

58. Ibid., p. 231.

59. Ridpath., p. 466.

60. Ibid., p. 427.

61. The estimates for the synodic and siderial periods were based on Copernicus, p. 231.

62. Copernicus, p. 231. Modern-day estimates are based on Mitton, Table 9.1, p. 161.

63. Asimov (1966), *The Universe, From Flat Earth to Quasar,* pp. 23, 24. The other exterior planets are Uranus, Neptune, and Pluto. They are, respectively, two, three, and four times as far from the Sun as the planet Saturn. More precisely, in terms of light hours (l.h.), their distances from the Sun are: Saturn, 1.321 l.h.; Uranus, 2.66 l.h.; Neptune, 4.26 l.h.; and Pluto, 5.47 l.h.

64. Copernicus, p. 265.

65. Ibid., p. 239.

66. David F. Tver, *Dictionary of Astronomy, Space, and Atmospheric Phenomena,* pp. 115, 116.

67. Copernicus, p. 275, 276.

68. Ibid., p. 87.

69. This quote is taken from the Introduction of Nicolaus Copernicus, p. 7 (p.iv$^b$ in the original). The Introduction is believed to have been written by Andrew Osiander, a Lutheran cleric and friend of Copernicus who managed the book's printing. It has been alleged that Osiander modified Copernicus' original introduction and thereby misrepresented the intent of the author by stating (on the first page of the Introduction) that "It is not necessary that these hypotheses should be true, or even probable; but it is enough if they provide a calculus which fits the observations—unless by some chance there is anyone so ignorant of geometry and optics as to hold the epicycle of Venus as to be a cause why Venus alternately precedes and follows the Sun at an angular distance of up to 40° or more." It is debatable whether or not this statement was a serious misrepresentation.

70 Hoyle, pp. 38–44.

71. Copernicus, p. 4.

72. Russell (1959), p. 119.

73. T. S. Kuhn as quoted in Hugh Kearney (1971), *Science and Change 1500–1700,* pp. 99, 100.

74. Edward Rosen, as quoted by Hugh Kearney (1971), p. 101.

75. Edward Rosen as quoted by Hugh Kearney (1971), p. 104.

76. Dreyer, pp. 346–350.

77. Ibid., p. 351.

## Chapter 9

1. N. M. Swerdlow, on "Astronomy in the Renaissance" in Walker, p. 237.

2. Durant (1961), *The Age of Reason Begins,* p. 595.

3. Jay E. Greene, ed., *100 Great Scientists,* p. 55.

4. Dreyer as quoted by Koestler, p. 86.

5. Durant (1961), p. 595.

6. Ibid., p. 595.

7. Pannekoek, p. 182. Shaped like a small cross it was widely used

around the fifteenth century for measuring the angular distance between two celestial objects. By pointing one end of the sliding crossbar at one object and the other end of the crossbar at a second object, the observer could read off the angular distance between two celestial objects on the graduated long bar. It was commonly used by navigators to measure the angle of the Sun or a star above the horizon.

8. Koestler, p. 87.

9. Figure 9.1 was adapted from the *Encyclopaedia Britannica*, "Navi gation."

10. Patrick Moore, *Watchers of the Stars, The Scientific Revolution*, p. 41.

11. Koestler, p. 90 and Pannekoek, p. 198; the "Alphonsian Tables," were superseded by the "Prutenic Tables" that were prepared by the Wittenberg mathematician Erasmus Reinhold, who based them on Copernican data.

12. Marie Boas, *The Scientific Renaissance 1450–1630, The Rise of Modern Science II,* pp. 92 , 109.

13. Koestler, p. 90.

14. Durant (1961), p. 496.

15. Koestler, pp. 85, 86.

16. Durant (1961), p. 596

17. Koestler, p. 86.

18. One degree is the 360th part of a complete circle and one second the 3600 th part of a degree. A ten-second accuracy implies that each degree was further divided into 360 parts. Enlarging the radius of a quadrant enabled astronomers to measure angular distances more accurately. If, to illustrate the principle, the radius of a quadrant were to match that of the Earth, each degree along the equator would measure 66 miles (106 km), each minute 1.77 km, and each second 32 yards (29 meters). (Also see Glossary, under degree.)

19. Pannekoek, p. 206.

20. Koestler, pp. 90, 91.

21. Durant (1961), pp. 575, 596.

22. Asimov (1972), *Asimov's Guide to Science,* p. 57.

23. Chet Raymo, pp. 186–188; *World Book Encyclopedia*, vol. 14, "Nova," p. 431; and Ridpath ed., pp. 329, 462.

24. Pannekoek, p. 207.

25. Moore, p. 95.

26. Tycho described these findings in his book *De Stella Nova*. While he re-ferred to it as a Nova (*Nova* is Latin for new and *stella* Latin for star), in modern-day literature Tycho's star is often referred to as a supernova because nowadays astronomers distinguish between a nova and a supernova. For more on this point, see Glossary under supernova.

27. Ridpath, pp. 388, 389; and Walker, p. 340: Radio astronomy began during the 1930's. The radio image of the remains of Tycho's Star was taken with the Cambridge radio telescope. Described as object 3C10, it was detected during the third Cambridge Survey.

28. Pannekoek, pp. 207, 208.

29. Marie Boas, *The Scientific Renaissance 1450–1630, The Rise of Modern Science II*, p. 111 and Koestler, pp. 92, 93.

30. Pannekoek, pp. 208, 209; Koestler, pp. 94, 95.
31. North, p. 301.
32. Moore (1974), p. 91; based on Tycho's *Astronomicae Instaurata Mechanica,* 1587.
33. Koestler, pp. 96, 97.
34. Ibid., pp. 96, 97, 98.
35. North, sp. 305.
36. Pannekoek, pp. 209–213.
37. Walker, p. 207.
38. Boas, p. 114.
39. Pasachoff and Kutner, p. 349: Adopted from Tycho de Brahe's illustration of his 1588 book, and North, p. 304.
40. Durant (1961), p. 496.
41. Koestler, p. 101–103.
42. Ibid., p. 107–108
43. Max Caspar, *Kepler*, p. 182.
44. North, p. 309.
45. Koestler, pp. 99–102.
46. Pannekoek, p. 216.
47. Koestler, p. 103; letter from Kepler to Ursus, dated 15. 11. 1595.
48. Ibid., p. 104; letter from Kepler to Tycho, dated 13. 12. 1597.
49. Ibid., p. 106; letter from Tycho to Kepler, *Gesammelte Werke.*
50. Ibid., p. 110; letter from Kepler to Herwart, dated 12. 7. 1600..
51. Ibid., p. 109–116, 120.
52. Ibid., p. 104, letter from Tycho to Kepler dated 1. 4. 1598.
53. Ibid., p. 106; letter from Tycho to Kepler, *Gesammelte Werke.*
54. Ibid., p. 121.

## Chapter 10

1. Born, p. 12. Max Born was the 1954 recipient of the Nobel Prize for research in quantum mechanics.
2. Weil-der-Stadt is located among forested rolling mountains, not far from Stuttgart and within easy reach from the Autobahn (national highway).
3. Caspar, p. 29.
4. Johannes Kepler as quoted in Koestler, pp. 22, 23.
5. Caspar, p. 34.
6. Ibid., p. 35.
7. Ibid., p. 33.
8. Ibid., p. 34.
9. Kepler as quoted in Koestler, p. 19.
10. Caspar, pp. 37, 38.
11. Ibid., p. 36, and Koestler, pp. 22–24.
12. Koestler, p. 26.
13. Ibid., p. 27.
14. Caspar, p. 39.

15. Kepler as quoted in Koestler, pp. 28, 29.
16. Caspar, p. 40.
17. Ibid., pp. 46, 47.
18. Ibid.., pp. 50, 51, 52.
19. Kepler as quoted in Koestler, pp. 36, 37, 38.
20. Caspar, p. 54.
21. Koestler, p. 39.
22. Kepler as quoted in Koestler, pp. 39, 256.
23. Ibid., pp. 39, 41, 256.
24. Ibid., pp. 43, 44–46.
25. Ibid., pp. 47, 48, 257.
26. Ibid., p. 51. For example: "the regular solids of the first order [i.e., of the exterior planets] have it in their nature to stand upright, those of the second order float. For if the latter were made to stand on their sides, the former on their corners, then in both cases the eye shies from the ugliness of such a sight."
27. Ibid., p. 52, 257.
28. Ibid., p. 54, 257. Kepler went much further. He claimed not only that the data Copernicus had used for his analysis were faulty but accused him of cheating: "He selects observations from Ptolemy, Walter, and others with a view to making his computations easier, and he does not scruple to neglect or to alter occasional hours in observed time and quarter degrees of angle."
29. Ibid., pp. 60, 258.
30. Ibid., pp. 60, 258.
31. Koestler, p. 61.
32. Ibid., pp. 69, 70.
33. Kepler, as quoted in Koestler, p. 73.
34. Koestler, p. 75, 76.
35. Ibid., pp. 52, 78, 79.
36. Kepler as quoted in Arthur Koestler, pp. 79, 80, 260.
37. Koestler, pp. 80–82.
38. Ibid., p. 84.
39. Pannekoek, p. 242. The full title of the book was *Astronomia nova, aitio-logetus seu physica coelestis* (New Astronomy, Causally Explained or Celestial Physics)
40. Kepler as quoted in Koestler, pp. 123, 124.
41. Ibid., as quoted in Arthur Koestler, p. 124.
42. Koestler, pp. 128. One of the motives for Copernicus' reform of Ptolemy's geocentric system was his dissatisfaction with Ptolemy's assertion that a planet did not move at uniform speed around the center of its orbit but around the equilibrating point *(punctum equans),* situated off center to give the appearance of uniform motion. Alternatively the appearance of uniform motion could be a-chieved by adding epicycles to the planets orbits.
43. Ibid., p. 131.
44. Caspar, pp. 127, 128.
45. Kepler as quoted in Koestler, pp. 132, 133.
46. Ibid., p. 133.
47. Ibid., p. 134.

48. Pasachoff and Kutner, p. 354. In 1801 the German mathematician and astronomer Karl Friedrich Gauss developed a precise and much less time-consuming method of predicting from a limited number of three or more observations of the orbits of objects in the solar system.

49. Based on Pasachoff and Kutner, pp. 353, 354.

50. Ridpath, pp. 289, 427. The sidereal year is the period of Earth-days it takes a planet to complete one orbital revolution around the Sun. The sidereal year of the Earth is 365.256 days and that of Mars is 686.980 days.

51. Abell, p. 40.

52. As shown in Appendix A to this Chapter, the Sine Rule states that in any triangle the ratios of its three angles to their corresponding (opposite) sides are numerically equal. The description is based on P. Abbott and M. E. Wardle, *Trigonometry*, pp. 100, 101.

53. North, p. 322.

54. Kepler as quoted in Koestler, pp. 139,140.

55. Based on *The World Book Encyclopaedia*, vol. 13, p. 181 and on *The Encyclopaedia Britannica*, "The Solar System, Basic Astronomical Data, The Orbit of Mars." Today's estimates for the Martian variations in distance to the Sun put the shortest distance at 128.3 million miles (206.6 million kilometres), the longest at 154.8 million miles (249.2 million kilometres), and the average distance at 141.6 million miles (227.9 million kilometres). It implies that the Sun-to-Mars distance ranges from 90.7% to 109.4% of its mean distance (set at 100%).

56. Caspar, p. 131.

57. A detailed description of Kepler's approach is given in Walker, pp. 214–230.

58. Park, pp. 175, 176. Kepler knew from his work on optics that the intensity of light varied inversely with the square of its distance from the source. According to Aristotle, however, the velocity of an object was directly proportionate to the driving force. In applying Aristotle's concept of motion Kepler expected to get the simple inverse of the planet's distance from the Sun for the driving force, but instead he got the inverse square for it.

59. Park, p. 150.

60. Walker, p. 222.

61. Timothy Ferris (1989), *The Coming of Age in the Milky Way*, p. 79.

62. Walker, p. 222.

63. Pannekoek, p. 241.

64. Actually, Kepler's geometric reasoning was far more complex and is described in greater detail by N. M. Swerdlow in *Astronomy in the Renaissance* in Walker, pp. 220–225.

65. Kepler as quoted in Koestler, pp. 145, 263.

66. Caspar, p. 134.

67. This simplified description follows Park, pp. 152.

68. Ridpath, p. 146.

69. The Diagrams 4 and 5 of Figure 10.5 are again simplified. They are based on Pannekoek, pp. 239, 241. A more detailed geometric and complex presentation is given by Swerdlow, "Astronomy in the Renaissance" in Walker, pp. 222, 223.

70. Kepler's equation is discussed in considerable detail by Swerdlow in *"Astronomy in the Renaissance"* in Walker, p. 223. Swerdlow also describes the reasoning behind the mysterious numerical values given in Diagram 4 of Figure 10.5. The numerical values differ slightly from the eccentricity of 0.0934 of the planet Mars given in *The Encyclopaedia Britannica*, "The Solar System, Basic Astronomical Data, The Orbit of Mars."

71. Dreyer, pp. 391, 392.

72. Abell, p. 40.

73. Ibid., p. 40.

74. As quoted by Koestler, pp. 264, 265. The Preface, written by Franz Gansneb Tengnagel, Tycho de Brahe's son-in-law, read as follows (you is substituted for thee, or ye) :

> *Greetings to the reader! I had intended to address you, reader, with a longer preface. Yet the mass of political affairs which keep me more than usually busy these days, and the hasty departure of our Kepler, who intends to leave for Frankfurt within the hour, only left me a moment's time to write. But I thought nevertheless that I ought to address a few words to you, lest you should become confused by the liberties which Kepler takes in deviating from Brahe in some of his expositions, particularly those of physical nature. Such liberties can be found in all philosophers since the world existed; and in no way affects the work of the Rudolphine tables.* [This refers to the planetary tables which Tengnagel had promised to produce, and never did.] *You will be able to see from this work that it has been built on the foundations of Brahe . . . and that the entire material (I mean the observations) was collected by Brahe. In the meantime, consider Kepler's excellent work ... as a prelude to the tables and the observations to follow which, for the reasons explained, can only be published slowly. Pray with me to the Almighty and all-wise Lord for the rapid progress of this much-desired work and for happier days..*

75. Koestler, pp. 160, 162.

76. As quoted in Ferris (1989), p. 79.

77. As quoted in Roy Porter, *Man Masters Nature, 25 Centuries of Science*, p. 60.

78. Koestler, pp. 165, 201.

79. Durant (1961), p. 539.

80. Koestler, pp. 166, 167, 203, 204.

81. Ibid., p. 205.

82. Ibid., p. 235.

83. Ibid., p. 208.

84. Ibid., pp. 213, 269. As Koestler points out, this "work is sometimes erroneously referred to as "Harmonices," as if the "s" stood for the plural, whereas it stands, of course, for the genetive."

85. Ibid., p. 214.

86. Caspar, pp. 275, 276.

87. *The World Book Encyclopedia*, "Harmonics," (vol. 9) and "Sound," (vol. 18).

88. Park, p. 155.

89. Kepler as quoted in Koestler, pp. 218, 269.

90. Kepler as quoted in Caspar, p. 286.

91. Abell, p. 41.

92. This numerical value differs slightly from that in Table 9.1 presumably because of rounding.

93. Kepler as quoted in Koestler, pp. 219, 220, 269.

94. Ibid., pp. 157, 264.

95. Ibid.., pp. 152, 264.

96. North, p. 326.

97. Koestler, p. 237.

98. Ibid., pp. 238–240.

99. Kepler had dedicated his book *Harmonices Mundi Libri V* to James I, as stated by Koestler in a footnote on p. 242.

100. Kepler as quoted in Koestler, p. 254.

101. Koestler, pp. 246–254.

102. Dreyer, p. 413.

103. The Sine and Cosine Rules are based on Douglas Downing, (1990), *Trigonometry the Easy Way*, pp. 99–107.

## Chapter 11

1. Born, p. 12.

2. *Encyclopaedia Britannica*, "Galileo."

3. Will Durant (1953), *The Renaissance, a History of Civilization in Italy from 1304-1576, The Story of Civilization*, p. 688.

4. Giorgio De Santillana, *The Crime of Galileo*, p. xxi.

5. Drake Stillman (1980), *Galileo (Past Masters)*, p. 22.

6. Allen-Olney as quoted in Stillman (1980), p. 23.

7. Colin A. Ronan, *Galileo*, p. 65.

8. Sidney Rosen (1958), *Galileo and the Magic Numbers*, pp. 22, 24, 25.

9. Ibid., p. 31.

10. Boas, p. 315.

11. Stillman (1980), p. 22.

12. Ibid., p. 23.

13. Ibid., p. 24.

14. Ibid., p. 24; and Spencer Armstrong (1950), *101 of the World's Greatest Books*, pp. 272–287.

15. Stillman (1980), p. 18.

16. Sidney Rosen, p. 69.

17. Hathaway, p. 134.

18. Stillman (1995), pp. 20, 414–416.

19. Ronan, pp. 81–85.

20. Sidney Rosen (1958), *Galileo and the Magic Numbers*, pp. 96, 98, 99.

21. Stillman (1980), p. 27; and Ronan, pp. 87, 89, 127.

22. De Santillana, p. xxii.

23. Stillman (1995), *Galileo at Work, His Scientific Biography*, pp. 34, 35.

24. Sidney Rosen (1958), p. 114; and Ronan, pp. 94, 95.

25. Hathaway, p. 134.

26. Boas, p. 170.

27. Sidney Rosen, p. 105–107; and Ronan, pp. 96, 97.

28. Stillman (1980), p. 29.

29. De Santillana (1955), p. xxii.

30. Koestler, p. 175.

31. As quoted in Nancy Hathaway, *The Friendly Guide to the Universe, A Down-to-Earth Tour of Space, Time, and the Wonders of the Cosmos*, p. 135.

32. Sidney Rosen, pp. 108–110.

33. Prowe as quoted in Pannekoek, p. 222.

34. Pannekoek, p. 186.

35. De Santillana, pp. xxii, xxiii.

36. Stillman (1980), p. 31.

37. According to Stillman, p. 32, Galileo's invention of the pulsilogium is often wrongly credited to him in his student days.

38. Ronan, p. 70.

39. Sidney Rosen, pp. 42–44.

40. Ibid., p. 115.

41. Ibid., pp. 115–117.

42. According to Stillman (1980), p. 33, with respect to timing the acceleration of falling bodies, Galileo was able to measure distances on a scale of millimeters, each approximately 4/100 of an inch, and time the positions of the balls at time intervals of about one-half of a second accuracy as judged by musical beats. According to David L. Goodstein and Judith R. Goodstein, *Feynman's Lost Lecture, The Motion of Planets Around the Sun*, p. 36, Galileo tried many different ways of measuring time intervals. The best of these was a "water chronometer" with which he might have been able to achieve an accuracy of two-tenths of a second.

43. Sidney Rosen, pp. 71–73.

44. Gamow (1988), *The Great Physicists from Galileo to Einstein*, p. 36.

45. Galileo Galilei (1974 [1638]), *Two New Sciences, Including Centers of Gravity and Force of Percussion*, pp. 166, 167; Galilei described this phenomenon as his Theorem II on Motion. Translated, it reads: "If a moveable descends from rest in uniformly accelerated motion, the spaces run through in any times whatever are to each other as the duplicate ratio of their times; that is, are as the squares of those times." He continues the theorem in Corollary I: "From this it is manifest that if there are any number of equal times taken successively, then these spaces will be to one another as are the odd numbers from unity, that is, as 1, 3, 5, 7."

46. Galilei, p. 170.

47. Motz and Weaver (1992), *The Story of Physics*, p. 40.

48. George E. Owen (1971), *The Universe of the Mind*, p. 85.

49. Halliday, David, Robert Resnick and Jearl Walker (1993), *Fundamentals of Physics*, p. 21; speed is a magnitude of velocity. Unlike velocity, it does not incorporate any sense of direction such as positive or negative, forward or backward.

50. Stillman (1973), "Galileo's Discovery of the Law of Free Fall," *Scientific American*, pp. 84–92.

51. Bernard I. Cohen, *The Birth of a New Physics*, pp. 109–117.

52. Galileo as quoted in Boas, p. 316.

53. Sidney Rosen, pp. 120, 121.

54. Ibid., pp. 122–130.

55. Ibid., p. 131.

56. Stillman (1980), p. 43; and Sidney Rosen (1958), p. 144.

57. Sidney Rosen (1958), p. 138.

58. Ibid., p. 138.

59. Stillman (1980), p. 43.

60. Boas, p. 319; Galileo published the *"Starry Messenger"* under the Latin title *"Sidereus Nuntius."* According to Menge's dictionary, *nuncius* is Latin for messenger or message, *siderus* is Latin for "of or from the stars, heavenly." Galileo, "When later, accused of arrogance for proclaiming himself a messenger of the stars, he pointed out that *'nuntius'* means messenger as well as message. Therefore the title might also be translated as *Message from the Stars.*"

61. Ibid., p. 320.

62. Sidney Rosen, p. 145.

63. Galileo as quoted in Stillman (1980), p. 44.

64. Stillman (1980), pp. 53–59.

65. Ibid., (1980), p. 1.

66. Ibid., pp. 60–61.

67. Ibid., pp. 61, 62.

68. Boas, p. 116.

69. Sidney Rosen, p. 49; Delo E. Mook and Thoms Vargish (1987), *Inside Relativity*, p. 5.

70. Paul Davies and John Gribbin (1992), *Unveiling the Edge of Time; Black Holes, White Holes, Wormholes*, pp. 19, 26.

71. Niels Bohr as quoted in Davies and Gribbin (1992), p. 27.

72. Stillman (1980), p. 28.

73. Ibid., pp. 63–68.

74. Ibid., pp. 71, 72.

75. Ibid., p. 7, Stillman writes that Gallileo named Simplicio "after a distinguished ancient Greek commentator on Aristotle" and that his arguments could be interpreted as those of Cremonini and Columbe, the former being his vociferous adversary in earlier public debates.

76. Morris H. Shamos, *Great Experiments in Physics, First Hand Accounts from Galileo to Einstein*, p. 16.

77. Galileo as quoted in Cohen, p. 145.

78. Stillman (1980), p. 76.

79. Ibid., pp. 78, 79.

80. Ronan, pp. 184, 185.

81. Galileo as quoted in Shamos, p. 18.

82. Galileo as quoted in Stillman (1980), p. 85.

83. Stillman (1995), pp. 78, 79.

## Chapter 12

1. Sir Isaac Newton (1934), *Principia, Vol. 1, The Motion of Bodies*, p. xiii, this dedication was prefixed to the *Principia* of Newton, 1686.

2. Goodstein and Goodstein, p. 3.

3. Pannekoek, p. 262.

4. Ibid., p. 262.

5. Richard S. Westfall (1993), *The Life of Isaac Newton,* pp. 1–3: Going by the Gregorian calendar, Isaac Newton was born on January 4, 1643. That is because the English calendar was then ten days out of phase with the Gregorian calendar of the Continent. The English adhered to Protestantism and regarded the Gregorian calendar as being adulterated by a Catholic Pope.

6. Ibid., pp. 4, 5.

7. Ferris (1989), p. 104.

8. Westfall, pp. 5–7.

9. Ibid., pp. 8–10.

10. Ibid., p. 10.

11. Ibid., p. 13; and Aaron Bunson Lerner, *Einstein and Newton, A Comparison of the Two Great Scientists* p. 30.

12. Lerner, p. 21.

13. Ibid., p. 20.

14. Westfall, pp. 12–16.

15. Ferris (1989), p. 105.

16. Westfall, pp. 16, 18, 21.

17. Ibid., pp. 19–23.

18. Ibid., pp. 23–32.

19. Ibid., pp. 33–35.

20. *Encyclopaedia Britannica,* "Wallis, John."

21. Westfall, pp. 42–44.

22. Pannekoek, pp. 262, 263.

23. This is a somewhat "modernized" version of Sir Isaac Newton's quote given in Westfall (1993), p. 39.

24. Ibid., pp. 42–44.

25. Ibid., pp. 45, 46.

26. Galilei, pp. 232, 233; conveyed this idea through Sacredo when he wrote: "It seems to me proper to adorn the Author's [i.e. Galileo's] thought here with its conformity to a conception of Plato's regarding the various speeds of uniform motion in the celestial motions of revolution. . . . he [Plato] said that God, after having created the movable celestial bodies . . . turned their straight motion into circulation, the only kind of [motion] that is suitably to be conserved uniformly, turning always without retreat from or approach toward any pre-established goal desired by them."

27. Westfall, pp. 49–51.

28. Ibid., p. 526; Boyle had discussed the issue in his *Experiments and Considerations Touching Colours (1664)* and Robert Hooke in *Micrographia,* as stated in Westfall, p. 52.

29. Ibid., pp. 52–55.

30. Ibid., pp. 61–62.

31. Ibid., pp. 62–65.

32. Ibid., p. 67.

33. Ibid., pp. 66–70.

34. *Encyclopaedia Britannica*, "Barrow, Isaac."

35. Westfall, pp. 70–72; and Dunham, p. 178.

36. Westfall, pp. 73–84.

37. Ibid., pp. 85–96.

38. Ibid., pp. 98, 99.

39. Ibid., pp. 100, 101.

40. Ibid., p. 101.

41. Ibid., pp. 192–105.

42. Newton as quoted in Westfall, p. 106.

43. Westfall, pp. 106–109.

44. Ibid., pp. 114–118.

45. *The Ottawa Citizen*, p. A4, October 30, 1999. Today, some three centuries after Newton, the debate on the question of Trinity is still going on.

46. Westfall, pp. 118–132, 137.

47. Ibid., pp. 133–135, 149.

48. Ibid., pp. 148, 149.

49. The trajectory would depend on the object's distance from the Earth and its speed. The greater its distance and the higher its speed, the greater its centrifugal force and the more likely that the object will orbit the Earth or fly beyond. At a shorter distance and at lower speed, the object will spiral toward the center of the Earth.

50. Westfall, pp. 150, 151.

51. William Bixby and Giorgio de Santillana, *The Universe of Galileo and Newton*, and the Random House Dictionary. The nautical mile, also called the geographical mile, is 6080 feet long compared with the statute mile of 5280 feet.

52. Westfall, pp. 154, 155.

53. Ibid., pp. 155, 158.

54. Pannekoek, p. 262.

55. Cohen, p. 150.

56. Ibid., pp. 150, 151.

57. Westfall, p. 159.

58. Bernard I. Cohen, *The Birth of a New Physics*, p. 174.

59. Goodstein and Goodstein, p. 18.

60. Bixby and Santillana, p. 131.

61. As quoted in Westfall, p. 162; with some minor simplifications in language.

62. Westfall, pp. 164, 165.

63. Ibid., p. 177.

64. Hatheway, p. 179.

65. Newton as quoted in Richard S. Westfall, p. 180.

66. Newton (1962), *Principia, Vol. I*, p. 46.

67. Westfall, pp. 178, 183.

68. Ibid., pp. 191, 193.

69. Pannekoek, p. 264.

70. Newton (1962), *Vol. I*, p. xvii.

71. Lloyd Motz and Jefferson Hane Weaver (1995), p. 9.

72. Newton (1962), *Vol. I*, pp. 1–12.

73. In the translations by Motte and Cajori the text of Newton's First Law

reads "right" line for "straight" line. Newton's Preface to the First Edition of *Principia, Volume I*, p. 13.

74. Halliday and Resnick (1993), *Fundamentals of Physics*, 4th ed. , p. 60.

75. Galilei, pp. 196, 197. To simplify, equable motion was replaced by uniform motion.

76. Cohen, p. 211.

77. Galilei, pp. 196, 197; Halliday and Resnick (1981), p. 13; and Born, p. 54.

78. In the translation by Motte and Cajori the text of Newton's Second Law reads "right" line for "straight" line. Newton, *Principia, Vol. I*, p. 13.

79. Galilei, pp. 298, 302.

80. In the translation by Motte and Cajori the text of Newton's Second Law reads "right" line for "straight" line. Sir Isaac Newton (1686), *Principia, Vol. I*, p. 13.

81. Newton, *Vol. I*, p. 13.

82. Ibid., p. 13, 14.

83. Goodstein and. Goodstein, pp. 19, 147: Richard P. Feynman received the 1965 Nobel Prize in physics for his work on quantum electrodynamics. He gave a guest lecture on planetary motion to a Caltech freshman class in March 1964. Material of his other lectures had been collected and been published in three volumes but this 1964 lecture was not among them. It was later discovered by David L. Goodstein, who together with his wife Judith R. Goodstein, described, elaborated on it, and published it. The Goodsteins wrote:

> Feynman was evidently intrigued by the fact that Isaac Newton, who had invented some of those more advanced techniques himself, nevertheless presented his own proof of Kepler's law using only plane geometry. Feynman tried to follow Newton's proof, but he couldn't get past a certain point, because Newton made use of arcane properties of conic sections (a hot topic in Newton's time) that Feynman didn't know. So, as he says in his lecture, Feynman cooked up a proof of his own..

Feynman proceeded to show that Newton's analysis leads to an elliptical orbit and that from it Kepler's two other laws can be deduced. Instead of using calculus or other advanced techniques of mathematical analysis Feynman, too, does it by geometric diagrams. He readily admits that nowadays it is usually done by superior analytical tools but for entertainment value and elegance he would like to offer "a ride in a buggy rather than in a fancy car." As the Goodsteins commented, the individual steps of the proof are easy enough and accessible by plane geometry but taken together the proof is still quite complex. In our description we draw partly on the Goodstein-Feynman demonstrations and partly on Newton's original work. In either case, be it Newton or Feynman, the reliance on their intuitive mathematical abilities is striking. It is in this context that Goodstein referred to Newton's most dramatic discovery, that is, the geometric links between Kepler's three laws.

84. Park, p. 183.

85. Newton (1962) , *Vol. I*, p. 40.

86. Newton (1962) , *Vol. I*, p. 41, Newton described this process as follows: "Now let the number of those triangles be augmented, and their breadth diminished ad infinitum, ... their ultimate perimeter ...will be a curved line."

87. Goodstein and Goodstein, pp. 88–90 and pp. 91–93. The geometric presentation is based on triangles of equal area. In Chapter 2 it was shown why in plane geometry the rule of finding the area of a triangle (by multiplying its height by half of its base) holds true for all triangles irrespective of their angles.

88. Newton (1962), *Vol. II*, p. 397.

89. Newton (1962), *Vol. I*, p. 47. Specifically under Proposition V. Problem I, Newton states: "There being given, in any places, the velocity with which a body describes a given figure, by means of forces directed to some common centre: to find that centre."

90. Newton (1962), *Vol. II.*, pp. 56, 57.

91. Ibid., pp. 56, 57.

92. Ibid., p. 62.

93. As quoted by Westfall, p. 190.

94. Walker, p. 225; and Westfall, pp. 192, 193.

95. Newton (1962), *Vol. I*, p. 3. Under Definition V Newton states: "A centripetal force is that by which bodies are drawn or impelled, or any way tend, towards a point as to a centre." This is a more general definition than that given here in the text but it applies to celestial bodies too. The question of what is the cause of the centripetal force. was not addressed until Einstein published his *General Theory of Relativity* some two centuries later.

96. Max Jammer, *Concepts of Space, The History of Theories of Space in Phuysics,* 3rd ed., pp. 215, 216.

97. Newton (1686), *Vol. I*, p. 250. According to Newton's Lemma II, "The moment of any genitum is equal to the moments of each of the generating sides multiplied by the indices of the powers of those sides, and by their coefficients continually." Although the meaning of this statement is not self-evident, in the text that follows Newton gives some examples of differentiation and generalizes the rule as an illustration of his method.

98. Struik, pp. 108–112; Richard P. Feynman (1997), *Six Not So Easy Pieces, Einstein's Relativity, Symmetry, and Space Time,* p. 106. Better notations can be powerful tools for the application and promotion of new mathematical concepts. Other calculus notations were due to Cauchy and Lagrange. Hollis R. Cooley, *First Course in Calculus,* p. 46, applied Newton's "dot" notation.

99. Westfall, p. 207.

100. Ibid, p. 215. During this time Newton was busy with alchemy. He wrote a treatise, entitled *Praxis,* which was a weird mixture of chemicals, imagery of the doves of Diana, the star regulus, all multiplied to infinity. He discontinued it and later, when his laboratoy burned down, abandoned it altogether.

101. Ibid., pp. 222–227.

102. Ibid., pp. 231–240.

103. Ibid., p. 234.

104. Lerner, p. 56; Lerner went on to say that "Newton spent a lot of time and money establishing his pedigree and was finally successful in linking his background to the British peerage."

105. Westfall, pp. 242–246.

106. Ibid., pp. 247–251.

107. Ibid., p. 252.

108. Ibid., pp. 260–262.

109. Ibid., pp. 267–269.

110. Ibid., pp. 270, 271; and Hathaway, p. 267.

111. Westfall, pp. 274–276, 291.

112. Ibid., pp. 276–282.

113. Ibid., p. 284.

114. Park, pp. 221–223; under the heading *Britain at War* Park quotes some letters of correspondence reflecting the tone of the debate.

115. Hollingdale, p. 256.

116. As suggested, for example, by Cohen, p. 148.

117. The importance of symbolism for making infinitesimal calculus more accessible to later mathematicians is noted by L. W. H. Hull (1959), *History and Philosophy, An Introduction*, pp. 228, 229. An example of the superiority of the Leibniz' notation is given in Owen, pp. 118, 119.

118. Westfall, p. 309.

119. Westfall (1980) as quoted by Timothy Ferris (1989), p. 104.

120. Lerner (1973), p. 58.

121. Westfall, p. 313. Not everybody was quite as generous. Hathaway, pp. 181, 182; Aldous Huxley reads: "If we evolved a race of Isaac Newtons, that would not be progress.... For the price Newton had to pay for being a supreme intellect was that he was incapable of friendship, love, fatherhood, and many other desirable things. As a man he was a failure; as a monster he was superb."

122. Donald E. Hall, "Isaac Newton" in McGreal, pp. 232–236.

123. Hollingdale, pp. 211–215.

124. Newton, *Vol. I*, p. 53.

125. Newton refers to these equalities of ratios as *proportions*. Newton, *Vol. I*, p. 57. Hollingdale, p. 214; provides an example by referring to them as *equalities of ratios*.

126. An excellent exposition of Newton's Proposition 6 is given in Hollingdale, pp. 209–212.

127. The concept of acceleration was described in Chapter 11 in Galilei.

128. Newton, *Vol. I*, p. 62.

## Chapter 13

1. Asimov (1972), p. 339.

2. Raymond A. Serway, *Physics for Scientists and Engineers*, pp. 1–3.

3. Gerald Holton, *Thematic Origins of Scientific Thought, Kepler to Einstein*, p. 107.

4. *Encyclopaedia Britannica*, "Sound: History of Acoustics, Early Experimentation."

5. Mersenne devised a mathematical formula that yielded prime numbers. Although his formula does not yield the complete set of such numbers, his pioneering effort inspired others to great advances in the theory of numbers.

6. *Encyclopaedia Britannica*, "Sound: History of Acoustics, Early Experimentation."

7. Coleman, p. 13.

8. Isaac Asimov, *The History of Physics*, p. 310.

9. Even at 3, 6, or 9 kilometers from the observer, it would have taken the light signals no more than 1, 2, or 3/100,000 of a second to travel the distance.

10. Hoffman, p. 44.

11. Coleman, p. 15; In 1610, with his newly built telescope, Galileo discovered the four most prominent of Jupiter's known moons.

12. Hoffman, p. 44.

13. The oldest forms of clocks are Sun dials, water and sand clocks. Wheelbased clock mechanisms appeared in the 13th century. The first such clocks in cathedrals, Churches and in Public places existed at the beginning of the 14th century, e.g., the clock of the Cathedral of Wells in England in 1335 and the clock of the Church Tower of San Gottardo in Milan, Italy, in 1336. These clocks were driven by weights. The first known spring-driven clock, still in existence, was built for the Duke Philipp of Burgund (ca. 1435). It was the forerunner of pocket watches developed some 70 years later. Keeping their spring-driven mechanism going at a constant rate posed a problem.. They were not accurate and could lose or gain as much as twenty minutes in twelve hours. This problem was solved by the Dutch physicist, mathematician and astronomer Christian Huygens in 1674. He described his invention, among other things, in his book *Horologium Oscillatorium* (1673). Following this improvement in accuracy led to the introduction of minute hands on clocks and watches.

14. Newton (1962), *Principia, Vol. II.*, p. 512.

15. Asimov (1966), p. 21.

16. Roemer had based the Earth-to-Sun distance on Cassini's estimate. Since it was about 6.8% below the actual value, it reduced the estimated distance the light had to travel and lowered the velocity of light.

17. Russel (1993), p. 26; Asimov (1984), p. 311; and Hoffman, p. 45.

18. *The World Book Encyclopedia*, vol. 9, p. 405.

19. The biographical notes that follow are based, in part, on the *En-cyclopaedia Britannica*, "Christiaan Huygens." They are also based on Motz and Weaver (1992), pp. 80-82; and on Serway (1990), p. 998.

20. *Encyclopaedia Britannica*, "Christiaan Huygens."

21. Serway (1994), p. 722.

22. Ibid., pp. 723–724.

23. Ibid., p. 712.

24. Pannekoek, p. 289.

25. Ferris (1989), p. 137.

26. Hoffman, p. 46. Bradley was not the first to observe some strange motions of the stars. By the middle of the seventeenthth century astronomers detected with the aid of the telescopes, some small but distinct movements of some of the stars. Bradley discovered, however, that the same motion affected many stars.

27. Ferris (1989), p. 139; North, p. 383.

28. Even if the Earth moved along a straight line, the telescopic aberration

would go unnoticed because the observed image of the stars would be shifted by a constant amount from the *true* image and the relative position of the stars would remain unchanged.

29.  To let rain rops fall trough the tube unimpeded by the walls would require adjusting the tilt as they pass through because they fall at a slow speed. Starlight would pass through almost instantaneously and continuously so that the tilt would need to be adjusted only with the orbital motion of the Earth.

30. Ridpath, p. 1. Technically, the aberration caused by the orbital motion of the Earth around the Sun is called the *annual aberration.* The much smaller aberration caused by the rotation of the Earth is called diurnal aberration. Planetary aberration is a combination of the Earth's motion and the time it takes light to travel from the planet to the observer.

31. As described earlier, Cassini and Richer had estimated the Sun-to-Earth distance at 87 million miles. Bradley and Molyneux had given it a range of 93 million miles (150 million km) to 125 million miles (201 million km). If Bradley had used the lower mileage and ignored the fact that the Earth's orbit is slightly elliptical (its orbital radius varies from 91.4 to 94.5 million miles), he could have arrived at a circular orbit of 6.28 x 93,000,000 = 584,040,000 miles. Given that a year has 365.25 x 24 x 60 x 60 = 31,557,600 seconds, he would have estimated the Earth's velocity at 18.5 miles per second (29.8 km/s), an estimate close to its actual speed of 19.3 miles per second ( 31 km/s).

32. North, p. 383.

33. *Compton's Interactive Encyclopedia* (1996), "Light."

34. *Encyclopaedia Britannica*, "Sir William (Frederick) Herschel.**"**

35. Ibid., "William Hyde Wollaston."

36. Ibid., "Johann Wilhelm Ritter."

37. Ibid., "Thomas Young." The same Thomas Young was also an Egyptologist who helped decipher the Rosetta Stone.

38. Tony Rothman, *Instant Physics From Aristotle to Einstein and Beyond,* p. 105.

39. Halliday, Resnick, and Walker (1993), p. 487.

40. Hoffman, p. 56.

41. Sidney Perkowitz.

42. Hoffman, pp. 49, 50.

43. George Gamow (1988), p. 161.

44. The human eye can not clearly see a light turned on and off because the image persists for about 0.1 seconds. Therefore, the light appears blurred.

45. Asimov (1984), pp. 313, 314.

46. Based on a formula in Halliday and Resnick (1981), *Fundamentals of Physics*, p. 576.

47. Based on Halliday and Resnick (1981), p. 676; and on the *Encyclopaedia Britannica*, "Light: Early terrestrial experiments."

48. Based on Asimov (1984), p. 314; Joseph F. Mulligan as quoted in Halliday and Resnick (1981), p. 676, Table 38-1.

49. Based on *Encyclopaedia Britannica,* "Light: Early terrestrial experiments."

50. Some authors, among them Peter A. Gabriel (1976), p. 21 and George Gamow (1988) p. 162, attribute the experiment of testing for change in the

speed of light by passing it through water to Armand Hippolyte Louis Fizeau. *The World Book Encyclopedia* and the *Encyclopaedia Britannica* attribute the experiment to Jean Bernard Léon Foucault.

51. Gamow (1988), p. 164.

52. *Encyclopaedia Britannica*, "Ether," and Newton (1962), *Vol. I* , pp. 6, 7.

53. *Encyclopaedia Britannica*, "Friedrich Wilhelm Bessel."

54. Simon Mitton, p. 406.

55. Hoffman, pp. 60–62.

56. Newton (1962), *Principia, Vol. I*, pp. 6,7.

57. Hoffman, p. 62.

58. Ibid., p. 62.

59. *Encyclopaedia Britannica*, "Faraday", "Maxwell."

60. John D. Barrow (2000), *The Universe That Discovered Itself*, p. 98; and *Encyclopaedia Britannica*, "Michael Faraday."

61. *Encyclopaedia Britannica*, "James Clerk Maxwell."

62. For a somewhat more detailed description see Maxwell's Equations in the glossary.

63. The biographical notes are based on the *Encyclopaedia Britannica*, "Albert Abraham Michelson."

64. Hoffman, p. 76.

65. Figure 13.7, Diagram 1 is similar to that shown in the *Encyclopaedia Britannica*, "Michelson Interferometer," and Diagram 2 is based on A.A. Michelson, and E.W. Morley, "On the Relative Motion of the Earth and the Luminiferous Ether," *American Journal of Science 34* : 333–345 as shown in Leo Sartori, *Understanding Relativity, A simplified Approach to Einstein's Theories*, p. 38.

66. Born, p. 218. Michelson and Morley were not the only advocates of this hypothesis. They were supported by the "elastic theory" of the British physicist Sir George Gabriel Stokes (1819–1903) and the "electromagnetic theory" of the German physicist Heinrich Rudolph Hertz (1857–1894).

67. Ibid., p. 219.

68. Ibid., p. 219. Lorentz was interested in resolving the ether-wind puzzle because otherwise his electron theory could not be reconciled with Michelson-Morley's invariant results.

69. Ibid., pp. 221, 222.

60. Ibid., p. 222.

71. Arthur Zaponc, *Catching the Light, The Entwined History of Light and Mind* p. 265.

72. Ibid., pp. 265, 266; and Albrecht Fölsing, *Albert Einstein*, p. 760.

## Chapter 14

1. Albert Einstein (1996 [1956]), *Out of My Later Years, The Scientist, Philosopher and Man Portrayed through His Own Words,* p. 61.

2. *Encyclopaedia Britannica*, "Albert Einstein."

3. Henri Poincaré (1904) as quoted in Fölsing (1997), p. 163.

4. Stephen Hawking, *Black Holes and Baby Universes and Other Essays*, p. 43.

5. Objects are said to proceed rectilinearly if they move in a straight course at constant velocity.

6. Hall, p. 478.

7. Denis Brian (1995), *Einstein, A Life*, p. ix.

8. Ibid., p. 1.

9. Michael White and John Gribbin, *Einstein, A Life in Science*, pp. 2, 3.

10. Philipp Frank, *Einstein: His Life and Times*, p. 6.

11. White and Gribbin, p. 5.

12. Maja Winteler as quoted in Fölsing, p. 12.

13. White and Gribbin, p. 6.

14. Frank, pp. 6, 7.

15. Einstein as quoted in Fölsing, p. 15.

16. *Encyclopaedia Britamnnica*, "Bieder meier-style,"the name Biedermeier was linked to Papa Biedermeier, a comic character often pictured by German painters. The Biedermeier style reflected family life, pursuit of hobbies, cultural interests in books, writing, and poetry readings of the middle class. It had a derogatory connotation as it referred, at times, to the life of the impoverished middle class of the early nineteenth century.

17. White and Gribbin, pp. 9, 11.

18. Frank, p. 10.

19. White and Gribbin, pp. 10, 11; and Frank, p. 7

20. Einstein as quoted in Fölsing, p. 14.

21. White and Gribbin, p. 11; the Luitpold Gymnasium was located in the Müllerstrasse 33. It was bombed during World War II, later rebuilt on a different site, and renamed Albert Einstein Gymnasium. Brian, p. 6, writes that the Greek teacher told Albert that "He would never amount to anything, that he was wasting everyone's time, and that he should leave the school immediately." But Fölsing, p. 18, reports that according to Dr. Wieleitner, a former principal of the Luitpold Gymnasium, and contrary to newspaper reports, Einstein did well in Latin and Greek. But no school records survived since they were destroyed during a bombing raid in World War II.

22. Frank, p. 10.

23. John Stachel, *The Collected Papers of Albert Einstein*, pp. 346–355. At the Luitpold Gymnasium Latin was taught from the first year on, natural science (Naturkunde) from the third year on, Greek from the fourth, but physics (Physik) did not appear in the curriculum until the seventh year.

24. Antonia Vallentine as quoted in White and Gribbin, p. 14, 266.

25. White and Gribbin (1994), pp. 13, 14 and Frank, p. 15.

26. Frank, p. 15.

27. Stachel, p. 20. To avoid German military service that Einstein would have had to serve in the year of his 20th birthday, he had to renounce his citizenship before his 17th birthday.

28. Frank, p. 17.

29. Ibid., p. 17.

30. Stachel, pp. 10, 11.

31. Einstein as quoted in Stachel, p. 11.

32. Stachel, p. xv.

33. Frank, pp. 18, 19.

34. Roger Highfield and Paul Carter, *The Private Lives of Albert Einstein*, pp. 24–31.

35. Fölsing, p. 36. Striking similarities have been found between Einstein's text and popular accounts of electromagnetic theory which appeared at this time.

36. Stachel, pp. 5–9, 15–18 and 384.

37. Frank, p. 20.

38. Fölsing, p. 39.

39. Brian, pp. 17, 18.

40. Ibid., p. 19.

41. Frank, p. 20.

42. Brian, pp. 17, 18.

43. Frank, pp. 20, 21; Highfield and Carter, p. 33; and Brian, p. 17.

44. Einstein to Mileva Marić, probably July 29, 1900, as quoted in Fölsing, p. 70.

45. White and Gribbin, p. 39.

46. Ibid., p. 40.

47. Brian, p. 22.

48. Stachel, p. 49.

49. Einstein as quoted in Stachel (1987), p. 44. 50. Brian, p. 28.

51. Ibid., p. 30.

52. White and Gribbin, p. 63.

53. Ibid., p. 64.

54. Stachel, p. 322–324.

55. Fölsing, p. 90.

56. Frank, p. 22.

57. White and Gribbin, pp. 67, 68.

58. Fölsing, pp. 106, 113. It has been hinted that Mileva's friend Helene Savić might have helped her with Lieserl, but how is not clear.

59. White and Gribbin, pp. 71, 73, 74.

60. Fölsing, p. 120.

61. Gamow (1988), pp. 171; and White and Gribbin, pp. 80, 81.

62. *Encyclopaedia Britannica,* "Albert Einstein." The title of his paper was "Über einen die Erzeugung und Verwandlung des Lichtes betreffenden heuristischen Gesichtspunkt" ("On a Heuristic Viewpoint Concerning the Production and Transformation of Light").

63. Brian, p. 63.

64. Ibid., p. 63.

65. Barry Parker, *Cosmic Travel, A Scientific Oddysey,* pp. 27, 29.

66. Halliday and Resnick, *Fundamentals of Physics,* p. 677; Pasachoff and Kutner, pp. 682 ff.; Leo Sartori, *Understanding Relativity, A Simplified Approach to Einstein's Theories,* p. 48; Coleman, pp. 44–52. The two postulates are described in such terms as: 1. The Principle of Relativity: The laws of nature are the same in every inertial frame, and 2. The constancy of light: The speed of light is an absolute of

nature and is the same in all reference frames independent of the velocity of the emitting body. Expressed in this manner the postulates are more precise.

67. Serway (1990), p. 6. More precisely the speed of light in a vacuum is 299,792.458 kilometers per second. It is measured with such precision that in 1983 the length of a meter was defined by the wavelength of an orange red light emitted from a krypton-86 lamp.

68. Holton, pp. 307, 308. Although reference to Michelson's estimates of the speed of light fits in well in this context, Einstein did not depend on Michelson's experiment. Instead, in leading up to his theory he referred in his paper to Faraday's (1791–1867) work and pointed out that the asymmetry between electrodynamics and optics of the presumed causes was unsatisfactory to him on aesthetic grounds.

69. Pasachoff and Kutner, p. 657. Astronomers have discovered that the radiation of stars is "red-shifted" in proportion to their distance from our solar system; the greater the distance, the wider the observed red-shift. The magnitude of the red-shift, in turn, was found to be correlated with the velocity at which the distant stars recede from Earth. A member of a cluster of galaxies in Virgo, for example, at a distance of 78 million light years was estimated to recede at a velocity of 750 miles per second (1200 km/s), and a member in Hydra at a distance of 4 billion light years was estimated to retreat at 38,000 miles per second (61,000 km/s).

70. Newton, *Principia, Vol. I*, p. 8.

71. Einstein, *Relativity, the Special and the General Theory, A Popular Exposition*, p. 25.

72. In this thought experiment we follow the Chapter on "Time Dilation" in Harald Fritzsch, *An Equation that Changed the World, Newton, Einstein, and the Theory of Relativity*. To convey the same idea Einstein compared the time interval of a person riding on a train and an observer standing on the embankment in Einstein, *The Principle of Relativity*.

73. To simplify, here the numbers have been rounded off and are given in kilometers rather than miles. For converting kilometers to miles divide kilometers by the 1.6093. For example, 300, 000 kilometers equal $300,000 \div 1.6093 = 186,416$. Because of rounding this result only approximates the true value of 186,287 miles for the speed of light per second.

74. Fritzsch, pp. 114–119. The derivation of the formula for the time-dilation follows his exposition.

75. As indicated by Serway, Equation (39.10) on p. 1120.

76. Feynman, *Six Not So Easy Pieces, Einstein's Relativity, Symmetry, and Space, Time*, p. 62.

77. Based on Fritzsch, pp. 124, 125.

78. Fritzsch, pp. 125, 145–147. Within 1.5 microseconds (i.e., 1.5 millionths of a second) exactly 50%, and after another 1.5 microseconds 75% of the muons will have decayed. That point determines their lifetime of 3.0 microseconds. In 1.5 microseconds light travels $300,000/1,500,000 = \frac{1}{2}$ km. That implies that we ought to expect most muons to decay after ½ km, some making it perhaps to two or even three kilometers.

79. Gamow (1988), pp. 315–317.

80. Fritzsch, p. 130.

81. Ibid., p. 133.

82. Hoffman, p. 110.

83. Fritzsch, pp. 149, 152; Hoffman, p. 110; and Mook and Vargish, p. 129.

84. Feynman, p. 94.

85. Serway (1990), p. 25.

86. Feynman, p. 97.

87. Fritzsch, p. 157.

88. Ibid., pp. 159, 160.

89. Hermann Minkowski (1908), "Space and Time," in Einstein, Lorentz, Weyl, Minkowski, *The Principle of Relativity, A Colection of Original Papers on the Special and General Theory of Relativity*, p. 75.

90. Gamow (1988), pp. 191, 192.

91. Fritzsch, pp. 162, 163.

92. Carl Selig as quoted in Fölsing, p. 245.

93. Cohen, p. 155.

94. Newton, *Principia, Vol. I*, p. 13.

95. Cohen, p. 156.

96. Serway (1990), pp. 161, 162.

97. Born, pp. 50–53.

98. Fritzsch, pp. 168, 169.

99. Einstein (1952), p. 45, 46.

100. This thought experiment is very similar to that of Fritzsch, who postulated that a bullet is fired from a high-speed spaceship while passing parallel to a wooden target board. Here, the bullet is fired from the spaceship parked parallel and at the same distance from the target board so that the speed of the space ship does alter the bullets penetration. Alternatively, the bullet could be fired at the target from a laser gun so that the bullet's path would not be affected by the high speed of the spaceship.

101. Halliday and Resnick (1981), p. 236. The linear momentum $p$ of an object of mass $m$ moving at velocity $v$, is given by $p = m\,v$ where $p$ and v are in the same direction. Both expressions, $p = mv$ and $F = \frac{1}{2} mv^2$ are non-relativistic.

102. Einstein (1952), p. 45.

103. Tullio Levi-Civita,(1977 [1925]), *The Absolute Differential Calculus (Calculus of Tensors)*, p. 297; the *intrinsic energy* refers to matter at rest and therefore excludes the kinetic energy imparted by motion. In computing the intrinsic energy $E = m\,c^2$ it is necessary to choose appropriate units of measurement for matter and speed. Sam Lilley (1981), *Discovering Relativity for Yourself*, p. 209; for example, the internationally agreed scientific units for the speed of light are 300 million meters per second. The corresponding energy unit is the *joule*. It relates the mechanical energy required to raise the temperature of water from 14.5 to 15.5 degrees Celsius. Careful tests have shown that it takes 4.186 joules of mechanical energy (i.e., 4.186 joules) to raise the temperature of one gram of water from 14.5 to 15.5 degrees Celsius, the equivalent of a one-gram calorie. Joules can be converted into kilowatt hours at the rate of 10 million joules to 2.778 kilowatt hours, where a *watt* is defined as 1 joule

per second. From this follows that 1 kilogram of matter has 25 million kilowatt-hours of intrinsic energy, the estimate given by Tullio Levi-Cevita.

104. Fritzsch, p. 183.

105. *Encyclopaedia Britannica*, Otto Hahn, Liese Meitner, and Fritz Strassmann.

## Chapter 15

1. Brian, p. 91.

2. Serway (1994), p. 256.

3. Brian, p. 76.

4. Ibid., p. 82.

5. Peter G. Bergmann, *The Riddle of Gravitation*, p. 22.

6. Sartori, p. 11.

7. Parker, p. 73.

8. Einstein (1951), pp. 61, 71, 72; White and Gribbin, pp. 127, 128.

9. White and Gribbin, pp. 127, 128.

10. Mook and Thomas, p. 141.

11. Einstein as cited in Sartori, p. 255; *Encylopaedia Britannica*, "Roland von Eötvös." Einstein referred here to the German-Hungarian physicist Baron von Roland Eötvös (1848–1919) whose study of the Earth's gravitational field yielded proof that the inertial and the gravitational mass are equivalent.

12. Ridpath, pp. 3, 194; The symbol $G$ in $G$-force refers to the gravitational constant that appears in Newton's law of gravitation. On Earth the acceleration of free fall due to gravity is $g$ = 9.807 metres per (second)$^2$, and the gravitational constant $G$ is the attraction of unit mass a unit distance apart at $G = 6.672 \times 10^{-11} N$ $m^2 / kg^2$.

13. Mook and Vargish, p. 149.

14. Einstein (1951), pp. 63–65, 69.

15. Parker, p. 75.

16. *Encyclopaedia Britannica*, "Riemann, (Georg Friedrich) Bernhard."

17. David C. Kay, *Theory and Problems of Tensor Calculus*, p. 88.

18. Jammer (1993), pp. 159–162.

19. Proceedings of the Cambridge Philosophical Society (1876) as quoted in Jammer, p. 163.

20. White and Gribbin, p. 130.

21. Parker, pp. 75, 76.

22. White and Gribbin, p. 123; Albert and Elsa were related on both sides of the family. Einstein's mother Paulina Koch and Elsa Löwenthal's mother were sisters; Einstein's father and her father were cousins.

23. Brian, pp. 87–90.

24. Garraty and Gay, pp. 981 ff.

25. John Archibald Wheeler and Kenneth Ford (2000), *Geons, Black Holes and Quantum Foam: A Life in Physics*, p. 235.

26. Brian, p. 91.

27. Banesh Hoffmann with Helen Dukas as quoted in Denis Brian, p. 92.

28. Born (1965), p. 321.

29. Feynman, p. 119; we are following here Feynman's suggestion to assess the divergence in curvature by looking at the difference between two radii but we are looking at their ratio instead. Sartori, p. 271; in a more traditional vein the divergence between a flat surface and a curved surface is measured by the *"Gaussian curvature"* calculated as the quantity $K_r = \{3(2\pi r - C_r)\}/\pi r^3$ where $C_r$ is the circumference of a circle.

30. Feynman, p. 124.

31. Ibid., p. 126.

32. Serway (1990), p. 27.

33. Bergmann (1992), p. 219.

34. Einstein and Lorentz, pp. 87–90.

35. Einstein (1951), p. 87, 88.

36. Levi-Civita, pp. 99, 100.

37. The subsequent description follows that of Born, pp. 321–327.

38. Figure 15.5 is based on Born (1965), pp. 321–326 and on Einstein (1951), pp. 87–90.

39. Born (1965), p. 325.

40. Valerie Illingworth, *The Penguin Dictionary of Physics*, p. 196.

41. Gamow (1988), p. 206.

42. Tullio Levi-Civita, p. 122; for example, in four-dimensional space we would need to compute the values of $N = 10$ coefficients, i.e., $N = \frac{1}{2}4\,(4+1)$, by solving 10 partial differential equations.

43. The formula for the Tensor Field Equation is based on Mook and Vargish, p. 161; and on *Encyclopaedia Britannica*, "Application of Riemannian Concepts."

44. The description of Einstein's tensor formula is based on Einstein, Lorentz, Weyl, Minkowski (1952), p. 149, and on Mook and Vargish, p. 177.

45. For denoting the dimensions the subscripts $i$ and $j$ are used here to concord with the earlier description of the Gaussian coordinates.

46. The derivation of Equation A15.4 is based on Feynman, p. 126.

47. A similar thought experiment was considered in a somewhat different context by Feynman, pp. 131–133.

48. In practice, the difference in time would not be measurable because the velocity would have to come very close to the speed of light. The velocity of today's spacecraft is far too low for that.

49. L. Marder, *Time and the Space-Traveller*, p. 19, 20.

50. *Encyclopaedia Britannica*, "Doppler, Christian." The article was published in German under the title *Über das farbige Licht der Doppelsterne* ("On the Colored Light of Double Stars").

51. *Encyclopaedia Britannica*, "Electromagnetic Radiation."

52. Bergmann (1992), p. 92.

53. Einstein (1951), p. 126.

54. Abraham Pais as quoted in Mook and Vargish, p. 160.

55. Until Thomas Young's work in 1802, light was believed to consist of corpuscles and, after Einstein's 1905 theory of the photoelectric effect in 1905, light quanta were thought to have some of the characteristics of particles again. In Chapter 12, Newton's corpuscular theory of light was briefly touched on in connection with

his reflecting telescope.

56. Born, p. 358.

57. Gamow, p. 196.

58. The text and diagrams of Figure 15.10 are based on Gamow, pp. 196-97.

59. Lilley, pp. 364, 365.

60. Highfield and Carter (1993), p. 189.

61. In 1920, Einstein's mother Paulina had passed away. Already diagnosed as terminally ill in 1918, she arrived in Berlin to spend her last few months with her son. Einstein made room for her in his study and Elsa cared for her. Suffering from abdominal cancer, only morphine could ease her pain. Einstein wept. "There is no consolation," he wrote to a friend.

62. Frank, pp. 167–176.

63. Ibid., p. 183.

64. *Encyclopaedia Britannica*, **"Albert Einstein."**

65. Brian, p. 101.

66. Ibid., p. 102.

67. Ibid., p. 103.

68. Ibid., pp. 103, 104.

69. Ibid., p. 104, 105.

70. Fölsing, pp. 462–464.

71. *Encyclopaedia Britannica*, "National Socialism, Anti-Semitism."

72. Stephen Hawking (1994), *Black Holes and Baby Universes and other Essays*, p. 70.

73. Highfield and Carter, pp. 191, 192.

74. Jamie Sayen, *Einstein in America, The Scientist's Conscience in the Age of Hitler and Hiroshima*, pp. 57–59.

75. Frank, pp. 239, 240.

76. *Encyclopaedia Britannica*, **"Albert Einstein."**

77. Sayen, p. 64.

78. Ibid., p. 83.

79. Ibid.

80. Ibid., p. 113.

81. Brian, pp. 316–321, 344.

83. Sayen, p. 85.

84. Brian, p. 339.

85. Sayen, pp. 81, 85 and Brian, pp. 306, 385.

86. Parker, p. 129.

87. Brian, pp. 431, 432.

88. Ibid., pp. 426, 433.

89. Lilley, pp. 396, 397, 398.

90. The variants of this equation are based on Born, pp. 306, 307.

91. Bergmann (1976), pp. 221, 222.

92. Ridpath, p. 196; and Bergmann (1976), pp. 221, 222.

93. Bergmann (1976), p. 212 .

94. Born, p. 348.

95. Einstein (1974), p. 90.

96. Levi-Civita (1977), pp. 406, 407, for example, puts it "...the maximum angular deviation to which a stellar ray can be subjected by the Sun's gravitational action...." at 1.7 seconds in radians. Bergmann (1992), *The Riddle of Gravitation*, p. 66, states "The displacement of the star images directly at the Sun's limb is 1.75 seconds of arc."

## Chapter 16

1. Barrow (2000), p. 200.

2. *Encyclopaedia Britannica*, "Unified Field Theory;" and Rothman, p. 88.

3. Dyson, as quoted by Barrow (2000), p. 200.

4. Rothman, p. 79.

5. *Encyclopaedia Britannica*, "Max Planck."

6. John Gribbin (1984), *In Search Of Schrödinger's Cat, Quantum Physics and Reality*, p. 36.

7. Text and diagrams are based on Serway (1990), p. 1148; Halliday, Resnick, and Walker, p. 1140; *Encyclopaedia Britannica*, "Development of the Quantum Theory of Radiation: Radiation laws and Plank's light quanta."

8. *Encyclopaedia Britannica*, "Electromagnetic Radiation."

9. Gribbin (1984), pp. 37–41; Isaac Asimov (1972), p. 351.

10. Halliday, Resnick and Walker (1993), p. 1140; and Seaway (1990), p. 1149.

11. More precisely, Max Planck's constant is $h = 6.626 \times 10^{-34}$.

12. Gribbin (1984), Gamow (1988), pp. 237.

13. Romano, Harré (1990 [1981]) pp. 157-165.

14. Zimmerman, Barry E. and David J. Zimmerman (1993), p. 147

15. *Encyclopaedia Britannica*, "Niels Bohr."

16. Gamow (1988), p. 237.

17. Ibid., pp. 237, 238.

18. *Encyclopaedia Britannica*, "Models of Atomic structure;" "Quantum theory of light," and Gamow (1988), p. 238.

19. *Encyclopedia Britannica.*, "Atoms: Their Structure, Properties, and Component Particles."

20. *Encyclopaedia Britannica*, "Electromagnetic Radiation." and Figure 16.3, Diagram 1 is based on Raymond A. Serway (1990), pp. 1152–1154.

21. *Encyclopaedia Britannica*, "Heisenberg, Werner."

22. To illustrate, a simple example of matrix multiplication is given in Appendix 16A of this chapter.

23. *Encyclopaedia Britannica*, "Born, Max."

24. Ibid., "Schrödinger's Wave Mechanics."

25. Gamow (1985), *Thirty Years That Shook Physics, The Story of Quantum Theory*, p. 105.

26. *Encyclopaedia Britannica*, "Dirac, P(aul) A(drien) M(Maurice)" and Timothy Ferris (1998), *The Whole Shebang, A State of the Universe(s) Report*, p. 209.

27. Gamow (1985), p. 119.

28. Based on Serway (1990), p. 854, Figure 30.28.

29. Ferris (1998), p. 209.

30. As quoted by Ferris (1997), p. 210.

31. Michio Kaku (1994), *Hyperspace, A Scientific Odyssey, Through Parallel Universes, Time Warps, and the Tenth Dimension,* pp. 113, 114. In particle physics the weak nuclear force, for example, creates the heat of radioactive materials. It is caused by the exchange of a W (weak) particle. The strong nuclear force that holds protons and neutrons together in the atomic nucleus relies on the exchange of π-mesons. Gluons hold all three together, i.e. the protons, neutrons and π-mesons. In quantum theory the weak and strong nuclear forces can be united with the electromagnetic force. To a non-physicist this is rather mysterious. In the present context, no attempt is made to go into greater detail on this point.

32. Nigel Calder (1977), as quoted by Kaku (1994), p. 118.

33. *Encyclopaedia Britannica,* "Cloud Chamber, Bubble Chamber."

34. Kaku (1994), p. 26.

35. A description attributed by Ferguson (1996), p. 3; to Wheeler (1990), *Journey into Gravity and Spacetime.*

36. Wheeler and Ford (2000), p. 229–231.

37. Ferguson, *Prisons of Light, Black Holes,* pp. 7–9.

38. Figure based on Pasachoff and Kutner, pp. 260, 261.

39. Wheeler and Ford, p. 293, 294; Ferguson, p. 115; Pasachoff and Kutner, pp. 303, 304.

40 Wheeler and Ford, p. 297.

41. Ibid., p. 312.

42. Ibid., pp. 313, 314.

43. Ferguson, p. 124–12;. Pasachoff and Kutner, pp. 331–333.

44. Kaku (1994), pp. 13–15.

45. Ibid., pp. 99–101.

46. Ibid., pp. 103.

47. Ibid., p. 102.

48. Barrow (2000), p. 207.

49. Crease, Robert and Charles C. Mann, *The Second Creation,* p. 192; *The World Book Encyclopedia,* "Chen Ning Yang and Tsung Dao Lee."

50. Kaku (1994), pp. 26, 27.

51. Ibid., pp. 118–120.

52. *The World Book Encyclopedia,* Year Book 2000, p. 323.

53. Gribbin (1984), pp. 256, 257.

54. Ferris (1998), p. 219.

55. Kaku (1994), p. 121.

56. Kaku (1994), p. 121, 122; and Ferris (1998), p. 138.

57. Kaku (1994), pp. 126, 127.

58. Heinz Pagels as quoted by Kaku (1994), p. 129.

59. Cole, *Sympathetic Vibrations,* as quoted by Kaku (1994), p. 130.

60. Gribbin (1984), p. 259.

61. Figure 16.7 and the commentary are based on Brian R. Greene (1999), *The Elergant Universe: Superstrings, Hidden Dimensions, and the Quest for the Ultimate Theory,* pp. 177–179.

62. Ferris (1998), p. 217.

63. Crease and Mann, *The Second Creation,* p. 401. For example, a short paper (three and a half pages) by Georgi and Glashow to the *Physical Review Letters* in January

1974 entitled *"Unity of all Elementary-Particle Forces"* was linked to many of the earlier discoveries in the quantum field theory and listed among them those of the physicists Yang and Mills, Gell-Mann, Glashow, Hicks, 't Hooft, Salam, Schwinger, Weinberg, and others.

64. Ibid., p. 400.

65. Ibid., pp. 407–409.

66. Kaku (1994), pp. 132–135.

67. F. D. Peat (1988), p. 76.

68. Ibid., p. 78.

69. Ferris (1998), p. 213. Gell-Mann named the symmetry pattern after the first sermon of Buddha (right understanding, thought, speech, action, livelihood, effort, mindfulness, and concentration).

70. Ibid., p. 213, refers to James Joyce 1939, novel *Finnigan's Wake.*

71. Ibid., p. 213.

72. Motz and Weaver (1995), p. 310.

73. *Encyclopaedia Britannica ,* "Analysis (in Mathematics), Topological Groups and Lie Groups."

74. Ferris (1998), pp. 213, 214; and Peat (1988), p. 77.

75. Text and Diagrams of Figure 16.3, Diagram 1 and Figure16.8 are based on Halliday, Resnick and Walker (1993), p. 1292 and on *Encyclopaedia Britannica,* "Subatomic Particles, SU(3) Symmetry.

76. Brian Greene (1999), *The Elegant Universe,* p. 137.

77. Kaku (1994), p. 143.

78. Ibid., pp. 148–150.

79 In the Superstring Theory the 10-dimensional space contains the *clockwise* vibrations and the corresponding 26-dimensional space the *anticlockwise* vibrations. Sixteen of the 26 dimensions can be condensed or *compactified*, leaving 10 dimensions.

Altogether they create a symmetry that is large enough to allow for the inclusion of all earlier theories.

80. Ibid., pp. 155, 164, 170, 171, 173, 177.

## Chapter 17

1. As quoted in John D. Barrow, *Impossibility, The Limits of Science and the Science of Limits,* p. 1.

2. Lee Smolin, *The Life of the Cosmos,* p. 179; and John D. Barrow (2000), p. 326.

3. Ernst Peter Fischer, *The beauty and the Beast, the Aesthetic Moment in Science,* p. 32.

4. Barrow (1999), p. 41, 42.

5. Stephen Hawking, (1994), p. 70.

6. Brian R. Greene (1999) , *The Elegant Universe,* p. 370; Steven Weinberg (1999), "A Unified Physics by 2050?" *Scientific American, End of the Millennium, Special Issue,* p. 71.

7. Weinberg (1999), p. 77.

8. Adapted from Brian R. Greene, p. 363; Steven Weinberg, p. 73.

9. The notes and Figure 17.2 are adapted from Holton, p. 443, 444.

10. Weinberg (1999)

11. Smolin (1998), p. 239.

12. Hawking, p. 102.

13. Greene, Brian R., p. 128 and Wheeler and Ford, p. 248.

14. Greene Brian R., pp. 284, 285.

15. Ibid., pp. 286, 287.

16. Ibid., pp. 306, 315 and 319.

17. Michio Kaku, *Hyperspace, a Scientific Odyssey Through Parallel Universes, Time Warps, fand the 10 th Dimension*, pp. 143, 146, 147.

18. Greene, p. 215.

19. Smolin (2001), *Three Roads to Quantum Gravity*, pp. 106–134.

20. Ibid., pp. 142–193.

21. Kaku, pp. 299–303.

22. *The Ottawa Citizen*, "Is Lambda theory just a cosmic fudge?," by Robert Mathews, Monday, August 10, 1998, Page B8.

23. *The Vancouver Sun*, "Scientist looking for the end of the universe, Traditional theories of an infinite cosmos being challenged," by Roger Highfield, October 23, 2003, P. A18

24. *The Vancouver Sun*, "A world discovered beyond Pluto," by Andrew Bridges, Octbober 8, 2002

25. *Harvard Gazette*, "New, far-out planet is discovered," by William J. Cromie, April 2003, p. 12.

26. Ibid., p. 307, 308.

27. William Harwood, *Space Odyssey, Voyaging Through the Cosmos*, p. 127.

28. Dennis Overbyte, "Scientists Press Their Search for Extraterrestrial Life," *New York Times*, Sunday, July 14, 2002.

29. Harwood, p. 154.

30. Ibid., p. 165.

31. Ibid., pp. 162, 168, 173.

32. Ibid., pp. 197.

33. Freeman Dyson as quoted by Kaku Michio (1998), p. 306.

34. Kaku (1998), pp. 317, 318.

35. Guy Gugliotta, "Asteroid hurtles towards collision with Earth in 2880, *The Vancouver Sun*, April 5, 2002.

36. At a distance of 4.3 light years, a light year amounting to roughly $(9.5)(10^{12})$ kilometers, and an escape velocity of 40,000 kilometers per hour, it would take roughly $[(4.3)(9.5)(10^{12})]/[(40,000)(24)(365)] \, [(40.851)(10^{12})]/[(3.5)(10^8)] = (10.7)(10^4) = 117,000$ years to reach the nearest star Alpha Centauri (Proxima).

37. Greene, Brian R. (1999), p. 79.

38. Pasachoff and Kutner, pp. 326, 327.

39. Michio Kaku (1994), pp. 224, 225; Barry Parker, pp. 4, 6.

40. Adapted from Pasachoff and Kutner, p. 327.

41. Hawking, p. 116.

42. Kaku (1994), pp. 226, 231, 245, 246.

43. Reinhard Genzel and Rainer Schodel, as reported under "Star's orbit firm evidence a huge, black hole exists," *The Vancouver Sun*, Saturday, October 19, 2002,

p. A20.

44. Wheeler (1998), p. 240. The term "Worm Hole" was first applied by Wheeler to field lines that could connect two places in a multiple connected space.

45. Kaku (1994), p. 247.

46. Ferguson, p. 182.

47. Stephen Hawking (1994), *Black Holes and Baby Universes and Other Essays*, p. 120.

48. John Gribbin (1998), *In Search for the Big Bang, The Life and Death of the Universe*, p. 308.

49. Kaku (1994), pp. 257, 264.

50. Paul Halpern, *The Cyclical Serpent, Prospects for an Ever Repeating Universe*, pp. 267, 271.

51. Ferris (1998), *The Whole Shebang, a State of the Art of the Universe(s) Report*, pp. 66, 67.

52. Eric J. Lerner (1991), pp. 121.

53. Sandy Fritz (2002), *Understanding Cosmology*, pp. 42, 63.

54. Smolin, pp. 37, 38, 39 and 43.

55. Ibid., p. 45.

56. Ibid., pp. 87, 89, 98, 101, 188.

57. Smolin (1998), p. 101 and Mathews, *The Ottawa Citizen*, August 10, 1998, p. B8.

58. As quoted in Ferris (1998), p. 271.

59. As quoted in Ferris (1998), p. 343.

60. Ferris (1998), pp. 303–312.

# GLOSSARY

**Aegean Culture** — refers to the cultures of the early civilizations that emerged on the islands of the Aegean Sea (located between what are now Greece and Turkey). There were four: the Minoan culture on the island of Crete, the Helladic culture on the Greek mainland, the Cycladic culture on the central islands of the Aegean Sea, and the Troadic (or Trojan) culture around the city of Troy and the Hellespont (now the Dardanelles). These cultures flourished between 3000 and 1100 B.C., and crumbled when invaders from the North overran Greece and advanced on the islands and Asia Minor. Their craftsmanship, the art of writing, and the building skills of these cultures faded when trade stopped and the economies stagnated.

**Aegean Sea** — an arm of the Mediterranean Sea between Greece to the west and Turkey to the east, narrowing down to the Dardanelles in the northeast.

**Alphonsine Tables** — in 1270 B.C. King Alphonso X of Spain gathered some Arab and Jewish astronomers in the city of Toledo, some 40 miles (64 km) southwest of Madrid, and had them prepare and publish astronomical tables. These famous Alphonsine Tables listed the data for predicting the celestial positions of the planets. They also had information on the future dates of solar and lunar eclipses. The Alphonsine Tables were later superseded by the Prutenic Tables, which were based on Copernican data. The Wittenberg mathematician Erasmus Reinhold prepared the Prutenic Tables for his patron the Duke of Prussia.

**Aphelion** — the point in the orbit of a planet or comet that is farthest from the Sun. Aphelion comes from the Greek *apo-*(αло-)"distant from" and *helios* (ἥλιος) the Sun.

**Apogee** — one of the two points, located on the major axis of an elliptical orbit of a celestial body, that is farthest from the Sun's center.

**A priori** — existing in the mind prior to and independent of experience, not based on prior study or examination.

**Apsides** — either of two points in an eccentric orbit, one farthest from the center of attraction (i.e., the higher apsis at the aphelion), and the other nearest the center of attraction (i.e., the lower apsis at the perihelion). Apside comes from the Greek words *hapsis* (ἁψίς) wheel, and *haptein* (ἅπτεὶν) to lock onto.

**Arc second** — a very small unit of angular measure equal to one-sixtieth of an arc minute or $1/3600$ of $1°$.

**Ascension, nodes of** — the point in orbit at which a celestial body crosses from south to north; a reference plane such as the celestial equator or the plane of the ecliptic.

**Astrolabe** — a device for measuring the altitude of stars. In antiquity it consisted of a disk suspended vertically, with a sight pivoted to point at a chosen celestial object.

**Astronomical unit (A.U.)** — a unit of length based on the average distance of the Earth from the Sun, one astronomical unit (1 A.U.) equals 93,000,000 miles (150, 000,000 km).

**Asymptote** — a straight line that is approached by a given curve as one of the variables in an equation goes to infinity, or as the equation of the difference between the straight line and the curve approaches zero.

**Atom** — is the smallest component of any element having all the properties of the element, consisting of an aggregate of protons, neutrons and electrons such that the number of protons determines the basic characteristic of the element. The word comes from the Greek *atomos* (ἄτομος) which means indivisible. Greek philosophers believed that each substance could be cut into smaller pieces until a basic substance is reached that could not be further divided. Modern science has shown that atoms are divisible.

**Atomic nucleus** — at the turn of the century not much was known about the structure of atoms except that they contain electrons. In 1911 Ernest Rutherford proposed that the positive charge of the atom is densely concentrated at the center of the atom. It forms the atomic nucleus which is responsible for most of the mass of the atom.

**Axiom** — a proposition assumed to be self-evident and accepted without proof for the sake of studying the consequences that follow from it.

**Binomial Theorem** — relates to expressions of the form $(a + b)^n$. If, for example:

$$n = 0 \quad then \quad (a + b)^0 = 1$$
$$n = 1 \qquad\qquad (a + b)^1 = a + b$$
$$n = 2 \qquad\qquad (a + b)^2 = a^2 + 2ab + b^2$$
$$n = 3 \qquad\qquad (a + b)^3 = a^3 + 3a^2b + 3ab^2 + b^3$$
$$n = 4 \qquad\qquad (a + b)^4 = a^4 + 4a^3b + 6a^2b^2 + 4ab^3 + b^4$$

The French mathematician Blaise Pascal (1623–1662) found that the additional terms could be readily derived from a number array of triangular shape (named after him, "Pascal's Triangle") that summarized the above coefficients as in

$$1$$
$$1 \quad 1$$
$$1 \quad 2 \quad 1$$
$$1 \quad 3 \quad 3 \quad 1$$
$$1 \quad 4 \quad 6 \quad 4 \quad 1$$
$$1 \quad 5 \quad 10 \quad 10 \quad 5 \quad 1$$
$$1 \quad 6 \quad 15 \quad 20 \quad 15 \quad 6 \quad 1$$

etc.

Newton formulated a more general version of the binomial theorem. His version was based on the series expansion of $(a+b)^{n/m}$ so that the exponent would not need to be a whole number, as in Pascal's Triangle, and could be a fraction or even be a negative number.

**Celestial Pole** — either of two points about which the celestial sphere appears to revolve each day. The celestial poles are located directly above the Earth's geographic poles and 90° from the equator.

**Centrifugal force** — refers to the inertial force that pulls an object away from the center of a circular path along which it is moving. It balances the centripetal force.

**Centripetal force** — is directed toward the center of a circular path followed by an object. For example, if a ball is rotating at the end of a string, the tension force of the string is the centripetal force. Or, if a satellite orbits the Earth, the force of gravity is the centripetal force.

**Compass** — unless otherwise mentioned, refers to a mathematical tool used in geometry. It consists of two movable legs, joined at one end and free to move closer or farther apart at the other. By holding one leg fixed the other can be moved to draw a circle.

**Composite numbers** — are non-prime numbers that are greater than one and are divisible by numbers greater than one ( e.g., 4, 6, 8, 10, 12, 14, 15, 16, 18, 20, . . .).

**Congruent** — in geometry it is a figure that coincides at all points when superimposed on another.

**Conic section** — also called a conic. In geometry, it refers to any curve created by the intersection of a plane and a right circular cone. Depending on the angle of the plane relative to the cone, and on the distance from the cone's central axis, the intersection is a circle, an ellipse, a hyperbola, or a parabola (pictured in Figure 4.3).

**Constellation** — refers to a group of stars in a region of the sky. The Greeks recognized and named 48 constellations. In 1928 the International Astronomical Union delineated the boundaries of 88 constellations. Also, see Zodiac.

**Coordinate system, celestial** — refers to any geometric system for locating the positions of objects on the celestial sphere. Geocentric coordinates, developed and used by Hipparchus and Ptolemy, give the position of a celestial object as it would be seen from the center of the Earth. Other systems have been developed, among them a heliocentric coordinate system.

**Coordinate system, two and three-dimensional** — on a two-dimensional surface any point can be identified by two numbers, in three-dimensional space any point can be identified by three numbers. These numbers need to be measured from a point of origin. For example, on graph paper the points might measure the width and length of an object from a point of origin. Points of origin can be quite arbitrary since one point readily translates into another (e.g., Figure 14.4, Diagrams 4 to 6).

**Corollary** — a proposition that is incidentally proved in providing the proof for another proposition.

**Cosine** — the ratio (in a rectangular triangle) of the side adjacent to a given angle, to the hypotenuse.

**Deferent** — the hypothetical circle around the Earth in which a celestial body, or the center of an epicycle of its orbit, was thought to move in the Ptolemaic system. See

Figures 6.7 and 6.8.

**Degree** — is a name given to various small units of measurement. Time is customarily measured in hours, minutes, and seconds. In mathematics, degrees are also used to measure angles and arcs of circles. An angle of 1 degree (1°) is 1/90th of a right angle (90°) and an arc of 1 degree (1°) is 1/360th of a whole circle (360°). Degrees in geometry are divided into 60 units called minutes and a minute is divided into 60 seconds. One degree (1°) consists of 60 minutes (60') and each minute of 60 seconds (60") and, therefore, of 3600 seconds.

**Eccentricity** — is a measure of the shape of the orbit of a celestial object. It denotes the amount by which a curvilinear form such as an ellipse differs from a circle. The eccentricity (denoted by $e$) of an ellipse is defined by the ratio $e = (R - r) \div R$ where $R$ is the semimajor axis of the ellipse and $r$ the semiminor axis. The eccentricity of a circle is zero when the orbit is a perfect circle because then both axes are equal and the denominator of the ratio $e$ is zero. The more elongated the orbit the greater is its eccentricity. When the ellipse is very elongated the value of the semiminor axis comes close to zero and the eccentricity $e$ of the ellipse approaches unity.

**Eclipse, solar** — the obscuration of the light of the Sun by the intervention of the Moon between it and a point on the Earth.

**Ecliptic** — the apparent path of the Sun against the background of the stars. The path is only apparent and not real because it is actually the plane of the Earth's orbit projected on to the celestial sphere of the stars. The angle between the Earth's equator and the orbital plane is technically referred to as the "obliquity of the ecliptic." It is the same size as the Earth's axial tilt. It is currently estimated at somewhat over 23° 26' and is gradually decreasing at the rate of 47"(seconds) per 100 years.

**Electrodynamics** — the branch of physics that deals with the interactions of electric power, magnetic fields, and mechanical phenomena.

**Electromagnetic radiation** — the process in which electromagnetic energy is emitted as particles or waves.

**Electromagnetism** — phenomena associated with the relation between electric currents and magnetism. It was only in the early part of the nineteenth century that scientists discovered by experimentation that electricity and magnetism are related. In 1873 the Scottish physicist James Clerk Maxwell (1831–1879) formulated the laws of electromagnetism based on their experimental results. See Figure 13.8 on Faraday's and Maxwell's field lines.

**Electron** — a subatomic particle with a negative charge orbiting the nucleus of an atom. An electron has the smallest unit of charge known in nature. No smaller unit of charge has been detected as a free charge. The antiparticle of an electron is the positron.

**Electron volts** — when referring to the mass of electrons or other subatomic particles it is convenient to express their energy in electron volts (eV) since they are usually given this energy by acceleration. For example, the rest energy of an electron is 511,000 eV (i.e., 511,000 electron voltss or 0.511 MeV million electron volts), the kinetic energy is 0.459 MeV and the total energy is 0.970 MeV.

**Ellipse** — the standard form of the equation of an ellipse in an $x, y$ coordinate system is:

$$\frac{(x-h)^2}{a^2} + \frac{(y-k)^2}{b^2} = 1$$

where $h$ and $k$ are the coordinates of the center of the ellipse and $2a$ and $2b$ are the lengths of the major and minor respectively.

**Entropy** — in statistical mechanics entropy refers to the principle that isolated systems tend toward disorder, and entropy is a measure of this disorder, that is, a measure of randomness. If nature is allowed to act without interference, a disorderly arrangement is much more probable than an orderly one. Entropy has also been defined as a measure of atomic disorder. As time goes on entropy and disorder will always increase. The trick is to define it quantitatively. A formal treatment is given in statistical thermodynamics. Suffice it to say that Ludwig Boltzmann (1844–1906) first defined entropy by the equation $S = k \ log \ W$ where $S$ is entropy (measure of the disorder of a system), $W$ is the number of ways the atoms of a system can be arranged and $k$ is Boltzmann's constant.

**Epicycle** — a small circle the center of which moves around on the circumference of a larger circle. A geometric concept introduced by the Greek astronomers Hipparchus and Ptolemy to explain the motion of the planets in the night sky. In this fashion they could explain the irregular motion of planets and their epicycles without changing Aristotle's hypothesis of perfect circular motion and the angular motion of the celestial bodies. For a fuller explanation of the motion of celestial bodies see chapters 8 and 10.

**Equant** — an imaginary point in the sky to one side of the Earth from which the motion of a celestial object would appear to be of uniform angular speed. The concept of an equant was discovered and first applied by the Greek astronomers Hipparchus and Ptolemy about 2000 years ago.

**Equator, celestial** — is the great circle which the Earth's geographic equator (at latitude zero), projects against the night sky.

**Equinox** — on its annual path, the ecliptic, the Sun intersects the celestial equator twice. If the elliptic and the celestial equator were two circles of the same size, centered on each other at an angle, the two would intersect halfway around. The Sun would pass through the intersections at equal time intervals twice a year. At these points in time night and day would be of equal length. Greek astronomers observed that night equaled day once on March 21 (vernal equinox) and a second time on September 23 (autumnal equinox). Hipparchus noted that the summer interval, from vernal (spring) equinox to autumnal (fall) equinox, lasted 187 days, whereas the winter interval, from autumnal (fall) equinox to vernal (spring) equinox, was only 178¼ days. He also discovered that the dates of the equinox were not fixed but moved slightly over the centuries, variations in time due to precession and nutation.

**Ergosphere** — the region just outside the event horizon of a rotating black hole in which an observer cannot be stationary but must rotate with the black hole.

**Exhaustion, method of** — the area circumscribed by a curvilinear figure (e.g., a circle) can be approximated by a succession of known elementary figures (e.g., triangles). Inscribing first a square composed of four equilateral triangles, then a hexagon of six equilateral triangles, and then double again the number of triangles, the area covered by such triangles will come ever more closely to that of the circle until it "exhausts" the circle's area from within.

**Exponent ( exponential powers)** — in the equation $2^3 = 2 \times 2 \times 2 = 8$ the exponent *3* indicates that the multiplicative product consists of three two's multiplied by themselves. The algebraic expression $a^3 = a \times a \times a = aaa$ stands for the multiplicative product of three factors *a*. Analogously the expression $(a + b)^n$ denotes the product of *n* factors *(a + b)*. In all cases the exponential powers of the expression are indicated by superscript specifying how many times the factors should be multiplied by themselves.

**Figurate numbers** — are numbers that match geometric figures. For example, the Pythagorean triangular and square numbers are created by basing their construction on triangles and rectangles as shown in Figure 2.1 of Chapter 2.

**Geodesic (or Geodetic)** — can be defined by the condition that for any two points close together on a surface, the length between them is shortest among all curves joining those two points.

**Gravity** — the force of attraction by which bodies tend to fall toward the center of the Earth or any other planet. Newton's laws of celestial dynamics were based on the force gravity (as described in Chapter 12 and in Figure 12.1).

**Hellenic era** — the era goes back to the eighth century B.C., to about 750 B.C. The Hellenic civilization was marked by an educational system in which the sons of nobility received their education at the courts of princes. The royal court attracted many of the best philosophers and teachers of the era. Under this aristocratic system the abstract was taught and performance was stressed. The cult of the hero was promoted. The ideal of a cultivated Greek patriot–warrior emerged. The Hellenic era ended when Philip II of Macedonia defeated the Greeks and made Greece part of Macedonia (338 B.C.). It was followed by the Hellenistic era.

**Hellenistic era** — this period of Greek civilization began at the time of Alexander's death (323 B.C.). Hellenistic Greece did not experience Alexander's death as the end of an age, but as a beginning of modern times. Greeks moved by the hundreds of thousands to Egypt, Macedonia, to the interior of Asia Minor, to Phoenicia, Palestine, Babylon, even to Bactria and India. Never before had the Greek spirit and culture wandered so far. In the new monarchies of Egypt, Macedonia, and Asia Minor a hundred Greek city states and Greek culture were loosely bound together with other cultures. Commerce flourished. The economies grew, cities were built and fortunes made. At a time when Greek literature and art was on the wane, Greek astronomy and philosophy reached new heights. The era lasted until the Romans conquered Egypt and the Near East around 50 B.C. Very likely the scientific treatises of this period would have been lost had it not been for the merger of the Greek-Oriental cultures.

**Hexagon** — refers to a figure with six straight sides of equal length whose six corners are equidistant from the center. It can be constructed by contiguously (adjacently) marking off along the circumference of a circle six sides of the same radius as the circle itself.

**Hyperbola** — a curve of two distinct and similar branches, formed by the intersection of a plane with a right circular cone as illustrated in Figure 4.3 of Chapter 4.

**Hyperspace** — a term used by physicists when referring to higher-dimensional theories such as Einstein's four-dimensional relativity theory, Kaluza's five-dimensional theory, and the more recent higher dimensional theories. Theories of hyperspace are discussed by Michio Kaku in *Hyperspace, A Scientific Odyssey Through Parallel Universes, Time Warps, and the Tenth Dimension.*

**Inclination** — in mathematics it refers to the angle between two lines or two planes. In astronomy it is defined as the angle equatorial and orbital planes of a planet (see Figures 8.3 and 8.5).

**Integer numbers** — positive or negative whole numbers as distinguished from fractions.

**Irrational numbers** — are not capable of being expressed exactly as the ratio of two integer numbers. For example, the base of a right-angled isosceles triangle (or the diagonal of any square) cannot be expressed as a multiple or fraction of the length to its two equal sides. For a proof, see Diagram 6 of Figure 2.3 (Chapter 2).

**Latitude** — in geography, latitude is the angular distance north or south from the equator of a point on the Earth's surface. In astronomy, latitude is the angular distance of a point on the celestial sphere from the ecliptic, the apparent path of the Sun projected against the night sky.

**Latus rectum** — an ellipse has two focus points that are located on the major axis, equidistant from its center. The *latera recta* (plural of *latus rectum*) are the chords that pass through the focus points of the ellipse perpendicular to the major axis. Each *latus rectum* runs parallel to the minor axis and intersects at two points with the circumference of the ellipse. The length of the latus rectum is a characteristic feature of an ellipse (see Diagram 8 and text of Figure 12.2).

**Lemma** — a subsidiary proposition or annotation helping to prove another proposition.

**Light** — in 1666 Isaac Newton discovered that a beam of white light could be separated into colors. He proposed that light consists of tiny particles which he called "corpuscles." Newton's theory became known as the corpuscular theory of light. The Dutch physicist Huygens (1629–1695) proposed an alternative wave theory of light. Today it is recognized that both, particle and wave, are essential aspects for a complete description of the properties of light.

**Logarithmic scale** — When numbers are to be plotted and some are quite small while others are very large it is convenient to use a logarithmic scale. For example, suppose the numbers 10, 100, 1000, and 10, 000 are to be plotted, then the problem becomes one of scale. The same numbers can be written as $10^1$, $10^2$, $10^3$, $10^4$ and they can then be simply plotted as 1, 2, 3, and 4, that is, as the exponents of 10. Thus, a logarithmic brings the numbers closer together. This is only one of the advantages. There are others. For example, multiplication can be converted to addition and division can be reduced to subtraction, thus geometric functions can be converted into linear relations. Before computers were invented, logarithmic tables could simplify computations.

**Longitude** — is the angular distance east or west on the Earth's surface, measured by the angle between a particular place and some prime meridian, as that of Greenwich, England (today) or that of Alexandria in Hellenistic times. The angular distance could either be expressed in degrees or by the corresponding difference in time. In astronomy it pertains to the angular distance of the celestial point from the great circle perpendicular to the ecliptic at the vernal equinox, measured through 360° eastward.

**Lunar parallax** — the angle created at the center of the Moon and by the Earth's equatorial radius. At 57' (minutes) and 03" (seconds), it measures almost 1° (60 minutes).

**Magnitude** — is a measure of the brightness of a star. Ancient Greek astronomers rated the brightest stars as those that first became visible after sunset. From there the scale declined to sixth grade for stars that could only be seen in total darkness. Today's scale has been put on a more refined system, one magnitude corresponds to a difference in brightness factor of 2.512 times, and a range of five magnitudes equals a hundredfold difference.

**Maxwell's equations** — applied to free space, Maxwell's equations take into account 1) Gauss' law, which states that the number of electric field lines penetrating a surface equals the net charge within the surface; 2) Gauss' law in magnetism, which states that the magnetic field lines entering a closed volume must equal the number that leave that volume; 3) Faraday's law of induction; which describes the relation between an electric field and a change in magnetic current. And 4), the Ampère-Maxwell law of the relation between magnetic and electric fields and electric currents.

**Meridian** — the terrestrial meridian is a plane through the Earth's center, connecting the south and north poles. The prime meridian is a circle of longitude that serves as a reference point from which other longitudes, east or west, can be measured. Today, the prime meridian on Earth passes through Greenwich, England.

**Mesons** — a class of elementary particles that are a major component of secondary cosmic-ray showers. They are unstable and decay into stable particles. They can be positively or negatively charged, or are electrically neutral. Mesons have masses intermediate between those of an electron and a proton.

**Muons** — are produced in the upper fringes of the atmosphere when cosmic rays collide with atoms. They have a very short lifespan.

**Near East** — this term was used by the first modern Western geographers. It refers to the lands around the eastern shores of the Mediterranean Sea, including northeastern Africa, southwestern Asia, and, occasionally, the Balkan Peninsula. Since World War II, the name has been largely replaced by Middle East and is frequently used interchangeably.

**Neutrino** — is a ghostly particle. Every second about 60 billion neutrinos pass through every square centimeter of our bodies without nudging a single atom. Neutrinos are born when cosmic rays strike the Earth's atmosphere.Collisions with atoms create a shower of secondary particles, such as muons and others, which decay after a short flight and create a spray of neutrinos. They were discovered by proton-decay detectors. Very likely they have a mass (in the neighborhood of 0.5 electron volts (eV) compared with an electrons's mass of 511,000 eV) and if so, together, they could outweigh all the stars in the universe (according to Kearns, Kajita and Tosuka).

**Neutron** — is an elementary particle with a mass slightly smaller than that of a proton but having no charge. It is a constituent of the nuclei of all atoms except those of hydrogen.

**Nova** — a star that suddenly becomes a thousand times brighter and then fades away. Based on their speed of decline they are divided into subgroups. In our galaxy of 100 billion stars, 25 to 50 novas occur each year but most of them go unnoticed because they are not nearly as bright as a supernova (see separate glossary entry for "Supernova").

**Nucleus** — in physics, a nucleus is the positively charged mass within an atom, composed of neutrons and protons, and possessing most of the mass but occupying only a small fraction of the volume of the atom.

**Numbers** — it is customary to classify numbers according to their characteristics. Natural numbers are the familiar counting numbers 1, 2, 3, .... The ratios of natural numbers are rational numbers like 1/2, 2/3, 3/4. Integer numbers are positive or negative whole numbers as distinguished from fractions. Even numbers are multiples of 2, odd numbers are not. A prime number is a number that is greater than one and only divisible by itself and one, e.g., 2, 3, 5, 7, 11, 13, 17, .... Irrational numbers cannot be represented by ratios of natural numbers such as, for example, the square root of 2. A composite number is the product of other numbers. Figurate numbers are formed by depicting and expanding geometric shapes (e.g., triangles and squares), as in Figure 2.1. Perfect numbers are numbers whose factors, when summed or multiplied, equal that number.

**Nutation** — A small variation in the position of the stars due to the oscillation of the Earth's pole about its mean position. Nutation is caused by the periodic attractions of the Sun and Moon. It is superimposed on the much larger effect of precession.

**Obliquity** — refers to the angle between the Earth's equator and the ecliptic, the plane of the Earth's orbit. It is of the same size as the Earth's axial tilt.

**Opposition** — when a planet lies opposite the Sun in the sky it is visible all night. It is the best time for observing outer planets since they are closest to the Earth at that time. See Figure 8.7, Diagram 1.

**Parabola** — can be described as the intersection of a plane with a cone (see Figure 4.3).

**Parabolic, hyperbolic** — refers here to the shapes of orbits, related to conic sections (illustrated in Figure 4.3).

**Parallax** — the apparent displacement of a celestial body when observed from two distant locations (e.g., from two distant locations on the surface of the Earth or from two distant positions along the Earth's orbit). The adjectival form of the word is parallactic.

**Parallelogram rule** — refers to the addition of vectors. The rules of vector addition can be geometrically described. Two vectors $A$ and $B$ are added so that the resultant vector $R$ is the diagonal formed with $A$ and $B$ as its sides, this is known as the parallelogram rule of addition (see Figure 12.1, Diagrams 6 to 9).

**Perfect numbers** — numbers whose factors, when summed or multiplied, equal that number. For example, the number 6 is the first of the perfect numbers factoring into 1, 2, and 3. Multiplied with each other or added to each other (as in 1x2x3=6 and 1+2+3=6), yielding the same value, 6. Pythagoras and his disciples discovered several others. Today 17 such "perfect" numbers are known.

**Perigee** — a point located on an (elliptical) orbit of a celestial body that is nearest to the Earth's center (see Figure 6.6) .

**Perihelion** — the point on a planet's or comet's orbit that is nearest to the Sun. Perihelion comes from the Greek *peri–* (περι–) "at, in the proximity of " and *helios* (ἥλιος) the Sun.

**Periodicity** — in general it is the tendency of events to recur at regular intervals. In astronomy it may refer to the time it takes a planet to complete one orbit or to the period of pulsating variables that may be associated with a star's mass, radius, density, temperature, and color.

**Peripatetic school** — Aristotle founded a school of philosophy in the Lyceum in

490

Athens in 335 B.C. It was his custom to teach philosophy while walking in the gardens of the Lyceum. His philosophy survived long after his death. His immediate disciples maintained and developed his teachings, but after them the school fell into decline. After generations, the quality of the lectures deteriorated. Eventually, in the first century B.C., the Greek philosopher Andronicus of Rhodes brought to light the long sequestered treatises of Aristotle, meticulously edited them and added detailed commentaries. This edition started a revival of interest in Aristotelian philosophy. Philosophers who followed it became known as peripatetics, from the Greek word *peripatein* (περιπατεῖν), referring to lecturing Aristotelian philosophy while walking, or simply pertaining to Aristotle.

**Perturbations** — refer, in astronomy, to deviations of a celestial body from its regular orbit, caused by the presence of one or more other celestial bodies. Newton mathematically described the gravitational interaction of celestial objects in terms of a two-body problem involving the Sun and the planet. But small deviations can be caused by mutual interactions of the planets (e.g., between the Earth and the Moon). Such perturbations have been described by computer simulations but not by a generally applicable mathematical formula.

**Photon** — a photon is defined as a quantum of electromagnetic radiation. For some purposes photons can be interpreted as light particles traveling at the speed of light.

**Positron**—an elementay particle having the same mass and spin as an electron but having a *positive* charge equal in magnitude to that to that of an electron.

**Precession** — in compiling a star catalog (completed in 129 B.C.) the Greek astronomer Hipparchus noticed that the positions of the stars had shifted from earlier observations recorded by the Babylonians. Although not recognized in his day, the precession was due to a cyclic wobbling in the Earth's axis of rotation. The Earth's pole takes about 25,800 years to describe one complete circle on the celestial sphere. The conical shape of this circle is about 23.5° and corresponds to the inclination of the Earth's axis.

**Prime number** — is an integer number that is greater than one and only divisible by itself and one (e.g., 2, 3, 5, 7, 11, 13, 17, . . .) .

**Proton** — is a fundamental constituent of all atomic nuclei, having a positive charge equal in magnitude to that of an electron.

**Pythian oracle** — oracular shrines were numerous in Greek antiquity. The most famous was that of Delphi. At Delphi the medium was a woman known as Pythia. Her counsel was most in demand to forecast the outcome of projected wars, political decisions, or other significant ventures. The Greek philosopher Pythagoras was named after Pythia of the Delphian oracle.

**Quadrature** — the occasion when the angle formed by the Sun and a planet measures 90° at Earth. See Figure 8.7, Diagram 2.

**Quantum Mechanics** — Quantum mechanics is a theory of the subatomic microcosm. Its main features were sketched out by the German physicist Heisenberg (1901–1976) while he was a student of Niels Bohr (1885–1962). Over the years it has been expanded into a full-fledged theory of quantum mechanics. According to Quantum Theory, some quantities in nature occur only in discrete packets or intervals called quanta. Heisenberg's Principle of Uncertainty sets probabilistic limits to observations at the subatomic level: it is not possible to determine both the position and momentum of a subatomic particle at the same time, but only possible to determine one or the other. Thus, it is a not a deterministic theory but one based on probabilities.

**Quantum Theory** — is a theory in physics in which energy exists only in discrete quantities. It originated in 1900 when the German physicist Max Planck (1858–1947) suggested that electromagnetic radiation is quantized (i.e., it can only be emitted or absorbed in tiny packets). Each quantum radiation has an energy equal to $hf$ where $h$ is Planck's constant and $f$ is the radiation frequency. Quantum Theory led to the modern theory of quantum mechanics.

**Radio astronomy** — beginning in the 1930s, radio astronomy is the branch of astronomy that uses extraterrestrial radiation in radio wave lengths (from 1 mm to 30 m) rather than visible light for the study of the universe. Radio telescopes employ different techniques to pick up the very weak radio waves coming from the sky. The most familiar method is the use of a parabolic dish that brings radio waves into focus. Several antennas or radio telescopes may be used together to achieve a higher degree of resolution and greater precision.

**Rectangular coordinates** — a coordinate system in which the axes meet at right angles.

**Retrogradations** — the apparent movement of an outer planet on its orbit as seen from the Earth when the Earth catches up and overtakes it. The planets are said to trace out a "retrograde" loop.

**Scholia** — is the plural of scholium, which refers to an explanatory note or comment that amplifies a particular aspect in a mathematical work (e.g., in Newton's *Principia*).

**Secant** — in a right triangle the secant is the reciprocal of the cosine. The cosine is the ratio of the side adjacent to a given angle to the hypotenuse, and the secant is the ratio of the hypotenuse to the side adjacent to that angle.

**Semi** — as in *semi*minor or *semi*major axis of an ellipse, denoting half of its smaller or half of its larger diameter respectively.

**Sexagesimal number system** — in industrialized countries today, the decimal system is used. It overshadows all other number systems. In Mexico and Central America, however, a system based on 20 is still in use. It became entrenched as it was used in earlier times by their astronomers. The Babylonians invented and used the sexagesimal system between 3000–2000 B.C., long before Arabic numbers became popular. Instead, they employed cuneiform (wedge-shaped) symbols. To differentiate between higher and lower orders of magnitude (e.g., $60^1$, $60^2$, $60^3$, . . .), they separated the orders by position and intervening empty spaces. One good mathematical reason for adopting this system might have been that 60 could be readily divided by many factors (2, 3, 4, 5, 6, 10, 12, 15, 20, and 30).

**Siderial year** — the number of days it takes the Earth to complete one orbital revolution around the Sun with reference to the fixed stars. The term sidereal comes from the Latin noun *sidus* for constellation and its adjective *siderus* meaning, pertaining to the stars. The sidereal period refers to the time it takes a planet to complete one orbit with respect to the stars of a particular constellation. This customary period of a year is nowadays timed at 365.25636 days. An alternative, but less accurate measure is the synodic year which refers to the time it takes to complete one orbit around the Sun (see synodic year).

**Sine** — pronounced like "sign," it is one of several numerical ratios of two sides in a right triangle. The sine of an angle $\alpha$ (in a right triangle) is the ratio of the side opposite the angle $\alpha$ relative to the hypotenuse. In standard notation the sine of an angle of 30°, for example, is expressed as sin 30° = 0.50 indicating that in a right triangle the side opposite an angle of 30° is half the size of the hypotenuse.

**Sinusoidal** — refers to a common form of wave function, specifically a function defined by sine ratios as in $y = k \sin x$.

**Solstice** — two points of the ecliptic on which the Sun reaches its greatest angle relative to the celestial equator. The summer solstice is on June 21 (or June 22) in the northern hemisphere and is winter solstice in the southern hemisphere. The winter solstice is on December 21 (or December 22) in the northern hemisphere and the summer solstice in the southern hemisphere. If the elliptic and the celestial equator were two circles of the same size, centered on each other at an angle, the two would intersect halfway around. The Sun would pass through the points of the solstice at equal time intervals twice a year. But in the northern hemisphere the summer time interval between the two solstices is 184.62 days and the winter interval is 180.62 days.

**Sphere** — in astronomy it refers to any of the crystalline, transparent, concentric shells, or layers on which, according to ancient belief, the planets, stars, and other heavenly bodies were revolving.

**Stadium** (plural: stadia) — an ancient Greek course for footraces, typically semi-circular, with tiers of seats for spectators. But also an ancient Greek and Roman unit of length. The Athenian Olympic Unit was equal to about 607 feet. If Eratosthenes had used this unit of length, his estimate of the circumference of the Earth would have fallen short. The Greeks, however, used various measures. The modern equivalent and commonly used conversion factor of a stadium is 10.218 per mile. That brings the Earth's circumference very close to 24,000 miles.

**Strong nuclear force** — the force that holds atoms together, the force that was first released in nuclear bombs, and the force that fuels the stars.

**Sublunar** — situated beneath the Moon or between the Moon and the Earth.

**Supernova** — a violent explosion ends the life of some stars. A supernova is an extremely bright nova that emits many times more light than a nova. The word "nova" was at first reserved for any star that showed a sudden increase in brightness. It was made famous by Tycho de Brahe and Kepler who referred to this phenomenon as "nova," but both novas they saw would now be called supernovas. Tyche's nova appeared in 1572. It was one of the few supernovas ever seen in our galaxy.

In the case of nova explosions, only the outer layers of the star seem to be involved in the sudden flare-up. Nova explosions are now thought to come from binary systems where some of the mass is drawn from the adjacent star. In contrast, a supernova is much brighter than a nova. It involves most of the material of stars with at least eight times the solar mass. In a supernova explosion the star may become a billion times brighter than the Sun. Different types of supernovas can increase in brightness, at times reaching the brightness of a whole galaxy.

**Synodic year** — the term synodic stems from the Greek word *synodos* (σύνοδος), for "reunion." In astronomy the synodic period or year refers to the average time it takes a planet to return to the same position with respect to the Sun as seen from the from Earth. An alternative but more accurate measure is the siderial year (see sidereal year).

**Tensor** — a set of functions that can be transformed in a particular way from one coordinate system to another.

**Tensor calculus** — provides a tool for the investigation of general formulations of distance. The most useful distance concept is the non-Euclidean one under which the Pythagorean relation for geodesic right angles is not valid. There exists a correlation between formulas of differential geometry developed to answer questions about curves and surfaces in Euclidian three-dimensional space and tensor identities. Tensor calculus was used to great advantage by Einstein in his development of relativity theory.

**Theorem** — is a proposition that is to be proven. The proof can be deduced from premises or assumptions of a system.

**Thermodynamics** — the science concerned with the relations between heat and mechanical energy, and the conversion from one into the other.

**Trigonometric ratios** — Six ratios of the three sides of a rectangular triangle can be related to one angle, say angle $\alpha$: the sine, cosine, tangent, cotangent, and the secant and cosecant. In a right triangle, the sine and cosine refer to the numerical relation between the side opposite the angle $\alpha$ and the side adjacent to it. The tangent and cotangent relate to the numerical relation between the two sides (adjacent to the right angle) and the angle $\alpha$, the secant is defined as the ratio of the hypotenuse to the side adjacent to angle $\alpha$, and the cosecant as the ratio of the hypotenuse to the side opposite to angle $\alpha$.

**Trigonometry** — is a branch of mathematics that unites the three disciplines of geometry, arithmetic, and algebra. Early Greek writers, including Euclid, based their calculations on the proportionality of similar triangles. The new rules of trigonometry made it possible to quickly find solutions for any shape of triangle if only three elements were known: three sides, two sides and the enclosed angle, or one side and two adjacent angles. It was a decisive break from the strict rule of straight-edge and compass, as was the practice in classical Hellenic geometry. The science of trigonometry is attributed to the great astronomer Hipparchus (ca. 180–100 B.C.). He was the first to summarize his trigonometric estimates in systematic tables.

**Vector** — describes a force applied to an object in terms of magnitude and direction. For example, Newton described the orbital motion of a planet in terms of the inertial force and the gravitational force. The combination or sum of the two dictated the orbital course of the planet.

**Weak nuclear force** — the force that creates the heat of radioactive materials, that can be as deadly as the radiation of nuclear reactors or that can be used in health care for cancer treatment.

**Zenith** — the point on the celestial sphere directly above an observer on Earth and at right angle to the horizon.

**Zodiac** — is the imaginary belt that extends about eight 8° on each side of the Sun's apparent path around the Earth. From the earliest times astronomers have divided the circular zodiac into 12 equal parts of 30° degrees each. About 2000 years ago each part was given a sign ( e.g., Aquarius (water bearer), Pisces (fishes), Aries (ram), etc). The final system of the twelve zodiac signs, 30° each, appeared in a Babylonian text around the fifth century B.C. It became the classical reference system for the positions of the planets and stars of all mathematical astronomy. It appears that this reference system was set in relation to the bright star $\beta$ Gemini, at 90°. The equinoxes occurred at about 10° of their respective sign in the year 500 B.C., an angle which was reduced, due to precession, to roughly 5° at the time of Hipparchus around 150 B.C. or approximately by 1.4° per century. The signs were named by the ancient Greeks after the constellations in each section. During the past 2000 years the constellations moved eastwards by over 30° so that the constellations of today no longer coincide with the zodiacal signs of 2000 years ago.

# Glossary

This Glossary is based on various sources that can be found in the bibliography. Among them: *The Encyclopaedia Britannica* (1997), John A. Garraty and Peter Gay (1972), *The Columbia History of the World*; D. Halliday, R. Resnick and J. Walker (1993), *Fundamentals of Physics*; Urdang, Laurence and Stuart Berg Flexner, eds. (1968), *The Random House Dictionary of the English Language* (1968), Ian Ridpath (1997), *A Dictionary of Astronomy*; Raymond A. Serway (1990), *Physics for Scientists and Engineers.*

## Bibliography

Abbott, P. and M. E. Wardle (1992 [1970]), *Trigonometry*, Illinois: NTC Publishing Group.

Abell, George O. (1980 [1964]), *Exploration of the Universe*, 4th edition, New York: College Publishing, Holt, Rinehart and Winston, The Dryden Press.

Alter, Dinsmore, C. H. Clemenshaw and J. G. Phillips (1983), *Pictorial Astronomy*, 5th edition, New York: Harper and Row Publishers.

Andrews, Robert (1993), *The Columbia Dictionary of Quotations*, New York: Columbia University Press.

Armstrong, A. H. (1965 [1947]), *An Introduction to Ancient Philosophy*, 4th edition, London: Methuen & Co., Ltd.

Armstrong, Spencer, ed. (1950), *101 of the World's Greatest Books*, New York: Greystone Press.

Asimov, Isaac (1966), *The Universe, From Flat Earth to Quasar*, New York: Walker and Company.

Asimov, Isaac (1972 [1960]), *Asimov's Guide to Science*, New York: Basic Books, Inc.

Asimov, Isaac (1977), *Asimov on Numbers*, New York: Doubleday & Company, Inc.

Asimov, Isaac (1984 [1966]), *The History of Physics*, U.S.A.: Walker Publishing Company Inc.

Asimov, Isaac (1992), *The Secret of the Universe*, New York: Pinnacle Books, Windsor Publishing Corporation

Asimov, Isaac (1995 [1994]), *A Memoir*, New York: Bantam Books.

Atkins, Peter Williams (1992), *Creation Revisited: A Distinguished Scientist Looks at the Origins of Space, Time and the Universe*, New York: W. H. Freeman and Company Limited.

Avery, Albert E. (1966 [1954]), *Handbook of the History of Philosophy*, New York: Barnes & Noble.

Barrow, John D. (1999 [1998]), *Impossibility, the Limits of Science and the Science of Limits*, Great Britain: Random House.

Barrow, John D. (2000), *The Universe That Discovered Itself*, Great Britain: Oxford University Press.

Bell, E. T.(1986 [1937]), *Men of Mathematics, the Lives and Achievements of the Great Mathematicians from Zeno to Poincaré*, New York: Simon and Schuster.

Bergmann, Peter G. (1968), *The Riddle of Gravitation, From Newton to Einstein to Today's Exciting Theories*, New York: Charles Scribner's Sons.

Bergmann, Peter G. (1976 [1942]), *Introduction to the Theory of Relativity,* New York: Dover Publications.

Bergmann, Peter G.(1992 [1968]), *Theories*, New York: Charles Scribner's Sons.

Bergmann, Peter G. (1992 [1968]), *The Riddle of Gravitation*, New York: Dover Publications.

Bernstein, Jeremy (1996), *A Theory for Everything*, New York: Copernicus, Springer-Verlag, Inc.

Bixby, William and Giorgio de Santillana (1964), *The Universe of Galileo and Newton*, New York: A Horizon Caravel Book.

Boas, Marie (1962), gen. ed.,*The Scientific Renaissance 1450–1630, The Rise of Modern*

*Science II*, London: A. Rupert Hall, Collins.

Born, Max (1965 [1924]), *Einstein's Theory of Relativity*, New York: Dover Publications, Inc.

Bowra, C. M. and eds. of Time-Life Books (1965), *Classical Greece, in Great Ages of Man, a History of the World's Cultures*, Time-LifeBooks, New York: Time Inc.

Brian, Denis (1995), *Einstein, A Life*, New York: John Wiley & Sons, Inc.

Bridges, Andrew (2002), in *The Vancouver Sun*, "A world discovered beyond Pluto," Associated Press, October 8, 2002.

Brody, David Eliot and Arnold R. Brody (1997), *The Science Class You Wish You Had ... The Seven Greatest Scientific Discoveries in History and the People Who Made Them*, New York: Berkeley Publishing Group.

Burn, A. R. (1972), *Herodotus, The Histories*, trans. Aubrey de Sélincourt, London: Penguin Books Ltd.

Caspar, Max (1993 [1959]), *Kepler*, trans. and ed. C. Doris Hellman, Don Mills, Ontario: General Publishing Company, Ltd.

Cohen, Bernard I. (1985), *The Birth of a New Physics*, Markham, Ontario: Penguin Books Canada Ltd.

Coleman, James E. (1954 [1990]), *Relativity for the Layman*, Markham, Ontario: Penguin Books Canada Ltd.

Commins, Saxe and Robert N. Linscott, eds. (1947), "On the Immortality of the Soul," *World's Great Thinkers, Man and Spirit: The Speculative Philosophers*, New York: Random House.

*Compton's Interactive Encyclopedia* (1996), CD-ROM, Softkey Multimedia, Inc.

Cooley, Hollis R. (1954 [1951]), *First Course in Calculus*, New York: John Wiley & Sons, Inc.

Copernicus, Nicolaus (1994 [1939]), *On the Revolutions of Heavenly Spheres*, trans. Charles Glenn Wallis Amherst, New York: Prometheus Books.

Costello, B. F. C. and J. H. Muirhead (1962 [1897]), *Aristotle and the Earlier Peripatetics*, New York: Russell & Russell, Inc.

Crease, Robert P. and Charles C. Mann (1986), *The Second Creation, Makers of the Revolution in Twentieth-Century Physics*, Toronto: Collier Macmillan Canada, Inc.

Cromie, William J. (2003) in the Harvard Gazette, "New, far-out planet is discovered," April 2003, p. 12..

Crowe, Michael J. (1990), *Theories of the World from Antiquity to the Copernican Revolution*, Toronto: Dover Publications, Inc., General Publishing Company, Ltd.

Davies, Paul and John Gribbin (1992), *Unveiling the Edge of Time: Black Holes, White Holes, Wormhole*. New York: Harmony Books, Random House Inc.

Davis, Joel (1985), *Journey to the Center of Our Galaxy, A Voyage in Space and Time*, Chicago: Contemporary Books.

de Santillana, Giorgio 1981 [1955]), *The Crime of Galileo*, Virginia: Time-Life Books Inc., Alexandria, Virginia.

Dickenson, Terence (1999), *Night Watch, A Practical Guide to View the Universe*, Toronto: Firefly Books.

Dörrie, Heinrich (1965), *One Hundred Great Problems of Elementary Mathematics, Their History and Solution*, trans. David Antin, New York: Dover Publications, Inc.

Downing, Douglas (1990 [1984]), *Trigonometry the Easy Way*, New York: Dover Publications.

Drague, Helge S. (1990), *Dirac: A Scientific Biography*, U.K.: Cambridge University Press.

Dreyer, J. L. E. (1953 [1906]), *A History of Astronomy From Thales to Kepler*, Toronto: Dover Publications Inc., General Publishing Company, Ltd.

Dunham, William (1991[1990]), *Journey Through Genius, the Great Theorems of Mathematics*, Toronto: John Wiley & Sons, Penguin Books Canada Ltd.

Durant, Will (1953), *The Story of Civilization, The Renaissance, A History of Civilization in Italy From 1304–1576*, New York: Simon and Schuster.

Durant, Will (1961), *The Story of Civilization, The Age of Reason Begins, A History of European Civilization in the Period of Shakespeare, Bacon, Montaigne, Rembrandt, Galileo and Descartes: 1558–1648*, New York: Simon and Schuster.

Durant, Will (1966 [1939]), *The Life of Greece, The Story of Civilization*, New York: Simon and Schuster.

Einstein, Albert (1951 [1916]), *Relativity, The Special and the General Theory, A Popular Exposition*, trans. Robert W. Lawson, New York: Crown Publishers.

Einstein, Albert, H. A. Lorentz, H. Weyl, H. Minkowski (1952 [1923]), *The Principle of Relativity, A Collection of Original Papers on the Special and General Theory of Relativity*, trans. W. Perret and G. B. Jeffery, New York: Dover Pulications, Inc.

Einstein, Albert (1974 [1921]), *The Meaning of Relativity*, 5th edition, New Jersey: Princeton University Press.

Einstein, Albert (1996 [1956]), *Out of My Later Years, The Scientist, Philosopher and Man Portrayed Through His Own Words*, ,New York: Random House Publishing, Inc.

*Encyclopaedia Britannica* (1997), CD-ROM, Inc., Chicago, Illinois.

Ferguson, Kitty (1996), *Prisons of Light, Black Holes,* Great Britain: University of Cambridge.

Ferris, Timothy (1989 [1988]), *The Coming of Age in the Milky Way*, New York: Doubleday.

Ferris, Timothy ed.(1991), *The World Treasury of Physics, Astronomy, and Mathematics*, Toronto: Little, Brown and Company.

Ferris, Timothy (1998 [1997]), *The Whole Shebang, A State of the Universe(s) Report*, New York: Simon & Schuster.

Feynman, Richard P. (1997 [1963]), *Six Not So Easy Pieces, Einstein's Relativity, Symmetry, and Space Time.* New York: Addison-Wesley Publishing Company, Inc.

Fischer, Ernst Peter (1999 [1997]), *The Beauty and the Beast, the Aesthetic Moment in Science*, trans. Elizabeth Oehlkers, New York: Plenum Publishing Corporation.

Fölsing, Albrecht (1997 [1993]), *Albert Einstein, A Biography*, trans. Ewald Osers, New York: Penguin Books.

Frank, Philipp (1953 [1947]), *Einstein: His Life and Times*, trans. George Rosen, ed. Shuichi Kusaka, New York: Alfred A. Knopf, Inc.

Fremantle, Anne (1965) and the eds. of Time-Life Books, *Great Ages of Man, A History of the World's Cultures:: Age of Faith*, New York: Time Inc.

Fritz, Sandy (2002), *Understanding Cosmology,*, New York, Warner Books Inc.

Fritzsch, Harald (1994), *An Equation that Changed the World, Newton, Einstein, and the Theory of Relativity*, trans. Karin Heusch, Chicago: The University of Chicago Press.

Galilei, Galileo (1974 [1638]), *Two New Sciences, Including Centers of Gravity and Force of Percussion*, trans. Stillman Drake, Madison, Wisonsin: The University of Wisconsin Press.

Gamow, George (1985 [1966]), *Thirty Years That Shook Physics, The Story of Quantum Theory*, Toronto: Dover Edition.

Gamow, George (1988 [1961]), *The Great Physicists from Galileo to Einstein*, Don Mills, Toronto: General Publishing Company.

Garraty, John A. and Peter Gay, eds. (1972), *The Columbia History of the World*, New York: Harper & Row Publishers.

Goodstein, David L. and Judith R. Goodstein (1996), *Feynman's Lost Lecture, The Motion of Planets Around the Sun*, New York: W.W. Norton & Company.

Gorman, Thomas L. Peter (1979), *Pythagoras, A Life*, Boston: Routledge and Kegan.

Greene, Brian (1999), *The Elegant Universe, Superstrings, Hidden Dimensions, and the Quest for the Ultimate Theory*, New York: W.W. Norton & Company.

Greene, Jay E. ed., Murray Bromberg, Brother C. James, Robert Lipton (1967 [1964]), *100 Great Scientists*, New York: Washington Square Press, Inc.

Gribbin, John (1984), *In Search of Schrödinger's Cat, Quantum Physics and Reality*, New York: Bantam Books.

Gribbin, John (1998 [1986]), *In Search of the Big Bang, The Life and Death of the Universe*, New York: Penguin Books.

Hall, Donald E. (1992) "Albert Einstein," *Great Thinkers of the Western World*, , Ian P. McGreal ed., New York: Harper Collins Publishers, Inc.

Halliday, David and Robert Resnick (1981 [1974]), *Fundamentals of Physics*, 2nd edition, New York: John Wiley & Sons.

Halliday, David, Robert Resnick and Jearl Walker (1993 [1974]), *Fundamentals of Physics*, 4th edition, New York: John Wiley & Sons, Inc.

Halpern, Paul (1995), *The Cyclical Serpent, Prospects for an Ever-Repeating Universe*, New York: Plenum Press.

Harré, Romano (1990 [1981]), *Great Scientific Experiments, Twenty Experiments That Changed Our View of the World*, Great Britain: Oxford University Press.

Harwood, William (2001), *Space Odyssey, Voyaging Through the Cosmos*, National Geographic Society, Washington D.C.

Hathaway, Nancy (1994), *The Friendly Guide to the Universe, A Down-to-Earth Tour of Space, Time, and the Wonders of the Cosmos*, New York: Penguin Books.

Hawking, Stephen (1994 [1993]), *Black Holes and Baby Universes and Other Essays*, New York: Bantam Books.

Heath, Sir Thomas L. (1956), *The Thirteen Books of Euclid's Elements*, 2nd edition, New York: Dover Publications, Inc.

Heath, Sir Thomas L. (1981 [1921]), *A History of Greek Mathematics, Volume I: From Thales to Euclid*, New York: Dover Publications Inc., and Don Mills, Toronto: General Publishing Co.

Heath, Sir Thomas L. (1981 [1921]), *A History of Greek Mathematics, Volume II: From Aristarchus to Diophantus*, New York: Dover Publications Inc., and Don Mills,

Toronto: General Publishing Co.

Heath, Sir Thomas L. (1991 [1932]), *Greek Astronomy*, New York: Dover Publications, Inc., and Don Mills, Toronto: General Publishing Co.

Highfield, Roger (2003), in *The Vancouver Sun*, "Scientist looking for the end of the universe, traditional theories of an infinite cosmos being challenged," October 23, p. A18.

Highfield, Roger and Paul Carter (1993), *The Private Lives of Albert Einstein*, London: Faber and Faber Limited.

Hoffman, Banesh (1983), *Relativity and Its Roots*, New York: Scientific American Books.

Hogben, Lancelot (1993 [1937]), *Mathematics for the Million*, New York: W.W. Norton & Co.

Hohn, Franz E. (1958 [1952]), *Elementary Matrix Algebra*, New York: The MacMillan Company, and Galt, Ontario: Brett-MacMillan Ltd.

Hollingdale, Stuart (1991 [1989]), *Makers of Mathematics*, Toronto: Penguin Books Canada Ltd.

Holton, Gerald (1988 [1973]), *Thematic Origins of Scientific Thought, Kepler to Einstein*, Cambridge, Massachusetts: Harvard University Press.

Hoyle, Fred (1973), *Nicolaus Copernicus, An Essay on his Life and Work*, New York: Harper & Row.

Hull, L. W. H. (1959), *History and Philosophy of Science, An Introduction*, New York: Longmans, Green, and Co..

Illingworth, Valerie ed. (1991 [1977]), *The Penguin Dictionary of Physics*, 2nd edition, New York: Penguin Books.

Jammer, M. (1954), *Concepts of Space, The History of the Theories of Space in Physics*, Cambridge, Massachusetts: Harvard University Press.

Jammer, M. (1993 [1954]), *Concepts of Space, The History of the Theories of Space in Physics*, 3rd edition, Don Mills: Dover Publications, General Publishing Company, Ltd.

Kaku, Michio (1994), *Hyperspace, A Scientific Odyssey Through Parallel Universes, Time Warps, and the Tenth Dimension*, New York: Oxford University Press Inc.

Kaku, Michio (1998 [1997]), *Visions, How Will Science Revolutionize the 21st Century*, New York: Anchor Books.

Kay, David C. (1988), *Theory and Problems of Tensor Calculus*, New York: McGraw-Hill Book Company.

Kearney, Hugh (1971), *Science and Change 1500–1700*, New York, Toronto: McGraw-Hill Book Company.

Kearns, Edward, Takaaki Kajita and Yoji Totsuka, "Detecting Massive Neutrinos," *Scientific American*, Special Edition, May 31, 2003.

King, Jerry P. (1993 [1992]), *The Art of Mathematics*, New York: Ballentine Books.

Kline, Morris (1980), *Mathematics, The Loss of Certainty*, New York: Oxford University Press.

Koestler, Arthur (1960), *The Watershed, A Biography of Johannes Kepler*, New York: University of America Press.

Leff, Lawrence S. (1990 [1984]), *Geometry the Easy Way*, 2nd edition, New York: Barron's Educational Series, Inc.

# Bibliography

Lerner, Aaron Bunson (1973), *Einstein and Newton, A Comparison of the Two Great Scientists*, Minneapolis, Minnesota: Lerner Publications Company.

Levi-Civita, Tullio (1977 [1925]), *The Absolute- Differential Calculus, Calculus of Tensors*, ed. Dr. Enrico Persico, trans. Marjorie Long, New York: Dover Pulications.

Lilley, Sam (1981), *Discovering Relativity For Yourself*, New York: Cambridge University Press.

Maor, Eli (1994), $\epsilon$ *The Story of a Number*, New Jersey: Princeton University Press.

Marder, L. (1971), *Time and the Space-Traveller*, Great Britain: George Allen & Unwin Ltd.

Mathews, Robert (1998), "Is Lambda Theory Just A Cosmic Fudge?" *The Ottawa Citizen*, August 10, Page B8.

McGreal, Ian P. ed. (1992), *Great Thinkers of the Western World*, New York: Harper Collins Publishers, Inc.

Menge, Hermann, Karl-Heinz Schäfer, and Bernhard Zimmermann (1986), *Langenscheidts Taschenwörterbuch der Griechischen und Deutschen Sprache*, Erster Teil: Altgriechisch-Deutsch, Berlin: Langenscheidt.

Menge, Hermann (1995 [1963]), *Langenscheidt's Taschenwörterbuch: Latein*, Berlin: Langenscheidt.

Mitton, Simon ed. (1977), *The Cambridge Encyclopaedia of Astronomy*, New York: Crown Publishers, Inc.

Mook, Delo E. and Thomas Vargish (1987), *Inside Relativity*, New Jersey: Princeton University Press.

Moore, Patrick (1974), *Watchers of the Stars, The Scientific Revolution*, New York: G. P. Putnam's Sons.

Motz, Lloyd and Jefferson Hane Weaver (1992 [1989]), *The Story of Physics*, New York: Avon Books.

Motz, Lloyd and Jefferson Hane Weaver (1995 [1993]), *The Story of Mathematics*, New York: Avon Books.

Newton, Sir Isaac (1962 [1729]), *Principia, Volume I: The Motion of Bodies*, trans. Andrew Motte in 1729, Los Angeles: University of California Press.

Newton, Sir Isaac (1962 [1729]), *Principia, Volume II: The System of the World*, trans. Motte, Los Angeles: University of California Press.

Neyman, Jerzy, ed. (1974), 'The Heritage of Copernicus: Theories 'Pleasing to the Mind'," *The Copernican Volume of the National Academy of Sciences*, Massachusetts: The MIT Press, Cambridge.

North, John (1994), *The Fontana History of Astronomy and Cosmology*, London: Fontana Press.

Owen, George E. (1971), *The Universe of the Mind, Seminars in the History of Ideas*, Baltimore: The John Hopkins Press.

Pais, Abraham (1982), *Subtle is the Lord: The Science and the Life of Albert Einstein*, New York: Oxford University Press.

Pannekoek, Anton (1989 [1961]), *A History of Astronomy*, New York: Dover Publications, Inc. and Toronto: General Publication Co. Ltd.

Park, David (1988), *The How and Why, An Essay on the Origins and Development of Physical Theory*, Princeton, New Jersey: Princeton University Press.

Parker, Barry (1991), *Cosmic Travel, A Scientific Odyssey*, New York: Plenum Press.

Pasachoff, Jay M. and Marc L. Kutner (1978), *University Astronomy*, Philadelphia, Toronto: W.B. Saunders Company.

Peat, F. D. (1988), *Superstrings and the Search For the Theory of Everything*, Chicago: Contempory Books.

Perkowitz, Sidney (1996), New York: Henry Holt and Company Inc., and Ontario: Fitzhenry & Whiteside Ltd.

Philip, J. A. (1966), "Pythagoras and Early Pythagoreanism," *Journal of the Classical Association of Canada*, Supplementary Volume VII, Toronto: University of Toronto Press.

Porter, Roy ed. (1987), *Man Masters Nature, 25 Centuries of Science*, London: BBC Books.

Raymo, Chet (1982), *365 Starry Nights, An Introduction to Astronomy for Every Night of the Year*, New York and Toronto: Simon & Schuster, Prentice-Hall Press, Inc.

Ridpath, Ian ed.(1997), *A Dictionary of Astronomy*, Oxford and Toronto: Oxford University Press.

Roberts, Royston M. (1989), *Serendipity, Accidental Discoveries in Science*, New York and Toronto: John Wiley & Sons, Inc.

Ronan, Colin A. (1974), *Galileo*, London: George Weidenfeld and Nicolson Ltd.

Rosen, Edward (1984), *Copernicus and the Scientific Revolution*, ed. Louis L. Snyder, Florida: Robert E. Krieger Publishing Company.

Rosen, Sidney (1958), *Galileo and the Magic Numbers*, Boston, Toronto: Little, Brown and Company.

Rothman, Tony (1995), *Instant Physics From Aristotle to Einstein, and Beyond*, New York: A Byron Preiss Book.

Russell, Bertrand (1917), *Mysticism and Logic*, New York: Double Day.

Russell, Bertrand (1959), *Wisdom of the West*, ed. Paul Foulkes, New York: Crescent Books.

Russell, Bertrand (1993 [1925]), *ABC of Relativity*, 5th edition, ed. Felix Pirani, Guernsey, Channel Islands: Guernsey Press Co.

Sartori, Leo (1996), *Understanding Relativity, A Simplified Approach to Einstein's Theories*, Los Angeles: University of California Press.

Sayen, Jamie (1985), *Einstein In America, The Scientist's Conscience In the Age of Hitler and Hiroshima*, New York: Crown Publishers, Inc. and Toronto: General Publishing Company Ltd.

Schäfer, Karl Heinz and Bernhard Zimmermann (1990 [1986]), *Langenscheidts Taschenwörterbuch der Griechischen and Deutschen Sprache*, Berlin, Munich: Langenscheidt.

Schneider, Michael S. (1994), *A Beginner's Guide to Constructing the Universe, The Mathematical Archetypes of Nature, Art, and Science, A voyage from 1 to 10*, New York: Harper Collins Publishers, Inc.

Serway, Raymond A. (1994), *Principles of Physics*, Philadelphia and Toronto: Saunders College Publishing.

Serway, Raymond A. (1990 [1982]), *Physics for Scientists and Engineers*, 3rd edition, Philadelphia and Toronto: Saunders College Publishing.

Shamos, Morris H. ed. (1987 [1959]), *Great Experiments In Physics, First Hand Ac-*

*counts from Galileo to Einstein*, New York: Dover Publications, Inc.

Smith, James H. (1965), *Introduction to General Relativity*, New York, W. A. Benjamin, Inc.

Smolin, Lee (1998 [1997]), *The Life of the Cosmos*, Oxford and New York: Oxford University Press.

Smolin, Lee (2001 [2000]), *Three Roads to Quantum Gravity*, New York: Basic Books.

Stachel, John ed.(1987), *The Collected Papers of Albert Einstein, Volume I, The Early Years, 1879–1902*, New Jersey: Princeton University Press.

Stewart, Desmond and eds. of Time-Life Books (1967), *Early Islam, Great Ages of Man, A History of the World's Great Cultures*, New York: Time Inc.

Stillman, Drake (1973), "Galileo's Discovery of the Law of Free Fall," *Scientific American*, May 1973, Volume 228, No. 5, pp. 84–92.

Stillman, Drake (1980), *Galileo (Past Masters)*, Reading and Toronto: Oxford University Press.

Stillman, Drake (1995 [1978]), *Galileo At Work, His Scientific Biography*, New York: Dover Publications, Inc. and Toronto: General Publishing Company.

Struik, J. Dirk, (1987 [1948]), *A Concise History of Mathematics*, 4 th Ed., New York: Dover Publications, Inc. and Toronto: General Publishing Co.

Taylor, Thomas (1986 [1818]), *Iamblichus, Life of Pythagoras*, trans. Thomas Taylor, Vermont: Inner Traditions International, Ltd.

Teller, Edward, Wendy Teller, and Wilson Talley (1991), *Conversations On the Dark Secrets of Physics*, New York and London Plenum Press.

Terry, Leon (1964), *The Mathmen*, New York and Toronto: McGraw-Hill Book Company.

*The Economist* (2003), "Planck Scale Physics, The Long and the Short of It," p. 72. March , Vol. 366, No. 8313, New York.

Tver, David F. (1979), *Dictionary of Astronomy, Space, and Atmospheric Phenomena*, New York and Toronto: Van Nostrand Reinhold Company.

Urdang, Laurence and Stuart Berg Flexner, eds. (1968), *The Random House Dictionary of the English Language*, college edition, New York: Random House, The Riverside Press.

Walker, Christopher, ed. (1996), *Astronomy Before the Telescope*, New York: St. Martin's Press.

Weinberg, Steven (1999), "A Unified Physics by 2050?" *Scientific American*, End-of-the-Millennium Special Issue, December 1999.

Westfall, Richard S. (1993), *The Life of Isaac Newton*, New York: University of Cambridge Press.

Wheeler, John Archibald and Kenneth Ford (2000 [1998]), *Geons, Black Holes and Quantum Foam:, A Life In Physics*, New York: W. W. Norton & Company, Inc.

White, Michael and John Gribbin (1994), *Einstein, A Life In Science*, New York and Toronto: Penguin Books.

White, Ron (1993), *PC/Computing, How Computers Work*, California: Ziff-Davis Press.

Wilford, John Noble (1998), "Revolutions In Mapping," *National Geographic Magazine*, Washington D.C., vol. 193, no. 2, February 1998.

Wilson, Colin (1980), *Starseekers*, New York: Doubleday & Company, Inc.

*World Book Encyclopedia* (1975), 22 vols., New York, Toronto: Field Enterprises Educational Corporation.

*World Book, Review of the Events of 1999*, Year Book, Annual Supplement World Book, Chicago: World Book Inc., Scott Fetzer Company.

Zaponc, Arthur (1993), *Catching the Light, The Entwined History of Light and Mind*, New York: Bantam Books.

Zimmerman, Barry E. and David J. Zimmerman (1993), *Why Nothing Can Travel Faster Than Light and Other Explorations in Nature's Curiosity Shop*, Chicago: Contemporary Books, Inc.